DEMENTIA AND MUM – WHO REALLY CARES?

Contents

DEMENTIA AND MUM – WHO REALLY CARES?

Contents

PART TWO

Foreword

"Why don't you call the book *Demumtia*?" exclaimed Kevin. It had been a remark from one of my colleagues at work that dominated my thoughts whilst jogging towards Kew Bridge one Saturday morning during the summer of 2010. Consequently, my failure to concentrate on the river path soon resulted in me tripping up on the uneven ground. Luckily, nobody was around to witness such an embarrassing fall, or hear the ensuing reactions, as my momentum caused me to slide further on, face downwards, for just a few more feet along the gravelly surface of the route. In between a few expletives, I spat out the dusty material, which had suddenly been disturbed to form a rising cloud around me, made all the more dry by a lack of rainfall over the previous few weeks.

Before picking myself up to inspect the cuts and grazes sustained, I spent some moments, flat on my stomach, reflecting on the suggestion offered by the PE teacher just a few days earlier. Yes, it seemed a clever play on words following my brief description of the story – one revolving around my mother's final few years that had been dominated by dementia and my attempt to look after her – but probably too flippant to use, given the seriousness of the illness. It is a condition that already must have blighted millions of lives around the world – its significance further compounded by acknowledging all those cases still awaiting a future diagnosis. Moreover, it doesn't stop there – with every passing year the number of relatives upon whom the responsibility of care is entrusted appears to show no signs of abating. And yet – perhaps because the experience with my mother was not all doom and gloom – it was a quirky title that I did not dismiss immediately.

For me there was no lack of motivation to write this biography, once sufficient time had passed following my mother's death, but for you – the reader – what might compel you to continue turning the pages? After all, she had, apart from the war years, led a relatively ordinary life. Her only claim to fame – that she was a cousin to an accomplished actor, Alfred Molina – was a rather tenuous one, not that the merits of reading this account should be determined, in my opinion, by such a fleeting factor as celebrity status. It may seem ironic, but in many respects dementia gave me a positive reason to write some sort of memoir of her life that went beyond one driven purely by sentiment. Sure, the debilitating nature of the illness means that some aspects of the chronicle inevitably can be harrowing and sad to read. However, that is not to preclude a very encouraging message that is an overriding theme running through the book – that it is possible to provide a level of care that makes those last few years still worthwhile and not just a mere existence. Amongst memories of the decline being experienced – mainly mental – but in the end even physical, there were still many moments of laughter, energy, accomplishment and hope.

Of course, one option is to bury one's head in the sand and pray that dementia never visits you, a close friend or member of your family. If you prefer escapism, then perhaps you shouldn't read on – this may not be for you. It is a real story – where the rawness of the account isn't meant to cause offence but – to avoid compromising the truth – it hasn't been sanitised either. However, before giving up, consider the next point for one moment – the wish for your life to be completely untouched by a problem that is so prevalent and pervasive remains, statistically, one that is unlikely to be fulfilled. If, on the other hand, you prefer to be prepared, or simply to allow you to compare experiences because you are, or have been, in a similar position, then my story should provide a fountain of information – maybe even a source of inspiration. It is not meant to serve as a model guide on caring and I would be the first to admit that along the way I made mistakes. Nevertheless, I believe anyone willing to invest the ten or so hours required to read the following chapters will emerge, maybe emotionally drained for a short while, but in a far better position to face some of the challenges that dementia can throw at both the carer and the person gradually losing memory and cognitive skills. It is quite possible that you might even be surprised by some of the unexpected twists that occur as the depiction unravels, especially when a beautiful young woman appears on the scene to offer help.

Perhaps the most important message that I would like to leave the reader with is this – that the situation isn't one that is just pitiful. A denial of its existence is likely to be the first reaction to any suspicion of dementia, but once the evidence increasingly points towards such a conclusion, then thoughts can be more constructively focused on trying to find solutions. With sufficient help, the sufferer can still experience a very worthwhile and purposeful life, even for most of the latter stages of the illness. As a result, living at home can be prolonged, especially if the burden of care is shared. Whoever provides such support, particularly if it is offered on a very frequent basis, will probably be rewarded by a sense of satisfaction at overcoming many of the obstacles that inevitably have to be faced. As the narrative unfolds, expect to gain a picture of the sacrifices required and strategies used to cope with the stressful challenges encountered at both a physical and psychological level.

What may come as a reassuring surprise is the likelihood that the care given to a loved one is often appreciated. Possibly even more of a miracle, but one that might only occur if daily contact is maintained for a reasonable length of time, is that you are still recognised as someone important – even if not correctly identified as a friend, son or any other close relative for that matter.

Anybody reading this account who knows me might be wondering why I have used a different surname. The one chosen is my mother's Italian maiden name. The main reason is simple. The content of this book is of a very personal nature and therefore to protect the anonymity of close members of the family, I have avoided using my father's East European surname. Containing letters not commonly used in Italian, notably k, w, y and, to a lesser extent, h, in an unusual combination, it was no surprise that Mum experienced difficulties in signing her married name towards the end. Moreover, for a more general readership, her original Fassio name is a much easier one to deal with.

Finally, and in a small way, its use also serves to pay a tribute to my grandfather by keeping his family name alive despite having three daughters but no surviving son.

DEMENTIA AND MUM – WHO REALLY CARES?

Cover design by Patrick Kilgarriff and Michael Fassio

Front cover photo

Mum in July 2003 by the newly-built shed

Back cover photos from left to right:

Row 1 ~ Mum in her teens riding a bicycle, Grandfather riding a bicycle (probably Turin in early 1940s), Mum at the age of eighteen (1944), Aunt Graziella (1955), Grandfather and Grandmother, Aunt Maria Teresa (1956).

Row 2 ~ Family home in *San Damiano* (near Turin), Mum and her cousin, Giovanna, in the 1950s, Mum and Dad at their wedding (1954), Mum at work in Waterloo Station (1981).

Row 3 ~ Mum in 1987, Mum checking the shed at the back of the garden (2003), Mum in 2005, Last-ever photo of Mum taken in October 2007.

Further Acknowledgements: Chris Duke of Blissetts, who provided much help in the final stages of printing this book; and Denis McGrath for setting up the website.

About the author:

Michael was born in London in September 1955, to Polish and Italian parents. He has an MSc in Economics, having studied at the University of East Anglia and Birkbeck College. His article, 'Beware of False Profits', was published in the Economic Review in January 1989. He is currently teaching part-time in several schools, namely Gunnersbury, St Mark's and Gumley House, as well as the University of Westminster. 'Dementia and Mum – Who Really Cares?' is his first book.

Chapter 1   Fear in Her Eyes

"What's up Mike?" enquired Noel on a grey, but not particularly cold, January afternoon. The year was 2008. In his early thirties, Noel was one of the PE teachers at Gunnersbury School where I also worked. Although I am about twenty years older than my colleague, the two of us still had much in common. Like me, Noel, with blue eyes and of average height, possessed the build of a mid-field footballer, rather than a rugby player. He kept his dark brown hair short. Whilst both of us showed no signs of a receding hairline, mine was a lighter shade of brown and, in contrast, had been greying for several years. Despite that, we shared, in varying degrees, some boyish facial features. As such these probably made us look younger than we actually were – particularly when we were clean shaven – Noel, all of the time; myself, most of the time.

Much to my relief, another trouble-free sports session had almost finished that Wednesday afternoon. The boys, either fifteen or sixteen years old, had all taken part in their games of football with enthusiasm. More importantly for me – there hadn't been any injuries. However, it wasn't just a concern over the welfare of the students that prompted such thoughts. For some time, due to the changing circumstances at home, I avoided hanging around school any longer than absolutely necessary. As we walked back towards the changing rooms, Noel could see that I looked troubled; and it didn't take him too long to work out what was on my mind. "Is it your mum? How is she?"

I paused for a second. I wanted to say everything was fine, but that was far from the truth. "No. God knows what state she's going to be in. I really dread going to the hospital today. I don't think she's going to make it." Noel put his arm around my shoulder and tried his best to provide some reassuring words. A few minutes later, he ordered me, in a nice way, to leave. "Go to the hospital, right now! Don't worry about the lads. Most of them have already gone home. I'll stay behind and sort the last few out. Go on, get going and don't be late!"

It is quite normal for PE staff to be delayed at the sports field beyond normal working hours, but once again, thanks to help from Noel and other colleagues, I was able to leave on time for what had become a daily trip to the local hospital, west of London. As I left, Noel promised to say a prayer for my mother. That, at least, was comforting, as I knew he was sincere.

The teachers at Gunnersbury School had been helpful in that way. This extended right up to the Head Teacher, John Heffernan, who had always been willing to reduce my teaching commitments as my responsibilities at home grew. The Head made a point of not spending all his time on tedious paperwork and was often seen patrolling the school during any breaks, either along the corridors or outside in the playground. Sometimes his short grey hair would be covered by a trilby, on other occasions a white panama hat, depending on the season. Encouraging the boys to tuck in their shirts or not to be late for their next lesson, his accessibility often provided me with opportunities to discuss timetable changes or any other issue on an informal basis outside his office.

A few years earlier, my teaching commitments had added up to about three quarters of a full timetable when combined with the extra hours at another school, St Mark's, and the University of Westminster. But then as the years passed, and with it the ability of my mother to cope on her own, so the hours were further cut. In 2006 I had to give up the University post. By the start of the new academic year of 2007, I was down to about one third of a normal timetable. Such reductions greatly helped, but there was an inevitable time lag before they could be implemented. Consequently, the hours agreed with Roger and Andy, the two senior staff entrusted to complete the timetable, in addition to teaching History and English respectively, always seemed to be pretty much obsolete by the time the new term had started in September. And yet, when reflecting on Mum's increasing need for help, they probably would have been perfect for the previous year. Mum's condition was deteriorating, not rapidly, but fast enough to render any forward planning as likely to be flawed. My mother, Renza Fassio, was suffering from dementia. Quite some time before that Wednesday afternoon games lesson of the 16th of January, 2008, she had already reached the final stage of the illness.

Until recently I had always set off on my bicycle with a sense of urgency, convinced that my visits to the hospital were important to Mum, as well as the staff treating her. I hoped that in some small way they might help and improve her chances of recovery and, on previous occasions, this belief was probably not misplaced. But not this time, sadly. The last few days had seen hope fading. She was slipping away from me. I felt despondent; all the more so as I was powerless to do anything about it.

The bicycle ride from the school playing fields to the hospital can be very pleasant, particularly in the summer. For a really scenic route, I could have cycled along the canal towpath past colourful barges while weaving my way past walkers, sometimes accompanied by their dogs, until eventually reaching the tail end of the High Street. But this was winter. Even though I wasn't in my usual hurry, for it felt as if a darkening cloud of apprehension was following me, I was nevertheless exhausted. Lack of sleep for the past fifteen months and the stress of the last six years were all taking their toll, so instead I opted to continue along an easier, though less picturesque, route, but at least the last part of the journey was pleasing to the eye; it involved cycling through a park boasting an imposing house within the grounds, whilst also providing a shortcut and break from the busy traffic of the main road. I finally reached the entrance of the hospital. Over the last few years the new building had periodically acted as a second home. It was probably about 4 p.m. by the time I locked up my bicycle and then made my way to her ward. For the last few nights Mum had been isolated in her own room. A tube ran through a nostril and down her throat for feeding. This had been the depressing state of affairs for a few days following the ominous introduction of the 'nil by mouth' notice that had been stuck to the wall behind her. She lay motionless on the bed – still breathing but helpless. Such a contrast to about ten years previously when I had broken my ankle – then I had been reliant on her for help.

So unlike her prior stay in the hospital over the summer of 2007, there was very little to do except hold her hand, sometimes gently stroking it, hoping that there was still some sort of communication despite the silence. The hours seemed to pass by very slowly. There were no longer any interruptions for tea or meals, when at least I could have spent time feeding her; not even requests for help from other patients to provide a distraction since Mum had been moved from the ward to a separate room. We were alone. Later, two nurses came in to change her pads and check her dressing. A few days earlier I had insisted on seeing the bed sore that had been developing on her bottom. By that point it had already become red in places, purple elsewhere. The opening in the skin was getting larger and turning into an ulcer. My sister Elizabeth, a nurse, had already told me how large such wounds can get – holes as big as a fist – for that had been her worrying description in an earlier conversation on such matters. On this particular night, I didn't want to look.

Over the previous four months while Mum had been bed-bound at home, I had taken special care to turn her regularly so that she wasn't stuck in a particular position for too long. It had worked, and the nurses who inspected her from time to time were very complimentary. Her skin had been completely unblemished when she was readmitted to the hospital about ten days previously. Consequently, it was sad to see her deteriorate so quickly. Was it due to a lack of care on the part of the staff? After all, they were always busy and had many other patients to tend to. Maybe – but I suspect it was a reflection that her body was falling apart – and not even doctors can work miracles.

For a while my thoughts turned to the following day. I would be taking the Upper 6th Economics group. I felt relaxed about the lesson, as for the first part of the morning they would be doing re-sit exams in one of their modules. This meant less preparation on my part. It was a small group, only six in total, and each had performed well on the coursework though, as usual, most of them had been late for my provisional deadlines. As a result, the Christmas holiday was interrupted by several visits by my students to check the progress of their final or, in some cases, penultimate drafts. I didn't mind giving up a bit of time as I was stuck in the house for most of the day, every day, and the meetings provided a surprising source of light relief, as well as an opportunity to help with their revision for the fast-approaching exam in January. And so there we were. Around my mum's house with her stuck in an electrically operated bed while discussions about the merits, or otherwise, of increasing tax on alcohol or tobacco were taking place only a few feet away. This year education was going far beyond the theories contained in an economics textbook.

A glance at the clock reminded me that I should really be thinking of making a move. It was getting close to 10 p.m., well beyond the end of normal visiting hours. Even during her earlier hospital stay in the summer of 2007, I had often been allowed to hang around for longer than other visitors. She may not have known I was her son by that stage, but she certainly seemed more relaxed in my company. Regardless of the debilitating effects of dementia – she still knew that I wasn't a stranger. For that reason it had always been easier to slip out of the ward after she had fallen asleep. The same challenge that I faced with any departure still applied even though it was some time since she had stopped calling out "Michael" on seeing me leave. Of course, not hearing the echo of her calls following me down the corridor helped to ease any feelings of guilt, but there was still the sense of sight to ensure that I wouldn't be entirely free from any self-recriminating emotions.

Although she was lying there quietly, I could still see anxiety in her face. Tonight was particularly unnerving. There was real fear in her eyes. That expression seemed to be all the more pronounced against the background of her short white hair, thin face and frail frame. She couldn't speak, but I knew exactly what she was thinking. There was a little, weak motion of her mouth, but no sound was coming out – and yet – it was as if she was screaming with all her will, pleading with me to get her out of there. I wished I could. She would now have been light enough to carry over my shoulders. We could have sneaked out. I did give it some thought for a few seconds, but soon dismissed the idea after working through the implications. Eventually she fell asleep and it provided me the chance to slip away. Back on the bike and soon I was home.

The house that I returned to was so quiet. The sound of my parents arguing, which had been so upsetting to hear as a child, would have been a welcome contrast at that moment. I spent a while packing things in my rucksack ready for the following day. I knew exactly what I would be doing; it was becoming a routine. As soon as I finished school around midday, it was odds-on that I would be cycling over to the hospital.

Later that night, despite feeling so tired, I was unable to fall asleep. As I remained lying awake in bed, I could feel tears rolling down my cheeks. The eerie silence was only interrupted by the occasional vehicle passing by – its headlights tracing a moving beam across the ceiling – and the faint tapping sound as each tear hit the pillow. That night my spirit, which had been sustained for nearly a decade by hope and a sincere self-belief, had finally been broken. I wondered if Noel had said any prayers for my mother. He was Head of Year 11, as well as a PE teacher, so was always busy, but I bet he had found the time. She certainly needed some prayers. And then it was my turn to pray. I said a few Hail Marys and then pleaded, "Please God, take her tonight!"

Where I turned for intervention that night was significant. The situation had moved on. It had gone beyond any help that could have been usefully offered by Elizabeth – my younger sister with all her years of nursing experience, Sara – a new-found friend, or Peter – a friend for almost four decades. Even the medical staff at the hospital seemed powerless. Mum's fate lay elsewhere.

Chapter 2   An Italian Background

My mother, Renza, was born on the 12th of February, 1926, during a very interesting time in world history. She was the first child of Clorindo Fassio and Maddalena Ramello, who had been married a year earlier and possessed surnames typical of the area. They lived in a small town called *San Damiano d'Asti*, about forty kilometres south east of *Torino* (Turin) in the northern region of Italy, called *Piedmont*. It was the year of the General Strike in England; Germany had recently been ravaged by the hyper-inflation of 1922-3 and Mussolini was already in power in Italy. The world was just a few years away from the upheavals of the Great Depression, only to be followed by a major war that engulfed so many countries and affected so many lives.

Born in 1902, my grandfather became a tailor, but much of his spare time was devoted to his favourite sport, cycling. He loved reading the pink newspaper, *La Gazetta dello Sport*, since it devoted a reasonable section of the editorial to his particular interest. He was well known and respected amongst the locals as he also ran a cycling club in the town. After much badgering, he successfully persuaded the authorities to redirect the *Giro d'Italia* (Tour of Italy) through *San Damiano* one year. A few years after his death, his remains had to be relocated to another part of the cemetery. Deposited in a basket at the front of a bicycle, they were transported by a worker to their final resting place, providing an unceremonious but seemingly appropriate end. It was an ironic story that greatly amused the three daughters, as the event occurred after a respectful interval of time and thus made it easier to appreciate the humorous aspect of this last trip. His other two daughters, Maria Teresa and Graziella, were born in 1931 and 1937 respectively. Mum would also have had a younger brother, but he was stillborn, and I can remember Mum describing how sad her father had been when carrying a tiny box, which served as a coffin for his son – possibly an end to any dreams of producing a future champion of the *Giro d'Italia*.

Mum's mother, Maddalena, concentrated on housework and raising the family but was also able to help her husband at work as she was a skilled seamstress. I met my grandfather only once – when I was far too young to allow any recollections now – but I did have the privilege of getting to know my grandmother as a result of visits to Italy over the years. Interestingly, I could see the characteristics of her in all three daughters. My mother seemed to inherit her more practical, pragmatic and energetic side as well as her height, being the tallest of the three. Maria Teresa was inclined to exhibit the more glamorous and flamboyant aspects of her character. Finally Graziella, who played an active role alongside her husband in running a paper recycling business in *Torino*, displayed her commercial acumen. All were blessed with their mother's good looks, but each had different hair colour: black, blonde, and light brown respectively. My grandmother continued to run a shop selling clothes and repairing garments well into her seventies, after being widowed in 1964.

Although times were hard, at least it was not all work. The family lived in a house on the corner of the town's main piazza, adjacent to the tailor's shop. The dwelling faced the rather grand town hall building that still dominates the skyline to this day. From there, it meant that the family could enjoy a good view of any important events in the community. Every year there was a festival, the highlight being a race staged through the town using the farmers' big workhorses and probably ridden by their sons, no doubt eager to show off. As with the annual firework display, the window overlooking the piazza must have provided the perfect vantage point to see the crowd gathered below – waiting in anticipation, especially those men who had wagered bets on the outcome of the race. "Boom ... body ... boom ...body ... boom ..." was the repeated and animated way that Mum described the loud thudding noise of the hooves pounding on the hard surface – all building up to a crescendo – as the horses approached the town square for the finale, which provoked a deafening roar from the awaiting spectators. And typically on those sunny summer days most families, including my mother's, would be treated to the delicious ice creams prepared by one of their neighbours having returned from a spell in the United States with many new recipes.

Apparently my grandfather had a good voice and I was told that he serenaded my grandmother with a guitar while courting her. Everybody in the family seemed to be good singers. It is such a shame that my grandfather died in 1964, far too early to see one of his granddaughters, Monica, performing *Madame Butterfly* and other operatic works in, for example, *La Scala,* Milan. Whenever my mother heard someone singing poorly, as she did in later years whilst watching some of the first auditions for programmes like the *X-Factor*, her thoughts would invariably drift back to her earlier days in *San Damiano* and I listened patiently to an often recounted, but still charming story. Out-of-tune singing reminded her of the banker who dreamed of being an opera singer but had absolutely no vocal talent, a fact that had escaped his notice but not that of the neighbourhood. During the long lunch breaks, a tradition in Italy, his grating practices would drive my grandfather out of the tailor's shop and into a bar – any bar – as long as it was out of earshot.

As a child Mum had attended the local school run by the nuns. Her favourite teacher was the Mother Superior who one day fell ill. None of the students were permitted to see her, but Mum kept pleading until she was finally allowed to pay her a visit. That revealed a trait of stubbornness that was maintained throughout her life. At school Mum didn't like maths and even in adulthood was never particularly confident when dealing with numbers. She did love reading, however. When she had spare time from chores around the house she would hide up in the attic, accompanied by a novel. That was where she would have a secret cigarette. Mum was also fond of going to the local cinema. If she came home with her eyes still red having seen a moving film, her father would laugh and suggest that he could have given her a slap for nothing if she wanted to have a cry.

Another story that she told me concerned her cousin, Giovanna, who was a year older. Along with my mother and her sister, Maria Teresa, as well as a few other friends in the town, sometimes the group of children put on a show for their parents. Borrowing dresses from my grandmother's wardrobe and acting out a play that they had made up, a modest admission charge contributed towards earning a little pocket money – possibly for those ice creams being sold in the town square. And maybe it was from such modest beginnings that the idea of a career in acting can be traced a few decades later when Giovanna's son, Alfred Molina, revealed signs of being talented in such an activity even from an early age. Unfortunately, her untimely death in the 1980s robbed Giovanna of the opportunity to be present at her son's nomination in 2010 for a BAFTA award as best support actor in the film, *An Education*, or to witness many of his preceding, or subsequent, achievements on the stage or screen.

By the time the war started, Mum had begun learning her father's trade and was soon becoming very adept at sewing, a skill that she later made use of when living in London. That she wasn't shy was also put to good use by the family. The farmers always seemed to have an excuse for not paying my grandfather for his tailoring work. Bad weather, crop failure, sick animals and falling prices were all used but that didn't deter Mum from extracting some money from them. Sometimes without any prompting from her parents, she paid the farmers a surprise visit. Having charmed her way in, she sat down and engaged in polite conversation for a while. But Mum could also hold a stern face when required, and soon followed through with a blunt threat that she wouldn't move until they paid her. Invariably she left with some remuneration – and even if it wasn't always the full amount – in more ways than one, she was proving to be an indispensable part of the family. She never lost this ability to get her own way, a tenacity that my dad, sister and I each confronted at some point in our lives.

Other chores included chopping up the firewood in readiness for the winter months, a skill that she held on to until her eighties. They must also have involved many hours helping in the kitchen – the proof being in the many tasty puddings and other dishes served up over the years. Mum wasn't a vegetarian, but she wasn't particularly fond of meat either. It was a sentiment that I seemed to share, particularly when I was a child. Just as I secretly transferred some of the meat from my plate to my dad's, apparently the same act had already been played out several decades earlier between my mum and grandfather. But while Mum excelled and probably enjoyed developing her culinary skills, there was one particular task that she didn't like – being asked to go down to the basement to fetch some provisions as she was scared of the prospects of encountering any rodents that might be scurrying about in the darkness. Maybe that was why, many years later when I was only about four years old, she let out a loud scream as I showed her a friend's white pet mouse. I can still just about remember the tickly feeling as it moved around on the palm of my hand. Much to my surprise, Mum promptly ordered me and 'it' out of the Fulham house. It was probably this unexpected reaction that helped to preserve a hazy recollection of this event from the summer of 1959, shortly before we moved out of Ashcombe Street to the larger house in Chiswick.

Despite his dictatorial style and all the upheavals caused by the war, Mum never really had a bad word for Mussolini. His siding with Hitler and the mistakes made, particularly over the campaign in Africa, may have contributed towards his eventual downfall, but he had been the architect for many improvements in Italy too. In her youth, Mum had been enrolled into the *Piccole Italiane*. This was the case with all the other girls in the town, since membership was compulsory. As a result, participation in such a movement may have influenced her opinion at a very formative age. Moreover, all the Italian children of those times had been brought up with no other leader or political system to make a comparison with. But this was not so with the older generation. Her mother certainly wasn't awestruck by *Il Duce* and, like most of the other women in the town, totally ignored the request to sacrifice any gold or jewellery to help fund the war effort.

Mum had great respect for both her parents, but she was particularly fond of her father. Nevertheless, she was also able to stand up to him when necessary, particularly as she got older and desired more independence. In fact I was once told by her that she reprimanded him when she caught him being a bit too friendly with one of the female employees. The threat of reporting the incident to her mother was enough to stop any further indiscretions, however minor, from ever being repeated. The end of the war brought changes for the Fassio family. There was a move to *Torino* and Mum also spent a period working in the mountain town of *Bardonecchia*, close to the border with France.

Sometime in the early 1950s Mum moved to England. At that time there were far more controls than now and 'aliens', as they were called, had to have a full medical inspection and report to the police on a regular basis. Maybe Mum was looking for adventure; she was in her mid-twenties by then and the fact that her cousin, Giovanna, had already secured work in London and reported back with positive comments, probably was enough to encourage her to take the plunge. Her first job was as an *au pair* for an affluent family with property in Chelsea and Lingfield. It provided Mum with an opportunity to learn English, and she later told me that going to the cinema had been a good way to improve her fluency in the language. For the family, my mum offered an introduction to the many Italian dishes that she had learnt from her mother, and which I would later enjoy.

Even from a young age, I can remember being incredibly spoilt as far as food was concerned. No doubt, many of those dishes must have been sampled by the wealthy couple in Chelsea. Homemade ravioli, along with many other varieties of pasta, were prepared. Sometimes she cooked polenta, a yellow cornmeal staple diet typical of rural areas in northern Italy. Unused portions were later fried and served with a sauce. Leftovers from other meals were also rarely wasted. Mixed in with eggs, Mum could quickly produce a *frittata*, an Italian-style omelette. Tasty servings with rice included *risotto* and amongst the many vegetables cooked, a favourite of mine was when she fried thinly sliced courgettes. Ranked a close second was cauliflower coated in breadcrumbs. Garlic heated in olive oil provided a sauce into which celery could be dipped, while pepper, mushrooms, onions and tomatoes often featured in her cooking. But it was with puddings that Mum particularly excelled. Peaches, sliced in half, were baked with a chocolate filling. Light pastry cakes were filled with a delicious *zabaglione* sauce and adorned with a thin coating of icing sugar, chocolate or vanilla. A trifle called *zuppa inglese* was a real treat. Sponges were cut in half and dipped in sherry. A chocolate sauce was then spread over the soaked sponges – that was often my job. From an early age, I learnt that volunteering to help with the washing-up provided an opportunity to dip my finger in the saucepan to finish off any of the delicious sauces that hadn't been scooped out. As for the trifle, the layers were gradually built up to form a rectangular block. This was covered with whipped cream and finally decorated by maraschino cherries. But it wasn't just Italian cuisine that appeared on the table – Mum learnt many English recipes over the years and even tried her hand at some Polish fare in order to please my father.

The spell with the wealthy family back in Chelsea seemed like a happy time for her. She was taken to concerts at the Albert Hall, and some weekends would be spent at Lingfield. I don't think she went to the horse races there because she told me she had only attended once in her life, and that was with friends in Italy. They had all won some money on the first race. After that Mum stopped betting despite the goading from her friends, but by the end of the meeting the others – unlike Mum – had all lost their earlier winnings. Her only other flutter on the horses spanned a few successive Grand Nationals in the 1970s when Red Rum duly obliged on each occasion. Similarly, she had only been to one live football match, again in Italy, and for the most part she seemed to be more amused by watching her uncle's cigarette excitedly waving up and down in his mouth rather than the action being played out on the pitch.

After a few years Mum left the family – though she continued to receive Christmas cards from them well in to the 1970s. Mum was probably getting restless again and needed a change. Her next job was at a hospital in Hammersmith, where she worked in the kitchen. It was only after she got married that she turned her hand back to what she probably knew best. To supplement income, Dad bought her a sewing machine, and from home she was able to make dresses and other garments. She was still very good and consequently there was always work. As a child, rainy days meant being stuck indoors. Mum was usually busy sewing, but at least I was also kept occupied. Many happy hours were spent sitting on the edge of the sturdy sewing machine cabinet observing Mum at work. Possibly her simplest task involved making the belts for the dresses that she was working on. She quickly threaded through belt after belt. Being so adept at such tasks, Mum found it easy to engage in conversation at the same time. My job was to cut the thread that linked the many dozens of belts that she had sewn together and then turn them so they were no longer inside out.

By the time I started Primary school, Mum, fluent in English, had already lived in London for about a decade. Like most immigrants, she retained much of the culture from her early life in Italy, but at the same time she was becoming influenced by the customs of her newly inherited country. She never forgot her roots, but with the arrival of my younger sister, Elizabeth, in 1965, her life became increasingly involved in England.

Contact was still maintained with her relatives back home, and there were several visits to Italy spread over a few decades. However, a wedding photograph of my aunt, Maria Teresa, showed one notable absence, my mum. I'm not so sure about Giovanna – I would need to check the photograph again. My mother's non-attendance remains a mystery and I can only hazard a guess when trying to offer an explanation. The wedding was in the 1950s, a very different time with respect to foreign travel or taking time off work. One can certainly speculate that the expense of journeying back to Italy may have been too prohibitive for her. I suppose I will never know for sure. Some questions just have to remain unanswered – especially if not asked at an opportune time. Whatever the reason, it was a pity because the wedding photo, shown to me by my aunt on a visit in 2008, would have captured an image of the whole family on the Italian side, had Mum not been on her adventure in England. At the time it had been planned to be a relatively short stay – it just didn't work out that way.

Chapter 3 Wars Apart

For my dad, the Second World War had life-changing consequences. On a few occasions Mum even referred to him as a 'mystery man'. It wasn't meant as a compliment – but in many ways it correctly summed up Dad's earlier life – for he had a complex background and personality, traits that became increasingly obvious to me as I grew older.

When I was young, I had always been under the impression that Dad was Polish. After all, he was born in Poland in the village of *Sukowate*, to be precise, not too far from a town called *Sanok*. Before World War II his birthplace was located in a reasonably central position in the south of the nation. By the end of the War, it was no longer even visible on a map since none of its inhabitants or buildings remained. However, had the community survived, the south east corner of Poland would have been its new position. Such a change in geography can be explained by the eastern border shifting backwards and forwards over time according to the balance of military power in the region.

As a child, in the 1960s, and brought up in London, initially I had very few doubts over the authenticity of my dad's links to Poland. With the passing of time he had built up a small network of Polish friends living in the capital, and even further afield in Essex. As for his relatives, he continued to receive letters from his original homeland, but when I observed that some had also been sent from the USSR (Union of Soviet Socialist Republics) some doubts began to surface. Did that mean that I was a bit Russian too, I wondered? To further complicate things, there was also post from Austria. Combined with the Italian connection on my mother's side, it meant that at a young age I started to acquire an expanding international stamp collection. This left me slightly bemused trying to work out my own ethnic identity – not that it caused too much of a problem – for in some respects the mixture had many positive aspects by supplementing the English upbringing shared with my peers. But never, in those early years, did Dad once mention the Ukraine. It was not until I had been teaching for over a decade that such a new link was first drawn to my attention. It was at a Parents' Evening when the Polish father of one of my students commented on my surname as sounding Ukrainian. Just like a jigsaw puzzle, more and more of the pieces were coming together. Not too long afterwards, the Ukraine gained independence and suddenly I found Dad taking more interest in the Olympics Medals table and Ukraine's progress in qualifying for the World Cup.

Two decades later and I was fascinated to discover that Sukowate, along with another twenty-nine villages in the region, formed the *Komancza* Republic with the aim of uniting with the West Ukrainian National Republic in 1918. It provided further confirmation, certainly from my grandfather's side of the family, that there was a Ukrainian background. Although the *Komancza* Republic only lasted for a few months until January 1919, my family's connection to Ukrainian culture seems to have been far more enduring. Much to my surprise it turned out that the name of the country's currency, the *hryvnia*, bore an uncanny resemblance to my father's surname. And so while it would be correct to assume Polish nationality for my dad, both legally and through his fluency in the language, culturally he still retained his links to the Ukraine. That might explain why of the two, he took far more interest in the opening of a Russian Orthodox Cathedral in Chiswick than in the Polish Centre a few miles away in Hammersmith.

According to his British passport – signifying his last adopted nationality – Dad was born on the 18th of April, 1923, but, as with so many other aspects of his life, even this fact is clouded with uncertainty. Whether or not he was joking with me, I can't be sure, but I distinctly remember a conversation with him revealing that there was some doubt over the validity of the date, since he may have changed the year of his birth before coming over to England. I never got a definite and unambiguous answer to this issue and now it is too late to ask. Even the name on his passport was liberally interpreted, further adding to the mystery of his early years; in his British version it appeared as John, but his original first name was Jan. He was even referred to as Hans during his spell in Austria.

I have no idea if his birthplace of *Sukowate* was touched by any confrontations during the Polish – Ukrainian War of 1919 but, as far as I can gather from accounts provided by my dad, fighting between German and Russian troops during the Second World War left the village completely destroyed. Whilst on a return visit many years later, Dad discovered that the whole area had been abandoned and reclaimed by the nearby forest. I know very little of his family members except that I believe his parents, Stefan and Olga, were born in 1888 and 1900 respectively and he had two sisters, Irena and Krystyna. These were two names with easily recognisable counterparts in English; the same could not be said of his two brothers whose names were written in Ukrainian on the back of a photo dated 1956 but would translate to Basil and Michael. My grandfather worked in forestry but also kept some livestock in a small farm near to the house – a modest dwelling through which chickens were sometimes known to roam. Maybe if the war hadn't happened, my dad would have continued living contentedly in Poland – possibly labouring on a farm – and never given emigration to England a single thought!

So when Germany invaded Poland in September 1939, Dad could have been at least fourteen years old, or possibly sixteen if the passport entry is accurate. What can be absolutely certain was that he was still in his early teens. One year later and Dad became separated from most of his family. For a long time I had known that he had been sent by the Germans to Austria. However, I recently discovered a document dated the 28th of August, 1940. It was stamped a few days later on the 4th of September with a German emblem of the eagle displaying its wings spread open and the Nazi insignia, the swastika, at its foot. It reveals that Dad was not travelling with strangers. His elder sister, Irena, born in 1919, was also being transported to Austria. Her document number 2107 gives some idea of the scale of the exodus. Their destination, along with other Poles on the train, was *Untere Fellach*. Near to the town of *Villach*, it wasn't a short journey given its proximity to the Alps, close to the borders with Italy. The route must have required a passage through Czechoslovakia and possibly Hungary too. On arrival they were taken to a hall where Austrian farmers were gathered, waiting to select who they wanted to take for work on their various farms. Such enforced labour was commonplace during the war and was not just confined to compatriots from Poland. I can remember Dad referring to French and Serbian young men also being in the same position.

Life was tough on the farm. Dad was expected to toil for long hours, but he was treated well by the Austrian family with whom he maintained correspondence for many years after the war. Beyond a shadow of doubt, Dad was very intelligent. After a year or two on the farm he must have learnt all the main tasks and could probably have run the operation himself. Compared to the fate of many other Poles at the time, this must have been an idyllic existence. Yes, hard work and away from the majority of his family, but at least he was safe and well-fed. Dad was good at languages, so he soon picked up German to add to the Polish and Ukrainian that he had learnt from childhood. He might have stayed in Austria for the rest of his life, but as the war ran its course towards a conclusion, the Germans had other plans for him.

Along with many other young men, Dad received notification that he was to be sent from Austria to France – not to work on a farm – but instead to help reinforce the German army which by then must have feared an imminent invasion from the Allies. The desire to defend the Third Reich suddenly called for a more pragmatic approach and the German military service could no longer be the preserve of just pure Nordic peoples. The Austrian farmer was saddened to see the loss of a good worker and an almost adopted member of his family. For Dad the moment of departure must have been made all the more poignant by the knowledge that this was likely to be the last he would see of his sister for some time to come – if at all. A letter from Austria in the second half of the 1950s reveals that Dad was still trying to trace his sister and the rest of his family from his new home in England. The reply from Josef Kleinbichler, most probably the Austrian farmer, apologised for not being able to help. He had not heard from Irena since her departure from *Untere Fellach* in May 1945.

Once again, another train journey taking Dad even further west through Europe beckoned. Unfortunately, details of this next part of his life remain extremely sketchy. It must be a common experience that over the passage of time, fading memories of events in our lives – unless accurately recorded – often means that the line between fiction and non-fiction can become blurred. This is particularly the case covering the period between Dad being conscripted to the German army and then ending up on the side of the Allies. When did he have to leave Austria? How long was he in the German army? Was he released or did he escape and if the latter, how? Was he helped by the French resistance for a while? I really don't have a clue, but amongst Dad's collection of war-time photos, one might provide some answers, but equally, it seems to pose even more questions. It was probably taken in the cold winter of 1944, possibly on or near Christmas as it shows a group of eleven troops surrounding an officer dressed in a distinctive German uniform. Other than the harsh wintry conditions, indicated by the frosted earth walls of their dugout, it appears to be a relaxed setting. One of the soldiers is clutching what looks like a bottle of champagne in his gloved hands. Next to him there is someone looking vaguely like my dad holding an accordion – an instrument that he could play well – and of the three that were smoking, one had a cigar. Was this part of the group from which Dad later escaped? Or maybe with the war virtually lost, this was a parting shot before they went their own separate ways – the Germans presumably retreating eastwards, back to their homeland?

Anyway, this is all pure conjecture. What I can be more certain about is that sometime after Dad acquired the photo, he was joining the Allies, along with a Polish friend, as British forces advanced through France. In a new uniform and ranked as a private, it was time for army serial number 30039672 to learn some English. I was told that he was involved in mine-clearing and took his part in blowing up some bridges – but I'm not sure if this was in France or later in Italy, the last part of his war effort. Amongst his collection of photos from this period, there are even a few that show him relaxing by the sea, more than likely in Italy, with other British or Polish comrades. In recognition of his contribution, he received a War Medal and the comment, 'always good', on the section of his Polish Resettlement Corps papers describing his conduct while serving with the colours in the British army.

"Is that where your dad met your mum?" asked Donna. "No," I laughed. "That would have been the romantic version, I suppose." I had been recounting some of this story with two very pretty Chinese girls whom I had taught A Level Economics over the two years prior to them finishing their exams in June 2004. Donna and Monica were good company, and I had been invited by Donna's parents for a meal at their restaurant near Kew Gardens as a thank-you for helping with their studies. It was December 2004 and this was one of the few evenings during the course of that year when I had been able to go out. Prior to us meeting up, I had to wait patiently at home until Mum had fallen asleep. It wasn't until about 7 p.m. before I was able to sneak out, quietly closing the front door behind me. All I could do was hope she would remain in bed for a few hours and not get herself into any trouble on her own. By that stage of her dementia, she had never wandered off, but there was always going to be a first time. The expectation of that eventuality added to the tension of any of my rare evenings out.

To my surprise, and despite the age difference, there were hardly any breaks in the conversation. The food was great too. We talked about many other things that night before I left a few hours later but they seemed fascinated by the adventures of my dad, so I continued. "No, that was a few years later," I replied. Dad probably spent at least a good few months in Italy before the war was finally over. Over that period of conflict on the continent, which more or less encompassed his teenage years, he had completely lost touch with his family in Poland. In addition, he had seen quite a bit of Europe, learnt new skills and languages and may have also witnessed scenes that he would not particularly want to recall. There were a few nights when I could hear Dad shouting and screaming in his dreams. I sometimes wondered if such nightmares could be explained by his mind drifting back to some events lived through during the war – ones that he never shared with us.

When the Second World War broke out in 1939, Mum was thirteen. In contrast to the events experienced by my dad in Poland at the time, she had a reasonably trouble-free war, but it didn't leave her family completely untouched either. During these tougher economic times, people must have been spending less money on new clothes. That could have hit my grandfather's business badly but fortunately for him the arrival of soldiers stationed reasonably close to the town provided sufficient work to get by. Mum had to collect measurements and deliver uniforms to the barracks, and as a teenager, she probably enjoyed the attention from the young soldiers. Photos from the early 1940s reveal that she had dark wavy hair and a very pretty face. Her ears, nose, mouth and jaw line were all well-proportioned, while her brown eyes and dark eyebrows were probably her most attractive features. She had long shapely legs and at about 5' 7'' had grown to a decent height for a young woman. By all accounts she had a number of admirers in the town and, of slightly more concern to my grandfather, even from further afield – recollections of which seemed sharper whenever she was annoyed with my dad.

Bombing raids that continued over England until the *Luftwaffe* lost command of the air in the 'Battle of Britain' probably remain common knowledge even to later generations – and certainly they have been well-documented. However, I was surprised to discover that Benito Mussolini ordered the *Corpo Aero Italiano* (Italian Air Force) to aid their German allies on sorties across the English Channel. One such mission, in the winter of 1940, involved towns on the East Anglian coast such as Felixstowe. Undoubtedly, Mum must have been totally unaware of such attacks at the time, despite the likelihood of it being reported in the Italian press. Regardless, she could never have foreseen that the Suffolk town was going to have a significant influence on her later adult life. As for its bearings on the outcome of the war – fascist propaganda would have prevented the campaign from being described as anything other than a success – but in reality little damage was inflicted by the Italians. Their old biplanes – with designs that conjure up images from a WW1 dogfight – were no match for the *Spitfires* or *Hurricanes* most likely to have been deployed by pilots from the RAF (Royal Air Force). Ironically, the British forces themselves meted out a bigger impact on the coastal town by demolishing a large part of the 852 m pier – until then the third longest in the country – to a more modest one of 137 m, less than one quarter of its original length. Hindsight now makes the decision look regrettable, but it was all part of a defence strategy being repeated along other parts of the British coastline – an understandable sacrifice given the real fear that a German invasion was imminent.

Mum didn't really see much of the Germans until the latter stages of the war when a division did pass through the town, resulting in the tanks smashing up some of the cobbled paving. During that period, young men were hidden as best they could, but some were rounded up to be drafted into the German army. Those that did return, because obviously some didn't, often came back little more than skin and bone – friends that were barely recognisable as a result of their ordeals. It was also a time when there were fights between the fascists and the partisans. A teacher at Mum's school was beaten up because he held opposing views to his assailants. A dog belonging to one of my mum's relatives, ironically a retriever, was shot dead in a similar act of reprisal. Like many other people at the time, my grandfather would have preferred to have been left to get on with his life without the hindrance of a war going on and didn't really hold any strong political views. But it was virtually impossible for families to escape entirely from some form of tragedy in those six years, and so it was with Mum. One of her cousins worked in a circus, and one day their convoy of caravans travelling along the road was mistaken for a German unit by an American pilot who opened fire. Unfortunately her cousin was killed as the bullets sprayed the road.

When the war was over in 1945, Dad was given a choice. He could either return to Poland or settle in any of the Allied countries. With Poland under the Soviet Union, his village already destroyed, and probably because he had no idea as to what had happened to the rest of his family, he opted for a fresh start. Some of his Polish comrades went to Holland; at least one took his chance in America, but Dad and a friend named Paul chose England. They both remained in the Army until July 1947. According to the Polish Resettlement Corps document issued by the British Army, Dad was demobbed in Essex where he was directed towards employment close to the very quaint village of Finchingfield as an agricultural labourer. Unlike Paul, who stayed in Essex, my dad eventually decided to seek his fortune in London but not before he used his savings to acquire a motorbike. Rather recklessly – maybe because of youth and the difficulty of adjusting to civilian life – he sometimes could be found speeding along the uncongested country roads. On one occasion he was spotted by a policeman who gave chase. However, the combination of Dad's riding experience in the army and a more powerful engine ensured that he eventually shook off his pursuer. Many decades on, and judging from the mischievous twinkle in his elderly eyes, recalling such a narrow escape still evoked a sense of delight. When he arrived and settled down in London he soon found work, yet he always retained fond memories of his time in Essex. Eventually he became a maintenance fitter, but as well as engineering he seemed to be able to turn his hands to anything – plastering, bricklaying, roofing, plumbing, rewiring, basic carpentry and even repairs of watches, clocks and televisions.

By the time peace descended on Europe, Mum was already nineteen. A new generation of young tailors, some of whom had been trained by my grandfather, meant that there wasn't enough business to go round in the small town of *San Damiano*. Consequently, it was time to move and shortly after the war the whole family relocated to the relatively large city of *Torino*. Mum continued to help her father in the tailoring trade. But not for the last time in her life she was probably getting restless and needed a change. An opportunity to join a younger cousin working in a hotel in the mountain town of *Bardonecchia* presented itself and Mum decided to leave home, much to my grandfather's disappointment and protests. Having tasted the freedom of living away from home, it probably made it easier for her to make her next move and follow another cousin, Giovanna, to London. Her first post was with the aforementioned wealthy family residing in Chelsea, where she soon began to improve her fluency in English. As this was still during a period of rationing in England, she was probably fortunate to enjoy a reasonable standard of living. But while there were the trappings of luxury on visits to her employer's second home in the country, Mum valued her independence and eventually left the residence. New employment was secured in Hammersmith – the hospital kitchen – where she even entertained the idea of training to become a nutritionist for a while. She found accommodation in a house nearby which was owned by a Hungarian couple renting out several rooms to a number of foreign tenants.

It was there, a few years after being demobbed from the army, that my dad met a pretty, dark haired young Italian woman named Renza. I had finally answered Donna's earlier question. Although my dad was slightly the shorter of the two and wasn't fluent in Italian, he must have remembered enough from his time in Italy to create a good first impression. Some time later in April 1954 they were married. It wasn't long before they had bought their first house in Fulham and then a year later in September, I was born. Before the end of 1959 the Fulham property had been sold. This helped to fund, along with a mortgage, the purchase of their next house in west London. It was a three storey semi-detached in Chiswick, located close to Kew Bridge. Mum had the good sense to encourage Dad to pay off the mortgage as soon as possible, hence the acceptance of a more frugal existence compared to the ones often expected by later generations of young couples. Second-hand furniture and no car or holidays abroad would have to do for a while. Whenever possible, they readily took on most of the jobs around the house themselves. Such thriftiness was quite unlikely to be everybody's 'cup of tea' – even in those days – but much to their credit – they would never again be in debt.

Before the end of the decade, Dad had discovered the whereabouts of his Polish family with the help of the Red Cross. Miraculously, all had survived the war. His parents and brothers had ended up in *Ternopil*, a Ukrainian city in the former USSR. They wrote back expressing their delight at finally being able to retrace each other, but also informed Dad of the hardships suffered during the harsh winters of the war, when they were forced to survive on discarded scraps such as potato peelings. Irena and Krystyna settled in *Przemyśl*, not their original village which had been wiped off the map, but at least a city in the region of Poland where they had been born.

During the 1990s, Dad encouraged me to correspond with the Austrian authorities enquiring if he might be entitled to a pension. I had my doubts as to whether the hours spent searching through a German dictionary in order to write such a letter would be worthwhile. But I was wrong to question German bureaucratic efficiency. Much to my surprise, a few months later and after completing a few forms, Dad began receiving a modest pension. Every three months a cheque of between £20 and £30 arrived in the post, the amount fluctuating according to the exchange rate between the pound and the Austrian schilling. To the great credit of the Austrian farmer, it showed that he must have been paying the relevant insurance contributions while Dad had been working on his farm for those couple of years during the war.

By this stage of the night all the other customers in the restaurant had left. The other tables had been cleared and made ready for the following day. It had been a really pleasant evening, probably even more appreciated as it was already becoming rare for me to go out socialising by 2004. And for a few hours I had been able to forget about the burdens of caring for Mum. Donna's parents were very good hosts and I was given several delicious dishes. I didn't want to take advantage of the hospitality so came armed with gifts for the two students: an econometrics textbook each. Probably not the most exciting of presents to receive, but hopefully ones that proved useful while they were studying for their degrees.

I suddenly became aware of the time. It was well past midnight. As soon as we had said our goodbyes, I ran over Kew Bridge hoping Mum had been all right on her own. When I got back home it was quiet. A few minutes later I heard a noise from upstairs. It was just Mum walking to the toilet. I breathed a sigh of relief. Everything was fine and she was none the wiser as to my little adventure earlier that evening.

Chapter 4   Carefree Holidays Drawing to a Close

Since my early teens, significant parts of the summer holidays have been spent in Felixstowe, a Suffolk seaside town about twelve miles from Ipswich, probably better known for its docks. My parents bought the semi-detached house in 1969 for £3,000 with the redundancy payment that my dad had received from J.LYONS, where he had been employed as a maintenance-fitter for many years. The house was conveniently divided into two flats. The ground floor was let which helped to pay for the local authority rates and other expenses, while the first floor and attic remained empty and ready to be used for a holiday whenever required.

As we didn't have a car, we travelled by train from Liverpool Street. Apparently, up until the 1940s, it had been possible to catch a train that ran straight through from London without the need to change at Ipswich. The suspension of that service was a pity as it lengthened the journey time, but at least the platform there provides a panoramic view of the town. At a very young age, the new scenery must have been a mystery to my sister Elizabeth and her questioning as to whether we were in another country never failed to amuse Dad. Another thirty minutes later and the train, comprising just one or two carriages, pulled into the station at Felixstowe. Built in 1898 towards the end of Victoria's reign, the still attractive structure boasted a very long platform, probably signifying its importance as a holiday destination in earlier times, but this was later shortened to allow space for a shopping development and car park.

Inevitably part of the holiday had to be devoted to maintaining the property. Dad might be repairing the roof while Mum would be doing some general housework as well as decorating. In fact, over the years, she managed to wallpaper nearly all of the rooms and, it has to be said, very neatly, maybe because the work was akin to her dressmaking skills. In those earlier years I did make some contributions to the chores, but it was really only from the 1990s that I became more actively involved in a few projects around the house. Nevertheless, time was set aside to enjoy the stay – one that was invariably carefree in comparison to the faster pace of life in London.

The house, which had sea views from two upstairs windows at the rear, was little more than a ten-minute walk from the beach. My sister preferred the route along the High Street as this provided an opportunity to visit a large toy shop. However, the most frequently used walk took us down a stepped path by the cliffs, past well-kept gardens near a theatre. Sometimes we could spend most of the day on the beach, particularly when the weather was good. I would go swimming to cool down, often accompanied by my sister who is nearly ten years younger. By the time she reached her teens, whilst never able to keep up with me on a bicycle or a run, positions were reversed when we were in the sea or a swimming pool. She was a better swimmer and despite my seniority, eminently more sensible. Elizabeth was quite content keeping close to the shore. Being a boy, I had to swim out as far as I could. I didn't get myself into any trouble, but it was foolish, causing Mum to suffer a few minutes of undeserved anxiety on one particular afternoon.

For lunch we would tuck into the sandwiches, fruit and cakes that Mum had prepared – a picnic that rarely escaped the attention of some curious, scavenging wasps. We nearly always chose the same spot on the pebbled beach which also revealed a small patch of sand as the tide retreated. It was a respectful few metres away from the occupants of the neatly maintained and colourful beach huts parked opposite the Spa Pavilion, the theatre that was set against the pretty backdrop of well-tended gardens by the cliff edge. Unless it was a very hot day, the fall in temperature, given the eastern breeze, prompted us to pack up at about 4 p.m. and stroll back home. Some evening walks involved going down the long promenade, past the pier that dated from 1887, towards the fun fair – or maybe just exploring the rest of the town to see if any houses were up for sale.

Despite inspecting many other properties over the years, my parents stuck with the one they had bought in 1969. It wasn't impressive from the outside with no front garden, but that turned out to be a blessing in disguise by giving us one less task to perform. Nevertheless, it had ample space, low council rates and even shared the same street as an imposing 'neo-Jacobean' listed building nearby. Dating from 1903, Harvest House started its life as a grand hotel. Its impressive clock tower, rising beyond the red tiled roofs, green domes and tall Tudor-styled brickwork chimneys, remains visible from many parts of the town. Above all, the central location of my parents' more modest property was perfect for close proximity to the shops, railway station and beach.

The last day of any holiday in Felixstowe was always one of great activity. In those earlier years this would invariably occur towards the end of August or – at the latest – the first week of September. If the house could be imagined as one busy bee-hive, you could be left in no doubt as to who played the role of queen bee on those occasions. All orders emanated from her – all notifications of completed tasks were reported back to her. Mum was in control. Even Dad had to fall into rank.

My task was usually to take anything that needed washing, including all the bed linen, to the nearby laundrette. Meanwhile, my dad concentrated on cleaning all the carpets with an old Hoover while my young sister went from room to room with a duster. Instructions were periodically issued from the kitchen. As well as preparing a simple meal before leaving and a few snacks for the train journey, Mum gave the sink and cooker a thorough clean. A similar level of attention was also paid to the adjacent bathroom. Bags were packed and when all the checks had been made that doors and windows were locked, it was time to turn off the gas, electricity and water supplies. The latter was possibly the most important – helping to avoid any pipes freezing as it was unlikely that we would be returning over the winter. Sometimes I was asked to run back from the station by a worried mother to make a final check of the property, anxious in case something had been forgotten. But when the train finally pulled out of the station with all of us on board, it signified that another carefree summer holiday was drawing to a close.

Sometime during the 1980s my parents stopped going to Felixstowe together. The advantage of one of them staying behind to look after the Chiswick property – mostly Mum for a few years – was given as an excuse, but probably the underlying reason was that their marriage was under a bit of strain. A few weeks break from living with each other was possibly welcome, particularly for her. Although never divorced or legally separated, Mum did move out of the Chiswick house in 1992 and stayed in my place in Hammersmith. From then onwards, I lived a fairly nomadic lifestyle, alternating between Chiswick and Hammersmith while also acting as an intermediary. It was also in that decade, particularly in the second half, that Dad seemed to lose interest in going to Felixstowe. And so, from 1993 onwards, part of the summer holiday was usually spent in Suffolk with Mum. Around this time, Mum was energetic, something that she held on to almost to the very end, but she was also still thinking rationally and despite approaching her seventies, there was absolutely no hint of the impending changes that were going to occur in her personality and cognitive skills brought on at a later stage by dementia.

When Mum returned to Felixstowe in 1993, after an absence of four years, she was shocked to see the extent to which the ground floor had been allowed to deteriorate. No longer let, it displayed a neglected appearance. But as well as requiring some decoration, structurally there was a problem with the hallway. The floor was sagging, leaving a gap below the skirting board. When I inspected it from underneath in the small basement, I could see the cause of the problem. Some of the joists had sunk, eaten away by a combination of rot and woodworm. Mum enthusiastically greeted my proposal to replace the entire floor and paid for the order of new floorboards and joists. All the rotten wood was removed and dumped in the garden. It looked unsightly so she suggested burning it in an old metal bath tub. The evenings were still cold but it was very pleasant sitting near the fire with a hot mug of tea and discussing future plans for the house. Within a week of that Easter holiday, I had completed the work achieving a perfectly level floor.

It must have been good because the job even met with praise from my dad – on one of his later but increasingly rare visits – which was unusual for me to receive! Mum was much more forthcoming with compliments. For the next few summers, there was real enthusiasm in continuing to make improvements. A new damp course was injected into the outside wall, while I added new electric sockets in quite a few rooms. In order to make visits to the place more comfortable throughout the year I also wired in the cables for storage heaters, significantly reducing the final bill from Eastern Electric when the appliances were finally installed in 1997.

In the early 1990s a friend, Jim, had helped remove some of the best furniture and carpets from the house by driving a van that we hired. It was a long journey there and back to London, probably over two hundred miles. We had a few hours break by the beach in Felixstowe, but it still must have been tiring to do so much driving in one day. In 1996, the trip was repeated but this time it was a friend from school, John, a PE teacher and a future coach of the Brazilian Rugby squad, who assisted in returning the items to Felixstowe. All this may sound like madness but it was a reaction to the changing policies by the government with regards to local government taxation. The decision to scrap the unpopular poll tax and replace it with the council tax worked in our favour and so the earlier decision to possibly sell the house was dropped.

The return trip from Felixstowe in the borrowed mini-bus must have been even more tiring for John since we had less time for a break. We also took a few wrong turnings on the way back when approaching London late at night which added to the distance. A few hours earlier, before setting off on the journey, we dropped in to visit Mum in Hammersmith for a meal. John, as did many other friends, enjoyed her cooking. But there was something else that struck me about that evening. It was the number of times that she kept repeating herself. She had probably done this before, but maybe because this time it was in the company of a friend, and therefore just a little embarrassing, it was more noticeable. At the time I put it down to her being just a bit forgetful, which could be reasonably expected from a seventy year old, but with the benefit of hindsight, I guess that evening was one of the first signs that the process of dementia was underway. If that was the case, then Mum was already on the start of a twelve year journey of gradual decline.

I probably missed other warning signs over the next few years but Lena, the next-door neighbour of my Hammersmith house, didn't. One day around the year 2000, she warned me that Mum might be starting to show some early signs of dementia. Having worked with elderly people suffering from the illness in the past, she had some insight on the matter – but it wasn't information that I wanted to hear. I dismissed it as a mistake and tried to look for other explanations for her changing behaviour. Nevertheless, the conversation did register in my mind and perhaps subconsciously better prepared me to accept the diagnosis a few years on.

Looking back at those last few years of the century, it is not surprising that I was either unable or unwilling to acknowledge that it was quite likely that the illness was already creeping up on Mum by stealth. It was a time when she continued to be independent, motivated and capable of doing many things, as the skills she had acquired over her lifetime remained unimpaired. She was still preparing meals as well as ever, dressing and washing herself, shopping and dealing with her own finances, corresponding with her sister in Italy, sewing and decorating. Above all, she was conversing normally and rationally and could switch between any of the three languages that she was fluent in, namely English, Italian or her own dialect, *Piemontese*. True, she occasionally went upstairs for something and then forgot the reason, but so what? Many young people do exactly the same thing and you wouldn't suspect that *they* had dementia, though John Suchet's book about his wife, *My Bonnie*, shows that the condition, tragically, is not just confined to the very elderly. With my mother, however, because the holidays in Felixstowe tended to take place on an annual basis, the location, in some ways, provided a barometer of how Mum's mental state was gradually changing.

On reflection, I would say the holiday of 2001 passed by without any problems. It was that summer when I had to work on the roof, re-fixing about thirty slates. Unlike jobs a few years later, I was able to get on with the work for a few hours at a time with Mum alone and left to her own devices. It took a couple of days to finish the work. Every time I attended to another section of the roof, I had to move the ladders, which then had to be tied up all over again. On finishing the job, I was glad to pack all the tools away in the long shed that Dad had built in the early 1980s. It now meant I could have a holiday. Some days found me cycling around the Felixstowe area with Mum. Sometimes we would go down to the docks and watch the ships being loaded. At the opposite end of the town an enjoyable afternoon could be spent cycling along the road that cut through the golf course. Continuing past a Martello tower, which has guarded that part of the coastline since Napoleonic times, we sometimes stopped at the Ferry Boat Inn for a drink to finally end up relaxing on the pebbled beach nearby.

But I was wrong to assume that my roofing work was complete for that year. In September I had to put up a different set of ladders again, because this time there was a leak in the attic of the Chiswick house. My dad, despite being in his late seventies, still had the strength to be able to come up and join me, though more in the role of inspector. But it was the last job that we ever did together. In December of that year, he started to look poorly and one Sunday evening close to Christmas, I came back from Hammersmith to find him in quite a bad way. Although I suggested calling for a doctor, he didn't want to know. It must have been about 9 p.m. when I followed him up the stairs to his bedroom, as he appeared to be a bit dizzy and unbalanced on his feet. "Are you sure you don't want me to call a doctor?" I enquired again. "No," he replied. "You can go now. I don't need you any more."

Those were his last words as I left his room. I went downstairs and spent about an hour tidying up in the kitchen and then went to bed myself. There was an uncanny silence in the house. No sound of my dad coughing – and that was unusual.

The following morning I woke up to a ghostly silence. Maybe Dad was still sleeping, although by that stage I was beginning to suspect another possibility. Assuming that the former was the case, and not wishing to disturb him, I left quietly to help Mum with some shopping as previously arranged. But what was happening back home, or not happening, was playing on my mind. I didn't stay too long in Hammersmith and as soon as an early lunch was over I was on my bike once more and cycling back to Chiswick. When I opened the front door and was again confronted by silence, I knew, more or less, that Dad must be dead. Nothing had been touched in the kitchen. I walked upstairs, but sat on the last step unable to go into the room. There wasn't a sound. No breathing or coughing. I wasn't used to dealing with death so it took a few minutes before I plucked up the courage and was ready to open the door. There on the bed in front of me was Dad, slightly curled up with his head resting on the left hand side of the pillow and his thumb in his mouth. It was obvious that he had passed away. I moved towards the bed and kissed him on the cheek.

As well as the doctor, I also phoned Mum and she cycled over to Chiswick. Despite their differences and the difficulties of their marriage, she attended the funeral in January. The Death Certificate recorded pneumonia as the cause and the official date was the 24th of December, 2001, but thinking back to the events of the previous night, I suspect he may have already been dead before midnight. For me there were mixed feelings. My dad had been good to me and taught me lots of useful practical things, but he was difficult to get on with and over the last nine years of his life, particularly after Mum moved to Hammersmith, he could be very unpleasant, regularly accusing me of taking his belongings – something that Mum had already been subjected to before leaving. Strangely enough, my fondest memory of my dad stems from a vivid dream that I had on Christmas Eve, the night following his death. When I woke up, I quickly jotted down a few notes to avoid forgetting it:

It seemed to be coming to the end of a day working out on the fields. The sky was a deep blue and the bundles of hay had a golden colour that stood out against the rich green background provided by the trees. The colours were incredibly strong. A beautiful young woman with blond, plaited hair and dressed in traditional Austrian costume smiled as she walked past. She was carrying a metal tray containing several tankards of beer. With each step it glistened, catching the rays of the setting sun. She made her way to a group of workers and when they glanced up at the approaching woman, I could recognise one of them as my dad. He wore a white shirt – the top-half unbuttoned – and so bright that it stood out in the sunshine. Still holding a sickle that he had been working with, he wiped the sweat off his brow with his free hand. No longer appearing frail – as he had done just a few days before his death – he was tanned, muscular and stood completely upright. He was like a young man in his prime, especially with his blue eyes and wavy light brown hair that had never shown any real signs of receding, right until his final days. He gratefully took the drink and looked so content in that rural setting. Out of the corner of his eye, he took note of my presence and turned towards me. He didn't say anything but pulled his shirt further open to reveal that his chest had been stitched and then pointed towards the area that had been operated on. It was as if he was saying he was fine. And then I woke up.

In some respects 2001 was a watershed. It was the year that I lost my dad and henceforth I would have the responsibility of looking after all the properties. That was somewhat onerous, but in many ways, and from a young age, Dad had been preparing me for such an eventuality. Meanwhile, Mum's dementia had not really manifested itself yet and so I was still able to enjoy a relatively high degree of freedom. It was still possible to go on a Geography field trip [1] with the school for five

---

[1] With Caroline, Paul M. and Luigi.

consecutive days in the summer term without too much concern about leaving Mum alone. Moreover, in November I took part in another outing, this time with the History department[2]. We took the Year 9 boys in a coach to *Ypres* in Belgium to inspect the trenches, museum and war memorials. On that morning I had to get up at about 4 a.m. and didn't arrive home until close to midnight. But that was the last time I was ever able to leave her unattended for so many hours in a day. From that year onwards it would get more and more difficult to go out – and so started the gradual restrictions on my liberty.

In the following year of 2002, I managed to fit in two journeys to Felixstowe, both with Mum. Prior to that, I had even got away with spending a few weekends up there on my own, allowing me to check that everything was all right as well as securing a welcome break. The first visit with my mother was in the February half-term, a few weeks after all the stress of organising the funeral for my dad. At last the storage heaters that I had helped to install were really proving their worth. It was only for three days and I can't remember much about it. Since my diary doesn't contain any significant entries, it must have passed by free of any incidents. The only memorable moment was the ride back when the Geordie coach driver, totally unfamiliar with the area, got lost and needed the guidance from one of the passengers to find both his way out of Felixstowe and then the location of the coach station in Ipswich. This greatly amused Mum as she pondered where we could have ended up by the end of the day had the passenger not intervened.

On the next excursion, this time in August, it was made easier as my sister drove us in her car. It turned out to be a good two weeks. We were still able to do normal things as in previous holidays and on some occasions, when Mum preferred to stay in, my sister and I could go out for a few hours together with little concern that Mum was on her own. However, one night particularly stands out as a worrying development. I was sitting in the front room upstairs when Mum suddenly came in looking very concerned. "Who is that woman in the kitchen going around like she owns the place?" she asked. It took me by surprise, but Mum looked even more shocked when I reminded her that it was just my sister, Elizabeth. "Oh, my God!" she exclaimed. "Please don't tell her!" she

---

[2] With Sarah, Paul B. and Roger.

implored. She had clearly not recollected her own daughter, albeit temporarily, but it was the first indication that she was beginning to have problems in recognising faces. This was possibly even more surprising given that my very pretty sibling shares many similar facial features to Mum, including brown eyes and curly hair of matching colour.

During 2003, two stays in February and August, but this time without my sister, once again provided pleasant breaks from London. The combination of walks, cycling, going to the beach, housework and watching some TV never allowed us to get bored. I also felt pleased that I had finished plastering the walls in the front room downstairs which meant that it was ready for decorating, probably the following year. However, I did have to abandon my planned bicycle ride to Ipswich. I had done this many times before and Mum had never questioned or made an issue about it. All of a sudden she seemed to become so anxious and concerned. And yet, when I had been fifteen, she made no objection to my desire to spend a few weeks alone in Felixstowe. It was the first of several summers when I found employment in a restaurant by the beach, first in the kitchen and then as a waiter. Exactly thirty-one years on and attempts to reassure her were futile. In the end I simply conceded to her wishes by taking the train. I can remember feeling a bit fed up. I didn't mind giving up horse riding. In fact it was my idea a few years earlier when I considered what could happen if I got injured and had two elderly parents to look after. But this objection to going along a perfectly safe cycle path seemed a bit over-the-top. Gradually my freedom was being eroded and there was a feeling of resentment.

But on that day I couldn't have had any idea of what further sacrifices I would be making over the next five years. If I'd had any inkling, I would have savoured the moment when I still had the opportunity to spend an afternoon by myself without having to worry about rushing home as soon as possible.

So far, touring around with Mum had never been a problem, although she could get a bit restless if we had to wait too long at a bus stop or train station. She was still fine in 2003 but the final journey back to London provided a warning that this was about to change. On reaching Victoria coach station at midday, we made our way to the Underground, about a five-minute walk. When we arrived there, Mum looked absolutely petrified. True, it was particularly busy as the normal volume of shoppers and tourists was swelled by football supporters travelling to the various grounds around London. But they were well-behaved – and there really shouldn't have been any cause for concern. In the past Mum would never have been unsettled by such a scene of energetic, yet harmless, activity. I expect it was the dementia causing her to feel alarmed by the sight of so many people, all rushing around in different directions. Reflecting back on this incident, it is hardly surprising that I would find travelling to Italy with Mum, three years later, so stressful.

Chapter 5   A Trip to Italy?

'What's that?'... 'Are you seriously telling me you considered … taking an eighty year old … with a severe case of dementia … on a holiday abroad?'... 'Are you crazy?' These might be your thoughts after reading the last sentence of the previous chapter, but it wasn't just a proposal made lightly on one particular day. By the autumn of 2005 plans were already under way to accomplish that very objective. There were further stays in Felixstowe after 2003 and these will be described later. However, I think I can safely promise that it might be difficult to provide you with a more interesting or engaging insight into the nature of the illness than the one about to be revealed. As a result, the story needs to move forward in time for a while.

Most people would be eagerly anticipating a holiday in Italy, but for me it was a journey that I was dreading. How on earth was I going to take my mother on such a long trip out of the country? By May 2006 she was certainly in the latter stages of dementia. To make matters worse she was just recovering from cellulitis, a nasty infection in the leg. Fortunately her fitness from all the walking completed each day, combined with treatment from the District Nurses who regularly visited to check and change the dressing around her ankle, all helped to prevent an ulcer developing. With a few days to go before the trip, both her doctor and the nurses felt confident that she would be well enough to travel. But it was her mind that I was more worried about, as over the last year her behaviour had become more unpredictable, especially on longer journeys. I could still get away with taking her on a thirty-minute bus ride to Kingston to visit my sister, but travelling all the way to Italy on a train for up to at least ten hours was another matter.

I had good reason to be worried. In the previous year, 2005, I had experienced a difficult coach journey to Felixstowe. Mum had been fine for most of the trip and there was no problem when the vehicle stopped at Chelmsford. But by the next stop, Ipswich, she was getting fed up with being on the bus. Most passengers travelling to Suffolk get off there. At that moment Mum must have thought, 'Why not us?' Sitting on my left next to the window, she moved to get out of her seat. "What's the matter, Mum? " I asked. "It's not time to get off yet," I added. But it was no use. She was determined to disembark. "Come on!" she insisted. "Everybody is getting off." This continued for a few minutes to the point at which she was becoming hysterical. All this was going on while the driver was outside helping passengers remove their luggage. There was only one other remaining traveller left on the coach sitting a few seats away. Looking a little worried he got up and moved to the back. Maybe I could have dealt with the situation better had I taken Mum off the coach for a few minutes. The only trouble with this alternative strategy was that it provided absolutely no guarantee that I would have been able to persuade her to get back on and consequently re-united with our belongings.

Fortunately the driver soon returned and then we were away on the last ten miles to the coast. My mother remained seated for the remainder of the journey, but she was still in a filthy mood and refused to talk to me. She alighted from the coach when it arrived in Felixstowe and walked ahead, still without saying a single word. She continued along the High Street and then, on reaching the focal point of the town centre, the road junction where a supermarket, chemist, cinema and recreational area can be found, she turned left without any prompting. That at least was a good sign as it showed she still could remember the street of her holiday home purchased as far back as 1969.

It was a sunny evening and in the small car park behind the food store, four teenagers were loitering. I was probably at least ten metres behind my mother and didn't make any effort to catch up with her. Since I had been left to carry all our bags, I was truly fed up with the whole situation. As my mother walked past the youths, I could hear their taunts and abuse. A few seconds later I caught up with the four lads and in a rage turned round towards them. They looked surprised, probably thinking that she was on her own. "Who the f***ing hell are you shouting at?" I exclaimed. "That's my mum!" They must have seen that the proverbial 'red mist' had descended. Before I had a chance to utter any more emotive language or make any threats, they apologised and moved off looking a bit embarrassed. I had been lucky. For all I knew they could have been carrying knives. But the combination of frustration from the coach journey and the anger provoked by their rudeness towards Mum, even if she had been getting on my nerves, meant that I was prepared to throw caution to the wind and my confidence and aggressive stance, while possibly a bit reckless, must have looked convincing enough.

Worse was still to come on the 2005 visit. This was the first year when staying in the Felixstowe house was causing a real problem. We had arrived on Wednesday evening. The next day, she had her hair cut at our neighbour's salon next door. Lynette was the hairdresser. As her mother had suffered similar problems, she was very patient when dealing with elderly people. By the following day, Friday, my mother had completely forgotten that she had been to the hairdresser less than twenty-four hours before, and no amount of persuasion on my part could convince her otherwise. Eventually I had to ask Lynette if she would be willing to spend a couple of minutes making a few adjustments to her hair without doing anything too drastic. She willingly obliged and the rest of the day passed by without any major crisis, although by the evening she was already demanding to go back to London, despite having return tickets booked for two days later.

Sunday arrived and finally it was time to go back to London. Thankfully Mum was very well-behaved on the coach, which arrived in Victoria in only two hours. But it was too good to be true. It then took nearly another three hours to get to Chiswick, an incredibly long time since the whole journey can be completed in no time if everything runs smoothly. Engineering works meant that we had to take two extra buses home, in addition to the Underground, and once again I was shunned for at least an hour. I suppose, in her mind, it had clearly been my fault. On returning home I then spent a bit of time working in the garden, mainly to let off a bit of steam. It wasn't too long before Mum's mood changed. She popped out from the kitchen where she had been looking at me from the window. Soon she joined me to offer some help. Thankfully there were some redeeming features of dementia – for when she was annoyed with me – at least it didn't last too long.

Nevertheless, if journeys around London or neighbouring counties presented such a challenge – this begged the question – why on earth was I entertaining the idea of a lengthy trip abroad with my mother when her condition of dementia was getting worse every few months? Well, the idea of going back to Italy probably has its roots in an International Rugby match being broadcast on the television. It was Saturday the 26th of February, 2005, to be precise. I think the Italians were host to one of the countries in the Six Nations; I can't even remember for sure who they were playing or the result, but I have a feeling that it may have been France. No matter. What was significant, however, was my mum's reaction to hearing the Italian national anthem. It is a colourful and cheerful piece of music and yet it prompted a stream of tears. Oddly enough she hadn't expressed any desire to return to Italy for years. Indeed, the thought of going there on holiday hadn't even crossed my mind, given the amount of extra work and responsibility I was taking on as a result of looking after her. But from that day on she expressed a real desire to visit her original homeland. I didn't take the request too seriously at first. I said I would try to organise something for later in the year, fully anticipating her to forget about it. But I was mistaken!

A surprising thing about dementia is that some thoughts are retained more strongly than you would expect. For instance, Mum had a pair of brown velvet shoes purchased in Felixstowe – very comfortable – and easily distinguished by the symbol of a crown on the front. Over the years, and particularly with all the walking, a hole developed in the sole. This resulted in her tights getting wet every time we went out in the rain or even shortly afterwards, while the pavements still remained damp or covered in puddles. Although this problem could have been avoided by her wearing the new pair that I had bought, Mum always insisted on selecting the ones with the crown. Despite giving it my best shot, the search for an identical replacement never succeeded. In the end the only way to get Mum to accept the new design was to hide the worn-out pair. Eventually, out-of-sight did mean out-of-mind – but only after a decent passage of time.

Surprisingly, that same selective power of memory extended beyond her preference for a particular shoe design. When I was reminded on several subsequent occasions that I had promised to take her to Italy, I found that by the summer of that year, despite her suffering from pneumonia in March, she was still determined to go. It meant I had to plan some way of getting her there and, more importantly, getting her back. At the time the actor, Tom Cruise, may well have been rehearsing for another spy film sequel. But for me – the proposed journey to Italy was going to be my *Mission: Impossible*.

Ideally, I should have taken her that spring. Better still, I should have organised the trip a few years earlier. The dementia was getting bad but even by that stage in 2005, her mind was sufficiently intact for her to get something from such a holiday. But there was a problem. Her passport had expired several years previously, unbeknown to me. This needed to be sorted out and quickly. I didn't want to wait until the summer holiday since travelling across Europe in July or August might prove to be too hot for her. If I couldn't get everything ready to take her in May, then it would have to wait until the following year as I also wanted to avoid the winter months as much as those in the summer.

Once the opportunity to go during the spring had disappeared, I decided that I would use the rest of 2005 for preparation. As well as the requirement of a new passport, I would also need to make enquiries regarding different modes of transport. A letter would also have to be written to my aunt expressing the possibility of a visit in May 2006 when the weather would be more conducive for an eighty year old to travel. Besides, the delay meant there was still time for her to either forget or change her mind – I hoped. It was particularly the thought of being stuck with Mum at a station or airport for hours or – worse still – days – that left me really worried. Mum would not have appreciated or understood any explanations in terms of unexpected strikes, inclement weather or natural disasters. Indeed – subsequent news bulletins over the years, showing stranded passengers desperately queueing by the ferries or at airports, serve to remind me of the genuine concern that I was experiencing prior to the Italian trip because, regardless of how meticulously planned the holiday was, I was still not looking forward to the risks and uncertainties posed by such a challenging journey. If anything was for sure – it was that I should expect the unexpected.

Chapter 6   Preparation

Clearly before any trip could be made, Mum would need a new passport. The source of such an essential document became something of a choice between a rock and a hard place. At first I felt tempted to apply for a British passport as she had been resident in England for over fifty years and it might only require filling in an application form. However, I later found out that there were too many obstacles that would make the process overly complex and time consuming. With that option looking increasingly less appealing, in the end I felt that there was little real alternative but to take Mum to the Italian Consulate in London. Inevitably, that would mean waiting in queues; and recent experience of the delays before seeing a doctor at the local GP[3] taught me that I only had a limited amount of time before her patience ran out – so it wasn't a particularly attractive choice.

Before having to endure what I anticipated would be a painfully stressful wait, I had to get some new passport size photos of my mother. There was a photo booth in the Post Office near Chiswick High Road. It was about a fifteen minute walk from the house. I did manage to get some photos – eventually – but only after I found a way to hold her down on the seat while staying out of view of the camera because on the first attempt Mum wouldn't keep still long enough to remain in shot.

Bit by bit things were falling into place. I had arranged to take my mum to the Italian Consulate on Monday the 24th of October as I was on half-term holiday. She was in a good mood that morning and there were no problems on the underground train from Gunnersbury to Sloane Square. We walked to the Consulate but still arrived too early and had to wait outside for at least half an hour. Normally this would be the maximum one could expect from Mum at this stage but she seemed quite relaxed; and for a while my thoughts were diverted by a tall and broadly built man with black hair and a Latin look ahead of the queue. Judging

---

[3] General Practitioner.

from a film that I had seen recently on DVD called *Chocolat*, he looked uncannily like my second cousin, an actor named Alfred Molina. There he played the role of the 'conservative' mayor obstructing any changes in the sleepy rural French town. It probably wasn't him, and even if it was, there was no way he would recognise us. Along with his younger brother, Roberto, we hadn't met since I last saw him acting in a play in East London in the late 1970s, just a few years away from his career taking off. But at least it provided an interesting distraction.

Briefly, thoughts wandered back to my childhood in the early 1960s when Mum had taken me to visit her cousin Giovanna. She had married a Spanish waiter and lived in the Ladbroke Grove area. I can remember walking past rows of big houses – probably all had been very elegant originally – each with a long flight of stairs leading up to an imposing front door. Typically, a list of names was visible by the side of each entrance indicating that nearly all the properties had been divided up into flats. Most of the buildings had paint peeling off – looking as if they were in need of some decoration to restore them to their former glory. Once inside, however, we were always made to feel at home by a friendly Giovanna. I got on particularly well with her son Alfred, despite being about three years younger. However, it was even more fun when *Alfredo*, as I remember him being called by his mother, was able to stay over for a weekend at Chiswick as the garden, basement and nearby recreation ground provided more areas to play. I can only recall one occasion when he annoyed me. That was the time he ripped out one of the Player's cigarette cards from an album of motor cars. Dated 1936, it had been donated to me by my next door neighbour and for all those years the collection had remained intact. Perhaps the Italian connection that I shared with my second cousin might help to explain both the motivation for his 'crime' and my 'indignation' at the theft of the *Alfa Romeo* – number two in the set. And maybe if I had known that such 'vandalism' was being perpetrated by a future movie star, it might have been less annoying. Decades later, it now seems rather trivial – an act that can be forgiven, but not forgotten.

Finally the doors of the Consulate were opened. On entering, it felt as if we had slipped into a small and seemingly timeless part of Italy tucked away in London; there was even an official dressed in the uniform of an

Italian policeman. It brought more memories flooding back. I could remember being taken there by Mum when I was young. Then I had felt somewhat wary of the official carrying a gun in his holster that for me, until then, had been an unfamiliar sight. It seemed as if most of the offices were filled with exactly the same furniture as that first visit in the 1960s but now the tables were adorned with computers. If memory serves me well, brown and grey were the colours that dominated the slightly dull surroundings – but ones that served to give the building its own distinguishing and charming character – and provided a welcoming flashback to times when Mum was well.

We were directed to a row of seats in a fairly large room. It wasn't too bad at first. Mum was remarkably relaxed and may have found it interesting to hear the conversations taking place all around in her native tongue. Thirty minutes passed, then forty-five. Eventually it was an hour, then incredibly, another fifteen minutes. The delay was understandable given the large number of people applying for passports, but for Mum, the notion of remaining stuck in one spot for too long probably appeared to be completely irrational. You could see the expression on her face changing ominously and I was feeling increasingly uncomfortable. I didn't want to have to go through this process again. Therefore it was essential to get the paperwork completed on that day. I asked the person in the nearby seat to keep our place in the queue and took Mum for a short walk as she was getting so agitated. "Are you mad, keeping me here all day?" she said in a reprimanding voice. Despite insisting on going home, I managed, somehow, to persuade her to return to her seat.

Another fifteen minutes passed – and then all hell was let loose. She exploded in an uncontrollable rage, shouting in Italian at me and even at some of the officials nearby. It was like a volcano, a mini Vesuvius erupting in that office. But instead of hot ash and lava, it was abuse – borne from the frustration of waiting for nearly two hours – that was being spat out. Amongst other comments, the phrase "*Porca Miseria* (Bloody Hell)!" was repeated a few times – not the strongest language that could have been used, but it left nobody in any doubt that her patience had run out completely. The room fell into silence as all conversations suddenly stopped. We were now the focus of attention.

Much to their credit the officials, whom I had warned earlier of Mum's condition and the difficulties of waiting too long, reacted very quickly by escorting us to the front of the queue. What a relief and what good common sense on their part! Unsurprisingly, nobody in the room objected. In fact I think they were all too scared to question the decision. Maybe some people would have been embarrassed by the scene but I was already used to her temper and in some ways I was quite proud of her. She still had spirit in her, so typical of many Italian women, which might have been quashed by a cocktail of drugs and tranquilisers had I allowed her to be sent to a nursing home – something that I wanted to avoid at all costs. Moreover her outburst did work. However, from that moment onwards, the thought of Mum having to wait too long for anything left me full of apprehension!

We were now at the front of the queue and although my mum still looked annoyed, at least she had calmed down sufficiently to continue with the proceedings. The lady dealing with our form tried to go through the questions as quickly as possible. When I told her that Mum was having problems signing her name, she didn't make any fuss whilst I held the unsure hand that was clutching the pen and helped Mum trace out something that looked like her normal signature. Payments were made and it was almost done. Mum would soon have her new Italian passport. With that accomplished, we left the Consulate, much to the relief of not just me but also quite a few staff. The only remaining task was to return a few days later to collect the document but this time, unremarkably, no longer accompanied by my mother. One more obstacle remained on that memorable day at the Consulate but this time it was actually a physical one. At Gunnersbury station she got stuck in the barriers at the exit. It provided a warning that future trips on public transport would become increasingly problematic, posing many new challenges that able-bodied and able-minded people often just take for granted.

So by the end of October, a new passport had been acquired and I had already written to my aunt proposing the following May for the visit. During a previous phone call, she had suggested coming over earlier so that the stay could coincide with the Winter Olympics to be held in and around *Torino*. Clearly she may not have realised the speed at which the dementia was taking its toll on my mum's ability to comprehend and appreciate different activities. Moreover, I just didn't fancy the idea of combining both unpredictable weather and temperament on the same journey so the winter invitation was politely declined.

The next decision was transport. The easiest mode to rule out was the coach. It might be the cheapest but, after experiencing the problems of the relatively short journey to Suffolk earlier in the year, there was no way I could risk such a long and uncomfortable trip through France to reach Italy. Obviously the plane would be the quickest means, but there were disadvantages. There was no direct flight from Heathrow to *Torino,* which meant extra travelling. The options were Gatwick or Luton to *Torino* or Heathrow to *Milano* (Milan). Either way would have involved adding quite a few more hours to the journey. An additional worry concerned how Mum would react on the plane.

One remaining alternative would be to take the train, which has always been my preferred form of travel. I was pleasantly surprised when I found out that the time involved would only be about ten hours, which was so much shorter than my first recollected trip to Italy with Mum back in 1964. The first part of the journey between the nearby Kew Bridge station and Waterloo would be straightforward. At that time the Eurostar service had yet to be moved to St Pancras International. As far as the cost was concerned, something which was low down in the list of priorities, the fare seemed quite reasonable. The only real worry was the inconvenience of having to change trains in Paris and use the Metro or a taxi to reach the other station. It was such a pity as the journey could have been cut by about three hours if this changeover could have been eliminated and replaced by a direct route.

Partly to keep Mum used to travelling on public transport and also because I didn't like to leave her alone in the house too often or for too long, I took her to the booking office up in London to get the tickets for Eurostar, a regular high-speed train service linking London and Paris via the tunnel under the English Channel. A few years on and I could have booked them on the internet, but at the time I wouldn't have had a clue where to start. This may sound strange but when you are looking after someone with dementia, you are increasingly drawn into their own little world. Technology was changing at an incredibly rapid pace, and despite some limited exposure at work, I was being left behind to such an extent that it felt as if I was stuck in some time-warp.

Anyway, back to January 2006 and much to my relief Mum was incredibly well-behaved in the booking office and within about ten minutes the tickets had been printed and paid for. We would be setting off from Waterloo on Saturday the 26th of May, first class to the *Gare du Nord*, Paris. I would later regret not booking first class for the whole of the journey to *Torino*. The only little glitch of the day was using the escalators on the underground. Mum looked terrified as we approached them and took a little coaxing before I could persuade to her to step on. But getting off also presented a problem. I needed to hold her in order to prevent her losing her balance as the steps started to flatten out. Well, she passed that test, but what unexpected challenges would meet us on the holiday in May, I wondered?

A few weeks before the trip I decided to take Mum on a practice train ride from Kew Bridge to Waterloo. Thank goodness I had the foresight. Because I cycle around London for most journeys I hadn't used this particular line for years. We didn't have to wait on the platform for too long, given the frequent service to Waterloo. When the train arrived and the doors opened, I couldn't believe my eyes. Not only was there a huge gap but the height of the carriage was equally scary. How on earth could most elderly people be expected to use such a mode of transport? You almost needed to be an athlete to board it. Luckily another passenger nearby spotted Mum's swinging leg repeatedly missing the floor of the carriage and kindly offered to help so that, together, we managed to lift her on. Fortunately, the step at Waterloo was much lower and she experienced no difficulties disembarking. I was later informed that I could book assistance on the platform, but never took up the offer as it is very difficult to arrange set times when dealing with someone with dementia. No, my mind was made up. On the day of the trip we would try to get to Kew Bridge early and just pray that someone was on the same platform both willing and able to help. Before leaving Waterloo Station, we made our way to the main Eurostar entrance to be more familiar with procedures and surroundings.

I had been given the timetable for the journey and a few weeks before going I had an idea that might simplify things. I would have lots of documents to carry which were vital to avoid losing. For a number of years, I had been ordering hundreds of T-shirts for the Charity Walk that I organise for the school. Each shirt has the design of the route and names of the participants printed on. 'Why not use the same method for the timetable?' I thought. Taking similar care, I neatly wrote out the times, train numbers and seats for both the outward and return journeys. My instructions requested that the writing should be printed upside down, so that wearing the shirt would enable me to read from it whenever necessary. The man in the Hammersmith shop looked a bit puzzled by the order, but after a few minutes he returned with the white T-shirt displaying the Eurostar train schedule. It later proved to be money well spent.

Everything was now in place. All that remained were things like the packing of clothes and other luggage that you would take on any normal holiday. I had planned as best as I could but still felt a bit anxious the night before going. Make no mistake, this was going to be a very stressful journey even if everything were to run as smoothly as possible – and I'm sure one that not that many would have taken in similar circumstances.

Chapter 7   A Setback

March 2005 had seen my mother contract pneumonia which forced her to stay in hospital for two weeks. She was strong for a woman of seventy nine and recovered well. A year on and as we had almost reached the end of March, it looked as if she was going to get through the month without a recurrence of any serious illness. Moreover, with spring approaching, I was feeling increasingly confident about the forthcoming trip – well – at least as far as her physical health was concerned. Sunday the 26th seemed like any other normal day. Mum got up at about 6 a.m. and was quite lively for an hour – but then suddenly became overcome with tiredness and went back to bed.

A tired Mum was unusual but, oddly enough, it was sometimes welcome because it gave me a few precious hours to myself. I was able to go for a run by the river, which was becoming a rare treat, and even had some spare time to catch up on marking the homework submitted by the

6th form. That freedom was great until about lunch time, but when she stayed in bed all day I became a little anxious. She had a temperature so I made sure she had a few drinks. As far as I could see she must have gone down with influenza.

Mum had a difficult night which meant I didn't have much sleep either. She was shivering and her body was very sensitive to being touched. All this seemed to confirm my earlier suspicion that influenza was to blame. She was going back and forth to the toilet and most times was getting caught short. Maybe to avoid wetting the carpet she held her nightdress between her legs to try to catch the urine which she couldn't hold, but that meant I had to change her nightdress at least eleven times that night – along with some sheets. I shouldn't have been too surprised because I had read a book describing the likelihood of encountering the problem of incontinence in the later stages of dementia. Still reeling from the workload, I really hoped that this was just a temporary problem and not the onset of a new phase in the downward spiral of the illness. I concluded it would be a waste of time going to bed, so when I wasn't changing either her or the bed linen, I tried to catch a bit of sleep on the floor next to her room.

In all, I probably managed to obtain about two hours of broken sleep and got up when my mum awoke at about 6:30 a.m. She stayed up long enough to drink a mug of milk shake made from a nutritional food supplement powder from one of a variety of flavours – vanilla, banana, strawberry and chocolate – all of which Mum sampled at some time. She then returned to bed and again slept for most of the day. I didn't have to go to school on Monday but had been booked in for an economics training day. One important early task that morning was to phone and inform the organisers that I wouldn't be able to attend as I wanted to keep an eye on my mother. I also felt extremely tired from the previous night's exertions, but kept that detail to myself during the short conversation. Later in the day I found time to watch a video called *The Body Story* which explained the flu symptoms, leaving me somewhat reassured that it was nothing more serious than that.

Thankfully I had a far more peaceful night and when I woke up on Tuesday I found a much brighter and livelier Mum. I was still a bit concerned so when my Upper 6th students were sitting a mock exam in the second half of the morning a Science teacher, Gillian, kindly agreed to look after my class so that I could go home to spend a bit more time with Mum over lunch. She seemed fine so I was able to leave her for the second time that day and go back to school for my afternoon lesson. Later in the evening she indicated that she was strong enough to go for a walk. There were further grounds for optimism when I found that even her appetite had returned, which is nearly always a good sign.

I knew that Wednesday would be a particularly busy day hence I was glad Mum had appeared to have recovered so well. The evening before, I worked out an itinerary. I had to cycle to St Mark's school in Hounslow early in the morning in order to teach economics to their Upper 6th and then return back to Kew to have dinner with Mum. This was to be followed by an afternoon of sport at Gunnersbury, then back home again to take Mum out for at least one walk, prior to an early supper. Because I was required to return to Gunnersbury for the 6th form Parents' Evening, this wouldn't leave much time to relax. All in all, it represented a challenging, but just about feasible schedule.

When I left home at midday – for the second time in the space of just a few hours – everything seemed fine with Mum. Moreover, the plan was running as smooth as clockwork. But after that there was an unexpected turn of events. About two hours later I came back home from football to find my mother in great pain. Her right foot and leg were both incredibly swollen and she had great difficulty in walking. I phoned the GP and was advised to bring her in. However, there was no way that she would have been able to make such a distance on foot – certainly not in her condition – so I had to call for a mini cab. With great difficulty she struggled to make it to the pavement, but was unable to get into the waiting car. I don't know if she had forgotten how to adjust her body to manoeuvre herself into the seat or whether her immobility was caused by being in such pain. I suspect it was a combination of both. Every time I tried to gently push her into the car, she screamed and held on to the edge of the car roof. She refused to bend her body at all. Each effort to encourage her into the car only served to increase Mum's anger further. The minicab driver was very patient, but eventually he had to give up. The next attempt was with a people carrier, but with the same unsuccessful result. In desperation I phoned the GP again and was now beginning to lose my patience. It's not as if I called that often. When I did, it was nearly always because I felt there was something serious. The receptionist finally agreed to request an ambulance and later that evening we were both driven to the hospital. I had mixed feelings. There was relief that she would soon be examined and treated, but there was also the disappointment that, despite all my efforts to avoid the hospital in March, she was once again being admitted. It was as if she had been destined to return.

It did not take long for the medical staff to diagnose the illness. She had not been enduring flu at all – as I had mistakenly thought. The severe swelling of her leg confirmed that she was suffering from cellulitis, a bacterial infection. Later tests revealed that she had also been victim to a urinary tract infection. Both would have caused great discomfort. Two years later I was in a better position to appreciate the pain associated with cellulitis when I too succumbed to the streptococcus bacteria.

It is a very deceptive illness. You think for a day or two that you have caught the flu. One of the early symptoms described in the literature is malaise. I can remember the Sunday in February 2008 when I didn't have the strength to do anything. Despite desiring a cup of tea, it took nearly two hours to find the motivation to get out of the chair that afternoon and walk a few metres to the kitchen. The complete loss of appetite, along with the tenderness, fever and chills, that my mum had also experienced two years earlier, serve to trick you into thinking you have the flu. The only odd thing at the time was that I didn't experience a sore throat. Then, just like my mum, I had a day when I felt I had recovered – great – but that was an illusion.

The next day when I woke up, I had a terrible itch in my left leg and a red rash covered the area below the calf muscle and above the ankle. As the hours passed I noticed that there was a definite swelling of the leg. Remembering the experiences of my mother, I started to suspect that I had cellulitis. Over the next few days I experienced the pain that my mum must have been suffering, but at least I had an understanding of what was going on. I could still walk but with difficulty. The worst part of the day was getting out of bed in the morning. The first occasion took me completely by surprise. When I stood up, I felt such a powerful jolt of pain that it just knocked me back down onto the bed. I found the only way to prepare myself for walking was to sit on the edge of the bed for about ten minutes. It was uncomfortable, since it seemed as if there was liquid draining down inside my leg, trying to find some new balance or equilibrium. When it felt as if it had stopped, I was then able to stand and limp tentatively downstairs. It was an unpleasant few weeks before I fully recovered, but it wasn't so bad that I couldn't go to work. Antibiotics and regular changes of dressing eventually cured the problem but not until all the swollen blisters had burst, leaving my leg in a pitiful state for a few weeks.

More than a year on and I was still left with a few brown patches on the skin – ones that, until a few months ago, I was convinced might serve as a permanent reminder of an illness I had the misfortune to share with my mum. Fortunately, such marks have been fading with the further passing of time, but the whole experience did at least help me to understand the discomfort that Mum must have suffered when she had been struggling to get into the waiting vehicles back in the spring of 2006.

Once again my mother spent about two weeks in hospital providing me with a period when I could enjoy some uninterrupted sleep and, outside the visiting hours between 2 p.m. and 8 p.m., an opportunity to catch up on some housework. To speed up treatment Mum was put on antibiotics to be administered intravenously, but unfortunately she pulled out the line into her arm on the second day and from then on the medicine was given orally. But Mum could be crafty. She would sometimes hide the capsule under her tongue and spit it out later. On some occasions I could see one discarded on the floor. One method I found useful in order to get her to take her medication involved opening the capsule and sprinkling the contents on a crème caramel or trifle that I had brought in. It probably helped to disguise any unpleasant taste and was certainly easier to swallow.

Because Mum was completely immobile for most of her stay, my visits to the hospital in 2006 were far more relaxing than the previous year. Then in 2005 she couldn't keep still for long, despite being treated for pneumonia. Nearly every day on arrival, I found her wandering around the adjoining wards talking to other patients – for this was a time when she could still communicate in English. Also, to help relieve her boredom, I had to take her for walks around the hospital several times during each visit. Unfortunately it was still very cold outside, so that limited the walks to the hospital shops and canteen, as well as nearly every corridor that we found access to – a pity because the hospital grounds could have provided some more interesting scenery. And I knew the area well; there were still some sections left unchanged from the days when I had worked there as a gardener in the summer of 1977 – a temporary job that commenced very soon after graduating from University. In fact, on my first morning back in Chiswick, rather than enjoying an expected lie-in, I was awakened abruptly by a bowl of water being thrown in my face and Mum ordering me to get out of bed to search for employment!

I attended every day while Mum remained in hospital and my sister also visited. On at least one occasion she was accompanied by her friend Jack who lived in Eastbourne. It was Grand National day. I was later informed that his good deed may have been rewarded financially when one of the horses that he had backed finished in the frame at generous odds. Friendly and easy to get on with, it was always effortless to engage in conversation with Jack as he had a wide range of interests, including sport. And so, with all these visits and care from the hospital staff – Mum was certainly not being left unattended.

By Sunday the 9th of April she was ready to be discharged from the hospital. Before being driven home in a modified mini-bus, a Philippine nurse took my mum for a shower. I could hear several shouts of protest but a few minutes later she emerged from the room dressed and looking fresh and ready to go. There was an undesirably long wait, made all the more uncomfortable by Mum's impatience to leave, but eventually we set off. Although some of the skin on her leg was still peeling off – made to look worse by a few areas covered in blisters – the swelling had gone right down. With her mobility regained, Mum declined the offer of a trip to the minibus in a wheelchair. My only remaining concern was that she had trapped her ankle in the bed guard a few days earlier and the injury had left an opening in the skin which left the risk of an ulcer developing.

Later that day, just as we were about to set off on a walk by the river, one of my neighbour's, June, a friendly Jamaican lady – always willing to talk whenever we met her – noticed Mum's wound. Straight away she looked concerned and advised me to seek further medical assistance. Fortunately I heeded her warnings against allowing the injury to heal on its own. Mum's initial care of the ulcer was very competently managed by

- 58 -

the nurse at the local GP. The responsibility for the last stages of her treatment was then handed over to the local District Nurses. They visited every few days and after cleaning the wound, reapplied a fresh dressing. This continued for several weeks, right up to a few days before the Italian holiday. Her strength was returning, along with her appetite, and soon we were back to the routine of walking round the block, or by the river, several times a day. All this exercise must have helped to speed up the recovery. Combined with the care given by the nurses and the medication provided, the likelihood that Mum would be fit to travel was increasing all the time. Just a few days before the departure date, both the nurses and her GP gave Mum the green light to go.

Chapter 8 The Journey

It was the morning of Saturday the 27th of May, 2006, and D-day had finally arrived. If that sounds overly dramatic then wait for the description of the journey to unfold. I certainly didn't anticipate a relaxing and straightforward trip, but this was no time to dwell on any misgivings. I got up early, having slept on the floor in the same room as Mum, and packed away the sleeping bag. I quickly dressed myself, remembering to put on the white T-shirt that had been printed for me with all the details of the journey. Next it was Mum's turn.

I was still able to wash Mum in the evening by this stage of her illness. That made it easier in the mornings, which was particularly helpful on this one. Furthermore, Mum cooperated fully by making absolutely no fuss about getting out of bed promptly. It meant that as soon as I was ready, I was able to concentrate on getting her dressed. The nightdresses were very easy to slip on and off and were surprisingly well-designed given their low price. I had bought them in a range of colours – pink, blue, yellow, purple and a pale green. I took off the yellow nightdress that she had been wearing overnight, quickly replacing it with a fresh sky-blue one. Then she smiled and performed her characteristic pat on the sides of her hips with the palm of her long hands as if to signify approval of my choice. I got her to sit on the bed and helped her put her tights on. Knickers were omitted from her attire as she might need to go to the toilet quickly at any point during our travels. In that respect, I didn't want anything to delay me providing help swiftly. After all, there was no guarantee that I would be given much, if any, warning.

She always looked very smart in the navy blue dress with small white spots. That was the next item. However, the comfortable nightdress remained underneath – for without it – there was the risk Mum would complain of feeling cold as soon as we stepped out of the house. Her white hair looked neat as I had been able to wash it two days earlier, despite her struggles and complaints. All the regular walking over the previous few years had left her slim. Her pretty face gave the appearance of a woman at least ten years younger and perhaps more feminine than in the past. I looked at her and thought to myself – yes, she was definitely presentable to my aunt. She certainly didn't look neglected.

Next it was downstairs for breakfast and then we were ready for the short walk to Kew Bridge Station. It was very early in the morning and consequently still cold, so I decided it would be appropriate for her to wear a cardigan and a thin, light grey coat. I took two rucksacks; one that I carried in my hand, the other larger one was on my back. Mum carried her black handbag, more out of habit than necessity. By then she had become prone to lose or misplace it. In order to minimise any worries, there usually wasn't much inside of any value or significance. Holding my mum's hand, we set off down the road on what was to be a long journey ahead.

Remembering, as we crossed the road by the traffic lights near Kew Bridge, the problems of boarding the train, I prayed that somebody would also be waiting on the platform to give some assistance. As we walked down the steps of the station, I could see in the distance a tall, well-built man wearing a Harlequin rugby shirt. Perfect, I thought. "No problem," he replied, when I explained the need for some help in getting Mum on the train. He stood about five metres away and didn't speak again but when the train arrived, and the doors opened, he took her right arm and together we lifted her into the carriage effortlessly. Great! The first hurdle had been overcome. In less than thirty minutes the train was pulling into Waterloo Station. It was relatively easy to get off without any assistance and soon we reached the Eurostar entrance. We passed through the barriers and completed the passport and ticket checks fairly quickly. So far, and much to my relief, there hadn't been any problems. I had reminded Mum that we were going to Italy a few times already that morning, but I wondered how much of this she was really able to comprehend or retain. We entered a huge lounge area for waiting and despite it being very crowded, we didn't have any difficulty finding seats. Our train was due to depart at 9:09 a.m. and thankfully we had arrived early with over forty minutes to spare. My only concern about this good punctuality was the length of time required to wait, and whether Mum would remain patient.

A few minutes passed and then an announcement called any awaiting travellers for the next departure to Paris. It was about 8:30 a.m., probably the last train before our one. The majority of people in the lounge must have been booked for this earlier train. Almost in unison, nearly everybody got up to make their way to the section designated for boarding the waiting train. I didn't move but to my surprise, Mum got out of her seat to follow. "Come on!" she implored. I grabbed her hand to hold her back and then tried to explain that this wasn't our train. But the more I tried, the more irate she became. 'I can't believe this!' I thought. We hadn't even got out of London and already she was making a scene. In a few seconds, memories of the difficulties experienced on preceding trips came flooding back – the similar problem on the coach stopping at Ipswich, her nervousness on a previous train journey to Weybridge and the challenge of boarding most forms of public transport. Then of course, there was the drama at the Italian Consulate and the hassle involved in getting her passport photos. Moreover, when looking ahead, all I could feel was apprehension – anticipating the likely difficulties that could be encountered in Paris and also the prospect of having to sit for another six or seven hours on the train with her for the last part of the journey.

While these negative thoughts were running through my head, Mum continued tugging me to follow her with the others. Then something just snapped. In that instant I decided to abandon the trip. "If you think I'm going to take you all the way to Italy with this carry on, then you've got another think coming!" I continued uttering a few more words of protest. But Mum looked puzzled by this outburst that, to her, must have seemed totally unjustified. "I've had enough, and as far as I'm concerned, we're going home and don't ever ask me to go to Italy again!"

I really believed I had made my mind up. In that brief moment, I didn't even care about the cancellation wasting hundreds of pounds. I was just so annoyed. I quickly thought things through and as soon as I got Mum home to Chiswick, I would phone my aunt, apologise and try to explain that it was now becoming impossible to take her sister on trips abroad. That was my intention but then I found it wasn't so easy to get out of the waiting area. I was pulling Mum now and we were going against the general flow of the crowd. How exasperating! "Where on earth is the bloody exit?" I murmured under my breath. Mum seemed to have given up her battle to join the others and must have been wondering where we were going by this stage. Finally I found a porter. "Excuse me, but how do you get out of this place?" He was very tall which seemed to add to his air of authority when he spoke. "Not that easy, sir," came his surprised yet calming response. "But what is the problem?" I then hurriedly tried to explain the troubles I had experienced. He patiently listened but was also looking around attentively at the same time. "Well, sir, I think you'll find it will take quite a while to get through all the checks in order to leave. And by the way, I've just noticed that your train is ready for boarding."

'Oh well,' I thought. 'Let's take one more chance – especially if getting on the train provides the easier of the two options.' And so the trip was back on! I thanked the porter for his help and, still holding my mum's hand, made a move towards the stairs that we had been directed to. The train was waiting and after consulting my printed T-shirt, I found coach 09 and seats 35 and 31 opposite each other and next to the window. It was first class and we received a full English breakfast, with the waiter popping back every now and again to check that everything was fine as we sped towards Paris. This was so relaxing and, as it turned out, the best part of the journey. It probably took about two hours and for the twenty or so minutes through the tunnel you feel totally unaware of crossing the English Channel. Mum was calm and had enjoyed her breakfast. How fortunate that the porter had intervened at the right moment. As a consequence, I was able to experience my first journey on the Eurostar service and was impressed with how smoothly everything ran.

It was midday when the train arrived in Paris. The station was the *Gare du Nord*. I got off the train and then held out my hand to help Mum. The door exit from the train was quite high in comparison to the platform but there were two steps to facilitate descent. At that point I had no reason to suspect that anything untoward was going to occur. After all, she was still reasonably agile. Moreover, she had been negotiating the steps over a railway bridge near home – one that we must have crossed several times a day over the previous few years – without any difficulty. Despite her age, I doubt very much if the events about to unfold would have happened had she not reached such an advanced stage of dementia. If it was difficult for me to foresee the likelihood of any problems, then it was nigh on impossible for the staff on the train. Unfortunately the next task that I set before her was just too much to cope with.

Mum put her right foot on the first step but then, for some inexplicable reason, she attempted to put her left foot on the platform and completely bypassed the second step. Of course it was too far for her and in a split second she fell through the gap between the train and the platform. It was quite deep and I believe she would have fallen completely down and out of view had I not been holding one of her hands. It helped to break the fall and luckily a porter nearby was very alert and acted straight away by grabbing her right arm, adding further support. Mum let out a scream from the shock of the sudden fall but at least she only went down to about waist level and thankfully was uninjured. But it was enough to alarm her. It wasn't long after we had pulled her out of the gap, and got her back on her feet, that fright turned into anger. It was much warmer in Paris. Mum took off her coat and threw it at me. Without any hesitation, she stormed off, quickly overtaking other passengers heading for the exit. Chasing after her with two rucksacks, her coat and handbag, I soon caught up but it was going to take a lot of coaxing to calm her down and we had just over two hours to cross Paris and reach the *Gare de Lyon* for the next train that was due to depart at 14:24. We had to press on. Besides, I had no choice. There was no turning back now.

Just for a few seconds I still toyed with the idea of catching the Metro. It would be very cheap, but by then I had a very volatile eighty-year old on my hands with severe dementia to travel with, so simplicity, regardless of the cost, was the top priority. Mum was still in a foul mood but I managed to persuade her to follow me and we headed for the signs indicating taxis.

This wasn't a time for shopping around, haggling or making price comparisons. I headed for the first available taxi driver. He showed me a card indicating that the relatively short trip, about six km, to the other station was 90 euros. 'What a complete rip-off,' I thought. I'm good at maths and didn't need a calculator to work out the cost. At the then current exchange rate, it would be over £60. Worse still the taxis in Paris aren't like the ones in London where my mother could simply stoop a bit lower to gain access. No, although this was a nice and comfortable car, it still involved quite a palaver trying to get her in. All this didn't help to allay her annoyance. The next thing that puzzled me was the route taken to the *Gare de Lyon*. I had already checked the map weeks before and even contemplated walking the journey with Mum as the distance was just within her range. However, the fear that to take just one wrong turning could prove disastrous was a sufficient deterrent, yet it had looked reasonably straightforward. That is why the meandering route taken by the driver puzzled me and begged an obvious question. Why was the driver seemingly taking us on a tour of Paris? Maybe it was to justify the extortionate fee being charged. Eventually we arrived outside the correct station. I begrudgingly paid the ninety euros and the driver seemed to wait as if expecting a tip. 'Huh. You'll be lucky,' I thought. He must have read my mind and soon left us outside the main entrance.

The *Gare de Lyon* is an old, small but pretty station – almost quirky in its style of architecture. We were greeted by an impressive facade, enhanced by a tall clock tower slightly resembling Big Ben, one of the famous icons of London. The position of the hands against the black roman numerals on its white face indicated that we were due for a long delay. Inside, steel columns and arched frames supported a glass roof that covered another white clock dominating the middle of the concourse. There it was surrounded by ornate, black metalwork and, even more surprisingly, a couple of palm trees. Built around 1900, this train shed had already been used in *Mr Bean's Holiday* starring Rowan Atkinson. Indeed, its odd and magical aura left me with the thought that this location would not have looked out of place in a *Harry Potter* film. However, this was not the time for day dreaming or lingering to appreciate the aesthetic properties of the surroundings.

There was a lot of bustle, as with any station, and all this must have been a bit too much for Mum. People suffering from dementia tend to prefer a tranquil atmosphere and this was going to be difficult to find whatever mode of transport I had chosen. It was probably over an hour since my mum had fallen in the gap by the platform, back at the other station. She was still in a bad mood – one that was being fuelled by her getting impatient with all the unavoidable hanging around. Sometimes she would sit down. Next she would go off for a walk with me on her trail, carrying our luggage – constantly trying to make sure she didn't get lost – fearful that she could just merge into the crowds that were crisscrossing the hallway to their various destinations. In between all this to-ing and fro-ing, I was grateful that we managed to grab something to eat and drink. As well as quenching any thirst or satisfying any pangs of hunger, sitting down to dine for a few moments served an even greater need – helping to keep her temporarily occupied during this painful interval of waiting.

Finally, thank goodness, it was time to catch the next train for *Torino*. Once again the T-shirt came in handy. A casual glance downwards revealed that we needed to find coach 15 and seats 37 and 38, next to each other with Mum sitting by the window. It wasn't first class on this part of the journey however. The carriage was fine, but it could have done with more leg room and it was a bit awkward for Mum to get out when she wanted to go to the toilet. On that issue, which had been a further worry for me, she didn't give me any real problems. I accompanied her to the toilet and helped, but it was a little awkward as there wasn't much room. Other than that, the remainder of the journey was thankfully uneventful. There was plenty of interesting scenery to look at, especially when the train progressed upwards and through the Alps. Many years ago when I was only nine, my mum had taken me to Italy for my grandfather's funeral. Like any child of that age I must have been pestering her with questions about how long it would take before we arrived. And I seem to vaguely recall her trying to occupy me by pointing out all the lovely views. Now the roles were reversed.

The train crossed the French border and we were at last in Italy, something indicated more by the passport checks taking place than any change in the surroundings outside the train. One of the stations that we encountered in the mountains was *Bardonecchia*, the small town containing the hotel where Mum had worked for a while after the war. I wondered if Mum still recognised the place. Did it stir any memories? Probably not, because she made no comment about the place as we passed through. Such a pity! Years ago she might have been able to point out the actual hotel if it was close enough to the rail track. And then you could feel the train descending and eventually reaching flatter ground. The Alps were now in the background and *Torino* would soon be reached. It had been a nightmare of a journey and I had been right to set off with a sense of trepidation, but as the train pulled into the station of *Porta Susa, Torino*, I felt a real sense of satisfaction that we had at least made it, even though my nerves had been more than a bit strained.

We were greeted at the platform by my cousin Germano, but Mum didn't recognise her nephew, despite having met him several times before. About 5' 9'' and two years my senior, his brown curly hair had hardly receded. Handsome, fashionably dressed and still fit, he had changed very little over the twenty or so years since I had last seen him. Effortlessly he helped put the luggage into the boot and once again I had to go through the ritual of encouraging Mum into the backseat of the car. Occasionally he managed a few words or phrases in English and his accent sounded like the stereotypical Italian portrayed in most films. Meanwhile back at the flat, my cousin Monica and my aunt Maria Teresa were busy preparing an elaborate meal to welcome us home.

Chapter 9 Some Holiday!

It must have been some time after 8 p.m. when we arrived outside a big block of flats. We made our way through the foyer and then took the lift to the third floor where we were greeted by my cousin Monica. Of similar height to Mum, and pretty, she had long black hair, dark eyebrows and brown eyes. Her light brown skin meant that she looked as if she was from Sicily, while her frame was typical of many of her fellow opera singers. After being kissed on the cheeks, we were led into the flat which opened into a reasonably large dining room where my aunt Maria Teresa was sitting. The last time Mum had seen her sister would have been in

1992 when she took a flight to Italy on her own to attend her mother's funeral.

The passing of the years had been kind to my aunt. Retaining her good looks and sharp mind while remaining physically active, she seemed able to maintain a wide range of interests. Her blonde hair, which had become white, had been allowed to grow to an unfamiliarly long length. Fourteen years later and the two sisters were in the same room again – but this time Mum showed absolutely no signs of recognising her. My aunt got up from her seat to greet her taller sister with a kiss. To my aunt's disappointment it failed to provoke any reaction whatsoever. It was sad to think, that after all the trouble taken with preparation and the journey itself, one of the main reasons for embarking on the trip was being totally thwarted by the memory loss which now wasn't just confined to short term recall.

The table had been carefully laid with the best cutlery and crockery, along with bottles of wine from the Piedmont region and mineral water. Very great care had been taken, but the setting was too formal for my mum in her present condition. In between the courses I was able to explain that we were both well, but my mum's mental condition had deteriorated over the months. It was also an opportunity to describe the difficult journey as best as I could in Italian. It was easier to talk to my cousins because they kept to formal Italian. In the case of my aunt, although she spoke in Italian, sometimes she would also slip into using her regional dialect *Piemontese*, particularly whenever she got more animated in discussions.

I sat at the table next to Mum. A sensible arrangement as it enabled me to cut up her food into small pieces. By this stage she had lost the ability to use a knife and fork, so a spoon would have to suffice. To avoid a mess on the table and floor, I thought it might be wise to help her. It was a strange evening – alternating between eating myself and feeding Mum – as well as trying to engage in conversation in a foreign language. Throughout the proceedings Mum was extremely agitated. She still didn't show any sign of recognising anybody at the table. This must have been upsetting for my aunt as she got very little response from her sister despite several attempts to communicate with her.

At one point during the meal, Mum nearly pulled off the tablecloth with all the contents still on it, but luckily I managed to spot her tugging and intervened just in time. She kept getting out of her seat and was extremely fidgety and on one occasion picked up a small button that she must have noticed on the floor. Well, at least her eyesight wasn't being impaired by the dementia! All in all, it had been a long and difficult day. Mum's brain had probably been over stimulated by too much occurring in the space of about fifteen hours. All the hustle and bustle of the long journey, combined with meeting her next closest relatives who, for her, may have appeared as total strangers, was just too much. My aunt left after the meal with her son, Germano, probably upset, although she did her best not to show it, but she was probably putting on a brave face. If Mum was tired, I was absolutely exhausted, so I was glad to have the opportunity to help Mum get washed and ready for bed. She didn't take long to fall asleep.

Before retiring myself, I had a chat with my cousin Monica. We were able to catch up on what we had been doing since the last time we had met in the 1980s. She told me about her career as an opera singer and what had happened to other members of the family and likewise felt proud of Alfredo's achievements in the film industry. On a sad note, however, she also recalled some of the similar experiences encountered while looking after our grandmother, who also suffered from dementia in her last few years. Maybe that was why Monica seemed the most relaxed with Mum and consequently got the best response from her. Sometimes when I was trying to tell Monica something, I would have to restart the sentence in search of another word that was in my limited vocabulary. But I was suddenly struck by how much my Italian had improved over the year during which Mum had virtually stopped speaking English and instead reverted back to her mother tongue.

After thanking Monica for all the trouble she had gone to in order to make us feel at home, I took the opportunity to have a quick shower and then joined Mum in the double bed. She was still asleep, so I took care not to disturb her as I didn't want to wake her up. Having a bed was an unexpected bonus, as I had been prepared to sleep on the floor when I requested that we share the same room. By this stage it was important to keep an eye on her, especially if she needed to go to the toilet in what would be unfamiliar surroundings to her.

The next morning started with me giving Mum a brief wash before helping her to get dressed. Following breakfast, Monica informed me that there had been a slight change in plan. Instead of heading to *San Damiano* for the day, which I had been looking forward to, we were going to be taken to the city centre. That would enable us to get back for a meal where a younger cousin of my mother, a chef, had received an invite as well as being enlisted to help. If I had not been so tired the previous night I might have remembered to point out that it would be better for Mum if we avoided having meals in a formal setting. But it was too late. I would just have to go along with the arrangement and hope Mum would be on her best behaviour. Germano and my aunt arrived later in the morning and so we set off leaving Monica behind to begin preparing the meal.

It took a while before Germano found a place to park, in that respect not much different from London. We got out of the car and took a short walk to the city centre. It was a hot sunny morning and we soon found ourselves in a very large square hosting, on that day, an exhibition of classical cars, some dating back to the early part of the 20th century. We then popped into the nearby church for a while and finally rested on a bench back outside in the square where I managed to take some photos. By this point in the day it was becoming uncomfortably hot, prompting the purchase of some ice-creams. In contrast to the day before, Mum was much calmer. About an hour passed and with all of us sufficiently rested, it was time to return to the flat.

If the previous evening meal had been a bit too formal, that was nothing in comparison to the sight that greeted our eyes on the return from the little tourist trip around the centre of *Torino*. It looked as if a banquet was about to start. It was such a shame my cousin had gone to so much trouble as Mum was just not going to appreciate such efforts. Once again she became very agitated. Her younger cousin, another Michael, the one who had arrived earlier to help prepare the meal, suddenly became visibly upset. For at that moment, it dawned on him that she did not have a clue as to who he was, despite his attempts to remind her of shared experiences at the hotel in *Bardonecchia*. Even though I was already used to this state of affairs, it was still upsetting to see his disappointed reaction. It was the first time I started to cry in public. How could such an illness rob somebody of so many memories? It wasn't just cruel for her; it was also sad for everybody close to her.

Finally the meal – with all those different courses of lovely food and all that work – was over. I know Mum would have enjoyed the occasion a few years earlier, but now it was almost torture. It had been an awkward affair and, not for the first time in those few days, I took her out for a walk. She was used to that, but unlike the house in Chiswick there wasn't the river nearby and I was wary of straying too far in case we got lost. Still – it was nice to be out of the flat. Without a garden it did feel a bit claustrophobic. My right hand held tightly to my mum, wanting to make sure there was absolutely no chance of losing her. I looked at my watch and thought – just under three days to go before we return to London. That was less than seventy two hours. Surely we could make it?

A trip to my aunt's house had been arranged for the remainder of the afternoon. It was an imposing detached property located on a hill not too far from the river Po. The front of the house had an impressive entrance with steps leading to a surrounding balcony. Beyond a sturdy front door we were ushered into a large hallway. Even though the property needed some work, it gave the impression of wealth but to a certain extent that was an illusion as it was rented by my aunt. In that respect the two sisters were quite different. My aunt was inclined to show off and for most of her life had led an ostentatious lifestyle; whereas Mum was more pragmatic and when it came to property – of greater substance – not that it mattered very much any longer!

It was still sunny, so in the late afternoon we were able to enjoy drinks and some delicious cakes, some of which were filled with *zabaglione*, a custard-like dessert that Mum had often made herself by whipping sweet wine or sherry with egg yolks. We sat outside in the garden in a grassed area. Enclosed by many trees, the space provided shade as well as a refuge for a dozen or more cats and kittens. My aunt tried to remind her sister of stories of their childhood, particularly how they used to sing together and would get up to pranks, but Mum still had a vague expression on her face. I wasn't just concerned to observe that the conversation was dominated by my aunt. All this talk in dialect between the two sisters was getting me worried. Would I return back to London with Mum speaking to me in Piemontese rather than Italian, I wondered? Then I would be really stuck trying to understand her.

Later on we returned to the house where there was a chance to look at some old photos. My aunt certainly looked very pretty and glamorous when she was younger and could easily have been mistaken for a model or film star. It must have been a time when it had been fashionable to copy the hairstyle of Marilyn Monroe. But the family photos, which also included her mother and father, again didn't provoke any reaction from Mum. Perhaps prompted by the earlier conversation about singing, my aunt then encouraged Monica to provide a demonstration of her vocal prowess. Slightly reluctant at first, she duly obliged by putting on a record from a Verdi opera and then began to accompany it. She has a very strong, impressive voice, but for the only time during the stay in Italy, my cousin seemed to annoy Mum. Dementia had robbed Mum of any previous sense of tact or diplomacy and she soon indicated her disapproval, so Monica took the hint and didn't continue for much longer.

We were now coming up to the end of the first twenty-four hours of our stay in Italy, but for me it had already seemed like a much longer period of time. Mum showed no signs of recognising her sister, or anybody else in the family for that matter, and was already beginning to question me as to why I hadn't taken her home, probably not realising that Chiswick was hundreds of miles away. But the evening, which often was the most difficult time of the day, unexpectedly provided the best part of the entire holiday. If only those next few hours could have been bottled and served up again for a few more days, then I expect we could have stayed until the planned leaving time of Thursday morning.

We had probably left my aunt's house after 6 p.m. Germano then dropped the three of us off by Monica's flat just a few miles away. Earlier in the day I had mentioned that while I appreciated her efforts, large and formal meals were no longer appropriate. Monica must have understood me because that evening she served up a bowl of soup with dumplings. It was a simple meal but perfect. Mum was relaxed when there were only three of us and she ate the lot. After some fruit and a hot drink, I took Mum out for a walk. It was a very warm evening and the light was gradually fading. Many other people were out walking but not in any particular hurry.

On the way back we stopped at a café and I ordered some ice cream. Despite being dark by that time of the evening, it still remained very warm. We went outside and gratefully found some spare chairs to sit on. Soon there were streams of green, chocolate and pink liquid running down the cones – no wonder we had been provided with paper napkins – so for a few minutes there was little conversation. We were under pressure to eat the delicious contents as soon as possible before it all melted away. Afterwards we didn't rush off. I can't remember what we talked about but it certainly didn't touch upon the issue of returning to London for a change. For the first time during the holiday, I felt free from anxiety. We then got up from our seats outside the café and continued the walk back to Monica's flat.

When we returned we sat down by the dining room table. The television was on in the background which suddenly caught my mum's attention. A film had just started. It had been dubbed in Italian and was a true life story about a French female singer, Edith Piaf. Mum watched the whole film attentively and this was for nearly two hours. That seemed odd to me, but maybe she recognised some of the songs. This was the first time she had done something like that for over a year. In recent times she had lost interest in all the soap operas that she used to watch and about the only things that would hold her attention on TV involved music or dance – so for her to watch a film was quite something. She looked very content and when the film finished, even engaged in a little conversation with her niece who, despite having such a strong voice, was speaking to her aunt as softly as if she was addressing a small child. Eventually Mum became tired, as it was getting close to midnight. I spent a bit of time getting her ready for bed, before rejoining my cousin to relax for a while. It provided an opportunity to review the day and discuss what to do with the time remaining. I then went to bed feeling more optimistic, hopeful that the next three days could pass off as smoothly as that Sunday evening.

Strands of light passing through the gaps in the wooden shutters of the window overlooking the street below indicated the beginning of a new day in Italy. Sounds of the shop awnings being pulled open and beeping vehicles passing by indicated that the city was gradually coming to life. Meanwhile, the noise of dinging bells from the passing trams transported me back in time to previous stays during my childhood at my grandmother's flat in *Torino* before she passed away. Despite the lapse of a few decades, the tone seemed unchanged. And then the smell of freshly baked bread and coffee wafted up to finally encourage me to get out of bed.

The morning started well, but as soon as my aunt arrived my mum's mood changed, and once again she became quite unsettled. It made me wonder why? Maybe it was because my aunt had an excitable nature which for some reason just seemed to wind Mum up. Although on previous trips I had witnessed the odd moment of disagreement between the two sisters, it had always been temporary – certainly never like this – where now my aunt appeared to be subjected to continual animosity from my mother. In some respects it mirrored the situation being experienced by my sister Elizabeth for a limited period of time. But whatever the reason, it added to the tension of the stay and for me was an unwelcome and unexpected development.

From what I could gather, the outing to *San Damiano* was to be delayed until either Tuesday or Wednesday. The plan for Monday morning was a short trip to the local market, which was within walking distance. When we were all ready to leave we took the lift downstairs, but as we got out I could see a concerned expression appear on Mum's face. She didn't say anything but from the way she was clutching her dress, I could see she wanted to go to the toilet and quickly. Before I had time to do anything, a large yellow pool began to spread across the marble floor. Because she wasn't wearing any knickers there was no need for her to go back to the flat to change. Nevertheless, it was an embarrassing moment and we did our best to soak it up by throwing on some discarded newspapers, probably left in the foyer for recycling. Although a similar accident didn't happen again while we were in Italy, it was an indication or warning sign that by the autumn of 2006, only a few months away, I would have to confront one of the next stages of dementia that involved dealing with her incontinence. And how did Mum feel about the incident? Hard to say, and yet she looked like a child who knew something had been done that was wrong but wasn't quite sure what.

Having left the porter with some unexpected and unpleasant work that morning, the four of us proceeded towards the market, with Maria Teresa and Monica at the front leading the way. As soon as we arrived, I knew it was a mistake. The market was extremely busy with people jostling as they were seeking to go in different directions to the stalls. My aunt liked to pause and examine the goods on offer, but Mum was having none of it. She was growing increasingly impatient and just wanted to carry on walking and get out of the congested place. There was enough time for my aunt to buy some cakes, but it was probably an outing that nobody really enjoyed. With my aunt being four years younger than her sister, Maria Teresa still wanted to do things that were becoming totally inappropriate for my mother at eighty and in her condition. The evidence was steadily mounting up to reach the conclusion that crowded and noisy places were to be avoided wherever possible. A year earlier, I had tried to vary the entertainment by taking Mum to watch a show at Richmond Theatre involving Latin American music. I had fully expected her to enjoy it, but we had to leave after about ten minutes because she was complaining it was too loud. The choice of seats had also been a mistake – too high up and frighteningly steep – and on reflection that was probably the main reason why we had to go home early.

As we left the hustle and bustle of the market behind us, I could detect a change in Mum's mood. She looked satisfied that she had got her own way in the end. I suspect that Mum still possessed a small degree of guile that belies any misplaced notion that dementia robs a person of all thinking capacity. When we returned to the flat we had a simple pasta meal. We were joined by my cousin Germano, who was taking a lunch break from his office where he worked as an architect. He gave his mother a lift home on his way back to work while Monica suggested going for a walk that afternoon.

She led us to an area of *Torino* that I had never seen before. Instead of neatly arranged blocks of apartments that are so common in the city, it contained streets of detached houses, much more in the style of an English town. It was yet another sunny day but by then it had turned quite breezy and Mum's white hair was occasionally being blown into her face. We ended up in a park where we were able to sit and rest for about an hour. Fortunately, many mothers had brought their children to play and since that amused Mum for quite a while, we didn't have to rush off. But even the calming effect of young children eventually wore off, and once again it was time to move on. After the difficult morning I felt relieved that the afternoon had ended on a good note. Would I be hoping for too much to expect a similar evening as the one enjoyed previously? After all, it seemed as if we had found a winning formula; a simple meal, an evening walk, followed by a nice Italian film. I was hopeful, but it wasn't to be.

Unfortunately for the remainder of the evening Mum became very irritable and extremely annoyed that I wasn't taking her home. "But why are you keeping me here?" she pleaded. I tried my best to explain, again and again, that we were hundreds of miles away from home and we only had another two days to go, but it was to no avail. The requests became more and more frequent but also more desperate. Even taking her out for several walks that evening didn't seem to be working any more. If those persistent but irrational demands – for what seemed impossible to deliver – weren't bad enough, my mind then started turning towards the impending train journey back to London. That could turn out to be another nightmare. I started to wonder whether it was worth staying another two days just to see *San Damiano* when it appeared that she was unlikely to get anything out of it. I then began to think of some of the benefits of arriving back earlier than originally planned. It would give me a few more days to recover before going back to school after the half-term holiday.

All these thoughts were racing round my head, as we were going on what had probably been our fourth walk that evening. But then something happened to dispel, once and for all, any indecisiveness. As we walked down the main road we reached the point where we had to turn left to join the street where Monica lived. Mum suddenly stopped and refused to continue. For a few minutes I wasn't too concerned, but when she continued to refuse to budge my mood changed. After a lot of persuasion she did eventually move but my mind was made up. Imagine the problems I would have faced had Mum suddenly stormed off. Of course I could have followed her, but there remained a chance that she could have got lost amongst the crowd. There was the added worry that there was no guarantee that I would have been able to guide her back to the flat in what was a relatively unfamiliar city. Although it would be costly and embarrassing to break the news to Monica, I couldn't see that another two days would be bearable, especially if Mum became even more uncooperative and unpredictable.

When I told Monica my intention of taking Mum back early, she looked disappointed but hardly surprised. She must have seen that it was a difficult situation for me. Much to my relief she provided no opposing argument when I told her that staying two more days wouldn't serve any purpose. I felt guilty about the decision to go early because they had all made their best effort to make the stay as pleasant as possible, but Mum was getting more difficult to handle and the problems were being compounded by being abroad. I needed to get her back to her routine in London, where she was already difficult enough to manage anyway.

Fortunately I had come prepared expecting to deal with a few unforeseen problems. I had brought with me at least one thousand euros, so I had just enough money to pay for the flight back to Heathrow organised by my cousin Germano. Following a call from Monica, that night he checked on the internet for availability of seats. About half an hour later, he called back to confirm that the flight was definitely booked. Monica just had to collect the tickets from a nearby travel agent in the morning. At last I was able to inform Mum that we were definitely returning home the following day. I didn't know what to expect the next day since I didn't have a clue how she would behave on a plane. But at least I had bought some peace. She seemed more content after receiving the news, and gave me no further trouble that night.

Chapter 10   An Unexpected Flight

I woke up on Tuesday morning with mixed emotions; happy to be returning back to England after the last few days of Mum's increasing demands to go home, but also pleased that I wouldn't be providing another taxi driver in Paris the opportunity to rip me off. I was disappointed for my aunt that we had to leave earlier than expected, and similarly for my mum as we had to leave out the planned trip to *San Damiano*. There was less concern about the latter point as Mum's ability to recall her distant past which, until about a year ago, had been so sharp, now seemed to be as weak as her short term memory. I was also worried about the flight back to London; any outbursts from her could be more serious on a plane.

Monica prepared a light breakfast for us. She appeared to be sad that we had to leave early, but still did everything possible in order to help. For a while she left us alone in the flat to collect the tickets ordered the previous evening. When my aunt, Maria Teresa, arrived we went for a walk. It was another sunny day. Even though it was early enough for some cafés still to be serving breakfast, the shade from the tall buildings provided a welcome respite from the sun, rays of which seemed to be intensifying with each passing step. Mum still ignored her sister – a great pity since this must have hurt my aunt. We didn't walk too far and soon we were back by the large wooden doors that served as the entrance to the block of flats. Monica took a bunch of keys from her handbag, and then we were in the foyer where the lift took us to the third floor. What was becoming a familiar metallic tone resonated throughout the building, as the sliding gate of the lift was slammed shut. My aunt beckoned my mum to follow her into the dining room to sit down. Monica went into the kitchen to prepare some drinks, while I took the opportunity to visit the bathroom.

Just before entering the dining room, my progress came to a sudden halt. I stood there by the doorway for a few seconds in silence – completely motionless. My aunt was talking softly and unhurriedly to my mother nearby and for the first time I could see Mum was relaxed with her, listening and responding. It must have been a special moment for my aunt. I was determined not to interrupt – so retreated as inconspicuously as possible – walking backwards slowly and quietly and left the two of them on their own. I went back to the bedroom and lay down on the bed for a few minutes – one might as well save a bit of energy for the journey ahead, I concluded.

Germano arrived at midday, having already spent a few hours working in his office. He was hungry and was happy to tuck into the salad that his sister had prepared for him. He also needed a break before the drive to *Milano*, which would take over two hours. With his meal finished it was time to set off for the airport. My aunt stayed in *Torino* and, of course, there were tears before we departed. That was natural but the parting was particularly poignant for another reason. I didn't say anything on the matter, but I think we both knew that this was probably going to be the last time she would see her sister alive. She could understand from those few days that I would never be able to return to Italy with Mum; my aunt wasn't getting any younger so it was almost equally unlikely that she would be travelling to England again. The word *addio* (good-bye forever) was never uttered but it would have been sadly appropriate.

Monica joined us in the car and sat in the front next to her brother. My mum got into the car with less difficulty this time, seemingly getting more used to the procedure, and soon we were driving out of the streets of *Torino*. It was an area that Germano knew well as he had lived there all his life. With his earlier studies in architecture, he couldn't resist giving us a short background to some of the historical buildings that we were passing. To some extent *Torino* tends to get overlooked as a potential tourist destination, which is a pity as it contains many places of genuine interest, in addition to the legendary and controversial Shroud of Turin.

Soon we were on the motorway, cutting through the countryside with a gradually descending mountain range in the background. It was only while passing through some of the smaller towns, as we were getting closer to *Milano*, that Monica was asked by her brother to check directions in the map. Although we weren't late, I became aware that we wouldn't have much time to spare at the airport. Recalling some of the earlier incidents involving long waits with Mum, this was probably not an unwelcome situation. Meanwhile, Mum was really well behaved in the backseat of the car. She was in a good mood as if she realised I had complied with her requests to go back home.

Finally we arrived. It wasn't the main airport serving *Milano*; nevertheless it was still quite large. We only had fifteen minutes to check in. From my limited experiences of flying, I began to wonder if there would be enough time. We queued up for a while, Mum probably oblivious to my growing anxiety. Then to my relief my cousins were allowed to cross the barrier to join us. They helped by encouraging the lady at the check-in desk to make a phone call to see if we could still board the flight. A minute must have passed, but it seemed like hours. There was no change in her facial expression to provide any clues as to how the conversation on the phone was progressing. Then at last – an announcement!

I was relieved to be informed that there was still a bit of time, but not much, and we would have to hurry. With their job done, my cousins kissed both of us goodbye and soon disappeared amongst the throng as they made their way back to the car. From that point onwards we were on our own. Vulnerable! That I was left in a predicament became even more obvious when suddenly I had an awful thought. 'Suppose we miss the flight?' The implications looked dire. I would be stuck in an airport many miles away from *Milano* and a hell of a lot further from *Torino*. I didn't have that much money left by then – certainly not enough to buy tickets for another flight – and I didn't have either a debit or credit card. Any help in the form of my cousins was rapidly disappearing down some motorway, so it was critical to catch the plane. We turned round the corner and entered a very large concourse. For a few seconds everything seemed a blur as there were so many signs in front of me. I started to get that feeling of panic and, of course, Mum – who had been such a source of security for most of my life – could be of no assistance. Luckily I found a member of staff who immediately directed us towards the correct area for the departure to Heathrow.

However, Mum could certainly pick her moments to wind me up. No sooner had I found the correct direction to head towards, than she decided to stop and plant her feet. It was like an obstinate racehorse refusing to leave the starting stalls. Regardless of how much a jockey kicks the sides of the horse, sometimes it can have no effect. And so it was with my mother! Of course I wasn't kicking her, but she wasn't responding to my tugging and imploring her to start walking again. We had less than five minutes left and the plane still wasn't in sight. The timing of such mulish behaviour was way beyond belief. Some days Mum would demand that I take her for maybe up to as many as a dozen walks. Why the hell had she picked this moment to decide not to walk? In the end I just had to pull her as forcefully as I could in the direction of the departure gate, hoping not to attract too much attention. Suddenly she seemed to get the message and started walking voluntarily again, but incredibly, frustratingly and irritatingly slowly.

When we eventually reached the entrance for departure my torment was not over – we still had to continue walking along a narrow corridor. As we turned the corner, I was finally able to relax. Ahead of us I could see a queue with about a dozen people waiting to board the plane of the Italian airline. At last we were on board. The air hostess, wearing a green uniform, hurriedly guided us to a row of three seats on the left and at the back. Elsewhere, the plane was already full. A young woman was sitting by the window, so we occupied the next two seats with Mum in the middle. The relief of getting our places on the plane was short-lived and was quickly replaced by a feeling of apprehension. How would Mum react, I wondered? Would she start screaming and go completely hysterical? I didn't have to wait much time to find out. Because we had been so late getting on, it wasn't long before the pilot sent the plane speeding down the runway, and soon we were taking off. Mum remained completely calm throughout and, if anything, I was the one showing signs of nervousness as my grip of Mum's hand tightened. I had been on a few flights before, but the last time was over twenty years ago so I had forgotten how bumpy the first few minutes during take-off can be. But once the plane had reached a cruising altitude the atmosphere on board became more relaxed. We were given a small but adequate lunch. This helped pass the time and it didn't seem long before I could see some familiar landmarks by the river Thames as the plane approached Heathrow. Apart from requesting to leave the plane every now and again, Mum was fine and much to my astonishment, showed that I needn't have worried about her potential to react badly.

But Mother had given me quite a few surprises on this Italian holiday and she still had one more trick up her sleeve. It was announced that the plane was now over Heathrow and that we should fasten our safety belts ready to land. Silence fell over the plane as you could feel the gradual descent. Was this the time when Mum would lose it? No, she was fine. She was quiet – and when the plane finally touched down and taxied towards one of the terminals, I felt so relieved. *Mission impossible* had been completed. I had taken Mum to Italy and back at the age of eighty and with severe dementia, and we had returned to England – well almost! We still had to get off the plane.

Once the cabin crew gave permission, people started to disembark in an orderly fashion. As we were sitting near the back, we had to wait. Eventually it was our turn to leave. I stood up, but Mum didn't follow. "Come on Mum, we've landed. It's time to get off." But she absolutely refused to move. I tried as best as I could to persuade her politely to get up and even combined it with some gentle pulling, but both failed to work. By now everybody had left the plane apart from some of the cabin crew and the two of us – plus the poor young woman who was still stuck in the window seat next to Mum. "Sorry, but I think you'll have to climb over her if you want to get out!" She paused for a second as if to think about my suggestion and then, left with little alternative, clambered over Mum who was still unwilling to cooperate.

A few more minutes passed and there was even an attempt by a stewardess speaking fluent Italian to get her to leave. Nothing seemed to work. Then, as if she was only going to move when she was ready, she rose and to my relief we were off the plane. We just had a few more metres to go along the platform that connected the plane to the terminal and we would be on terra firma, so to speak. Then, suddenly in the middle of this platform she stopped again and refused to budge. We were in no-man's-land; neither on the plane nor in the building. All the frustration of the last few days just converged into one second of pure, undiluted anger. Such emotions were intimated not only vocally, in a despairing exclamation that contained one or two swear words, but also visually, in my next course of action. I took the rucksack off my back and threw it on the floor in front of me. Taking aim, I then channelled all my energy into kicking the bag quite a few metres into the building without any care for the contents or anybody who might be unfortunate enough to be passing by at that moment. I really needed to do that – to dissipate all that pent-up anger – and fortunately nobody was hurt. Mum turned towards me and gave me a look that seemed to be asking if I had gone mad. Then she casually moved on, as if all this drama had nothing to do with her.

Once again we were on the move, but there still remained a few more challenges – the passport checks and journey home. The queue to leave the terminal was fairly long, but it was moving quickly, and as we only had hand luggage we were able to get out of the building without any further problems. I saw the signs for the underground but walked straight past. We were going to get a taxi, no matter what the cost! We soon found one and, in complete contrast to Paris, it was so easy for Mum to walk straight in. They say 'beauty is in the eye of the beholder' and that expression couldn't have been more appropriate for that particular journey back towards Chiswick. Some sections of the Great West Road can look quite ugly – drab and grey – but on that particular Tuesday afternoon, I couldn't think of beholding a more welcoming sight.

The charge was only £30, but I was so relieved to arrive back home that I told the driver to keep the change when I handed over the two £20 notes. Yes, it was a great relief to be back but the trouble with looking after someone with dementia is that you don't get much of a break. It wasn't long before I had to take her for a walk. Then after a light supper there was the little battle over getting her to have a wash and be ready for bed. It was only then that I had an opportunity to unwind and reflect on the last few days. I was glad I had taken her back to Italy, but was determined never to do that again. In fact, Mum never made a further request to go abroad, and in some ways I wonder if she fully comprehended, or even remembered, much of the visit a day or two later.

Chapter 11   Remaining Holidays in Felixstowe

It really shouldn't have been too much of a surprise that the Italian holiday ended up being such a challenge. Two years prior to that remarkable trip of 2006, Mum's behaviour on a visit to Felixstowe confirmed my suspicions that her mental health was declining; although it wasn't until a year later in 2005, when she spent over a week in hospital, that I first began to hear the word dementia being used by some of the medical staff. Then she was in their care for many hours and I wasn't able to cover up for her inevitable confusion. One could imagine her repeatedly asking for directions to the toilet on the ward or looking confused when being questioned by a consultant during those hours when I wasn't present. One poor woman repeatedly had to remind Mum not to pat her on the foot; it was just an affectionate form of greeting but Mum kept forgetting that it was painful for the bed-bound patient.

For the first part of 2004 I planned to make some improvements to the kitchen in the Chiswick house. A new sink and small water heater had been plumbed in as early as 2002 – all the more memorable as the job coincided with the World Cup. At the time Mum was still living in Hammersmith. When she moved back to Chiswick in July, everything in the kitchen was working but it still needed some finishing touches to make it look neat. However, embarking on such improvements kept getting postponed as there had been a lot of clearing out to do during 2002 following my dad's death. Then in the following year, I decided to build two small brick sheds in the garden. As a result, I never got round to tiling and decorating the kitchen.

Mum couldn't have been particularly happy with the situation in the kitchen, but she never voiced any complaints, and in 2003 she was proud of the two sheds I had built. The first one was at the end of the back garden and made use of the two existing brick walls. Once the foundation had been finished, I made a wooden frame and then built the remaining brickwork around it, adding a nice window that I found in the basement and an even more impressive white front door that had been dumped in a nearby skip. Within the two weeks of the Easter holiday I had completed the project, finishing the roof just in time before the weather changed and the rain set in. Mum agreed that it had been finished well, particularly the yellow brickwork, but she did have one criticism levied at the design. This concerned the use of some glass blocks that had been donated by our neighbour, Jim. There was an odd number and as a consequence of using all of them on either side of the door frame, the end result wasn't symmetrical. For an eye trained in tailoring, this was a fault that was not going to be left unnoticed, a point that Mum reminded me about several times over that summer. It's never easy to accept disapproval, but at least it was reassuring to see that Mum's critical faculties still remained sound to some extent.

However, there was no controversy with respect to the next shed built, one that was indisputably more pleasing aesthetically. My dad had constructed an open timber frame shed next to the kitchen many years earlier. But by 2003 the corrugated metal roof was rusting and although not leaking, it certainly didn't look attractive. I ripped off the roof but kept the frame. This time the brickwork at the front was organised in alternating colours. One course was with red engineering bricks; the following course was made with new yellow stock bricks. It was looking very pretty, almost Italian in style, and Mum helped most days with the mixing of the mortar. I had always wanted to build a wall with an arch and since my bricklaying skills had improved, this seemed as good a time as any to give it a try.

First I had to construct a wooden frame in the shape of a semicircle. As soon as the brickwork had reached the right level, the curved frame was put in place to support the bricks that were going to form the arch. A few days later I removed the frame. The arched brickwork remained firmly in place. Completing the final part of the brickwork was a bit more time-consuming than anticipated as I had to cut several small triangular shaped pieces to fill in the gaps as each course met the arch. But the end result made it all worthwhile. Mum was proud of my work and gave me a lovely smile as she posed in front of the camera while I was taking a photo of her opening the door of the new shed in July. It was a really nice photo taken on one of those many hot evenings in that summer of 2003. As usual, she provided a warm smile in front of the camera, but the shot was almost symbolic. The way Mum held the handle, with the door slightly ajar, was as if she was inviting you to peer into her future, a dark and empty background that lay ahead. But that was for later. On that evening in 2003 the sun continued to shine on Mum. It captured a memorable moment from easily the best year out of the whole period whilst looking after her with dementia.

With the major shed building programme over, it meant that 2004 could be devoted to sorting out her kitchen. I figured that as I was working unaided on the project, it would need more than a week to complete. Since this required turning off the water supply for several hours on some days, which would have been very disruptive, I encouraged Mum to move back to the Hammersmith house for about two weeks. Each day during the Easter holiday, I cycled from Hammersmith to Chiswick without feeling the need to worry too much about leaving her alone for a few hours. The dementia still wasn't too bad and her Irish neighbour, Lena, could keep an eye out for her as well as provide some company. About ten years younger than Mum and of similar height, she too spent some of her time sweeping the front of the house on most days. Indeed, all the energy devoted to housework not only guaranteed that her home was maintained like a show house, but also may help to explain her slim figure. Pretty, with short, grey curly hair, she always remained very close to her husband during more than fifty years of marriage. Not surprisingly, she was left distraught for a considerable period of time after losing him to cancer several years later. I could have mentioned the old adage that 'time is a great healer' but, from personal experience, dealing with grief rarely works as easily as that.

Meanwhile, back in Chiswick, I disconnected the sink and then built a wooden frame on the wall to the left to hide any copper pipes connected to the water heater. By the kitchen window, I took off the old tiles and rebuilt the wall so that it would be flush with the sink, ensuring that as soon as I had reconnected the pipe work, it was ready for re-tiling. With that job finished and no leaks either, I re-decorated the kitchen. Of course, if I could have left Mum alone for longer periods of time, I would have stayed more hours each day and finished the work sooner – but that would never have been possible by 2004. As the job was nearing completion, Mum seemed to be getting more restless in Hammersmith. Eventually the room was ready, and on that day she gladly cycled back to Chiswick with me. My sister also came round to see the improvements. There was a curtain in front of the small kitchen and it was a bit like one of those makeover programmes on the TV. I was fully expecting to receive a similar reaction to the one expressed about my bricklaying work the previous year, but to my surprise she seemed totally underwhelmed by the improvements – and instead expressed annoyance at being kept at Hammersmith for so long!

So largely due to all the work in Chiswick, the first and only trip to Felixstowe for 2004 didn't take place until the 22nd of August. Luckily there were no problems with Mum on the coach; although I did have an uncomfortable journey over the last few miles due to cramp in the leg. As usual on arrival at the house, there was a pile of unopened post, newspapers and flyers to greet us – even larger than usual as we hadn't been there earlier in the year. I took what appeared to be the most important ones upstairs, but then proceeded to connect the electric, gas and water so that we could make a hot drink and have something to eat. Later in the evening, I opened an electricity bill. My face must have turned red. My Mum was sitting in the same room. Even though she had dementia, her mind still had the wherewithal to notice that something must be amiss. "What's the matter?" she enquired. And not for the last time, I found myself withholding the truth from her – but it was all for her own good. "Oh, nothing too important, Mum. I'll sort it out tomorrow," came back my white lie. In fact it was an absolutely ridiculous bill for over £2,400. Given that the property was only being used for a few weeks in the year, there had clearly been a mistake. With a phone call the next day, I was promised a new and greatly reduced bill, but it was also a relief to see my mum's awareness the evening before – showing that she could still comprehend emotions from facial expressions.

The next day, and without any renewed prompting, I finally replaced the cracked glass in the window at the front of the house. It was a job she had been asking me to do for years. It had looked untidy but, I guess because I'm a man, it never really bothered me that much. True, there had been a small crack in the corner, but I had never shared my mum's concern that it was dangerous and about to fall on someone passing by on the nearby pavement. Still, with the glass replaced, I had to admit that it did look much better. But just as with the work in the kitchen a few months earlier, once again there was a muted reaction. In the evening we watched the Olympics from Athens. It was the night Kelly Holmes won a gold medal in the 800 m. This was a time when Mum was still taking an interest in sport. So having a couple of weeks of athletics, cycling and gymnastics on the TV was a great help in keeping her occupied. Overall, the first three days went well and Mum was still able to use her bicycle – which wasn't bad for a seventy-eight year old. On Wednesday we took the train to spend the day in Ipswich. After going around the shops we stopped at Woolworth's for a meal. It was a very large store and as well as the usual mixture of merchandise, there was space for a restaurant. She had a bit of trouble with the peas rolling off her fork, but tucked into the fish and chips as it was still a time when she could eat unassisted. But that evening, when we were back at the house, she tripped up in the hallway and even though she was unhurt, her pride seemed to be injured. As a result she was quite sad for the remaining hours before she went to bed.

Mum had an appointment with one of her two chiropodists on the following day. Compared to visits to the GP, this was far less stressful. It just involved a predictable ten minute walk and on arrival, there was very little time to wait before she was called into the surgery. Her toe nails were too thick for me to cut so it was worth paying a visit every few months, whether in Felixstowe or London, to keep things in check. Both men were charming with elderly women and this helped to put Mum at ease. In later years when it became more difficult to take Mum to appointments, the chiropodist visited her at home. Mum was always cooperative, which wasn't always the case with other people.

That Thursday evening proved to be difficult, maybe because Mum experienced another fall in the hallway. Her reaction to tripping up this time was anger and frustration rather than the sadness shown the previous day. Suddenly she wanted to return to London. I looked at my watch and it was already past 9 p.m. There was no way we could just pack up and turn everything off and leave for London at that time of night, certainly not on public transport. Worse still was to come. It turned out that one of the reasons she wanted to go back was that she wanted to find Michael. Two years ago she had problems recognising my sister. That night it was my turn. It was all the more surprising as I was with Mum for many hours each day. It took quite a while, but eventually I was able to persuade her that it might be a good idea if we stayed the night in Felixstowe. Then suddenly, and without warning, she seemed to recognise me again. It was as if her brain had momentarily experienced a short circuit – then the connections were rewired and all was fine again – for a while.

The next day went well. It was sunny for the first time that week so we spent the morning by the beach, followed by a walk after lunch. Later in the afternoon I put a new plug on the record player and found that it was still working. There was a Glen Miller record that had been bought from a charity shop on a previous stay and, after listening to a few tracks from the American jazz musician and Big Band leader of the 1940s, Mum wanted to dance and encouraged me to join in. It would be an activity that she enjoyed right through to almost the very last stages of dementia. During the course of the day there had been no further talk of returning to London until, once again, the same recognition problem re-occurred in the evening. "Where is Michael?"... "We must go back to London!"... "Why are you keeping me here?" I had quite a lot of these statements and questions being fired at me for a few hours. In the end, I needed a break and thought it might be worth trying a different tactic. I left her in the house and sat outside for about ten minutes – not too far just in case she wandered off. When I returned, she immediately recognised me. "Where have you been, Michael?" was her greeting, in a slightly reprimanding voice. Even though it had earned me a ticking off, at least it had succeeded. But I would later find out that any strategy I devised for dealing with her dementia would only work for a limited time. Soon there would be a new problem to test me and I would have to try and think up a new solution to deal with it.

There were no further trips to Suffolk that year. She was becoming a bit difficult with travelling for long periods of time. And the new development of having trouble recognising both me and my sister meant that holidays in Felixstowe would never be the same again. Instead of looking forward to an opportunity to relax and enjoy a change of scenery, from henceforth such trips would bring a certain degree of trepidation. As we made our way back to London on the 1st of September, close to my birthday, I wondered what the year 2005 would deliver with regards to future stays in East Anglia.

Despite any misgivings, we were back in Felixstowe in March of the following year. It was quite cold but at least the storage heaters could now keep the house warm. Mum popped next door for a haircut and then later in the day we tidied up the garden. Unfortunately, she may have caught a chill because two days later she had diarrhoea. While paying for some items at the chemist, Mum suddenly told me that she needed to go to the toilet. We walked back home as quickly as possible but the time taken, certainly no more than five minutes, was too long. When we got back I helped her get out of her tights and knickers. After washing her and helping her to put on some clean underwear, I then washed the dirty laundry. I didn't mind, which is just as well because, for the next three years, I would be spending a considerable amount of time repeating similar tasks. A few hours later Mum became quite delirious. It turned out to be a terrible night with her not only wanting my sister, who was miles away in Kingston, but worse still, she was shouting out for her mother and father, both having already died in 1992 and 1964 respectively.

Eventually she did fall asleep, but when I got up the next morning, I decided to cut the holiday short and return to London as I was sure Mum was unwell. We took the train back. For the remainder of that Wednesday she didn't seem to deteriorate any further, but it was probably a wise move to get her back to London. On the following day Mum seemed a bit better, and we even went for a walk. We had an early dinner, and then I popped out for just under two hours. When I returned home, I found that Mum had left two gas rings on and she was very confused. She went to bed early in the afternoon and just seemed to be mumbling nonsense. I phoned the doctor and she was later admitted to hospital, suffering from pneumonia. Thankfully after about a week of treatment, she made a full recovery.

A further attempt at having a holiday was made in early August. This was the journey when Mum was insisting on getting off the coach at Ipswich rather than Felixstowe – which didn't augur well for the remainder of the stay. In fact it only lasted for five days and once again the vacation was spoilt by frequent demands to go back to London. Marred by sudden and inexplicable mood swings, she was also getting very frightened by unexpected things. Finding ourselves caught in the rain without an umbrella wasn't just unpleasant; one day it suddenly caused real anxiety, despite us taking shelter under a large arch of a nearby building. She looked so nervous, holding on to my hand tightly and so out of character with the way she had been for nearly all her adult life. These much shorter visits were such a contrast to earlier holidays when we could remain by the coast for anything up to five weeks on some occasions. Now the place was increasingly becoming a millstone round my neck.

And so to the very last trip to Felixstowe with Mum. It was Sunday the 6th of August, 2006. She had recovered from the cellulitis earlier in the year and the very challenging holiday to Italy was already behind us. In some ways the journey to Suffolk looked relatively easy in comparison, but if going abroad could be considered a waste of time by this stage, so too were stays in Felixstowe. This year we were there for only three days. Clearing out the garden and plenty of walks, because she was always restless, were the main activities. Cycling had already become less of an option by 2005. She became increasingly frightened, finding it more difficult to maintain her balance. One year later, and such an activity was definitely off the agenda

Once again, the evenings proved to be the most difficult times with her. Restless and insecure, she sometimes gave the impression that she was being held there against her will. Although relatively more relaxed during the day, there still remained a problem in looking after her that was specific to the Felixstowe property. Because we were there only for relatively short periods, there had never been the time to modify the house, for safety and security, on anywhere near the same scale as in Chiswick. This meant that it was virtually impossible to leave her on her own.

Unfortunately on the last day, while returning from one of our walks, I noticed that two roof slates had slipped down. I didn't really want to start such a job on the day we were leaving, but if I didn't, then it would just give me more work to do in the following year. So out came the ladders again. I was soon up on the roof hammering a galvanised nail through the loop that I had made in one of the copper wires. This was attached to the wooden batten, nailed in between the small gap between two already fastened slates, just as Dad had taught me all those years ago when I was a child. With that done, all that remained was to slide another slate into place and twist the copper wire up, preventing it from slipping down again. Meanwhile Mum was below, protesting that I had locked the front door and that she couldn't get out. 'Exactly,' I thought. This time, before going up the roof, I had remembered to take steps to prevent her leaving the house because by this stage there was no telling where she could wander off to.

Late that afternoon we were on the train departing the station of the seaside town. She would never return there again. With my sister, we had planned to take her to Felixstowe in 2007. I had even bought a special cushion that could rotate on the car seat. The hope had been that it would have made it easier for Mum to get into the car, but the device was never used. By the following August, Mum's health had deteriorated dramatically. Consequently, a major part of that summer was spent in a Middlesex hospital rather than on a Suffolk beach. I didn't make it to Felixstowe at all in 2007 and, for the foreseeable future, felt that as far as keeping an eye on the property was concerned, I would have to pass the baton on to my sister. My hope was that the work that I had been doing on the roof over previous summers would hold good for a few more years.

I suppose the investment made by my parents back in 1969 in the Felixstowe property had not only been financially worthwhile, but also provided many fond memories. However, the holidays from 2004 to 2006 were sad affairs that really marked out the decline in Mum's mental state. I can remember, many years ago, Mum observing an elderly lady sitting motionless outside a care home near our Suffolk house. Still in her late fifties at the time, Mum commented that she hoped that she wouldn't end up like that. But unfortunately time stands still for no one. Perhaps, to some extent, each current elderly generation serves to provide an unwelcome reminder to the young of their possible future fate – and eventual mortality.

Chapter 12 Social Life, 2002-5

Mum's dementia didn't really have too much impact on my social life in 2002. The year started quietly because my dad had passed away in December of 2001. However, by February I seemed to have got over his death and by the middle of the month I asked a nice South African supply teacher out, but was disappointed when informed that she was going back home in early March – so nothing developed there. With sport I was able to go running regularly and also played a few games for the staff football team after school on Friday afternoons in the spring. The games were followed by a beer and even though I didn't stay till late, I didn't feel any pressing need to leave early because of Mum.

The same applied with the 6th form Leavers' Ball at the end of June. It was always a very pleasant evening. The students all turned up smartly dressed and determined to enjoy themselves, the pressure of 'A' Level revision finally behind them. During the meal, Joe, one of my friends on the staff who taught English, paused from eating for a few moments. A handsome, tall and well-built Irishman with grey hair, his blue eyes had been glancing around from behind his spectacles at the other tables. It seemed to provoke a favourable comment concerning our younger guests. "It's great to see how so many of our students have matured into such nice young men and women. They're a real credit to the school." And this in turn elicited a contented smile from the Head Teacher who always made a point of attending the annual social gathering. A further factor that contributed towards making the occasion enjoyable was how relaxed Mum had been about the evening. She even paid me a compliment about the way I was dressed in dinner jacket and bow tie, as I left a few hours earlier. I was happy to stay until the end and join in on the dance floor – often the best part of the night. It also meant that I didn't have too much to drink, helping to avoid getting wrecked just a few days before the 2002 Charity Walk.

Scheduled for Wednesday the 3rd of July, it turned out to be another success and Mum was fine about being left alone for most of the day. A tidy sum of £2,000 was raised from the sale of the white T-shirts, illustrated on the back by the names of participants tracing out three pyramids. This was partly helped by a Japanese tourist, crossing Richmond Bridge at the time, who generously contributed with a £50 note, having persuaded Annalice, a teacher at Gumley, to part with the one that she had been wearing!

A few days later and it was time for Mum to make her return to the Chiswick house, the one bought with Dad when she was thirty-three years old. There was no need for a removal van as many of the belongings that she had left behind, when leaving for Hammersmith in 1992, were still there. My dad's annoying habit of hoarding had at least ensured that nothing had been thrown out. Nevertheless, Mum must have been itching to get started on the clear-out as she had always preferred a tidy home. By chance, the day chosen coincided with another Jubilee Street Party. This unintentionally gave the event the feel of a welcoming reception, but it was really organised to celebrate the fifty years' reign of Queen Elizabeth II, born in the same year as Mum. Although we set off from the Hammersmith house together, I was the first to arrive back on the bicycle ride to a street where a number of the neighbours were busy preparing for the afternoon's festivities.

When, after about fifteen minutes, she still hadn't appeared, I began questioning the wisdom of complying with Mum's request to leave her to cycle at her own pace and alone. I, along with a few other concerned neighbours, were only a few minutes away from organising a search party when, in the distance, I was relieved to see an elderly lady with white hair cycling down the road on the old and familiar brown bicycle with a metal basket at the front. It later transpired that she had mislaid the turning near Chiswick School and continued over the bridge towards Richmond. Fortunately she asked someone with knowledge of the area who was able to redirect her and she completed the remainder of the journey without any further assistance.

The street party was an opportunity for her to meet a few old acquaintances, some not seen for nearly ten years. However, she no longer recognised or remembered most of them. She politely listened to Mr and Mrs North, a very pleasant elderly couple whom she had known since moving into the street in 1959, but there was a vague expression on her face when they talked about their children and grandchildren. Another factor, reducing the significance of the event as a possible re-union, was that over the years some people had either left the street or passed away.

However, Mum had no problem in remembering her friend Odette, a French lady, who had visited her nearly everyday for many years. She could speak and write English well, but she never lost her strong accent. As a child I often sat with them and listened to their conversations. Amongst other things being discussed – some of which were probably not intended for my ears as they forgot my presence – were accounts that touched on their experiences of the war. That was probably when I first heard the story, repeated many times during the earlier stages of her dementia, about Mum's bicycle trips to France. Although she lived in a rural area, shortages still existed, one of which involved olive oil. In the main, she had accompanied her father on the long bike rides south. Sometimes, however, she was trusted to complete the journey with a friend. On one occasion the return journey was made easier when some American soldiers offered the two girls a lift. The bicycles were thrown in the back and the jeep then made its way along the meandering scenic route hugging the coastline to *Genova*, where they were dropped off. Almost sixty years on and Mum was still cycling and although the distance between Hammersmith and Kew sounds less impressive, it wasn't a bad achievement for a seventy-eight year old. Despite getting lost on that Saturday afternoon in July 2002, her cycling days were still not over.

The day for the street party had been blessed with good weather. Mum seemed to enjoy the afternoon, but by the evening she was getting tired and so didn't bother with the live music that entertained the remaining residents until late into the night. Not surprisingly, Mum didn't play any role in organising the event this time, but it had been very different back in 1977. I was in Norwich then, awaiting the results for my final year on the Degree course at the University of East Anglia, following a few days break exploring Newcastle and Edinburgh. Although I missed the party celebrating Queen Elizabeth II's Silver Jubilee, recognising her first twenty-five years as monarch, other neighbours later told me that Mum had made a big contribution to both the organisation of the day as well as helping to prepare the food.

Although leaving Mum alone for a few hours didn't present me with any problems during 2002, the uneasy feeling that accompanied any other outings involving longer periods of time can be traced back to May, the usual month for staging the FA Cup final. For quite a few years it had become a custom for me to watch the football match with John Kitchin, a remarkable teacher whom I had first met at Gunnersbury. By then his balding head and handsome features reminded me of Winston Churchill. Teaching is not the easiest of jobs, making John's return to the profession – following an accident that left him partially paralysed – an even more exceptional achievement. Despite such a handicap, he was able to conduct his duties extremely well from a wheelchair until retiring in the late 1980s. He still maintained a keen interest in sport so we made a point of keeping Cup Final day free to watch the televised game. This was followed by a meal prepared by his wife, Bridget, who devoted her life to caring for him – and often provided advice when I had to take on that role for my mum later on. A slim and pretty woman, Bridget had been evacuated from Singapore, along with her mother, during the war due to the threat of invasion by Japan. She spent a few years in Australia before returning to England where she later met John, a graduate from Oxford and teacher of the Classics and Mathematics. Later, an injury denied him the possibility of participating in his favourite sports of rowing, golf, football and cricket. Henceforth, much of his spare time became devoted to reading books and listening to Classical music. But above all – he loved talking.

Unfortunately it had now become a little more difficult to maintain this enjoyable day in the calendar after they had moved from Hampton to a bungalow near Aylesbury. So in 2002, with the option of taking Mum with me unlikely to work, I left Chiswick at about 8 a.m. and didn't return from watching Arsenal beat Chelsea 2-0 until 9 p.m. Although I did phone Mum during the day to check that she was all right, perhaps for the first time I was beginning to feel that the length of my absences needed to be considerably curtailed. Despite getting away with it, on the train journey back I was left pondering as to how many more years we could keep that particular fixture going.

The next main event when I felt a bit restricted about going out occurred on Saturday the 3rd of August. I was invited to a wedding reception in Thorpe. Because it would have been awkward getting there by public transport I decided to cycle, consequently reducing the journey time to roughly one hour. I can remember Mum looking concerned about being left alone as I set off, which had never really happened before. It must have been playing on my mind because I didn't feel particularly at ease during the reception. Despite the good food and music, I left early, apologising to the bride and groom, both teachers from Gunnersbury, and so missed a significant part of the evening's revelries.

Nevertheless, it was still a period in Mum's life when she maintained an interest in what was going on. When I was in Felixstowe that summer with her and my sister, we spent an afternoon going round the museum in the Fort located near a Martello tower not too far from the docks. I can remember that Mum stopped for a few minutes by each of the exhibits that we passed. She even took the trouble to read the notices. Later in the evening she commented on what we had seen earlier in the day. Clearly she could still recollect experiences from the not too distant past – definitely those from the very distant past – it was the bits in the middle that she had trouble with.

She also retained a reasonable level of independence. Two days earlier there had been no problem in leaving Mum in the house when I went to Ipswich Town Football Club with my sister to see a friendly against a Chelsea reserve team. It was a sunny evening, made all the more pleasant due to the amiable atmosphere in the stadium. And because it wasn't a well-attended fixture we had really good seats. A few hours before the game I had been interviewed by a film crew from Anglia News. They sought my opinion with regards to a key player, Matt Holland, who was leaving the club. I didn't feel qualified to comment, as I wasn't really an Ipswich fan, but I think most of the crew were desperate to wrap up and so they almost pleaded with me to do the interview, especially as at that time the area was completely deserted. I found it strange seeing myself on Anglia News the next day, when I was watching TV, but at least the comments I had made seemed appropriate, even if not voiced with a Suffolk accent!

Toward the end of September I was able to go to a concert with Peter, my best friend from secondary school days. We had known each other since about the age of twelve. Our first common interest had been football. In Year 9 we organised our own soccer team, even producing programmes for each match. Much of the artwork was completed during supervised lessons when the supply teacher was just grateful that it meant there were two less unruly pupils to worry about. We even started writing a book in our spare time about a football club, Chatham City, with Jeff Bromley as the hero. Our long lunch breaks meant we had time to go over to the nearby Public Library to write some more each day. We got quite far with it, writing over fifty pages. But as Year 9 was drawing to a close, we started losing interest, especially as the walk to the library involved passing by a Girls' School, which increasingly provided a new and more interesting distraction!

By the time we were doing A Levels, we tried to form a band as we both played the guitar. It was good fun, but the hundreds of hours of practice never led to any real success. In those days Peter allowed his brown hair to grow quite long. I can remember my mum tying it up behind his head out of concern that it was in danger of falling into one of the meals that she had prepared for us. Over the years, Peter never lost his interest in music, but as for his hair – the passage of time was a little less kind. Although we went to different universities, we both studied economics and ended up in teaching, even attempting to write a textbook, but once again the enthusiasm faded before it could ever be completed.

Despite maintaining a good friendship over the decades we hadn't been to a concert for some time so it was refreshing to go out and see a band. We had tickets to watch *Bad Company* appearing in Hammersmith. It turned out to be a very good evening and there was no problem in leaving Mum, but it was almost the last concert I would see for the next six years. By coincidence, Paul Rogers, the lead singer of the band, again played the same role – but this time for *Queen* – when I went to my next major concert. However, that was not until November 2008 – at the Wembley Arena and accompanied by my sister. The night was made all the more memorable not just by the faultless performance of the band, but also by the long walk from my sister's parked car to the stadium in really foul weather.

Two parties in November, admittedly ones where my presence was limited to about two hours, and the end-of-term Christmas dinner at school meant that, overall, 2002 hadn't been too bad a year as far as socialising was concerned. I had still been able to go out for more than a dozen evenings without too many worries, and even managed to have a few days when I was able to get away with leaving Mum on her own for most of the day. This still applied in the following year because the pace of deterioration with dementia was still quite slow.

In the first few months of 2003 I was again able to play a couple of games for the staff football team and visit Peter a few times. But Mum was slowly changing. She was having difficulty in remembering how to sign her name in public and this prompted the move to turn her savings into joint accounts. Every now and again there was a search throughout the house for her misplaced black handbag. She also got upset when she left her trolley in one of the shops at the top of the road. It wasn't a big deal as we soon retrieved it, but it was showing that her short term memory was deteriorating.

By the time April arrived, I was starting to regret accepting an invitation to help out with a Charity Walk over a marathon course in the Chilterns. Paul, an adventurous geography teacher, had asked me about six months earlier when Mum's condition was less of a worry. Anyway, it turned out to be a good day. Although I was out for nearly twelve hours, at least I had borrowed my sister's mobile phone enabling me to keep a check on my mum about every two hours. Nevertheless, it was another occasion when I got the feeling that it was too long to leave Mum alone.

At least there were only four more days in the year when I would have to abandon her for quite a few hours – but the infrequency didn't make the situation any less uncomfortable. The next occasion to cause such anxiety was the visit to John and Bridget when I saw Arsenal win the FA Cup again, but this time beating Southampton 1-0. The other long day was in July for the 6th form Charity Walk when the choice of sky-blue as the colour for the T-shirts proved to be most appropriate given the hot weather. Colin Clifford was the first student back, running the 14 km course in 64 minutes. I trailed in much later but at least for that gloriously sunny day I was able to keep in touch with Mum on my recently purchased mobile phone. The remaining two outings involved a school trip to the Bank of England and then the school's Sports Day held in Hayes, but these were more like normal work days in terms of the time involved. All four days passed by without any problems.

Luckily that summer of 2003 provided plenty of athletics to watch as the World Championships were being held in Paris. This year was particularly special as one of the art teachers from the school, Jo Lodge, represented Great Britain in the marathon and although she didn't win it, she ran well and everybody in the school was proud of her. A few years earlier that joy might have been shared by Mum, on being informed, but this time when I pointed out that the runner on the screen was a friend, she just sat there impassively.

In August I took Mum to the funeral service of Hélène, another one of her French friends. For many years a teacher at the Lyceé, unfortunately she passed away at the age of seventy-nine having lost her battle with cancer. One by one, Mum's social circle was diminishing. But the time spent in the church was slightly embarrassing because Mum kept on talking throughout the service and sometimes quite loudly, even laughing at one point. It was as if dementia was making it difficult for her to know how to behave appropriately in different social settings.

In September, I managed to watch a football match at Fulham with Joe. Nearly always charming and complimentary, with a strong sense of fairness, he was very articulate and quick-witted. Being particularly adept at spinning a yarn when a situation warranted one, he had no trouble in going along with me innocently pretending that we needed to attend the school for a meeting. This may have given the impression of two very dedicated teachers giving up their Saturday afternoon in the public interest, but it was designed to give Mum less to remember or worry about. It was a harmless white lie announced as we sat together in the sun-drenched garden appreciatively sipping cold drinks – and it worked. Mum didn't seem concerned when we left her a little before 2 p.m. After what turned out to be an entertaining game at Craven Cottage, which finished in a 2-2 draw with Manchester City, we had a quick beer in a pub near the house and I was home by 6 p.m. The following month I was picked up by Bridget and John to be taken to the Royal Festival Hall for Berg's Violin Concerto and Beethoven's Symphony No 3. By about 10 p.m., I had returned home but this really was the very last concert of any type until 2008.

After my dad died in 2001, and with the use of a dictionary, I had managed to write a brief note to some of my relatives in Poland informing them of the sad news. In the summer of 2003, the daughter of a niece of my dad was working in London. Anna, pretty, with blonde hair and in her early twenties, came over to visit in the autumn and then towards the end of December we agreed to meet up again. We had a meal in Hammersmith and then went to see the film, *Cold Mountain*. I had told Mum that I would be out that evening and did phone her before the movie started. But when I phoned her again, after the showing, she had completely forgotten where I had gone and sounded quite annoyed. That was the last time I went to a cinema for at least another five years and it also meant that from henceforth I needed to write notices every time I went out – a system that worked well for a few years until she eventually forgot to check what I had written down.

The Staff Christmas dinner at school signified that the end of 2003 was approaching. It had been a year when I had still gone out but unlike 2002, it was starting to get more difficult. I was now spending more of my free time with Mum, which wasn't too bad as she was good company, and with regard to TV, at least we still had some common interests. She would enjoy watching music programmes, even those that included contemporary R&B artists, and most sports. We watched highlights of the *Tour de France*, which also prompted her to recount stories of her father. Mum's proficiency at cycling must have been a great pride to my grandfather. When he told his friends that his daughter would be joining them on a planned excursion to the mountains, one of the men objected, protesting that he didn't want the group to be held up by a girl. My grandfather must have told his daughter because it seems that she set off with a point to prove. She bided her time and waited for the right moment. When Mum could see that the grumpy friend was showing signs of struggling as the gradient increased, she stepped up a gear and breezed past, making the point to turn round and pull a face. "Who's holding up the group now?" she laughed. Needless to say, whenever it was suggested that Mum might be joining the group of men on further bicycle trips, it no longer prompted any objections.

Perhaps the cinema trip with Anna, my first cousin one generation removed, was the turning point, because 2004 saw far less opportunities to go out. Between January and May there were a few visits to my sister and just one meeting with Peter for about two hours. The annual outing to Aylesbury went ahead, but this time I had to leave shortly after Manchester United beat Millwall 3-0. I took Mum to a music event at the school, but she didn't really enjoy it, complaining that it was too loud. Unfortunately this comment was in front of the Head of Music, but Kevin took it well as he knew about her condition. That was a few days before the Charity Walk. This was going to be the fifth one that I had organised. The previous four had been very successful and raised significant sums of money. More importantly, they had gone by without a hitch, and for each one, Mum had been fine. But this time I was worried. It was now getting difficult to leave her alone, hence the need to ask Nadia, one of the French teachers attending the aforementioned school concert, to look after my mother whilst I popped out briefly during the interval. In many ways 2004 was the worst year of the journey with dementia.

This was the year when Mum became scared. She realised that her condition was worsening and sometimes she would get very upset. She knew that her memory was going. On one particular day, while she was sitting next to me in the dining room and expressing concern about what would happen to her in the future, she suddenly started to cry. "Don't worry Mum, I will be your memory," I said to her, trying to reassure her – but it was also a promise I meant to keep. That seemed to comfort her for the time being, but it wasn't the end of her problems. This was the period when she started hallucinating. There was nothing wrong with her eyesight; she could still thread a piece of cotton through the eye of a needle, but one day she thought my rucksack was a person in the room. The tall flowers at the back of the garden, probably arum lilies, were also confused as representing people and frightened her. But this may not be as illogical as it sounds. The previous year Mum had got quite annoyed by a group of workers who climbed over the garden wall in order to carry large sheets of glass destined for the roof of the neighbour's new conservatory, but too large to pass through their front door. From that date onwards, Mum may have felt suspicious of any movements at the back of the house.

So when I left the house that morning on the 7th of July, 2004, I was anxious not just that the fund-raising event would be a success, but also that Mum would be all right left alone. Most of the work had been completed in the weeks before, but in the run up to the event, other staff began to help. Successive heads of sixth form from the three schools, Christine, Fiona, Cherie, Carmel, but particularly Catherine and James, galvanised the students into buying a shirt. Other staff, notably Bertram, Avion, Simone, Mark, Paul and Dave, assisted with deliveries. However, some things had to wait until the day of the walk. Nick and Pat set up the barbecue and gazebo, while Luigi, Bob, Andrew, Amanda and Larry took turns in preparing the food. Another important and time-consuming job was to fill up the many bottles with water for the drink stations. I usually did that, starting at 6 a.m. There was a big order from the local Iceland frozen food store to attend to later in the morning, while Carol, Roshni and Bridget assisted with any last minute administration or by selling some more black T-shirts from their office[4]. In the meantime, a team of students volunteered to help in the kitchen, while I had to check that all the marshals were present and knew where to go. By about 2 p.m. hundreds of students had assembled next to the 6th form block. After registering with Carolyn and Ena, they were ready to set off in smaller groups, each equipped with a map. Two long-serving teachers, John and Jonathan, usually led the way. However, with a few pubs on the route, they were never the first back.

Unfortunately the day seemed to be cursed with the worst possible weather imaginable for what supposedly should have been the height of summer. It threatened to rain all morning but almost as if it to tease, it waited about one hour into the 14 km walk and, when it started, it couldn't stop. As well as contending with the heavy downpour, it was very windy, and for July, particularly cold. Conditions were so bad that a decision was made to shorten the distance to 12 km by crossing at Richmond Lock Bridge rather than further along the river, an arrangement

---

[4] As did Elly, Jane, Julie Lorraine, Lynette, Mary, Veronica and Valerie, while the Head Teachers, John Heffernan (Gunnersbury), Sr Brenda Wallace FCJ (Gumley House) and Paul Enright (St Mark's) helped with promotion.

that was adopted for subsequent years. A group of teachers, including Sue, Nelson and Pat, took temporary refuge in a pub by the river.

Hundreds of walkers arrived back at school completely soaked through, but only to be welcomed by a most inappropriate cold buffet. What a year to decide to give up on having a barbecue! There was live music with the school jazz band but, unlike previous years, the damp students started drifting home a bit earlier than usual. Just as well because when I phoned home at 6 p.m., I knew straight away that there was a problem. I had been phoning earlier in the day and Mum seemed fine, but not this time. She was hyperventilating and could hardly speak. "Where... are the children?"..."Shall I... phone... the police?" she kept repeating in between trying to catch her breath. "Don't worry, Mum, I'll be home in a few minutes," I replied.

Luckily things were winding down in the hall where those still present were taking shelter from the rain, so I asked Noel if he could take over and supervise the last hour or so while I went home to sort out Mum. When I returned I found her trembling with fright. Somehow Mum had convinced herself that she had lost her two children. She may have been going round each room frantically looking for me and my sister, assuming that we were still infants. Her brain must have regressed to a few decades earlier. She was breathing very quickly – short, sharp intakes being repeated rapidly – making it a distressing sight to witness. After sitting with her in the front room, holding her hand and trying to reassure that everything was fine, she gradually calmed down – but not before at least an hour had passed by. At last – and much to my relief – her breathing returned to normal.

That evening I started to question if it was worth staging this Walk again if Mum was going to suffer so much. Clearly if the event was to be repeated in 2005, I would need to get more help and make sure I found time to visit Mum a few times on the day. There was no way I could have a repeat of the trauma she had suffered in 2004. Later that night I worked out the Walk had raised £1,400, which was still pretty good as the unpleasant conditions had wiped out last minute T-shirt sales, but whether it compensated for the upset suffered by Mum was questionable.

Finally it was the summer holiday, but despite all the extra free time, I didn't go out for another evening until a few days before Christmas. I did have two tickets for the *Gabrielle* Concert at the Hammersmith Apollo, but as the event drew closer, I started to wonder if I would really enjoy the evening. After deliberating for a while I finally gave the tickets to Peter. He took Joy, his young and very attractive Nigerian wife, while his mother looked after his three young children. So in the end, the main evening of the year turned out to be the meal with the two Chinese students. I was lucky that Mum had gone to sleep before leaving her that night. It meant that I had been able to really enjoy the five hours in their company whilst being treated to a lovely meal that included beer, soup, duck with onions in a pancake, chicken and noodles, ice cream, toffee apples and jasmine tea.

Chapter 13 Almost Grounded

From 2005 onwards I was never actually 'grounded' but increasingly it felt that way as the years passed by. Towards the end of 2004 it was becoming obvious that I would need to curtail my social life but I still hoped that it wouldn't become non-existent. The next main social event, and the first for 2005, was back at the Chinese restaurant near Kew Gardens. Mum was in hospital in March and because she was being looked after, it was an opportunity to go out with my sister, made all the more significant as her birthday was approaching. It was another great meal. I wanted to pay, but once again Donna's mother refused to take any money. Surprisingly the only other time I took advantage of this unexpected week of freedom involved a visit to Peter to watch an England football match. On other nights I felt obliged to stay in the hospital until late in the evening.

Mum was already home at the end of April when I went to another fixture at Craven Cottage. It was a sunny Saturday afternoon, and on this occasion Fulham beat Everton 2-0. Not a bad game – but I didn't really enjoy it – because suddenly watching twenty-two men running after a ball didn't seem that important any more. What a contrast to the emotions experienced at my first ever live match on the 11th of February, 1967. Eleven years old at the time, I was taken by a neighbour to watch Fulham beat Newcastle 5-1. Decades later, and at the same stadium, I kept my unenthusiastic thoughts to myself, not wishing to spoil my friend's enjoyment of the game. But Joe was well aware that the situation with Mum had deteriorated since the previous year and so we agreed not to bother with a beer afterwards. I also missed watching the FA Cup Final with John, when Bridget informed me on the phone that her husband had still not really recovered from a chest infection.

It was also a period when I escaped from two accidents on the bicycle relatively unscathed. This convinced me that there must have been a guardian angel looking after my welfare, even if it was just to make sure I could fulfil my promise to continue caring for Mum until the end. The first was in October of 2004 when I was cycling along Wellesley Road in Chiswick. As I approached a junction next to a church, I could see a woman driving towards me in a red car to join the road that I was on. 'Surely she's going to slow down,' I thought, but she continued looking the other way. When she hit me, I landed on the bonnet and then slid off to land on the road standing on my feet. I was completely unhurt, but the front wheel of my recently purchased bicycle was utterly buckled. The woman looked quite shocked, but at least she had the decency to pay for a wheel replacement, eventually!

The next incident could have been more serious. It occurred a few months later on a rainy night in March 2005 whilst cycling back from the University of Westminster on Marylebone Road. I was always in a hurry to get home as I felt uneasy about leaving Mum unattended for over four hours on those Wednesday evenings. Because the road surface was wet, the reduced friction seemed to allow me to go faster than normal. After following the winding road through Hyde Park, there was a straight run along Kensington High Street. I felt lucky that night for each set of traffic lights turned green on approach. It meant that I was able to continue going along at maximum speed. Ahead of me was a bay with some parked vehicles. I thought they were unoccupied as none had lights on. Suddenly and without any warning a car door was flung open about two metres in front of me. There was no time to think let alone react by pressing the breaks. The next thing I knew, I was flying through the air like Superman – with a rucksack, yellow helmet and matching raincoat in place of a red cape – but devoid of any supernatural powers. The whole incident may have been over in little more than the blink of an eye and yet it felt as if time had stood still with me being suspended in a sequence of slowly run film frames ...both arms were outstretched as if I was diving into a pool ... luckily no cars ahead of me ... Finally, I landed on the road some distance ahead of the car, still sliding forwards for another few metres but now feeling as if everything had returned to normal speed. Looking back, I could see that I had completely cleared the car door, leaving behind my bicycle in a crumpled heap.

A little awkwardly, I got to my feet, relieved to find that, apart from a few bruises and minor cuts to the hand and knee, I was fine. But the front wheel of my bike had been twisted into a figure of eight. The overweight and unpleasant looking driver gave me his details, but they turned out to be false when I checked with the police at a later date. Adding insult to injury, he never even offered to help and seemed more concerned about being late for a meal than for my well-being. If I hadn't been so concerned about how to get home due to worrying about Mum, I might have checked his number plate and phoned the police there and then.

Walking the seemingly cursed olive-green bicycle back to Hammersmith was no easy task. It required holding the handlebars to keep the front wheel, which could no longer turn, off the ground – until it could be safely locked up. The last part of the journey was completed by bus. I arrived home in Chiswick over an hour later than usual, but I needn't have worried. The quiet house indicated that Mum – who ironically had made me a complete Superman suit when I was about eight years old for a fancy-dress competition – had probably been blissfully asleep throughout the whole incident.

Every now and again, Mum would have problems recognising me. Once or twice I had to leave the house for a few hours because she thought I was an intruder and wanted to phone the police. That might explain why she once hit me on the back of the neck. It was quite a powerful whack and although it hurt for a few hours, at least I felt confident that she could probably still look after herself if she was ever in danger. Mum could have periods of bad moods and aggression, but always apologised afterwards and, for the most part, was affectionate. She was relatively easy to look after compared to some of the people documented in case studies that I had read about in the medical books on dementia. Nevertheless, she often had worries – and although some were misplaced – all seemed to impact on me. They may have stemmed from her growing inability to distinguish between different periods of her life. One involved her frequently expressed concern about children potentially falling into the garden pond, despite the absence of any youngsters in the family for many decades. Finally one day in May, after many reminders from Mum, I dug out the pond's plastic container. It had been there for years and used to fascinate our black cat for hours as he watched my sister's goldfish swimming around. Both cat and goldfish had long since passed away, so it wasn't controversial when I filled up the vacant hole with earth. A few weeks later the grass-seed had grown to cover it, extending the lawn area and removing at least one of the many sources of anxiety for Mum.

Many people advised me to try and get help. One day, after making an appointment, I took Mum over to the local Day Care Centre, about twenty minutes walk away. The idea was to try and start in the summer and if Mum got used to the centre, then maybe I would be able to leave her there for a few hours so that my time at work would be less stressful – less worrying about what she was getting up to on her own, I hoped. When we arrived, we were taken on a little tour. It looked very clean and colourful. We were then guided to some spare seats to join a few other elderly people. Mum was given a crossword, which was totally inappropriate. The lady next to her did try to talk to Mum. However, after only five minutes Mum already looked irritated. Turning towards me, she asked, "What are we doing wasting our time in here? Let's go home!" And that was it. Mum got up, probably thinking that no further explanations were necessary. She didn't even acknowledge the poor old lady who may have thought, a minute earlier, that she had found a new friend. I was only able to offer a brief apology to a member of staff as I quickly followed Mum towards the exit and we were out of the centre in a shot.

Oddly enough, I felt a bit relieved – as if our freedom had been regained. I chuckled to myself. Mum's reaction seemed to confirm that I knew her better than doctors, social workers or even some well-intended colleagues at school. I had correctly anticipated how Mum would respond to any institutional setting, friendly or not. As long as Mum could walk and still think, even if just a little bit, she was not going to be told what to do. She might have dementia, and by 2005 it had already advanced into the middle stages, but she was still strong willed and, as far as possible, an independent woman. Besides, the opening hours of the centre were totally out of line with the school day; consequently attendance would have presented another logistical problem. And that was typical of many of the government services provided for the elderly where, despite large sums being allocated, there was a frustrating lack of flexibility in the system which often prevented optimum usage of the facilities.

Although opportunities to socialise dwindled during 2005, they didn't entirely disappear. As well as seeing my sister, there were a few visits to Peter, but usually lasting for little more than an hour. The same duration applied to my attendance at a party in Twickenham, hosted by Paula, one warm, sunny Saturday evening in June. I was also present for Sports Day, but for me it was the last one for a few years – a pity – as I had always found it to be one of the highlights of the school calendar. Unfortunately, I had less luck with another eagerly awaited event. I had paid for the 6th formers Leavers' Ball in July, but it turned out to be an awkward night. Mum was restless and just couldn't get to sleep. By 10 p.m. I knew I had missed the dinner, and when she still hadn't gone to bed an hour later, I just gave up and put the tuxedo back in the wardrobe. On a more positive note, the Charity Walk went much better than the previous year. For a start, my workload was dramatically cut when Irene, along with some of the other teachers at Gumley House School, offered to act as hosts. That left them with the responsibility of organising the catering arrangements for the social that always followed the Walk. The weather was perfect, and I was able to fit in two visits to my mum during the course of the day, which helped to keep her calm.

Another change was with my running. In 2005 I had to replace the longer routes with several laps around the block in order to achieve the desired distance. When I was particularly worried about leaving Mum by herself, I would instead run on the spot for about half-an-hour in the kitchen. Boring – but it helped keep me fit – and that was something I was determined to hold on to. In that respect there was no conflict of interest with regards to the many walks that Mum was insisting on taking each day. But when we walked by the river, I often glanced across to the

Surrey embankment and longed to have the freedom to go on those carefree runs in the morning that I had once taken for granted.

There were trips out for Mum as well. Sometimes we would take the bus to Kingston to visit my sister. The bus stop was on Kew Bridge very close to our usual walking route. This could sometimes cause problems when I took Mum for a walk on those mornings before I had to go to school. On seeing an approaching bus she could suddenly demand to catch one to Kingston completely forgetting or, even more likely, not comprehending my work commitments. And when I ignored her request, it could leave her annoyed right until I had escorted her home. We also took the train to Weybridge for a day out. Then I was surprised at how nervous Mum could get when travelling on the train, but it was good to maintain the experience of journeys on public transport. During that summer of 2005 we even included a boat trip from Kew Pier to Richmond. It was a sunny Sunday afternoon and Mum really enjoyed the outing, though she was a bit hesitant about both boarding and disembarking from the vessel.

At the very least such outings provided a useful diversion for Mum, but in many respects they served another purpose too. As it became clearer, certainly by the summer of 2005, that the Italian holiday planned for the following year was still on the cards, the significance of such preparation became increasingly more apparent. And up to a point such perseverance did work – because when we finally boarded the train from Kew Bridge on that eventful journey to *Torino* in May 2006, she at least didn't appear to be nervous.

As far as keeping Mum occupied in the house, the TV still proved useful. But there was a smaller range of programmes that could hold her attention. In August I found a record that she had liked, *Tie a Yellow Ribbon round the Ole Oak Tree*. She loved dancing, particularly to that song. It was an activity that nearly always featured at some part of the day, being very helpful in raising her spirits if she wasn't in a good mood. It may have reminded her of earlier times in *San Damiano* when her parents regularly took the whole family to the local dance hall. Sometimes whilst we were dancing, I caught a glimpse of our reflection in the brown glass of the cabinet in the front room. Because it was displayed on a dark background, Mum's figure, particularly with her white hair standing out, had a ghost-like appearance. It made me wonder about the future – whether I would look nostalgically at the cabinet one day and try to recall those moving images that were being captured momentarily in the glass.

Although reducing the hours at work proved to be an absolute necessity, I was well-advised by colleagues at school not to give up the job completely. Not only ensuring a moderate stream of income – even if limited – it also provided a link to the outside world. As my life increasingly revolved around caring for my mum it was important to avoid being left completely isolated – and a few hours in the company of school children definitely guaranteed against that particular fate. One memorable afternoon was spent at Griffin Park, Brentford FC, watching the victorious Year 9 football team in the Middlesex Cup Final.

Despite the obvious benefits of continuing to work, it did add to the stress. There were clear expectations to achieve high grades from all quarters – the students, the parents and the school itself, although at least I did notice fewer and fewer memos appearing in my staffroom pigeon hole as awareness of Mum's situation increased. Nevertheless, in some years the structure of the time-table could be far from ideal. The academic year of 2005-6 proved particularly difficult every Tuesday. It was a day when I taught economics for each one of the six periods to both the Upper and Lower 6th – morning and afternoon respectively. For me that added a further challenge – one concerning time. How was I going to fit in a visit to see Mum during a lunch break that only lasted fifty minutes?

As soon as the bell started ringing, I usually dashed from the classroom, like a greyhound out of the traps, rushing to the school gate as fast as a heavy rucksack on my back would allow. With the bike unlocked I was off – pedalling as fast as possible towards Kew Bridge, about two miles away. After greeting Mum, I discarded any notes linked to the morning lesson and headed straight to the kitchen. Soup was quick to prepare, followed by a pudding. Having been cooped up in the house all morning, Mum was nearly always itching to go out – just like the boys at school when reluctantly kept in class during a wet break. Usually there was just enough time to take Mum around the block. On returning about ten minutes later, I left a jug of squash and a few cakes or biscuits on the table, hoping these would provide a sufficient distraction to ease my departure. It was then back on the bike which was hurriedly locked up by the school railings on arrival. This ritual was inevitably accompanied by the unwelcome sound of *that* bell again. It signified that afternoon lessons were about to start. A little run to the 6th form block and soon I entered the classroom, sometimes a few minutes late but always ready to deliver the next lesson – even if feeling a bit flustered.

One of the last really significant events of the year was the sad news from Bridget concerning the death of her husband. The funeral was scheduled for Friday the 9th of September. I had been given permission from the Head to attend along with Mark, another teacher who, like John, also shared a passion for golf. It was held in a pretty village called Haddenham on a sunny afternoon. At the end of the service, the gathering of relatives and friends stood outside the church to observe the cortège departing in the distance with John's coffin, the silence only being interrupted by the resident ducks failing to respect the solemnity of the occasion. This was followed by the wake in a nearby hall. It was interesting to see the photos of John on display, outlining different periods of his life, and some of which I had never seen before. Despite leaving just after 3 p.m., it still remained a bit of a rush to get home.

I had already bought tickets to take Mum to the Richmond Theatre that evening, but it was a show featuring the Latin American music that proved to be a mistake. We left after a few minutes as she didn't like it, but to make matter worse this was followed by being caught in a monsoon type shower on the way back. Later that evening, after Mum had gone to bed, I was left with the task of scooping buckets of water out of the flooded basement.

For a change, the Gunnersbury Staff Christmas dinner for 2005 was held outside school in Syon Park in a huge marquee. It was arranged by Nick for the evening but unlike the July Leavers' Ball, Mum did fall asleep at the appropriate moment. It allowed me to sneak out for two hours – the maximum period before leaving Mum alone would cause me anxiety. I had the meal and a chat with a few of the teachers, but even though it looked a lively venue and the music was tempting me to stay a bit longer, I knew I couldn't. As I got on the bicycle to make the short journey back to Kew, I had no idea that apart from a few short visits to Peter and my sister, plus the trip to Italy with Mum in 2006, I wouldn't be able to attend another evening social event until 2008. From then onwards my life was going to revolve around caring for Mum, and either through lack of time, tiredness or a reluctance to leave her alone for too long, I had more or less to give up trying to maintain a social life for the foreseeable future.

Chapter 14 Modifying the Chiswick House

Before Mum's return to her home in Chiswick, in August 2002, the plumbers had put in new pipe work for the gas, replaced the sink unit and installed new boilers for the kitchen and bathroom. Although it had to wait until 2004 for me to finish the tiling near the sink, the new appliances were functioning and ready for use. As Mum had lived in the house for over three decades, she soon settled in. For the first two years I didn't need to adapt anything to cope with her dementia. But as her condition worsened both mentally and, to a lesser degree, physically, I gradually found I was being forced to make more and more modifications to protect her from possible accidents or danger.

One of the first changes required was with the gas cooker. On a few occasions I returned home, maybe from school or shopping, to find that she had left the gas rings on and unlit. Sometimes the smell of gas was so strong that I was alerted to the problem as soon as I entered the front door. The solution was simple, though slightly inconvenient. Every time I left the house when I knew I wouldn't be returning promptly, I took off all the knobs from the gas cooker and put them out of reach and out of sight. I also couldn't leave any boxes of matches lying around; they too had to be hidden. I did the same with the iron eventually, but in the transition years when Mum could still do quite a range of housework, I taped the dial to its lowest setting. I figured that if she left the iron switched on but unattended for too long, at least it wouldn't cause a fire. Mum was none too pleased by the new arrangement, as it took much longer to iron an item of clothing, and sometimes I could see that she had attempted to remove the tape. Despite enquiring, I never found an appliance where the power can automatically cut out when left stationary for an inappropriate period of time.

To avoid Mum getting locked in either of the two toilets, it became necessary to tape up the door latches. At the same time, I didn't want to get locked out of the house so was forced to do the same to the chain on the front door. As for the bolt at the bottom of the door, I felt confident that it would be too awkward for her to reach comfortably – so left it. My intuition was correct, as I never had any problem gaining access to the house in the later years.

Another concern was her tendency to go up to the attic on a fairly regular basis. I sometimes wondered why she wanted to. On reflection, it may have been because she had slept there alone for quite a few years before her eventual move to the Hammersmith house. Typically, and not long after Dad had returned home from work, the meal that Mum had prepared for him was unceremoniously dumped on the dining room table. The door was then shut firmly to be followed by equally loud footsteps as she marched up to her retreat in the attic where she had a bed and TV.

So maybe it was quite rational for her to visit the top floor – to a room that she may still have had some attachment to. But for me it was a worry because I noticed that Mum was placing her size 9 feet on the narrowest part of the winding stairwell. I feared that one day, on returning from a few hours at school, I might find her lying injured at the bottom of the stairs. A little construction work was required. Soon after buying some material at the nearby DIY store, I was able to make a gate. Placed at the start of the final flight of stairs, it prevented her gaining access to the attic. It was probably the first example where I had to restrict her movements around HER house, but unless I could stay with her every single minute of the day, which was impossible, realistically I didn't have any other option.

Actually thinking back, there may have been another reason why Mum may have found the return to Chiswick confusing. I decided to use the larger of the bedrooms upstairs for myself because I felt that despite having a storage heater she might, at her age, find it too cold in the winter. But this had been the main bedroom that she had shared with my dad for many years before retreating to the attic. As an alternative, I suggested to her that she should use the smaller room at the back which would be much easier to keep warm. This used to be my sister's room until she moved out to Kingston in 1990. Mum agreed, and by and large the new sleeping arrangements worked very well. However, there were a couple of times when I went upstairs, a few hours after Mum had retired, only to find her sleeping in my bed. Obviously she must have gone to the toilet and then instinctively returned to her original bedroom. I didn't mind. Usually on such occasions I tried to sleep on the floor in the room next to hers. If I was awakened by her going to the toilet again, it provided me with an opportunity to guide her back to her room without the need to make her aware of any mistake having been made.

By the time Mum reached her late seventies, although she remained very fit in terms of walking, I did notice that there was definitely less strength in her arm and thigh muscles. This meant that she found getting off the toilet seat more difficult and taking a bath on her own was impossible. To help out with the former problem, I fitted rails in both toilets and also a device to raise the toilet seat, but these were only of temporary assistance. By 2006 I needed to accompany her to the toilet and help clean her bottom which was good preparation for the level of care that was necessary by the autumn of the following year. When I found a stool left on the lid of the toilet seat one day, the remedy was simply to tape the lid up to the pipe. Why Mum had also thrown one of her nightdresses in the toilet was a mystery, but one that didn't pose much of a problem and for which I couldn't think of an appropriate solution anyway.

As for taking a bath, the easiest remedy in the end was to just give up. Instead, I brought a bowl of warm water up to her room and simply washed her with a flannel. Washing her hair wasn't easy and was definitely unpopular with Mum. It couldn't have been comfortable, particularly for her back, because I needed her to lean forward over the sink for a few minutes. Because she nearly always complained, this particular part of her personal hygiene tended to get a bit neglected. But if, for some reason, I found Mum particularly annoying on a certain day, it was usually a good time to wash her hair. It meant that I was less sensitive to her shouts of disapproval.

If Mum hated having her hair washed, the same could not be said of her treatment for facial hair. It was a problem that she had been cursed with since her teens. She once confided with me that it was an issue that greatly upset her when she was young. I suspect it was a concern that never left her right up until the last stages of dementia – because I never once received a negative reaction when I applied the cream to remove any facial hair that would eventually become noticeable if left untreated. It was as if she still understood. Nearly every time, she calmly sat still for the ten minutes required before I could scrape off the cream. Of course I never attempted the method that I had once observed as a child whilst curiously peering behind drawn curtains. There in the kitchen she had melted some wax in a small saucepan over the stove. After application, the temporary brown mask that partially covered her features did look strange. But either means to epilate produced the same result – a smooth and fresh skin that made her look younger – and which brought a smile back to her face.

For most of the years while Mum was suffering dementia she still liked to spend time in the garden. I know this was the case as I often found her there when I returned from work. I also felt that she didn't take any delight in relinquishing her role as being the person in charge of many of the household chores, even towards the end. One annoying habit of hers remains difficult to forget. Sometimes after I had washed the laundry and put it out on the line to dry, I would then get really frustrated when a few minutes later I could see, from a window inside the house, that Mum had gone out to the garden to bring in the washing while still wet. Occasionally this could be repeated several times in a day! That was irritating, though hardly a great source of anxiety.

But one worrying concern over her visits to the garden centred on a small metal rail that Dad had put on the right hand side of the steps leading up to the lawn. This was fine for going up the stairs but somewhat useless for coming down. When I saw Mum leaning forwards to reach the low bar, I was worried that one day she would fall and land on the concrete floor. When Mum stayed in hospital for over a week in March 2005 it provided an opportunity to use my free mornings, before visiting her in the afternoon, to build two brick piers. These were designed to support a scaffold pipe that I found in the basement, which served as a rail on the left hand side of the stairs. When Mum came out of the hospital she was soon well enough to go into the garden. However, I noticed that she was still using the old and unsuitable rail when returning to the house. But my time had not been wasted. Eventually, with a bit of training and much reminding, I got her to use the new rail and fortunately she never once fell.

My bedroom upstairs also acted as an office. It was a bright and spacious room at the front of the house and consequently a good place to mark homework, prepare lessons or, for that matter, any other administrative work related to the school or University. Nevertheless, concentration was not always easy to maintain. From my writing desk, which was located next to the window, I could see what was going on outside. Sometimes I would be distracted by my mum, but at least it was a reassuring sight. Often she would be outside by the front of the house, sweeping the pavement or chatting with a neighbour or somebody passing by. She took pride in the appearance of the property and enjoyed the opportunity to meet other people, but allowing her to have this degree of freedom came at a price.

Back in 2004, in fact New Year's Eve, I left Mum alone in the house for about three hours during the afternoon. When I came back, I found her looking upset. Although her dementia meant that I couldn't get a very clear explanation, it appeared that a couple with two children had stopped by the gate to talk. Probably wanting to give the small children a gift, Mum must have taken her purse out of her handbag to give them a few coins. When the couple saw a purse full of notes, they must have grabbed the money and run off. I know the purse had contained at least £270 because I was becoming increasingly concerned that she might lose the contents one day. I had wanted to deposit some of the cash in her building society account a few days earlier but, unfortunately, Mum was going through a paranoid stage of dementia at that time and didn't seem to trust me.

From that day on, and regardless of whether she liked it or not, I took more control over her money. Her purse was now to be just a store for coins. I hid all her savings books and replaced them with some old ones where I wrote down the amounts in each account. I knew this would provide Mum with the reassurance of financial security, but would be of no use to a thief. Any cash that wasn't used for shopping was deposited in her account. For the next few weeks, I was a bit nervous about leaving her on her own, but thankfully the same couple never returned, although a woman did call a few days later and looked surprised when I opened the door. When I asked her what she wanted she said she had got the wrong number – but she did look suspicious, especially as she ignored my directions when guiding her to the house number she had apparently been looking for.

With no further incidents, Mum was still allowed to have her freedom. But another worrying aspect of leaving somebody with dementia unattended, aside from security issues, is the possibility that they might wander off and get lost. In that respect I was fortunate with Mum for it was only in the last stages that this became an issue. On one occasion, she got out of the house while I was home, but luckily I quickly noticed. I ran around the block and knew I was on the right trail as I soon found her white hat and scarf on the pavement. Not before long I caught up with her and, without making any fuss, escorted her for the remainder of the walk home feeling relieved that I found her so soon. On another day the wife of the shopkeeper up the road brought Mum back when she found her wandering outside the shop. There was nothing irrational about Mum wanting to go out by herself. After all she was an adult and had been free to do that most of her life. But it became a problem when she couldn't remember how to get back home.

I didn't want to imprison Mum but I had to restrict her movements. In the end I went for a compromise. For a few days in the week, the pavement would just have to remain unswept. I worked out that she wasn't agile enough to climb over the brick wall, so all I had to do was lock the gate whenever I left her alone in the house. I used a lock designed for a sash window and screwed it on the post just above the latch of the gate. Before leaving for school I pushed the bicycle outside and left it leaning on the wall. I then went back into the front garden and used the key to lock the bolt in place. I was then able to leap over the wall – not quite like a cowboy mounting his horse in the films – but at least I could confidently ride off, knowing that she could still go outside and chat to the neighbours if she wanted, without the risk of her wandering off.

The system that was introduced on the 26th of October, 2005, worked well for about a year but it wasn't without its problems. Sometimes Mum would get locked out and if I was away for about three hours, that would be a long time for her to wait outside, particularly if it was very hot or cold or, perhaps worse still, raining. As well as a bottle of drink, I did leave a chair outside so that she would at least have something to sit on, other than just the steps, but she kept on putting it back in the house, probably thinking it looked out of place. It didn't matter how many times that I told her the purpose of the chair, it was never left outside by the time I had returned. Looking for a more permanent solution, I ended up building two brick seats on either side of the front door under the porch. Of course, locking the gate then denied access to the postman. In order to deal with that newly created problem, I built a brick mailbox next to the gate ensuring that any post could still be delivered. For a permanent cover I cast a concrete slab – it was very strong – but so heavy that it required the assistance of a neighbour to help lift it on to the mailbox. A few other neighbours were also given keys to the house so that if they noticed that Mum had been locked out, they would be able to let her in – as long as they didn't mind clambering over the brick wall!

So for just over a year Mum was able to enjoy a relative degree of freedom, but because she was on her own for a few hours with a weakening memory, eventually the system broke down. Unfortunately I couldn't ask anybody to look after Mum while I was out – certainly not in those years whilst she remained so restless. Unless somebody was fluent in English, Italian and her dialect, but also willing to take the responsibility of taking her out on several long walks, regardless of the weather, there was no point. She would have given anybody trying to keep her in the house a very difficult time. As the dementia progressed, the number of times that neighbours informed me that they had found her locked out increased. The last straw came on the 9th of November, 2006, when I returned home from school. Mum wasn't downstairs so I went up to her room and found her lying on the bed. The expression on her face seemed to be one of resigned sadness associated with failure. It was hard to work out what was the matter with her.

Later I went into my room and straight away noticed that there was an empty space on my desk that had been occupied by my laptop a few hours earlier. I looked around the room and then the rest of the house to check if Mum had moved it. But that would have been impossible. With her dementia, there was no way she could have disconnected all the leads so carefully to remove the laptop. My neighbour, Jim, later told me that he had noticed that the front door had been left open. If only Paul, the friendly and helpful postman had been doing his rounds at the time. Maybe his presence would have been enough to deter any intruder even thinking of entering the house. But it would have just postponed the inevitable. It started to become obvious. Somebody passing by may have seen an opportunity. It could even have been one of those youths often seen cycling up and down the road looking into any unoccupied parked cars. Quickly rushing into the house maybe the laptop was enough to take since nothing else was missing. Maybe Mum disturbed the burglar? Maybe she didn't have a clue that somebody had entered the house? Who knows? There was no way I would be able to get any useful information from her. Although I reported the incident to the police they certainly didn't have much to go on. The main thing, however, was that Mum was unharmed. But I couldn't just leave the house open to any random thief passing by. Regrettably I would have to take more drastic action and if Mum would not cooperate in having someone sit with her while I was out, then her freedom would have to be restricted even further.

The next morning after washing and dressing her, giving her breakfast and taking her for two walks, I had to do what, until then, had seemed unthinkable. It was necessary to lock Mum in. She was imprisoned and I could still hear her distressing howls of protest and banging on the window as I left to buy a replacement for the stolen item. Ignoring any televisions, digital cameras or other electrical goods on display in the store, I quickly selected a reasonably priced laptop. It must have been the fastest sale that the shop assistant had ever experienced as I was desperate to get home as quickly as possible. I had left the back door to the garden unlocked so she wouldn't be completely trapped in the house in case there was a fire, but I still felt terrible about locking her in. As the weeks progressed I got more used to the idea since I didn't have much alternative, but it meant that every trip outside was worrying and guilt laden.

Another and more immediate concern, however, was the way she had been banging the glass of the front door. Would I return home to find that she had smashed the pane and, worse still, got herself seriously injured? It was while I was cycling back with the laptop that I decided I would also need to cover the glass. That evening, after taking the measurements, I ran to the DIY store and bought a sheet of MDF which I then screwed on the door frame to act as a cover. From then onwards, her frustrated banging would be safer and a bit more muffled. Moreover, it would be less likely to cause distress to anybody passing by who would probably have wondered if they needed to call the police. Imagine the scene – an elderly woman with her distraught face pressed against the frosted glass pane – and looking desperate to escape from the house! With Mum out of sight, it also made it a bit easier for me to leave for school in the morning. It had the unfortunate effect of making the hallway darker but a partial solution was found a week or two later. A carpenter working nearby kindly offered to drill a series of large circles in the board which would allow five streams of light to shine through.

At least by this stage I had cut my hours at work to the point where I would never be out for more than three hours on any one day. Nevertheless, it was still a much longer time to leave her than I felt comfortable with. It dominated my thoughts for some time because I knew just how much Mum hated being trapped inside. Her anger and frustration was evident in the damaged curtain next to the front door. In a rage she must have been pressing the material so hard against the light switch that it made a large hole in the fabric that, all those years ago, she had carefully crafted on her sewing machine. Consequently, for a few weeks at school, but particularly during a weekly dinner-break duty shared with Ian, this topic seemed the focus of most conversations. As an assistant to the CDT [5] department, he had the practical knowledge and experience to consider other possible options. But the need to keep other people out, while allowing Mum the freedom to enter and leave the house, was a tricky combination, especially with her seriously diminished cognitive skills. We never came up with a satisfactory solution, and neither did any other members of staff willing to engage in such discussions. In the end I just had to accept that sometimes you have to be cruel to be kind.

Locking Mum in was the last major modification, but the strategy didn't work on FA Cup Final day in 2007. In previous years I had watched the football match with John. But this year the day turned out to be memorable for a different reason and it had nothing to do with the game between Chelsea and Manchester United which, later in the

---

[5] Craft, Design and Technology.

afternoon, I completely missed. It was Saturday the 19th of May. Because I was in the house I didn't bother locking the door but I also forgot to bolt it. I left Mum downstairs while I looked for some electrical tools for a job that I was planning to do later in the day. I must have been upstairs for just a few minutes, rummaging through a brown tool bag, but it was long enough for her to sneak out quietly. When I became aware that she had gone, she was already out of sight. At this point I wasn't too concerned. It had happened once before and I soon found her.

I started my search by running around the block but this time there was no sight of her or any clues from mislaid personal belongings. I then checked the other smaller block where we sometimes walked but worryingly there were still no sightings. 'Okay,' I thought. 'Let's get on the bike and cycle around the usual walking routes.' When I was met with the same lack of success after going along the river and even crossing over Kew Bridge, I started to panic. Maybe she had boarded a bus and some unfortunate driver, unable to understand her, might have allowed her to stay on? That meant she could have ended up anywhere.

I had done all I could do. It was time to phone the police. Because I had dressed her, like every previous morning for the past two years, I was able to give a perfect description of every item that she had been wearing that day – white cap, dress with narrow red and white horizontal stripes, red cardigan, light brown tights and dark brown shoes. A few minutes later I got a call back from the police. She had already been spotted by a patrol car, having fallen over, close to the Pilot pub on Wellesley Road. Maybe she had been walking to the GP? Maybe she had been looking for me but had not thought to call or look upstairs? Maybe she just wanted to go out? Who knows? But because she had been found injured, she was taken straight to hospital. This time it was closer to central London.

When I later arrived at the hospital, I could see her face was badly cut and bruised, but fortunately nothing was broken. What a relief to find her again! She was kept in overnight as a precaution, and there was also a brain scan to check for any internal injuries. The result of that was fine, but it also yielded some very useful and interesting information. The scan revealed, through areas of infarction in the brain, that Mum had suffered several strokes over the years, which can be a cause of vascular dementia. Now the diagnosis of her worsening condition wasn't just based on observation of her behaviour or even tests revealing an inability to count backwards from twenty to one or recall the name of the current Prime Minister. There was also physical evidence as to what had been going on with Mum over the last few years – and a medical explanation for her changing demeanour. But Mum's energy levels never quite returned after that fall. While the scan revealed no internal bleeding in her head, I'm still left wondering as to whether the same level of attention had been applied to the rest of her body. Any bleeding left unchecked might have explained the condition of anaemia that she began to experience over the forthcoming months but one that had yet to be diagnosed.

Chapter 15 Unlearning

Clearly the process of dementia had an impact on me both socially and practically. But what was the journey of decline like for Mum? The impression that I got and the best analogy I can think of would be to picture a lengthy journey on a barge along a canal. It wasn't a smooth decline as if going down a hill, but neither was it a sudden fall off a cliff edge. Imagine travelling on the barge, taking in the scenery with nothing dramatic happening; then you reach a lock and are lowered to a new level, at which point the load is lessened. Boxes containing fresh produce are exchanged for a fewer number of boxes full of inferior contents. Again, there is a passage of no significant change for a while until ahead, lies another lock. A similar exchange of boxes occurs – each time reducing the value of the cargo – each lock taking you down to yet a lower level. Sometimes the gaps between the locks are a long distance, sometimes only short. As the journey nears its end, such gaps get smaller, while the drop to the next water level becomes even greater. And so it was with Mum's mind – as one looks back at the changes that occurred between 2000 and 2007 – a series of stepped declines but with the rapidity and severity increasing as time passed by.

In 1996 Mum was seventy years old. At that stage there really was no indication that she would later suffer from dementia – although the death of her mother in 1992, after suffering from the illness, did provide some sort of warning sign. As far as losing an interest in current affairs was concerned, it is impossible to pinpoint an exact date. It didn't happen suddenly – but by recollecting some significant incidents that dominated the media, I shall attempt to give some idea of the timing. In 1997 at the age of seventy-one she was still following the news. She was aware that Tony Blair had replaced John Major as Prime Minister. A few months later in August I received a phone call early one Sunday morning. It was Mum expressing her shock at hearing the reports that Princess Diana had been killed in a car accident in Paris. Three years later and we watched the opening New Year's Eve celebrations from the Millennium Dome and she fully comprehended the meaning of the occasion. But after that...?

The last major event that I can remember having an impact on Mum was when she had reached the age of seventy-five. It involved the awful images being broadcast on the screen when the planes were crashed into New York's twin towers at the World Trade Centre on the 11th of September, 2001. Probably not too long after that atrocity, Mum's perceptions of the outside world, beyond her own immediate needs and experiences, were quickly shrinking. By 2005, the bombings in London, only a day after the capital had won the bid for staging the 2012 Olympics, meant nothing to her. This was made all the more noticeable by the absence of any demands on me to avoid setting foot on public transport.

So between 1996 and 2001 there were very few signs that there might be a problem with Mum's brain and any such changes were made all the more difficult to detect by being fairly imperceptible. As well as repeating herself sometimes, there were a few occasions when her thoughts seemed slightly irrational. One example that springs to mind occurred in the late 1990s. It was a Saturday afternoon when my sister was driving us to Hammersmith. The car broke down very close to the busy roundabout. We managed to push it into a nearby side road but had to wait for what seemed like ages – but probably wasn't that long – before help arrived. Eventually the car was towed to Kingston and the meal with Mum had to be abandoned. It was Mum's reaction when my sister phoned initially to say we would be late that was surprising. Mum appeared more concerned about us missing her meal rather than the fact that the car was immobile. It was totally out of character.

Another example when Mum seemed to be acting strangely was her falling out with her neighbour. She had known Lena for many years before moving to the Hammersmith house in 1992 and they had been good friends. And yet sometime in the late 1990s Mum was convinced that Lena had been rude to her. This couldn't have been the case, but either from a certain degree of paranoia that may have already been there, but which only came to my notice in 2004, or just simply from mishearing or misinterpreting something, Mum was offended. For quite a while she refused to speak to her neighbour. That put me in an awkward position. But having grown used to being the diplomat and intermediary between Mum and Dad over the years, I was able to work out a compromise arrangement. I told Lena not to be offended but whenever I met her while I was with Mum, I wouldn't say hello for the foreseeable future. Years later, when Mum's dementia was far more advanced, she greeted Lena as if nothing had happened and so I was able to feel more relaxed whenever they met.

So by the end of 2001, Mum was still capable of doing the majority of things that she had learnt in her adult life. Her short term memory was no longer perfect and there were those few cases of odd behaviour, but other than that she seemed very normal. What might be termed higher order skills were all there. She could write, speak fluently in three languages, made perfect sense when talking, had no problems with reading and when watching a film, drama or documentary on TV, could still concentrate and follow the plot. She could deal with her own finances, go shopping independently and had absolutely no trouble signing her name. Her social skills were unimpaired. She recognised everybody whom she knew well and had a very good sense of direction. She was able to cycle from Hammersmith to her house in Chiswick without any guide or assistance. All the more practical skills that she had acquired in her youth and developed as an adult such as sewing, cooking and decorating were all still intact. And of course her basic skills of eating, dressing, washing, going to the toilet and sleeping at appropriate times were all totally unaffected. These basic skills were probably the first that she had acquired as a child and so maybe it is not too surprising that in the regressive process of dementia, they were the last ones to be surrendered. The arrival of the new millennium probably accompanied the start of Mum's life journey turning full circle. For by the end, every single one of those skills was lost without exception.

There still didn't seem to be any really significant change in Mum by 2002 but because she had moved back to Chiswick in the summer, the different location and routine probably made me aware something wasn't quite right. It prompted me to remember an earlier conversation with Lena when I hadn't particularly welcomed her conjecture that Mum might have dementia. Unlike the previous bicycle ride between the two houses that Mum had completed on her own, about seven months later the same journey between Hammersmith and Chiswick involved Mum getting lost, albeit temporarily. It showed her memory was changing. I was also concerned to see what a mess her medicine box was in. As far as I could make out, Mum must have been taking the medicines prescribed by her doctor in a completely random manner. I wondered for how long. It was now time for me to intervene. I found some suitably sized plastic boxes. They were navy blue with orange lids, ones that Dad had used for storing photographic slides, and labelled them appropriately for their newly intended use. From then on I took on the responsibility of administering her medicines each day. Other than that everything else carried on normally. Mum could still prepare really nice meals and was in charge of the garden; there was also the added benefit of having my laundry washed and ironed. One afternoon I worked through a memory check, which I discovered in a book on dementia. It was reassuring to find that in 2002 Mum could still gain a high score. Several years later, I repeated the identical test and tried to apply the same level of honesty as before. Unfortunately, but not too surprisingly, it revealed a significantly lower result.

I suppose it was in 2003 that it became more obvious that Mum's problems weren't just confined to short term memory loss and repeating herself. From this point onwards, I had to keep a much closer eye on her. Some things could be potentially dangerous – like her tendency to leave the iron on. Thankfully I was spared from another potential fire hazard as a result of her decision to quit smoking in the mid-1960s. At the time I was very pleased as I found it an irritating habit. Despite starting in her teens, as soon as Mum had made the decision to stop she had the willpower to resist ever picking up another cigarette again. At the time it made life at home far more pleasant and must have benefited her health; forty years on and that earlier decision had an unintended but beneficial consequence given the onset of dementia. It meant that at least I was spared the worry of her leaving discarded matches or lit cigarettes around the house and with it, all the ensuing risks.

Before the end of 2003 another significant change emerged; she was no longer able to go shopping on her own. Sometimes she could forget what she had originally gone out to buy. Alternatively, there was the risk that she could end up leaving the purchases behind. A successful shopping trip increasingly depended on the honesty of any shopkeepers as she was also starting to become less aware of the value of different notes and coins. I seemed to find myself buying clothes for Mum at this point and must have spent hours searching for a retailer that sold the thicker, winter tights from Italy that she preferred. It also marked the moment when phone calls to Mum from work weren't always helpful. "Are you okay, Mum?" "Who is it?" she would reply. "It's Michael," I would answer. "He's not here. I think he's at work," came back her response – still in a helpful tone. "No, I'm Michael. I'm at school." And so it would go on for a while until I could sense Mum had become either too anxious or irritated for me to press the matter any further. This type of conversation wasn't too representative of 2003, but by 2005 it had become the norm. The calls had originally been intended to give some reassurance when I was away at work for a few hours. For a while this wish was being fulfilled but eventually they just caused confusion. By the end of 2005 I found it better not to phone at all, especially if there was the possibility that any one of the calls could have caused her to rush downstairs and maybe suffer a nasty fall.

A significant change in 2003, and one that had financial implications, became evident one day when we were in Hammersmith and popped into a bank. It should have been like any other routine cash withdrawal but without any warning Mum suddenly forgot how to sign her name. Maybe Mum had already realised herself that she was having a problem. Prior to this incident she had got into the habit of signing her pension book at home in advance of collecting her money from the Post Office. The bank clerk then started to ask Mum security-type questions like date of birth. Mum was getting flustered and, under pressure, couldn't remember her birthday. I was shuffling around impatiently which probably made the whole transaction look even more suspicious. Eventually, when I suggested it might be easier if we could find a quiet spot to sit down,

Mum was able to sign. If she hadn't withdrawn any cash on that day, it wouldn't have been a disaster. But it was a warning for the future.

In the following few months we went to all the building societies where Mum had savings and turned them into joint accounts. It was a precaution in case the day came when she couldn't sign at all in public. By May, all the accounts and the will had been sorted out – and just in time. I had been right to be cautious. Not that Mum gave up without a struggle. In those couple of months I often found sheets of paper lying around the house where I could see that she had been practising. Each page had her signature copied out hundreds of times. But regardless of the repetition, the quality of her signature just deteriorated – until eventually she could hardly hold a pen. Hence by 2005, when her signature at the Italian Consulate was required for the passport, I had to hold her hand to trace it out. Had Mum not thrown such a tantrum a few minutes earlier, I'm not sure if we would have been treated so sympathetically.

Other than that, the dementia didn't manifest itself in any other negative way. Mum needed a bit of looking after but it wasn't too time-consuming. She was good company and it was nice hearing her stories about Italy even if they got repeated quite a few times. In some respects her memory was starting to operate like a Video Cassette Recorder that I had bought in 1980. Despite working well for many years, eventually it did stop recording, and yet it was still perfect for showing videos. Mum's brain seemed to be mimicking the VCR – it could play back the earlier recollections of her life that had been well etched into her long term memory, but it was failing to record more recent events which relied on short term retention. Nevertheless, even the long term memories may become erased eventually. For that reason, and regardless of any risk of tedium setting in from listening to such repetitions, one should try to be a good audience – not just out of politeness – but also because a time may arrive when such recollections will be missed.

Physically there was no deterioration in Mum's health during 2004. If anything she was getting fitter due to the amount of walking she was achieving each day. In the previous two years she had found a walk of a relatively short distance a bit tiring, especially on a hot day in the summer. However, by 2004 Mum was able to walk by the river, probably about 2 km, several times a day. She was also still able to cycle between

Chiswick and Hammersmith comfortably. By then nearly everybody whom we cycled past prompted Mum to comment that the person was somebody from a TV programme. That clearly wasn't the case. At first I pointed out that she was mistaken, but after this had been repeated a few times, I didn't bother challenging her any more. Besides, it wasn't that annoying once you got used to it, but it did provide an indication that she was increasingly having problems recognising or remembering faces accurately. She had already experienced such a difficulty with my sister. A year later the same was to happen with me. But as far as cycling was concerned, she could still complete a journey of a few miles, making appropriate use of the brakes and even hand signals. And because she was still perfectly balanced there was no fear of her falling off.

Mum remained in charge of preparing meals and she continued to do most jobs around the house. She often spent some time in the front sweeping the pavement while at the back she continued looking after the garden. In the summer we cut and chopped the wood out in the garden that Dad had stored in the basement. It helped to clear out that part of the house and provided useful fuel for the winter. Mum liked to take part in sawing the wood, using breaks to recount stories of such activities from her past, as it reminded her of a task that she had been asked to do in Italy during her youth. She was still able to chop the wood into fine pieces suitable for kindling, but the sight of Mum wielding a sharp chopper at her age did make me flinch sometimes.

As far as her personal hygiene was concerned, 2004 was the time when I took over washing her hair because, without my intervention, she would have let that go, either because she forgot or simply didn't want to. By October I found that I had inherited the responsibility of washing her entirely. For about two years Mum was happy for that chore to be completed in the evening before she went to bed. It was also the year when I had to begin helping her to dress, though not completely to start with. It was during that autumn that I started to hear, on more and more frequent occasions, a knock on my bedroom door at about 6 a.m. Mum walked in rather awkwardly because she had got her tights twisted the wrong way round having put her right foot in the side meant for her left foot. It didn't take long to sort out. And at least for that year she was still able to deal with the rest of her clothing on her own.

More worrying were the changes going on in her mind. As well as the start of some recognition problems, she also became scared as she realised that her condition was worsening. It was also the time when she experienced hallucinations: seeing and hearing things and becoming scared of flowers in the garden, discarded rucksacks on the floor or parked vehicles outside the house. For about two weeks a neighbour's yellow motorbike caused her much unwarranted consternation. This continued until I had the embarrassing task of asking the neighbour if he could park his bike further up the road and out of sight. And then as mentioned earlier with the traumatic day of the Charity Walk, she might have times when she convinced herself that she had lost her children. One day I had to go over to a skip parked opposite our house to check that there weren't any children trapped inside. I knew that until I had been seen completing that necessary but, in all other respects, futile task, she would not relax.

A year on and Mum's health still didn't show any signs of physical decline. An occupational therapist from the hospital came over to visit Mum after she had been discharged in the spring of 2005. Given that Mum was still sweeping, walking, chopping wood and even cycling, I was confident that Mum would pass the mobility test. When the lady left, Mum gave me a funny look. "What was that all about?" she asked me while walking up the stairs. However, by the summer Mum started to get a bit nervous on the bicycle. That was definitely a new development. She became more conscious of the surrounding traffic and for the first time she wasn't so confident with her balance. There were no more bike trips to Hammersmith in 2005, but on Sunday mornings we walked over Kew Bridge with her bicycle and then she cycled in the quiet area near Kew Gardens. She was a bit wobbly at the start, but it was a skill that she still held on to – but only just. For that reason and in order to try to ensure that she didn't have an accident I always ran close by. That continued for a few Sundays until autumn. Once it had become too cold to consider such an activity, it got neglected over the winter, and sadly by 2006 it was too late for her even to use the tricycle that I bought her in the previous October. She had started cycling as a child but at the age of seventy-nine she was forced to stop, not due to any lack of strength, but because the dementia was affecting her ability to co-ordinate the different parts of her body, skills that, up until then, had been taken for granted.

For my entire life Mum had reigned supreme in the kitchen and even up to 2005 she remained in charge for most of the year. But the dementia was affecting this activity as well. Quite frequently on my evening of teaching at the University I arrived home about 9:45 p.m. to find three beautifully arranged salads on the dining room table. Even though I was the only one staying with her, Mum must have forgotten and prepared extra meals for my sister and Dad. It wasn't too much of a problem because I covered the other two meals and placed them in the fridge ready for the following day. However, on one occasion I had a nasty surprise when I started to tuck into one of Mum's prepared salads. A second after taking the first mouthful, I became aware of a terrible taste and immediately spat it out. When I walked into the kitchen, I realised the mistake that she must have made. From that date onwards I never bought another bottle of yellow washing-up liquid because Mum obviously mistook it for olive oil and used it as a dressing for the salad! Some later incidents which involved Mum burning the food and cooking very odd dishes meant that by the winter of 2005 I had to take over the cooking.

A few times I was ordered out of the house and at least on two occasions this was accompanied by a threat to call the police. They were times when she couldn't recognise me. The only solution was to pop out for an hour, sometimes to the shops, and then when I returned she seemed to remember me again. By June of that year I completely gave up on phoning her as it was just causing more problems instead of the intended reassurance that was desired. Indeed 2005 was the first year when I often heard her saying, "*Non riesco* (I can't succeed)!" as she was finding various tasks around the house increasingly difficult to accomplish.

That summer she occasionally came out with other short expressions in Italian. But in October I was about to experience another surprising consequence of dementia. Mum had arrived in England in the early 1950s without knowing a single word of English, but she soon mastered the language. From my earliest childhood memories I can remember her being fluent even though she never entirely lost her Italian accent. But that all went in reverse in the autumn of 2005. From that point onwards she spoke predominantly in Italian. Thankfully I had studied the language up to 'O' Level standard in the year after graduating from University. My friend Peter also attended the evening class, motivated by an Italian holiday that had been planned for the summer of 1978. However, that joint decision suddenly took on a much greater significance. Almost thirty years on it meant that while communication wasn't perfect, I had enough knowledge to understand most of what she was saying and answer back in her mother tongue. But it wasn't easy. It made looking after her that bit more tiring, but it did sharpen up my Italian, and so I tried to look upon it as a positive development. And Mum was still speaking her language well at that stage. The verbs were being correctly conjugated and she was adeptly switching between past, present and future tenses as required in a conversation. In that respect she still seemed capable of holding complex thoughts in her head. Nevertheless, the possibility of losing any acquired foreign language should act as a warning to anyone entertaining the idea of moving permanently abroad, particularly to a country where the mother tongue isn't spoken or understood.

The increasing tendency for Mum to speak, and presumably think, in Italian prompted me to start signposting things in her language. Labels to distinguish between *sale* (salt) and *zucchero* (sugar) seemed useful. Also to serve as a reminder of the location of the toilet, I taped a sign with *gabinetto* on the door. Regrettably I had to put up a note on the MDF that covered the glass pane of the front door. It read '*MADRE, QUANDO IO VADO A SCUOLA, LA PORTA È CHIUSO PER SICUREZZA, IO RITORNO*, MICHAEL'.[6] It was meant to reassure Mum that I would be returning and gave the reason for locking the door – security – while I was out at school. But actions often speak louder than words. It was obvious what Mum thought of the note and it probably had nothing to do with my mistaken use of the word *chiuso* rather than *chiusa*.[7] On some occasions I found it discarded on the floor, either crumpled or in pieces! To make the notice more permanent, I had to protect it behind a piece of clear Perspex that I screwed onto the MDF.

She clearly hated being locked in and was probably frustrated that she was being denied the opportunity to go out for another walk during my absence. Indeed all the walking was good for her. She even added to her

---

[6] MUM, WHEN I GO TO SCHOOL, THE DOOR IS CLOSED FOR SECURITY, I'M RETURNING, MICHAEL.
[7] Nouns ending in –o belong to the masculine gender; those ending in –a belong to the feminine gender.

activities by dancing and encouraging me to join in when I found one of her favourite records. Because I was washing her every day, I could see the benefits of this daily exercise in terms of her body shape. The fat on her waist had completely disappeared and her buttocks were taut. From the back she looked like a woman of about thirty. Most of the time I don't think Mum minded me washing her, but as winter approached, and maybe because the rooms in the house weren't so warm in the evening, I did notice that Mum was getting more uncooperative. This went on for quite a few months until 2006 when the washing switched to the morning. At that time of the day she was a bit too drowsy to object. As soon as she woke, I had a window of opportunity, perhaps no more than about ten to fifteen minutes, when she would be agreeable to the task. I had to rush down to the kitchen and return to her room with a bowl of warm water. With a flannel, I was able to give her a complete wash in her room. It worked most days and as a result she kept clean and, unlike some elderly people that may be neglected, never smelt badly. Of course some days she was very lively and that meant that I had to follow her around the room with flannel and towel – and one day she spilt the entire contents of the bowl of water onto the carpet. But other than that, the switch over from washing from the evenings to the mornings was a success and helped avoid the angry confrontations I had been experiencing during the latter part of 2005.

If anything, Mum's energy levels, particularly for walking, increased over 2006. There was a short interruption when she was immobile due to the cellulitis during spring, but she quickly recovered and even during the time when the district nurses visited to attend to the ulcer on her ankle, she insisted on going on her walks again. The exercise may also have contributed towards speeding up the healing process. Most of the time, the route of the walks were of a circular nature. They involved either going around the block or, more scenically, by the river, where it was always pleasant to sit down on the benches near Kew Bridge. Up until 2005, I could take a few pieces of homework to mark and if Mum was content to sit there for a while it often provided me with an opportunity to catch up on some schoolwork. There she could watch the boats or canoeists going by or, even further in the distance, a passing train on the railway bridge which reminded her of past journeys when she worked at Waterloo. But by 2006 although we were still doing the walks, she was far more restless and the breaks by Kew Bridge became shorter, until in the end they usually lasted little more than a minute. For me that was a pity. I had already given up on using the breaks for marking, but now that the rests were so short it meant that the time taken out for each walk had been reduced. Unfortunately this left even more spare time to fill up back at home trying to keep Mum occupied. This prompted, during one desperate week when it couldn't stop raining, the purchase of some games and toys. However, when Mum showed no interest, I passed them on to my friend Peter to amuse his young family.

Sometimes we would walk over Kew Bridge and stroll on the Green. One day Mum insisted on prolonging the walk. As we continued along the Kew Road for over one mile and passed the London Welsh Rugby ground, I was beginning to wonder where this walk was going to take us. Eventually I managed to persuade her to turn back before reaching Richmond, but it showed that she was still an energetic woman. And that energy was also channelled into her still trying to help when I was doing a job. In earlier years such assistance was welcome. When I was building the two sheds in the garden during that hot summer of 2003, Mum aided with the mixing of the cement. Maybe that reminded her of the help that she had given my dad when I was a child and they had moved into the Chiswick house which required much renovation during the early 1960s. But now it was unintentionally having the opposite effect. When I was building the brick seats near the front door and the brick mail box, she often came out and neatly rearranged my tools. That was tolerable, but when she did the same to my recently laid brickwork, I would lift my head up to the heavens in despair and pray for some patience!

The year of 2006 was the time when most of her skills disappeared. I had already taken over the cooking in the previous year but now I had to help feeding her. When she lost the ability to use a knife and fork, I encouraged her to use a spoon. To make things easier for her I sliced up the food into small pieces. That worked for a while but eventually she began using the spoon upside down. Soon afterwards she abandoned cutlery altogether. It was at that point – when she resorted to using her fingers – that I felt obliged to start feeding her myself. By then all writing and reading had stopped. Sadly, the creative sewing work that she had been doing, since her early teens, also finished. All around the house were examples of her handiwork spanning several decades. All the curtains and many of her clothes had been made by her at the sewing machine that now stood idle. How strange it felt for me suddenly to find myself sewing on press-studs for one of Mum's dresses!

The World Cup of 2006 also revealed how the dementia was affecting her comprehension and awareness of what was going on. Mum had never been particularly interested in football but she did take great pride when Italy won the World Cup in 1982. Twenty-four years later a very different woman was sitting in the same front room watching the match between Italy and France. I don't think we had even got into fifteen minutes of the game when Mum was already becoming restless and we had to go out for a walk. In the end I saw very little of the final. The news that Italy had won the World Cup, even if only by penalties, had absolutely no effect on her.

Another lost link to Italy had already been revealed to me a year earlier. The purchase of the *Spiderman 2* film on DVD was partly motivated by the appearance of my second cousin, Alfred Molina, as *Dr Octavius*. "Look Mum, there's Alfredo!" The fact that he was in a costume with tentacles, along with such a long absence of seeing him, didn't exactly help to recognise her first cousin, one generation removed. That was understandable. What was more surprising to me, however, concerned the blank expression on her face as I explained that Alfredo was Giovanna's son. Sadly it seemed that she no longer had any recollections of her cousin whom she had known so well and for such a long time during the earlier part of her life.

As well as losing interest in the outside world, Mum was also losing a certain degree of inhibition. I was fairly lucky on that score because the number of incidents were quite limited. Mum's behaviour at the funeral of her friend in 2003 had been slightly inappropriate. Her tantrum in the Italian Consulate had been embarrassing, but worked in getting her passport application through more quickly. Journeys on public transport also became more problematic, given her shortening length of patience. There was also the day I discovered her standing outside the house with a faeces in her hand. Another, but unforgettable example of unexpected behaviour was when I came home from school one day and found her sweeping the carpet in the hallway. Nothing extraordinary about that, but this time it was with absolutely nothing on except for an apron round her waist! Admittedly, it was a hot day – but I was thankful that I had arrived back unaccompanied.

As already indicated, Mum was still very fit physically, but 2006 was the year when certain changes showed that even her body – not just her mind – was in decline due to the dementia. She was experiencing falls on a more frequent basis and this was always a source of worry when I left her alone in the house. But it was the incontinence, starting in the autumn, that presented the biggest problem - not every night - but she was starting to wet the bed on a more frequent basis. However, at least she was still managing to get to the toilet during the day. To try to minimise the frequency and consequences of the problem during the night, there was a need to be able to respond swiftly. For that reason I started to sleep on the floor, first of all near her room and then eventually in the same room.

Coping with her incontinence was the main challenge of 2007. Occasionally I had to deal with some excrement left in inappropriate places, but this wasn't very frequent and mainly occurred when she had a spell of diarrhoea, which may have followed a few uncomfortable days with constipation. Switching from the system that solely relied on plastic sheets and towels in the bed to one where Mum was happy to use the incontinence pads helped greatly, especially as, by the middle of the year, Mum had completely lost control of her bladder and had only limited control over her bowel movements.

As far as making use of other people in terms of her personal care, there were mixed outcomes by 2007. A year earlier it had become impossible to take her to the dentist. Such treatment requires a certain level of understanding and co-operation from the patient. When neither state was forthcoming from my mum it made the task for the very calm and understanding South African dentist futile. This was especially the case on her last visit. Whatever limited composure Mum had possessed at the start looked spent towards the end of her treatment with Mandy the hygienist. By the time Quintus was ready to examine her a few minutes later, Mum refused to open her mouth. That definitely spelt the end of her dental care! But at least her teeth were in a healthy condition – possibly still benefitting from the private treatment that she received while in the employment of the wealthy family in Chelsea – a service that the dentist kindly continued to provide for her at a discount until his retirement in the 1960s. Before leaving the dentist in Chiswick that afternoon, we agreed that I would try my best to maintain her teeth through brushing as regularly as possible, neither of us realising that more serious challenges to her health were just round the corner.

The services of the chiropodist, in contrast, were used right until the end. Mum didn't seem to mind. All she had to do was sit still for a few minutes while her toenails were being cut and filed. Her last haircut in public was just before her Italian holiday in 2006, but she did make a bit of a scene in the salon. After that I attempted to cut her hair myself at home, usually when she had fallen asleep in her chair. That way I couldn't be interrupted by her protesting or, worse still, moving around to avoid the scissors which could be dangerously close to her eyes.

When she fell ill during July of 2007 and then stopped walking, nearly everything that she had learnt over her lifetime had gone. She could still eat and drink but only if assisted. All her other skills had, one by one, disappeared. She was still talking but the conversation was now quite limited. The extent often depended on her mood. At this point I suddenly found myself missing the often repeated stories from her past that she was either unable or unwilling to share any more. It was very sad to witness such a decline, particularly the swiftness of it during 2007 – but at least I was around to realise that nobody was to blame other than the illness itself.

Returning to the analogy of a journey down a canal over several descending locks, each new level presented problems and challenges. However, after each descent, the previous level suddenly looked so desirable! But there was never any way back. Each drop was irreversible. It seemed like a journey on a one way ticket. And yet when Mum was driven to the hospital in the summer of 2007, I was still optimistic that, as with all her other stays, the doctors and nurses would perform another miracle. While they wouldn't be able to repair her mind, maybe there was a chance that before the holidays were over we would be walking by the river again. That was my hope.

Chapter 16 Height of Walking

Whilst Mum may have been losing skill after skill over the years, there was still one area where she was able to excel and for some time bucked the trend of decline – walking! This activity, frequently mentioned before, became an increasingly important part of her life and, because I was obliged to accompany her all the time, an evermore dominating part of mine too. Mum had always been a very active person, perhaps hyperactive, a description that has also been directed towards me and probably quite justifiably. As a result, it shouldn't have come as too much of a surprise when the vacuum, created by the end of cycling and various chores around the house, had to be replaced with something else. Of course, the beauty of walking was that it was so relatively straight forward. In many ways 2006 marked the height of walking as an activity in both our lives. But from where did this seemingly new found passion emanate?

In her early life Mum must have gone on countless walks with her family. Encircled by farms, vineyards, undulating hills and picturesque countryside, the town of *San Damiano* and its surrounding area provided the perfect backdrop for outings on foot. That would have been a typical way to spend a summer day after attending mass on Sunday – no doubt summoned by the bell-ringing that resonated from the towers of surrounding Romanesque churches. Weather permitting, which was usually the case in Italy outside the winter months, this would often be combined with a picnic. It was also an era when very few families owned a motor car, so walking or cycling was often the only practical choice for short journeys. And family rambles were probably not just confined to the weekends. An evening walk or *passeggiata* through the town was typical during the warmer seasons with most families making an extra effort to dress as smartly as budgets, in those economically difficult times, would allow.

Maybe it is because of that background that I can recall from an early age being taken for walks by the river. Mum attempted to keep the tradition going because most Sundays involved a walk after lunch, maybe to Kew Gardens or on other occasions along the river embankment between Kew and Chiswick Bridge. It is a route that I still run along to this day, and sometimes my mind can drift back to the walks when my sister was still being pushed in a pram by either Mum or Dad. In those earlier years I can remember disappearing excitedly through a dark tunnel under one of the bridges, and then letting my imagination run wild as I wondered who or what might inhabit one of the small islands that we passed by on our travels. As I got older, I can remember feeling impatient as I was eager to get back home to watch the highlights of the football about to be televised on Brian Moore's, *The Big Match*. But it's not just visual props that stir the memory. The occasional waft of an unpleasant smell from the sewage-works, located next to the path, often evokes flashbacks to those walks of the 1960s.

The other main strolls involving the whole family tended to take place in Felixstowe. The promenade must be over a mile long, providing a pleasant and ever changing sea view with so many different ships passing by. However, one sight seemed to remain in a fixed position and its purpose remained a mystery for many years. About 10 km from the coast and just visible, two concrete towers rise from the sea to support a platform. The Principality of Sea Land originally was a fort constructed in the 1940s as an addition to coastal defences, but by 1967 it was declared a sovereign state by Roy Bates. However, that is another story.

With a fun fair and the docks as further attractions along the coast, it would be rare for us not to be ambling along from one end of the wide walkway to the other and quite often more than once in a day. And despite going there for many summers, there always seemed to be somewhere either in the town, or on the outskirts, that provided some interesting scenery to justify a walk. More recently a new view, offshore and in the direction of Harwich, includes a row of white wind turbines rotating in the sea breeze.

I think Mum always found walking quite therapeutic, especially following a row with Dad. Sometimes she liked me to accompany her. At other times she preferred some solitude and used a long walk as a means of calming down in an upsetting or stressful situation. The main thing was to get out of the house for a while. But as I got older the walks became less frequent, particularly in London, although they never entirely ceased. I would see Mum on most days, but I had my own life to lead and it was usually very busy. We would still go shopping and help each other with various jobs around the house. Sometimes we watched the television together and often during a meal we shared stories about what was going on in our lives. But the habit of going out as a family for a simple walk had regrettably been allowed to slip.

As mother and son relationships go, there had always been a very strong bond, but it was nothing out of the ordinary. I loved her – but for most of my adult life with work and friendships developing, she still remained an important figure but far more in the background – always reliable and supportive – but certainly not a dominating force any more. I suppose like any son, I took advantage of the free meals and laundry service being provided and, for the most part, was probably guilty of taking such goodwill for granted. But the ironic thing about Mum's dementia was that our relationship which had always been good, if anything, was strengthened. As each year passed and her vulnerability increased, we were being drawn closer together. In many ways the increasing number of walks, on which I found myself accompanying her, provided the catalyst for that deepening friendship.

When Mum moved back to Chiswick in 2002, she wasn't particularly fit. She was definitely overweight and most of the walks were only for a specific reason, say to the nearby shops up the road, and they were short distances. The closure of the Post Office around 2003 helps, in particular, to provide some gauge as to how unfit she was at the time compared to a few years later. Collecting the pension at the alternative Post Office near Strand-on-the-Green involved a slightly longer walk. I can remember one extremely hot afternoon when Mum had to stop and sit for a while because she was so tired. Nevertheless, as the months passed, the dementia seemed to cause her to become increasingly restless. She needed to go out but, unlike in the more distant past when I could have just left her to go on her own, the risk that she could get lost meant that I had to accompany her on every trip. And so commenced, the start of many, if not thousands, of walks together.

As I began to find that Mum's fitness levels improved so too did the frequency and the length of the walks. We became increasingly more ambitious. It started off with the two blocks round the street. The shorter would typically take about ten minutes while the longer could occupy up to fifteen. But it was the even more distant walks by the river that became the most popular. Those could be anything between half-an-hour to an hour, depending upon whether the route was extended to the Grove Park area or not. The way back nearly always involved passing three pubs along the path by the river and sometimes we popped in. On one occasion we met a group of teachers from my school which included Noel. By that stage Mum was speaking mainly in Italian. Consequently it was just Włodek, a charming Pole resembling the actor Roger Moore and fluent in most European languages, with whom she was able to engage in a short conversation. I think she appreciated that. She must have got frustrated when often bypassed in a discussion. Other people may well have felt uncomfortable speaking to her directly, perhaps incorrectly assuming that just because she was finding it more difficult to express herself, she was totally devoid of any thought. However, that understandable conclusion was very far from the truth.

The area by the river provides a perfect example showing that even in the latter stages of dementia, Mum's perceptive abilities and awareness of her surroundings were not entirely lost. On one particular summer day there was a sharp, cold wind blowing from the east. As elderly people tend to be more sensitive to cold weather, it made sense when Mum expressed her desire to wear a coat. Yet by the time we reached the section of the river where the pubs are, the wind had dropped and the sun made an appearance from behind the clouds, suddenly warming our backs. This prompted a cheap jibe from a young man, amongst a group sitting on the benches outside one of the pubs, directed at Mum's attire which may have appeared inappropriate for the time of the year. I'm sure it had been a casual comment thrown out to impress friends but despite it possibly lacking any intention, the remark did cause Mum offence. It was immediately picked up by her and she made sure that her annoyance didn't go unnoticed as she turned round to give them an angry glare. For a few seconds afterwards she continued to express her displeasure as we carried on with our walk.

On reaching Kew Bridge we sometimes bumped into a young, rather eccentric Kenyan man. Articulate and with an athletic build, he nevertheless had a neglected appearance, possibly explained by a drink problem which fortunately he has shown signs of recovering from in recent years. With a friendly disposition, he befriended – not just us – but anybody willing to spare a few minutes in conversation. I think Mum found his directness a little overbearing, especially when he took hold of her arms to start dancing in the street. However, since his motives were harmless and well-intended – even helping to pass the time – I didn't particularly mind.

The last part of the route invariably involved a visit to one of the shops at the top of the road, regardless of whether or not we needed anything. It was a part of the walk which Mum rarely forgot and nearly always insisted on including as part of the itinerary. Yet because the walks were so frequent on any one day, it was important to discourage Mum from selecting too many perishable goods. For that reason we often returned home with a bag full of tinned food, toilet rolls and her favourite selection of chocolates, typically the Italian ones which include hazelnuts as an ingredient, and were all the more difficult to miss given their distinctive gold coloured wrapping.

Returning to Mum's growing prowess with walking – a passage to Chiswick High Road from Kew was well within her comfort zone, while some walks involved crossing over Kew Bridge to explore the Surrey side. Her longest walk was achieved at the age of eighty when oddly enough she reached the height of her walking powers. On one particular day she actually managed to walk the complete circuit between both Kew Bridge and Chiswick Bridge, which is easily over three miles. We never tried it again because even with her energy levels, she found it tiring. But not for too long! After a drink and short break at home, I could hear another "*Andiamo!*" It meant "Let's go!" and soon we were back out for another, admittedly shorter, walk.

Given that a few elderly people can still run marathons, the above achievements may not sound that much in terms of distance. And yet in the years 2005 and 2006 when she was probably at her fittest, the frequency of the walks, to my mind, were still quite impressive. On some days we could go on up to a dozen walks. It was then, whether in Italian or dialect, that I heard the command words *andiamo* or *anduma* repeated many times over. Considering very few of the routes were less than a mile, it meant that she was covering something like half a marathon in a day on quite a frequent basis. No wonder she was getting so fit and her body so well-toned. It also helped to explain why she was going through several pairs of shoes each year!

I didn't mind joining her on all these walks as I have always loved sport and to me it was a good way of keeping her occupied while also maintaining a reasonable level of fitness myself. My only problem was that it was time consuming, and Mum's increasing persistence to follow one walk immediately by another could hinder my need to prepare for school. The requests could also come at odd times. One night I was awakened at 3 a.m. with her demanding to go to Italy. Immediately! I was getting nowhere trying to discourage her, and it was only after we had completed the walk in the dark – to a still closed and deserted Gunnersbury Station – that I was able to persuade her to return home and get some more sleep. Her occasional storming out of the house in a huff presented another problem. You could be sure that she wasn't in the mood to hold hands. The walking pace was fast and there was no telling where it would end. I had to follow at a respectable distance, and wait until I could detect a change in mood which would provide the opportunity to re-direct her homewards. It had been the fear that Mum was getting close to throwing a similar tantrum in Italy that prompted my decision to take an unexpected flight back to England. Losing her in such circumstances in Chiswick would have been bad enough – her disappearance down some unknown back streets in *Torino* and the likely consequences thereupon would have been unthinkable.

But overall the walking was beneficial and also served some other purposes as well. Because we were out for quite a few hours in the day, it meant that there was a good chance of meeting neighbours and even making new acquaintances, one of whom was a beautiful brunette. Her significance only became evident at a later phase of Mum's dementia. Whilst on our strolls, we would often engage in conversations between ourselves or with other people, and all that helped to pass the time. I'm sure the walks improved Mum's quality of life – and probably preserved my sanity too! However, the main driving force behind the necessity to go on quite so many walks on any one day still remains a mystery. Was she bored? Did she forget that she was at home and feel the need to be somewhere else? Maybe she needed to channel the spare energy into something because most types of housework were no longer an option for her? I suspect there was no single explanation, and each of the above conjectures might have been appropriate at different times.

Regardless of the reason, I wasn't left with much choice. She never lost her strong will and stubbornness and, if anything, the dementia seemed to exaggerate those characteristics. I was going to be dragged off for a walk whether I liked it or not and without any consideration of conditions outside. Any weather – sunny, cloudy, windy, hot, cold, raining, even snowing – it didn't seem to matter. Fortunately we were never trapped indoors by heavy snowfall as the winters were reasonably mild during this energetic phase of her life. The prospect of being confined to the house for many days in a row to avoid dangerous and slippery pavements would have been unbearable. Even when she was sitting down it was clear that she was restless. I could often observe her repeatedly folding any material close at hand or even the hem of her dress. Consequently the opportunity to allow her to get out was a real necessity and for the most part, walking with her was a pleasure. I was proud of the way Mum had retained, dare I say developed, her athletic ability when so much else seemed to be disappearing. Moreover it was very comforting to go round holding her hand, feeling the affectionate gratitude shown to me, most of the time, despite her weakening powers of recognition.

Chapter 17   A Swift Decline

I can remember listening to warnings on BBC breakfast news in the summer of 2007; there was a shortage of junior doctors due to a change in the recruitment system which was predicted to put pressure on hospitals, particularly over the month of August. I wasn't particularly concerned at the time. True, Mum had spent a period of time in hospital over the previous two years but in both cases it had been in March. This year we had got through that dodgy month without experiencing anything too serious. Nevertheless there were a few days of vomiting and diarrhoea, which both of us succumbed to.

Probably the worst day of that seemingly 'jinxed' month was on the 16th. I had to ask one of the neighbours to stay with Mum outside the house for ten minutes so I could clear up the mess in the dining room. There was excrement everywhere and Mum had been walking through it backwards and forwards in an agitated fashion. If I hadn't got her outside it would have been spread all over the place. As soon as I had time to clean the carpets of the dining room and hallway and then the lino of the kitchen, I was able to bring Mum inside to attend to her and, of course, relieve my neighbour from her temporary duties.

On the next day, Mum was still experiencing diarrhoea but to make matters worse she also fell over in the kitchen. Although I was able to help her up again without noticing any apparent injury, it was still a worry, so I phoned NHS Direct which provides medical advice from the National Health Service. Later that evening, there was a visit from a doctor who discovered that Mum had a hernia, which would help to explain why she had been experiencing pain for most of the day. Almost miraculously, the doctor was able to push the hernia back in place and you could see the immediate relief in the transformed expression on Mum's face. A similar procedure was adopted by the local GP with the same positive and soothing effect on her later in May. I wondered if the bouts of constipation had been contributing to the problem recurring; maybe she was straining too much, thereby causing the hernia to pop out.

That night of the 17th, St Patrick's Day, Mum went to bed at around 8 p.m. By the time I was ready to crash out on the floor after watching the football highlights on *Match of the Day*, she was getting noisy once more. At 4 a.m. I got up because she was again in pain so I phoned for an ambulance and an hour later we were back in the hospital. We just couldn't seem to avoid the place in March! But this time she wasn't admitted to a ward. If she wasn't seriously ill, they may have wanted to avoid having somebody in who could spread the bug that seemed to be responsible for so many cases of diarrhoea and vomiting around the country that month. It would have been a nightmare for the staff in a hospital having to deal with such an extra workload. So instead Mum was put on a drip for a few hours, which probably helped as she must have been dehydrated, while a blood sample was taken. By midday we had been taken home in one of the hospital's small minibuses. So with March out of the way and summer approaching, I felt reasonably confident that there was a chance of avoiding the hospital again for the remainder of the year, not that her previous experiences had been unpleasant; in some respects they provided me with some respite.

Although we continued to go for numerous walks each day, I noticed that for the first time in several years there wasn't the same spring in Mum's steps. A year before she could sometimes skip up the stairs of the railway bridge, near to Strand-on-the-Green School, like a gazelle. But not any more – her head was tilted slightly downwards and she was taking less notice of her surroundings. In previous years she might stop to admire the flowers in someone's front garden, particularly the well-kept properties by the river. The delay might be extended by her considering whether or not to take a cutting or simply just to appreciate the fragrance from the colourful florae in full bloom. Surprisingly, she made less fuss of any children passing by. Back home Mum began taking longer naps. Putting on a record in the front room would no longer always guarantee a positive response from her seeking to dance. Of course she did have good days, but her energy levels in 2007, and particularly after May, were definitely lower. That wasn't such a bad thing for me; her slowing down gave me just a little bit more spare time. I put such lethargy down to the weather; some days it could be very close and so I didn't feel too concerned. But unknown to me, there was a radical change going on in Mum's body – something that would only be revealed by a blood test – but her reluctance to have injections meant that those potential warning signs were missed. I even took Mum to the doctor one afternoon, but halfway there she complained that she was tired and so we turned back. Perhaps a missed opportunity to gain an early diagnosis and appropriate medical treatment, I later wondered?

Another challenge was with Mum's own internal plumbing. There had been occasional nights of incontinence in the autumn of 2006, but from January 2007 onwards the frequency became more regular. There were a few exceptions, but by March wetting the bed had become so much the norm that it no longer became a noteworthy entry in the diary that somehow I still found time to maintain. At first, the sheets needed to be changed every time, but this wasn't very practical so I had to devise a more efficient way of dealing with the problem. I wanted to avoid her lying in wet bed clothes, while at the same time minimise the amount of washing. Working out where her bottom would typically be in relation to the bed, I placed a cut bin liner on the area and covered it with some towels. This system was eventually replaced with bed mats, but as a starting point the earlier improvised method served its purpose. Crucially, it kept both the sheet and mattress dry.

As long as I inspected Mum about every two or three hours, I would be able get some sleep and, at the same time, ensure that she wasn't lying in a soaking wet nightdress for too long. As I usually stayed up until after midnight, it meant that I could keep a check on her until then. Before trying to get some sleep myself, it was also worth trying to encourage her to go to the toilet. However, later in the night, Mum wasn't too grateful for being disturbed from her slumbers, sometimes expressing her annoyance or even resisting my attempts to get her to move. I could usually grab over two hours sleep by setting the alarm for 3 a.m. If I was unlucky, which more often than not was the case, I usually found that she had wet herself. So off came the damp or soaked nightdress and the towels were quickly replaced. With a clean and dry nightdress back on, Mum was back in bed within a few minutes. It was then time for me to go downstairs and wash the dirty laundry, place it in the spin dryer and hang it up to dry. This soon became a bit of a game to see how fast I could complete all the tasks. My personal best for the whole operation was about thirty minutes. For me – that was one way of dealing with the situation – treating it as a sporting challenge! The same procedure was then repeated at about 6 a.m., after which it was hardly worth going back to sleep. Sometimes I would be very lucky and wake Mum just before she wet herself. So if I could get her to the toilet at the right times, she could have a completely dry night and I would have no washing to do, leaving me with the following thought, 'What a result!' Returning to school on Monday, I often found some of the teachers talking about the football scores from Saturday – but for me – the highlight of the week-end was whether Mum had managed to have a dry night!

Nevertheless, I should have counted myself fortunate that in those months Mum's incontinence was mainly confined to urine. There were a reasonable number of days when I had to clear up the house when she suffered from diarrhoea, but thankfully only a few times when I found any faeces left on the floor. But I will probably never forget the day when I came back from school in the afternoon to find Mum standing outside the front door with a very large turd in her hand. It seemed as if she was clutching it proudly, relieved to be free of it after experiencing a few painful days with constipation. I wondered how long she had been standing there and, more from curiosity rather than concern, whether anybody had noticed. But when she had diarrhoea in the bed – well – that was a real mess! On the first occasion, I made the mistake of taking her nightdress off in the usual way with her co-operatively raising her arms while I pulled it over her head. Unfortunately, I didn't realise how much shit was inside the dress and, as a result, spread some of the contents all over her hair. Clearing that mess up, followed by washing and drying her hair, meant I didn't get much sleep that night. And yet the next morning I was back at school, covering the possible drawbacks of a Public Sector Borrowing Requirement. No wonder I looked a bit tired some days. And that may have been the morning when I noticed a sympathetic glance from Christian, a senior teacher at the school, as I almost dropped off to sleep, my exhausted head resting against the door frame of the entrance to the staff room, in the middle of a briefing at the beginning of the week.

When Mum wasn't sleeping during the day, she would still talk quite a bit, but by 2007 it often wouldn't make much sense to me. Maybe it was because she was speaking in Italian, interspersed with her dialect and the occasional English word thrown in, but I suspect the dementia was also robbing her of clear thought – though I must add – not from thinking completely. And it varied from day to day. On some occasions she could still be articulate but these were becoming less frequent. Some nights she would talk in her sleep and when it was particularly loud, I had to retreat to my bedroom, where I had the luxury of sleeping in a bed for a few undisturbed hours. Sometimes Mum could be funny. One morning she woke up and started laughing. "What on earth are you doing sleeping on the floor?" she exclaimed in genuine bewilderment, as if she had only just taken notice of what I had already been doing every night for several months.

For the previous two years, going to work proved to be difficult. It wasn't just that I needed to get up early to wash and dress her; the real difficulty was leaving her. Certainly prior to 2007 she was nearly always very lively in the morning, and so I had to take her on several walks. Along with breakfast, it meant that every so often I would be setting off as late as 8.45 a.m., leaving just five minutes for a ten minute bike ride to school. Most of the time the walks would be sufficient to tire her out so as to make it easier to set off without her getting upset, but the exercise wasn't always guaranteed to work. I also left some cakes and a jug of squash on the table that provided a distraction, but sometimes even that wasn't enough and I would feel bad when I had to abandon her despite her begging me to stay or even take her with me. It was strange to see what dementia could do to such an independent woman. The medical books had forewarned me of this 'clinging' tendency; now I was beginning to experience it first-hand.

During 2007 leaving for school on time became difficult for a different reason. It started in the winter and initially I put it down to the dark mornings. But even when it began to get light earlier as spring approached, I noticed that on most mornings Mum was waking up much later in the day. I didn't want to leave her in bed as she couldn't dress herself and there was no guarantee that she would get a drink or any food on her own. This meant that on some mornings I literally had to pull her out of bed. The latest I could delay such intervention was about 7:45 a.m., if I was to avoid being late. Evenings could also be difficult because there was a growing tendency for her to fall asleep downstairs. Most often it was in the spacious sky-blue wicker chair that I had repaired. Maybe with its soft cushion, one that she had covered herself when she was still adept at sewing, it was too cosy. As a result it wasn't always easy to persuade her to go upstairs to her even more comfortable bed.

Of course for me there were some benefits in Mum sleeping more hours; it meant it was much easier to slip out without her even noticing my absence. That was fine for short trips but it was a worry if I had to go out for longer. Maybe once in every few weeks she experienced a fall around the house – not very often but, nevertheless, frequently enough to be a cause of concern. It could have been a problem with her balance or maybe she was being less careful and tripping up more often. One fall in the dining room left her in such an awkward position that I phoned for an ambulance crew to provide assistance and also to check nothing was broken. Fortunately she was fine and really it was only the falls outside the house that left her with any injuries, but at least they were only confined to cuts and bruises – nothing ever broken thankfully. On another occasion, Mum fell over in her bedroom and it took a while before I could find a way to push her gently forward to open the door sufficiently for me to squeeze into the room and help her up. Then came the fall on Cup Final day when she ended up in hospital and where the scan revealed the likelihood of vascular dementia.

That year of 2007 presented another unwanted challenge. I needed to go to the Hammersmith house and mend the roof as there was a leak that was damaging the plaster of the ceiling in the upstairs hallway, but it was a job like no previous one. The ladder was tied up between April and August, during which time I gradually completed the improvements. The task had to be spread over so many months because I was reluctant to leave Mum on her own for more than three hours per day; so that left a maximum of about two hours for work after taking into account travelling time. It wasn't a small job either. Slates had to be replaced, a section of the brick wall rebuilt, while a small hole in the zinc gulley that separated the two roofs required repairing. To my relief, the work was completed before returning to school for the new academic year in September.

Earlier, during the spring of 2007, there had been several visits from the District Nurse and a Social Worker to see if some help could be provided. Sometimes it would be hard to keep Mum in the house for the appointed time of the visit. A few minutes beforehand Mum would start demanding to go for one of her walks. I found the best way of dealing with her on those occasions was to walk her up and down the street keeping the house, and any potential visitor, constantly in view. Mum observed the futility of this and in a slightly annoyed tone asked, "What's the point of walking up and down the same street? We're not going anywhere!" It was also never easy to plan too far ahead and this was particularly true with the bureaucracy surrounding social care.

During some of the visits from Social Services, I was asked if I would like to share my experiences with other carers in similar circumstances. It sounded like a good idea, but it was one that I never had time to take up. I was already finding it difficult to keep in touch with long-standing friends, let alone try to make new acquaintances. Besides, the people whom I already knew provided a useful sounding board to explore any new ideas or strategies for dealing with Mum. For instance Stuart, an old friend who had changed very little in appearance from our days at school, was a useful source of advice. His mother was also experiencing dementia, but the decline had started a few years earlier. As a result, Stuart was able to provide me with some idea of what to expect later down the line. Unfortunately, it was rarely reassuring.

However, I was able to implement one of the suggestions from Social Services quickly and it did help considerably. My system of plastic sheets, to be eventually replaced with bed mats, was working. Consequently Mum's skin was in good condition, but the pads that they recommended proved to be even more useful. Better still, and much to my surprise, Mum didn't object to using them. From the 22nd of May they helped to cut down the amount of washing considerably. Nevertheless, the proposals offering greater involvement by Social Services, while well intended, could never be implemented. Mum's condition worsened too much and more quickly than anybody could have anticipated.

If Mum was a bit sluggish in the morning, she could make up for it by still being quite lively for a couple of hours during the remaining part of the day. As a result we still managed to go on a few walks each day – even in June – but she was definitely showing signs of slowing down. It was the time of the year when I would start to get busy selling T-shirts for the annual Charity Walk. The event, which again involved Gumley House and St Mark's school as well as the hosts, Gunnersbury, was scheduled for Wednesday the 4th of July. In the few weeks before the Walk, Mum was suffering periods of constipation. I kept a record of when she went to the toilet over the preceding weeks. It was therefore worrying to see that as we got nearer to the event, quite a few days had passed and the calendar hadn't recorded any entries. With no personal experience to draw upon – either of the condition itself or the analogy once provided by Mum – I was still left in no doubt of the extreme discomfort being suffered when she compared constipation to child birth!

Where was all this food going? I wasn't with her 24 hours a day, but she couldn't flush the toilet and my nose told me there wasn't anything unpleasant lying around out of view. Phone calls to the doctor and NHS Direct didn't provide any conclusive advice. In the end, I followed my own intuition and just felt I would have to take more direct intervention. I didn't feel confident about using a suppository. In fact I had attempted, rather apprehensively, to use one a few months before. When I tried shoving the yellow capsule up my Mum's anus it just popped out, prompting such a filthy look, as well as screams of protest and indignation from her. Exclamations such as *"schifoso* (disgusting)!" left me reluctant to try that again. No, instead, I enlisted help from several different brands of laxatives, as well as a diet of prunes and any other food that might serve to stimulate her bowels. Although I had read the instructions advising against the use of a cocktail of aperients, I decided to take a chance. Besides, it was the day before the Walk and she hadn't had a bowel movement for a week! That worrying thought preyed on my mind as I took another look at the calendar hanging on the wall behind where Mum was seated.

The next morning, after being washed and dressed, Mum was sitting at the breakfast table. She hadn't finished eating when she suddenly got up. Before taking more than two steps it started. The laxatives had finally got things moving. First a trickle, then over the next few seconds, I just stood there motionless, almost unable to believe my own eyes. I am not exaggerating – there was now a torrent of soft, partly liquid, shit gushing out from under her nightdress and noisily hitting the carpet; it was like a brown Niagara Falls. And it just kept pouring out – all eight days' worth. But it wasn't just shit coming out. Mum would never be the same after that. It was as if all her spirit, motivation and energy were being drained out of her body in those moments. When I look back now I can see the significance of that day in the demise of her health, but early on that morning I had more practical problems to worry about as I surveyed the spreading brown lake that needed to be cleared up. "Oh, my God, where do I start?" I mumbled to myself.

Luckily Mum didn't wander about this time so when I got her sitting in the adjacent room, where at least the floor was covered with lino, I was able to start working out what to do. I quickly phoned the school and, without elaborating too much, told them I would be a bit late coming in that morning. With that done, I felt I wasn't rushing against the clock and so could think more calmly. Using a trowel, some empty ice cream containers and a few plastic bags, I gradually scraped all the mess off the carpet. The next task was to wash Mum and get her changed. I then turned my attention back to the carpet. That needed a thorough cleansing with disinfectant. Once all that was complete, I was ready to go to school.

Awaiting me was the task of organising a 12 km walk for over 300 students and 100 teachers all wearing conspicuous green T-shirts, the colour chosen for 2007. This was then to be followed by a barbecue. No pressure then!

My sister arrived before I left for school. She was doing the first shift of looking after Mum before going on to watch the tennis at Wimbledon with her friend Jack. I had organised a rota of volunteers to stay with Mum all day so that I could have less to worry about while organising the Walk. As I made my way to the school, I was just so thankful that Mum still had some sense of timing. I dread to think what would have happened if the events of the morning had occurred a few hours later while one of the neighbours had been in attendance!

As it happened the Walk was a success, raising £1,900 for various charities. Mum didn't give any problems to the neighbours and the only thing that marred the day was that my sister picked up a £50 parking fine, despite purchasing and displaying a ticket. We didn't realise it at the time but she had parked her car in a section that was reserved for permit holders only.

In spite of that minor, but irritating setback, I felt very content – it was finally time to get some sleep. There is rarely any respite from looking after somebody with dementia, but with the Charity Walk over, at least I would have less pressure from school, and of course there was the summer holiday to look forward to. Six weeks without marking or preparing lessons! It is a necessary break for any teacher regardless of additional responsibilities – especially if one is expected to return refreshed and ready to motivate new groups of young students. Additionally, I was relieved to know that I would be going back to school in September with a considerably reduced timetable. The Business Studies teacher, an elegant and very understanding Indian lady from Singapore named Gurpreet, was willing to help by taking Year 12 for economics. Although fewer hours would result in my already low income being further reduced, at least it meant I could just focus on Year 13 and one games session with Year 11, leaving any remaining time to care for my mum.

Chapter 18 An End to Walking

It may be a bit ironic but the Charity Walk of 2007 almost coincided with the last few times that Mum was able to go out for a walk unassisted. For several years it had been such an important part of her life, both in terms of quality and longevity, since it helped to keep her occupied and must have improved her health. But eventually the dementia caught up with her. It was all predicted in the medical books, something that my sister had also reiterated with her years of experience in nursing. Yet despite the overwhelming evidence against me, I was always a bit sceptical because in some ways Mum had averted most aspects of the physical decline forecasted. But in the weeks following the Charity Walk, I was to discover that dementia spares no victims, if they live long enough, from reaching the very final stages, even someone as fit and strong-willed as my mother.

Up until 2007 the deterioration in Mum's health seemed to be confined to her thought processes. In the space of six years virtually every single skill that she had acquired over a lifetime disappeared. But in all those years, there were very few outward signs of any physical change. Even the slight droop at the right-hand side of her mouth, probably caused by strokes, were only temporary and in many ways she looked in better shape at the start of 2007 than in any of the previous ten years. But if the following six months was a period of rapid decline, the two weeks after the Charity Walk saw the pace accelerate. It was a good job that she was still under my care while this was going on. Had she deteriorated so quickly while staying in a nursing home, I'm not sure if I would have been able to forgive myself for delegating such a responsibility.

Mum seemed quite tired on the day after the Walk, probably still recovering from the preceding week of constipation. She only managed one trip around the block, spending most of the remaining part of the day sleeping in her blue chair downstairs. The following two days gave rise to a spirit of increased optimism as she seemed more like her old self, completing a couple of walks around the block and at least one of the 2 km long circuits by the river. It was the next day, Sunday, which stands out as marking the real beginning of the end as far as walking was concerned. She didn't get up till 10 a.m. and then after washing and breakfast, she fell asleep in her chair. When she woke up again, we had lunch, and then set off for a walk by the river. It must have been about 2 p.m.

As with so many times before, we went down to the end of the road and then turned right, over the railway bridge and past the primary school that I had attended a few decades earlier. We didn't go left this time for the longer river route past the Post Office. Instead we turned right and joined the river and continued on, passing by Café Rouge. It was a hot afternoon and Mum was walking slowly. She seemed to be finding the gradual upward incline on the last section before Kew Bridge more tiring than usual so we took a rest on the bench facing the Water Tower – a 60 metre tall landmark that has continued to dominate the skyline since as far back as 1838. After a few minutes we set off again and turned right to go back down our street. Then about thirty metres from the house, her legs suddenly gave way. Because I was holding her hand, I was able to prevent her from falling over. Luckily a neighbour, Lynne, was walking behind, and she was able to help me get Mum back to the house because she no longer had the strength to walk unaided. Once I got Mum back inside and sitting down, I was able to give her some drinks and then she fell asleep. We did go for one more walk later in the evening, but it was just around the small block near the railway line. I didn't know it then, but that day was the last time she ever walked near the river again, a route that we must have walked several thousand times over the previous couple of years.

Over the next few days the walks became fewer and also shorter. Gradually the block was replaced by walks up and down the road. Friday the 13th of July was the last day that she ever walked outside the house. It was also the night that she struggled going upstairs to her bedroom. When she experienced similar difficulties going down the stairs the following morning, I took the decision to convert the ground floor front room into a bedroom. It had the same settee – red with black sides, though a little faded now – that my parents had bought decades ago. It could be unfolded so that it was flat like a bed. I then brought down the mattress to make it more comfortable for her and for the next twenty three nights we slept in the front room. For me, it really didn't make much difference which floor I slept on.

Ever an optimist, I was still hopeful that this decline was temporary. I tried to encourage her to walk in the house. Her balance didn't seem right so I had to hold both her hands to give her support. Facing her and maintaining a tight grip, I slowly walked backward. She followed nervously – for with each step it felt as if she could keel over at any moment. Each day her strength just seemed to be draining away. When I enquired at the GP's reception, I was asked to get a urine sample. A few minutes later I left with a small plastic bottle that wasn't much bigger than a test tube. I hadn't thought of asking for any advice but on the way home I was suddenly struck by the following thought, 'Great! How on earth am I going to get Mum to co-operate to get a sample?' Well, I did get one, but only with great difficulty.

Mum was finding it almost impossible to stand up on her own. There was no way I would be able to hold her with one hand and hold the bottle, with a diameter of less than one inch, for Mum to pee in it accurately. So instead I washed an empty tub of ice cream and eventually found the opportunity to catch her urine in it, but it wasn't easy. As I guided her to sit on the toilet seat, I had to quickly slip the box behind her legs and then hold it there while she was sitting on my arm. Fortunately the container was big enough to catch the urine, despite my having no view of what was going on below. However, I had to wait over ten minutes, swapping between kneeling and sitting positions intermittently, and my arm was starting to feel numb. Eventually I could hear the sound of her urine hitting plastic and, judging from the heaviness of the box, I knew I would have more than enough for the sample – as long as I could get her to stand up without dropping it in the toilet. I managed to avoid that and, as soon as I had transferred some of the warm contents into the bottle and completed the label, I took it to the GP. Unfortunately, when the results came through a day or two later, it was found that the sample had been contaminated. The receptionist explained that I should have used a sterilised container, so all my efforts had been a waste of time. But more significantly, there had been a further and possibly unnecessary delay in gaining a diagnosis of Mum's worsening condition.

Following the morning of trips between the GP and home, I left Mum asleep in her chair after she had lunch, to attend the end of year barbecue at the school. I didn't time it very well. I arrived at about 2 p.m. but the leavers' speeches didn't end until 3:45. Once again, Włodek delivered his articulate tributes to those members of staff moving on – but only after each person had been cleverly cast into a wittily woven story, usually based on some historical setting. As ever, he was most entertaining but I wasn't in the mood to appreciate the humour. I didn't feel at all relaxed and this wasn't just concern about leaving Mum alone. Although I had six weeks of holiday to look forward to, uncharacteristically, I felt quite gloomy. Was this just a temporary problem with Mum or did I have to start accepting an unwelcome possibility – that she might never be able to walk again? Would my sister be able to take us to Felixstowe in August? It didn't look too likely unless Mum could soon recapture her energy and start walking again. Finally the speeches were over. I grabbed some food and had a short chat with a few colleagues but didn't stay long and was back home by 5 p.m. That evening didn't provide any encouraging signs either, since I had to carry her back from the toilet to her bed in the front room.

The next day required me to go to the Hammersmith house as a plumber had been booked in to inspect and clean the boiler. When I set off on the bicycle it had already been raining hard for a few hours. Just a few minutes into the journey and it became like a monsoon. Parts of the Great West Road were transformed into a river and some cars, including a black Porsche, were left stranded. A torrent of water was rushing down, completely filling a subway, while some houses on the approach to Hammersmith looked in serious danger of being flooded. I became a little worried for my mother. She was so vulnerable. She couldn't walk unaided and even if she could, would she know how to react? But at least the house was quite high up, relative to the road, so it would have required very serious flooding before she could be in any danger. But it did cross my mind, and so as soon as the work had been completed, I hastily cycled back. On the return journey I was relieved to see that the water had receded and the heavy rainfall of the previous few hours had dwindled to a mere drizzle.

When I finally returned, I was shocked to find Mum lying on the dining room floor near to the blue chair that had toppled over. She must have tried to get out of her seat and lost her balance. Thankfully she appeared to be uninjured, but it would make later trips out of the house very stressful. To make matters worse, a few days later I found out that my sister had been involved in a serious accident in her car. She was hit while turning right into her road and was very badly concussed, leaving her with virtually no recollection of the incident. The navy blue car was a write-off. As I was speaking to her on the phone, more worryingly it became obvious that the accident had affected her brain as she kept repeating things. Fortunately she returned to normal after about a week. Later she gradually became able to recall some of the events of that night, but it was frustrating not being able to go over to Kingston to give her some help during that time as I was ever more needed at home in Chiswick.

For the remaining few days I was still able to get Mum to walk a few steps around the house. In that respect her condition stabilised, but it was getting more difficult to wash her in the mornings. She had lost the strength to stand on her feet for long and that meant I had to wash her by the dining room table to give her some support. As soon as she had been washed, she was relieved to be put back in her seat. This went on for a few more days. The only physical sign to explain her difficulty in walking was the slight swelling around her right ankle that may have been connected to her fall a few days earlier. I can't remember why there was a delay before Mum received a visit, but eventually a GP was able to come round. It was Thursday the 2nd of August and the doctor took a blood test. This time there was no resistance or protest from Mum – she was obviously too weak. A prescription for antibiotics was written out as a precaution and the doctor said that she expected to have some of the results of the blood test on Monday, by which time she would have a better idea if Mum needed to go to the hospital. Intuitively the doctor gave me a pessimistic diagnosis. She must have seen many other patients close to death over her years of practice, and before she left she bluntly told me that she didn't think Mum would have many more months to live. I was quite shocked to hear that, but maybe because I'm an optimist at heart, it wasn't long before I had put it to the back of my mind and had Mum's ankle elevated and was applying an improvised ice pack.

On Friday morning I received a phone call from the GP. According to the provisional results from the blood test, the main problem identified was that Mum's haemoglobin level had worryingly dropped to 8.5, far below the normal levels of 12 - 13. There was not enough iron in her blood and this would help explain her anaemia and, moreover, her pallor and lack of energy. I don't know why Mum wasn't admitted on that day but the doctor promised to put pressure on the hospital on Monday. I felt a bit uneasy because that meant I was on my own over the weekend, although I knew if there was a real emergency I could always summon help. For the next few hours, I checked books to find out which food would be best in providing iron so it was steak with spinach for lunch. Well, I got through the weekend with Mum somehow, but it was a relief to receive a phone call from the GP on Monday morning. It couldn't have come sooner for me. The previous day I had to resort to washing Mum on the floor. She was just too weak to stand on her feet, even if aided by leaning on the table. Without any further examination, but based on my report on her condition and further negative results from the blood test, the doctor soon phoned back and informed me that she had received confirmation that Mum would be admitted to hospital. Although I was relieved, I was still a little anxious as I recalled that the NHS was experiencing staffing difficulties in August. That was why, along with the general MRSA [8] bacterium or 'superbug' scares, I had delayed medical involvement until I knew I had exhausted all possible avenues on my own.

The ambulance came round later. Mum was carefully placed on the stretcher and then we were off to the hospital again – a procedure I was getting quite familiar with. Before the end of that first day, the X-ray confirmed that there was nothing wrong with her ankle so her difficulty in walking must have been linked to the iron deficiency. The cause of that, they explained, was what they needed to investigate over the next few days. Mum was put on a drip which helped with any dehydration. When I left about 10 p.m., there was no reason to believe that the staff couldn't perform the same miracles as in the previous two years – after all she had recovered fully from pneumonia and cellulitis, so why not anaemia?

---

[8] Methicillin-resistant Staphylococcus aureas.

Chapter 19 A Welcome Respite

Observing Mum deteriorate so quickly, over the two weeks prior to her admittance to hospital, made it a tough start to the summer holiday. Her inability to walk on her own and growing lethargy combined with the need, in the last few days, to carry her to the toilet had been wearing me down. Maybe for those reasons I was relieved that Mum would be spending a little time in the hospital again. In the previous year, she had stayed in for two weeks. As we were being driven along in the ambulance, I was fully anticipating a similar time period. Two weeks of not having to deal with her toilet issues and the knowledge that she would be looked after was just the sort of respite that I needed.

For the first few days of Mum's stay in the hospital, there were some encouraging signs. She was talking a little and even calling out my name. She had stopped dribbling and seemed slightly stronger. Because she was stuck in bed all day, each time that I visited her I went through some exercises with both her arms and legs to try to make sure that all her joints didn't just seize up from lack of movement. Her legs felt a bit stiff at first and from the disapproving expression on Mum's face and her occasional questioning, I expect such exercise wasn't entirely appreciated and may have been uncomfortable. But with the enforced movements – backwards and forwards – twenty times in each session – some flexibility was gradually restored. As far as I was concerned I was still very hopeful that Mum would leave the hospital within two weeks, once again able to walk.

With respect to personal hygiene, Mum was washed each morning and changed into a fresh gown. I wasn't sure if the nurses had enough time to brush her teeth, so each day I ensured that this aspect of her care wasn't neglected. Many of the other patients had liquid to wash their dentures but this was not required for Mum. She had always looked after her teeth really well and still had a full set, something that one poor nurse found out painfully in 2006, when she got bitten on the arm while attempting to take a blood sample! By 2007 there was little risk of that embarrassing incident being repeated. I purposely put very little toothpaste on the brush because by this stage Mum had forgotten the procedure for rinsing out her mouth. This had already started months before at home. Then, I would demonstrate how to swill my mouth with water and spit it out in the sink. That usually was enough to get her to copy, but in the hospital she was either less capable physically or maybe the dementia had worsened to the point where even spitting out the contents of her mouth had become too much of a challenge. So instead I rinsed her mouth out as best as I could by using the brush dipped into clean water. It wasn't a perfect system but it seemed the best available, and swallowing a very small amount of diluted toothpaste probably wasn't doing any harm.

Although I was hopeful that the stay wouldn't be too long and was still confident about her prospects, there were some differences with this visit compared to previous occasions at the hospital. On the third day a young consultant from South Africa took me to one side and sought my opinion regarding resuscitation, should it be necessary for Mum. I was a bit shocked to be confronted by such a choice, but remembering Mum's expressed wish many years previously that she shouldn't be revived if she ever had a heart attack, I indicated that I thought it best to let nature run its course and not intervene. It seemed a very gloomy conversation and for me was totally unexpected, but I guess it was just a standard question posed to close relatives of elderly patients. Given that Mum was eighty-one and still very poorly, it was probably something that had to be asked.

The other major difference was that for the very first time at the hospital staff began questioning Mum's ability to drink. There was concern that Mum could aspirate – which involves breathing in some liquid while drinking – a typical problem for the elderly suffering from the last stages of dementia. It was a serious issue because, as they later explained to me, any liquid in the lungs could lead to a chest infection and possibly pneumonia. It was only Mum's second day in the hospital when I met a speech therapist who explained that Mum had failed a swallowing test earlier that morning and would need to have a white, thickening powder added to any drinks. It was recommended that a custard-like consistency should be aimed for and drinking had to be administered by spoon. That guaranteed my visits to the hospital were going to keep me quite busy. When I wasn't exercising her limbs, I was stirring powder into her drinks and, spoon by spoon, Mum was encouraged to take in some fluid. Getting her to drink a glass of 'thickened' orange squash could take anything up to fifteen minutes. No wonder I occasionally found Mum with a dry mouth when I arrived at the hospital early in the afternoon. How could a short-staffed ward find time to ensure that all of the many elderly patients were supervised to eat and drink sufficiently? It was a job that I had to repeat many times again when Mum eventually returned home, but it was so time-consuming, especially if I was to hit the daily two litre target recommended by the doctors. I once worked out that over three hours could be devoted to that one task each day.

On Mum's fifth day at the hospital, she was put in a hoist and, I assume, 'enjoyed' her first trip out of bed for nearly a week. As well as providing an opportunity to move Mum into a sitting position in the chair next to her bed, the hoist was also a means of weighing her. I wasn't there at the time as this had taken place in the morning before visiting hours, but according to the records, in the red folder near her bed, she weighed 61 kg, or 9st 8lbs, considerably lighter than she had been a few years previously. Already at this stage there was some concern over Mum's lack of ability to balance by herself and, possibly for that reason, she was never put in the hoist again. A pity – because I felt it would have been safe for her to sit in a chair while I was there as I would have been willing to provide her with some support. After all, it would have given Mum some relief from the routine of being stuck in the same bed all day long. But maybe another reason could have been pressure on the staff's time. However, Mum was certainly not being neglected and after a few days her mattress was changed. It was replaced by one that inflated and deflated in different sections on a regular basis to help avoid bed sores. And so the first week ended on a reasonably positive note. Surely just one more week and Mum would be returning home, I thought.

Although I was visiting Mum each day and sometimes staying up to eight hours, it was an opportunity to make some progress with the roofing job in Hammersmith that I had started way back in the spring. The ladder had been tied up for months. After leaving Mum at home, I usually had just over one hour to work before it was time to return. This was a frustrating way to do such a job, especially as it meant that I had to be careful not to start something that I couldn't finish on the day. There was still a time constraint while Mum was in hospital, but now at least I would have a few more hours each morning and if I was unexpectedly delayed, I had the option of phoning the hospital, knowing that she was in safe hands. Nevertheless, I did try to avoid being late as much as possible because it was useful to arrive before lunch was served so that I could help her with feeding.

In order to aid swallowing, Mum's meals tended to be soft, like minced meat, mashed potato and vegetables in puree form. The portions were always far too large for her so I ended up finishing it off and usually found the meals were good, contrary to the opinions of other patients on the ward. Perhaps the main problem was that the porters often came back a bit too early. For some of the elderly patients that weren't being helped, there wasn't enough time to finish. I usually remembered to bring in a plastic container which meant I could transfer the pudding out of the bowl before the tray was whisked away. Sometimes other patients had trouble opening the containers, especially for the desserts. Quite often they needed the table that extended over the bed to be moved closer to where they were seated so that it was easier for them to reach the food on the tray. All this meant that as well as feeding Mum, I was often drafted in to help a few of the other patients. But there was a reward. As I got to know the staff delivering the meals, quite often I was also given a cup of tea on their rounds and, if I was particularly lucky, a cake or a few biscuits.

As well as remembering a container, it was also a good idea to bring metal cutlery, particularly a spoon when providing Mum any thickened drinks outside normal meal times. Plastic spoons could be obtained from the canteen, but proved unsuitable – too weak for Mum's strong teeth. On one occasion, Mum crushed a spoon into several sharp pieces which I feared she could swallow or get caught in her throat. Although successful initially, my attempts to remove the final few pieces were thwarted when Mum's mood changed and she refused to co-operate. Fortunately a metal spoon was quickly found in the ward kitchen. That enabled me to prise open her jaws with the improvised implement acting as an effective wedge between her teeth. With one of my fingers, I managed to scoop out the remaining pieces of plastic confident that I too would be unharmed. After all, she may have experienced difficulties with swallowing but she could still bite!

Mum's second week at the hospital started with a worrying development. On arriving that Monday morning I soon noticed that her arm was badly swollen. The medical staff didn't seem too concerned and explained that it was one of the effects of being on a drip. As well as helping to deal with dehydration, the drip also allowed antibiotics to be given intravenously to deal with the confirmed chest and urinary tract infection. What was more of a worry to her consultant was the result from a blood test indicating that Mum's haemoglobin level had dropped from 8.5 to 7.8, even further below the recommended level of 12-13. Iron tablets were prescribed but when it was realised that Mum had problems with swallowing, this was promptly switched to a dark orange liquid called ferrous fumarate – an iron salt designed to help transport oxygen from the lungs and round the body through the red blood cells.

By Friday I felt that although Mum was showing some small signs of improvement, she was still too weak for me to consider – even with my optimistic disposition – her leaving the bed, let alone the hospital. In the meantime the doctors were receiving information from the tests and scans but still remained puzzled by the exact cause of the anaemia. They were looking for some signs of internal bleeding but never found a source. As the weeks progressed less emphasis was placed on such investigations. Their energies were instead increasingly turned towards how to manage the new situation. This was especially the case because one of the consultants felt that Mum would be too weak to undergo any surgery anyway. So unlike her previous stays, which had never lasted more than two weeks, this one looked like it could stretch through the summer.

Luckily Mum was in a pleasant ward. It was on the top floor and the large windows ensured that it was bright. It provided a good view of the surrounding area. The skyline was dominated by trees but within a gap in the green scenery, a sports stadium was visible. There were, if I remember correctly, eight beds in the area and all the other women patients were friendly, seemingly not to mind me being there for most of the day and evening. The lady next to my mum was Scottish, and quite talkative. Her daughter visited each day, sometimes accompanied by her teenage sons. On most days we had a chat about our mums' conditions. Her mother seemed quite happy staying in the hospital. However, the daughter and I shared similar worries as to what would happen to our mothers when it was time for them to be discharged. The Scottish lady was a few years older than my mum, but her dementia was in a much earlier stage, and for that reason she was still quite articulate.

Gradually I got to know the other patients and their regular visitors and so it was quite sad to arrive one day to learn that somebody had passed away in the night. One man visited his mother, who was already in her nineties, every day. She had trouble with her legs, but in no way did she have dementia. She had lived in the area all her life and when her son arrived with the newspaper she enthusiastically attempted the crossword. It often surprised me how active her brain was. She would also pick a few horses for her son to place a small bet, eagerly awaiting the results on his next visit. The night before she died she was particularly lively and optimistic about the prospects of going home a few days later. That made it even more of a shock to find out the sad news the following day. I never saw her son again but, as looking after his mother had become such a large part of his life, I guess he must have been devastated. But my next thought took me completely by surprise. Of course there would be the grief, but that might pass eventually and at least in the meantime he had been freed from the heavy burden of responsibility. Looking across at the unoccupied bed-side chair, ashamedly for a few seconds, I almost envied him. And yet it was a selfish sentiment, which left me annoyed with myself. It was quickly dismissed as I returned to tending to my mum's needs with renewed vigour.

With Mum's haemoglobin level hovering between 7 and 8, a decision was taken to give her a blood transfusion in the third week. Two days later, Mum was moving her legs on her own while she was lying in bed and there were definitely signs of some improvement. By the following week her haemoglobin level had risen to 10, the first time it had reached double figures since the initial measurement back in July. She was also speaking a bit more during my visits, which was a further encouraging sign. Another development was putting Mum on a catheter to help deal with her incontinence and the danger to her skin from lengthy exposure to urine. Although the pads had helped, they needed to be monitored regularly. Unchanged pads eventually became saturated. Consequently, it was great whenever my sister visited. She had worked as a nurse on the ward before and if we spotted that Mum needed a change she just closed the curtains around the bed and went to the appropriate cupboard. She quickly returned with a pair of pads, bed mat and gloves. Within a few minutes and without any fuss, Mum had been expertly turned, cleaned and put into dry, fresh pads. Once again the curtains were opened without anybody being any the wiser, but with Mum's dignity restored.

And so, with Mum on a urinary catheter there was at least one less reason for a pad change. I was quite surprised that Mum didn't make too much fuss about the new arrangement since a small tube had to be inserted into her vulva and gently pushed up the urethra. I was present while one of the nurses administered the procedure and Mum didn't even react once during the entire operation. Once inside the bladder, a small balloon at the tip of the tube is inflated to provide a seal and, as long as there is no leak, the urine can then drain into a bag and be periodically emptied via a valve. Clever stuff! But it wasn't without its drawbacks. The catheter made life easier for the nurses and helped with skin care, but there was an added risk of a urinary tract infection. These pros and cons formed a large part of a later debate between two consultants with different opinions on the appropriateness of its use.

By week four, the physiotherapists came back on the ward and checked whether Mum could sit up in bed without assistance. This was to assess whether or not she could be allowed to sit unaided on a chair. Mum was helped into a sitting position on the edge of the bed. As soon as the physiotherapist let go of her shoulders, Mum started to keel over. She still hadn't regained her balance and although there was a further visit and test, the conclusion drawn was that it was safer for her to remain in the bed. I was disappointed with their evaluation and politely argued that it wasn't easy to remain balanced on a mattress where different sections were inflating and deflating. Anyway, regardless of their pessimistic assessment, I still went ahead and ordered a ramp, wheelchair and commode from the pharmacist in Brentford, anticipating that when Mum eventually returned home I would be able to get her out of bed and maybe even out of the house, weather permitting.

It was also the week when I met Stephanie, a social worker employed at the hospital and who played a key role in the process of discharging patients when care was a central issue. She had a cute, friendly face with long, wild, light brown hair. In all my dealings with her she was always polite and calm. Indeed, such a laid back temperament also found expression in her informal dress sense – colourful and slightly hippy outfits – that reminded me of some friends from University days back in the 1970s. But her folder, containing meticulously taken notes on Mum, revealed another, very efficient side to her character. Right from the start I made it clear that I didn't want Mum being sent to a nursing home, despite this being an option that was put to me for consideration. At this initial meeting it was hard to work out if she was going to be on my side on the issue of getting Mum home. However, when I told my sister that Stephanie was dealing with the case, she was pleased. Elizabeth knew her from earlier days of working at the same hospital. Stephanie had already gained a very good reputation for being helpful and considerate in such matters.

The very last day of that week was my birthday. It was a Sunday in early September and the summer holiday was almost over. It seemed hard to believe that Mum had already spent a month in hospital. As such it was the longest stay in her life. There were a few small signs of improvement, but the closest we were to the prospect of her being discharged was the conversation two days earlier with Stephanie when she indicated that we were at the start of what could be a lengthy process. Moreover, since decisions are rarely made over the weekend, I knew that at least another week was on the cards. I must have mentioned that it was my birthday to somebody on arrival because many of the nurses made a bit of fuss and one of the visitors of a patient in the same ward came back from the canteen with a box of chocolates for me. These were people I didn't know and would probably never meet again, but it was nice to feel that a certain amount of camaraderie was developing.

Unfortunately the day was slightly marred by the apparent lack of staff on the afternoon shift. Mum had made a mess in her pads and it took hours before a nurse was able to change her. Although I had seen my sister performing the task so adeptly, I didn't know where they kept the pads. It was very frustrating having to wait. Each request for help was met with a polite promise to attend in a few minutes, but it never materialised. Eventually the ward sister, friendly – but not the sort of person to be messed around with, summoned a nurse. Appearing annoyed that standards had been allowed to slip during her absence on holiday, it was Sister who noticed I had left Mum uncovered in order to expose the mess that she had been lying in. I too got a bit of a ticking off as Sister expressed, in her *Brummy* accent, concern about respecting the dignity of both my mum and other patients. But on a practical level it did the trick and Mum was soon washed and changed.

The incident made me realise that I would have to take an even more active role on my visits. If I was going to look after Mum, as I had indicated to Stephanie, it was the right moment to learn some new skills. In other words it was time to receive some training to be a nurse, albeit unofficially and at only a rudimentary level. It was a process that probably had already got underway, perhaps subconsciously, from the start of Mum being admitted back in August, if not before.

Chapter 20 Training to Be a Nurse

Although it may have been on my birthday when I made a conscious decision to use my hospital visits to glean as much information about the care of my mum as possible, my 'training' to acquire some basic nursing skills had already started well before then. Visits from the District Nurses during 2006 provided examples of good practice to follow, and of course my sister was always a readily available source of advice. Already in that summer of 2007, I quickly got into the habit of adding the thickener to Mum's drinks from the second day of her being admitted. But the main knowledge gained, often came from simply helping out to make things easier for both Mum and the nurses looking after her while I was on my visits to the ward.

Because incontinence had already become a dominating problem to deal with during 2007, it was only natural that I was curious, from the outset, to see how the nurses managed to change Mum while she was lying in bed. I had got used to changing her from a sitting position when the pads were in the shape of a pair of knickers. Whether she was sitting on a chair, the toilet seat or the bed, it was easy to put her legs through the two holes before getting her to stand so I could pull them up. If Mum did not recover her mobility, or simply to make life easier when she required a change in the night while lying in bed, I needed to learn a new technique. Nevertheless, some nurses thought it was inappropriate for a son to see his mother being changed. Despite my protests that washing her every day for the past two years – which meant there wasn't a part of her body that I hadn't seen or touched – I was still asked to stand or sit on the other side of the drawn curtains.

Mum didn't particularly like strangers washing her, regardless as to whether or not they were medically trained. So with me out of view, she was probably feeling insecure and often shouted during the ten to fifteen minutes while the nurses got on with their work. It was just as well none of them understood because on some occasions I could hear her screaming out *"vaffanculo!"* which, amongst Italian swear words, would rank top of the charts. *"Bastardi!"* was also emitted sometimes, but anybody in the ward within earshot must have understood her sentiments without any explanation. Despite the outburst at the Italian Consulate, it still sounded strange to hear Mum swearing and now even more strongly, as I have no prior recollection of hearing her use such language.

However, some nurses were fine regarding my presence while Mum was being changed. My help was particularly welcome when, as sometimes happened, the nurse was alone. It meant I could hold Mum in position while the nurse was sorting out the pad. Also to make turning Mum more comfortable, I could hold her by the head as she was gently rolled over from the side. I observed the methods used by the nurses and eventually requested to be allowed to have a go myself. I explained that it would give me more confidence to look after Mum at home. The nurse at the time looked slightly anxious as this probably was going against hospital procedure or etiquette, but the curtains were drawn and we both hoped that Sister wouldn't make a surprise appearance. Once Mum had been cleaned by the nurse, it was then my turn to take over. At this stage there was no need for me to get involved in washing around Mum's genital area – that would come later. The first task was to roll up the long cotton belt that was attached to the pad. We carefully turned Mum to her side so that she had her back facing me. I then had to press on the air mattress, near her bottom, and push part of the pad, along with the rolled up belt, underneath her. With that in place, Mum was now ready to be rolled towards me so that she was lying on her back and her bottom was fully on the pad. Next, we turned Mum slightly towards me so that it was easy for me to lean across and pull out the belt that was poking out by her side. With the belt unrolled and Mum allowed to turn gently down on to her back again, the front section of the pad was then pulled up between her legs to cover her up and then the Velcro belt was fastened to hold it all together. I didn't request to repeat the procedure again as I didn't want to undermine the rules of the hospital any further, but it was enough for me to feel more satisfied that I was ready to look after Mum even if she remained bed-bound for the remainder of her life. But one could question why the acquisition of such skills had to be gained in an almost clandestine way. Surely it was in everybody's interests for such knowledge to be disseminated?

By September I found that the staff were getting more and more used to me being on the ward. After all, I was there every day and on some occasions I was probably doing a longer shift than they were. I sensed their growing awareness that I was not put off by the impending challenges that lay ahead if I was to stick to my stated intention of caring for Mum at home. As a result I found I was increasingly being given advice from both doctors and nurses. I was even entrusted to fill in some of the sheets in Mum's medical folder. While present on the ward, there were some days when I completed the page that recorded Mum's food and liquid intake for the relevant hours. After a pad change the nurse would often leave me the job of recording the type of stool. Such information was monitored on a sheet that tracked the patient's bowel movements over the week. The spectrum of stools ranged from Type 1, 'separate hard lumps like nuts', to the other extreme of Type 7, 'watery, no solid pieces, entirely liquid'. I remember recording Type 4, 'like a sausage or snake, smooth and soft', but mostly it was Type 6, 'fluffy pieces with ragged edges, a mushy stool'. Other information that I got used to observing were colour, amount and whether the stool contained any blood.

When Mum's temperature and blood pressure were taken, again to save the nurses a bit of time, I sometimes recorded the readings and plotted the points on the graph. As Mum was on a catheter, it was important to look out for any spike in temperature. In addition, and as part of a further guidance to help avoid any potential urinary tract infection, one of the doctors reminded me of the importance of cleaning Mum from front to back. It was advice that I later felt compelled to pass on to some of the carers who called round to help later in the year. The same significance of temperature readings also applied to her growing propensity to fall ill from a chest infection linked to difficulties in swallowing. Getting into the habit of recording such information in those summer months formed an important part of the preparation for Mum's return home.

And so my time was usefully spent while I was on the ward. As well as gaining valuable experience and advice, I'm sure it must have helped in providing evidence that I was committed to meeting the demands of looking after Mum properly at home. In the meantime it also kept me occupied. Not that I didn't already have plenty to do. As well as feeding Mum, I was also providing her drinks and still continued to exercise her legs and arms. I was even sent out on my bike one day on a mission to track down a bottle of ferrous fumarate. The hospital pharmacy had completely run out of the liquid. To make matters worse there were problems with all the suppliers, for some unknown reason, temporarily suspending production. Eventually I found a chemist which still had some in stock. Although the doctor said that a lack of iron supplement was by no means life threatening, I was determined not to allow anything, if possible, to delay Mum's recovery.

To a certain extent all this activity helped to pass the time because by this stage conversation with Mum was very limited. But it didn't matter. Maybe it was just sufficient to be there and hold her hand. As far as it is possible to comprehend the feelings of someone who is unwilling or unable to talk, I got the impression that Mum was getting completely fed up by the middle of her fifth week in hospital. Although she had a slight change of scenery as she had been moved to another ward, the routine was much the same. On the 6th of September, Mum said only one word during my entire stay at the hospital. It was "*perché?*" which means "why?" Indeed, Mum must have wondered what on earth she was doing stuck in a bed for so many weeks, particularly as for the previous eight decades she had been so active and energetic. For the next two days Mum didn't utter a single word. It was later found that she had a chest infection which probably accounted for her spirits being so low. Fortunately it was caught in time. After a few days of treatment with antibiotics, her health and willingness to speak both showed signs of recovery.

While all this had been going on, discussions were still taking place with Stephanie. I had a slight disagreement with her at one meeting. Only nine days earlier she had delivered the great news that Mum would be allowed to go home as long as there was a care package put in place. Now all of a sudden there appeared to be questions raised. It was extremely difficult to work out why or who was blocking the move and unfortunately I shot the messenger. Altogether it hadn't been a particularly good day. Mum was still in the middle of her latest chest infection. On top of that, one of the other patients, who couldn't stop talking, was really getting on my nerves. When I finally got home and had time to reflect, I felt that I had been unnecessarily rude to Stephanie so the next day one of my first tasks on arriving at the hospital was to find her and apologise. But at least by the end of the sixth week there were some positive signs. Mum was definitely recovering from her infection. Additionally, a further meeting with Stephanie and a former nurse named Mark, who was also working with Social Services, gave the impression that the possibility of getting Mum home was still alive.

Another weekend arrived. Life in the hospital tends to be much calmer over those two days. Unless there is an emergency, fewer crucial decisions are made. The nursing staff, without the pressure and demands from consultants patrolling the wards, can be more relaxed. With nearly all the key players away, as far as decision-making was concerned, any further information regarding Mum being discharged from the hospital would have to be deferred for at least another week. As explained by one of the doctors in charge, the delay was just as frustrating for the medical staff as it was for me. Perhaps because it was a weekend, the Indian doctor was willing to spend a bit more time explaining things. Even on the busy days he had a pleasant bed-side manner and was popular with the patients. He had a friendly face and looked a bit like Elvis Presley. On purely medical grounds he felt that there was very little more that the hospital could do. In addition he was concerned that by prolonging Mum's stay, especially at her age and in her condition, she ran the risk of picking up more infections. For that reason, as well as the benefits of releasing a bed for another patient, he too was keen to see the issue of when Mum would be leaving resolved as soon as possible.

Fortunately we didn't have that much longer to wait. On Monday I had a meeting with Stephanie which lasted almost two hours. It really went through a lot of the detail involved in setting up a care package. I still felt I was being left reasonably in control of affairs – but it was also clear that I would have to accept a lot of help, or interference, from Social Services, depending on which way you looked at it. I needed to arrange cover for any times that I would be out of the house for significant periods like going to work. As this only involved four sessions lasting no more than three hours at a time, it didn't seem such an insurmountable obstacle. However, the recommended number of visits from carers of three per day started to make me feel a bit anxious. With my income drastically cut over the years I began to wonder about the cost. Were so many visits necessary? And after all, I could do most of that myself, surely? These were some of my thoughts which may have been transmitted visually by what probably was an increasingly concerned expression on my face. "Don't worry, the package is guaranteed to be free for the first month." Yes, these words from Stephanie were reassuring, but what about subsequent months, years or even decades, I wondered? In the end, I felt obliged to co-operate as much as possible and just hope for the best. The main objective was to get Mum home – to her home – not a nursing home.

Who would have thought getting somebody out of hospital was going to be so difficult? All I could do was hope that the information I had provided Stephanie with would help to win the argument to get Mum discharged; and also gain the funding to cover the cost of the care package that I seemed obliged to accept as a condition of getting her out. Although Stephanie couldn't make any promises, she felt that there was enough evidence that Mark could present at a meeting scheduled for Thursday. There he would argue that Mum needed care on medical rather than social grounds.

The distinction was significant. As long as the committee agreed on the former, that is medical grounds, and although I would still be left with plenty to worry about, at least the concerns would be less likely to revolve around finance. All the care would be provided free of charge – and indefinitely. On the other hand, if the verdict came down on the latter interpretation, in other words social grounds, I would be facing a financial meltdown. I had purposely cut down my hours at work to the bare minimum so that I could find time to look after Mum. If I had to suddenly fund three visits per day, the attendance allowance provided by the government wouldn't have been enough to cover even one day's worth of visits per week. The only option then would have been to dig into my savings for the unforeseeable future. Yes, many positive things came out of that meeting with Stephanie on Monday, but there were still many important questions left unanswered. I would just have to wait until Thursday to hear the outcome of the meeting. In the meantime all I could do was to carry on trying to remain positive and continue transforming part of Mum's house into a mini-hospital ward, ready for her return home.

Chapter 21 The Great Escape

Following the meeting with Stephanie, the next few days passed by uneventfully until Thursday finally arrived. As soon as I had finished my economics lesson with the Upper 6th around midday, I cycled over to the hospital eager to find out if there was any news about the funding. It must have been about 3 p.m., just before the trolley with tea and biscuits arrived on the ward, when Stephanie appeared. She could have played games with me and kept me guessing for a few minutes, but judging from the way she bounced in and the smile on her face, I felt confident that she was going to deliver some good news. "Hi, I've just got a call from Mark and he's told me that you've got the funding!"

For a second I wondered whether or not I should give her a hug. 'Might be a bit too informal,' I thought, but it was certainly great news and a big relief. It was a brief announcement but one that was responsible for removing a heavy burden of anxiety. It meant that when Mum was discharged, she would have visits from a nurse three times a day, morning, afternoon and evening, for at least a month, and some form of care on a similar level could continue afterwards – with no charge. Possibly to help keep down the costs for Social Services, I had to be present to give a hand. That was fair enough. Besides, it was something I would have requested anyway and, as a further bonus, visiting times were even arranged to fit in with my timetable at school.

Things were definitely moving in the right direction. After leaving the hospital that evening, I decided to cycle over to the Hammersmith house and sleep there. A plumber had been booked in for the morning to replace a cistern for the toilet, and I also wanted to take down the ladder because over the previous few days, I had finally managed to finish all the roof repairs. With all the main jobs in Hammersmith completed, I was able to leave the house that morning with plenty of time to reach the hospital before lunch was served and with the knowledge that I could now turn my energy towards preparing the Chiswick house for Mum's imminent arrival. Given the amount of work required, it suited me that there was a delay of a few days while some of the necessary paperwork and planning were put in place. Stephanie needed to book in nurses for the visits and this took longer than she expected. Meanwhile over the weekend, I checked the availability of the helpers who were to sit with Mum while I was at school. It meant that already by Tuesday, week 8 of Mum's hospital stay, I was able to give Stephanie the final list of names. As well as my sister Elizabeth, it also included Sara, Jim and Andrew, the latter three all living close by.

For a few days I had been uncertain which room would be the best to use for looking after Mum. Because she would need to be in an adjustable electric bed, which takes up quite a bit of space, the choice was narrowed down to one of the two large rooms on the ground floor. I particularly liked the front room. It was south facing and therefore brighter during the day. Although it hadn't been decorated for years, the wallpaper, which Mum had put up, was still in very good condition. But whilst the appearance of the room was important, it wasn't the most significant factor. As well as attending to Mum, I would have to spend time washing laundry and preparing meals. The need to avoid her being left alone for significant periods of time during the day meant that the front room was increasingly falling out of favour.

At the back of the house there were three rooms that were all connected to each other in the shape of the letter L in reverse. Of course the area wasn't as bright as the front of the house because it was north facing, but the main dining room was large and could easily accommodate the electric bed. The adjacent room – linked by the wide opening in the wall that Dad had made in the 1960s – also had a fireplace built into the chimney breast. There, wood could be burnt in the winter to raise the temperature to a comfortable level for Mum, especially in the evening when the power of the storage heaters faded. It had always been a comfortable place to sit and do some reading and was especially relaxing when the extra light from the yellow and orange flames flicker on the pages. Years earlier, coal had been used as the main source of fuel. Even our black cat had seemed to be enchanted by the changing colours of the flames skipping and dancing in front of him – for surely the hours spent gazing at the spectacle couldn't have been explained solely by a desire to seek a place of warmth.

The last room was the small kitchen where I would be able to prepare meals or get any warm water required to wash Mum whilst she still remained in full view. Perhaps just as importantly, Mum would be able to see me while I was working in the kitchen. Hopefully as a result she wouldn't feel abandoned when I was busy. So weighing up all the pros and cons, in the end I plumped for the back of the house as the most suitable location. I knew I had just a few days to transform the rooms and make them pleasant, and effectively serve as a mini-hospital ward.

To brighten up the rooms I first of all washed the ceilings. These were jobs that didn't make much noise and, with the preparation completed, I felt it wouldn't disturb the neighbours to use a few nights to carry on painting until about 2 a.m. The wallpaper in the middle room looked all the worse for wear. After stripping it off the wall and making a few minor repairs to the plaster, it was ready for painting. To make the room as bright as possible, I opted for white. The vinyl wallpaper in the dining room, a cream colour with light brown streaks, was still in good condition. It was again the handiwork of my mum from an earlier decade and just needed to be washed down. The doors, window frames and chimney mantelpiece were all painted white, again contributing to the rooms looking brighter and fresher.

My carpentry skills had also been put to good practice over the previous few days as I added some shelving on adjacent sides of the chimney. This extra storage space was useful for sheets, medicines and the many bags of incontinence pads that would soon be used. It was even home for the blood pressure wrist monitor that I had bought as well as the thermometer. The latter was similar to the one used in the hospital, where temperatures were taken from the ear. Mum had hated this procedure at first and always flinched when the end piece was inserted in her ear, but as the weeks progressed, she eventually became quite indifferent to it.

In order to create more space, out came the upright piano. The musical instrument had a history and probably deserved a better final resting place. It had been carefully restored by my dad in 1972 – much needed work – after Peter helped me push it for over a mile along uneven pavements in Isleworth. It probably hadn't been the cleverest of ideas, requiring the use of a van to assist with the final leg of the journey to Chiswick, but at the time we were still in our early teens. A few years later the piano provided the focal point during a memorable visit from my aunt, along with other relatives and friends. All were treated to an elaborate meal prepared by Mum. Afterwards, Uncle Franco played a medley of Italian tunes on the piano, encouraging all the assembled guests to join in with his singing. But almost forty years on – it was no longer time to be sentimental. The old piano had to make room for a more practical piece of furniture. So out it went – pushed into the garden and sadly exposed to the elements.

I then noticed a potential problem in the dining room. There wasn't a single electrical point. This hadn't presented any difficulties in the past, but if the room was going to be Mum's home for the foreseeable future it would need some sockets to operate the electric bed, TV, Hi-Fi, video and DVD player that I intended to install. So the next task was to add three more double sockets to the circuit that ran under the floor of the adjacent room. Access to the cables was made easier as I was able to work from the basement below. Fortunately, it was a type of job that I had done many times before and as such this further contributed towards speeding up the process. I was able to pack away my tools well before the arrival of the electric bed on Wednesday the 26th of September from a company used by the authorities to loan out medical equipment.

The bed came in separate parts that had to be assembled. It didn't take long for the delivery man to put it together to look just like one of the beds in the hospital. It was set up in the middle of the room to face the back garden so that Mum would have a view of the flowers that, until a few months ago, she had tended. In order to test the equipment, the cables connected to the bed and air mattress were both plugged in. Everything worked fine. The handset to operate the bed was similar to the one used in the hospital, so I quickly found out how I could raise the head rest and then the other end of the bed for the feet. The whole bed could be raised or lowered, either level or at an angle. Once the mattress was inflated the motor, which made a low humming noise, changed the sections of the mattress that were either inflated or deflated. Rails were also attached to the sides to ensure that Mum wouldn't fall out but could be easily lowered when it was necessary to wash or change her

To the left of the bed I placed a trolley that Mum had bought years ago. It was originally designed for carrying food from the kitchen. Henceforth its new planned role was to provide a surface to place the bowl of warm water to wash her. Behind the bed was a cabinet that was to be used for the Hi-Fi so that she could listen to some music. I moved an armchair from the front room and placed it in the corner of the room near the French windows, which would be an ideal location for anyone sitting in with Mum. It was comfortable and provided a good view of her as well as the garden. The other corner of the room where I had placed a new socket was reserved for the TV, DVD player and video. Looking around the house on that Wednesday, I was pleased with my few days of intensive work. The room was ready. It had the facilities of a hospital, and yet would provide Mum with a familiar setting. With the electric bed set up and working, I then switched off the power. It was time to go and visit Mum in the hospital.

After a few minutes by Mum's bedside, I noticed that there was something different. There was no bag for the urine. I checked the other side of the bed and on lifting the sheets I couldn't see a tube between her legs. Her catheter had been removed. I made some enquiries as to the reason, which then provoked a disagreement between two of the consultants on the ward. The amiable Indian doctor was in favour of its removal, expressing concern over its link to urinary tract infections. Because the tube is inserted into the urethra, it also provided a passage for harmful bacteria to cause infection, hence the importance of keeping the area near the vagina as clean as possible. The female doctor, on the other hand, felt that Mum should go home with the catheter in place as this eliminated the skin's exposure to urine and therefore reduced the risks of bed sores developing. I was caught in the middle of this debate.

Not wishing to offend either, I expressed the opinion that both sides had valid points but in the end my preference was swayed by some very practical issues. As long as there were no leaks due to blockages in the tube, it would be easier to look after Mum with the catheter in place. I would just have to be vigilant, cleaning Mum as frequently as possible, and try to prevent any excrement coming into contact with the tube. Given the close proximity between the openings for the urethra, vagina, and anus, that was going to be some challenge. And so the debate was settled. They went with my wishes, and the next day the catheter was re-installed.

Thankfully, Mum never succumbed to any further infections during that eighth week. In fact she was eating and drinking with more enthusiasm and even speaking on a few occasions. Whether or not she understood my explanations, that she would be returning home in a few days time, is hard to judge but her spirits seemed to lift. Maybe she just picked up a changing and more positive attitude from me during the visits. When the notice for discharge came, it was sudden and took me by surprise. It was the Monday afternoon, the start of her ninth week. I was told that Mum would be going home the following day. Although I was very pleased to hear the news, I had a temporary pang of anxiety. Her room was fully prepared at home, but was I?

In some ways I had grown used to the arrangement at the hospital. It wasn't perfect, but for the most part, she had been well looked after. I didn't have to prepare her meals or wash her laundry. All my visits, even though on some days they were lasting up to ten hours, could all be fitted in around my school timetable. From Tuesday onwards I would have the main responsibility for both her medical and social care. Mum was a very different person to the one who had been walking by the river just two months previously. It was a bit frightening, but then I thought back to all the preparation that had taken place over the preceding few weeks both at home and in the hospital. I had learnt much from the doctors and nurses. In the meantime Stephanie and Mark had completed their part in securing her return home. This was no time to bottle out. The self-doubt soon evaporated, especially after some of the compliments and well wishes from the staff on the ward. By the time I left the hospital that evening, I was beginning to feel more confident and ready to face up to the new challenges ahead. Moreover, my rucksack was full of spare pads and a few nightdresses that some of the nurses had sneaked in before going!

The next morning I briefly popped into the ward to deliver a nightdress, scarf and hat to keep Mum warm during her transfer. On the way back from the hospital I purchased some more pads from the chemist in Brentford by Albany Parade. It was the place where I had ordered the wheelchair and commode and frequently visited because the pharmacist was always helpful and specialised in stocking equipment for the elderly. After returning home for lunch, I cycled to school for a lesson but instead of going to Mum's ward as usual, I went straight back home to wait for Mum to be transported from the hospital. Later that afternoon, and much to my surprise, I received a phone call from one of the hospital staff enquiring whether there were steps to the front door. When I replied that there were, I was shocked to find out that this simple bit of information had jeopardised the possibility of Mum being discharged. Health and Safety was given as the reason.

"Oh leave it out!" I exclaimed. "You can't cancel Mum leaving because of three small steps!" It was unbelievable, but it looked like Mum would be stuck in hospital until this issue was resolved. And yet I knew, from past experiences of the ambulance crew collecting Mum, that they had never made any fuss about the steps. Suddenly, whilst still on the phone, I remembered the ramp. It was another item that I had bought from the Brentford pharmacist, but one that suddenly took on an unexpected significance. It had cost about £160 and had been standing idle in the conservatory for weeks. Now it could be put to good use. "Look, I've got a ramp," I told the man at the end of the phone. "Surely that will be okay?" I continued. "I'll have to check and then I'll get back to you as soon as possible," was his reply. Well, he kept to his word and soon afterwards phoned back to inform me that his superiors were happy with the arrangement.

That left very little to do other than to wait. My sister also came over to help. When the ambulance arrived at about 5 p.m., I could see that Mum appeared to be on a trolley that looked quite heavy. It wasn't a simple stretcher as I had expected, hence the concern about the risk of back injuries for the ambulance crew. We did use the ramp for the steps and then Mum was wheeled into the dining room. Within a few seconds the height of the bed was adjusted to the same level as the trolley which made it easier to transfer her. I later made a note in a diary that she was lying on her side facing the kitchen. She was home at last. It had taken over eight weeks. Of that time, probably about two or three weeks were necessary for medical reasons. The remaining time in the hospital was less justified but at least it had served to allow me some breathing space to recover and prepare for her return.

The first visit from a nurse was scheduled for 8 p.m. She came round promptly for Mum's first pad change back home. Mum had already been fed. With three of us, it didn't take long to complete the task of washing her and changing her pad. We altered her position so that she was lying on her back. This was again noted in my diary along with a description of the stool as 'small, soft, No 4' and then once the preliminary paperwork in the official folder was complete, the nurse left. My sister stayed a bit longer, but eventually it was time for her to go as she was working in the hospice the next day. It was very peaceful sitting there with Mum by my side. There was enough room to put a chair between the bed and the chimney. From that position I could hold Mum's hand and even watch television. I had found a cassette, *Tutto Pavarotti,* full of Italian songs, which I put on later, and so Mum's opening night at home started reasonably well. She was obviously tired from the events of the day, but appeared content to be encircled by such familiar surroundings and sounds.

Just after midnight, I opened her pads to check. She was still clean. The catheter was functioning perfectly. All that was required was for me to drain the bag of urine and empty the contents in the toilet. The colour of the urine was quite dark – changing to a healthier-looking yellow as the next few days progressed and I was able to get Mum to drink more regularly. It was time for me to get some rest. I laid a blanket on the floor at the foot of Mum's bed, along with a sleeping bag and pillow. It wasn't particularly comfortable but it wasn't that bad either. I left a light on but it was from a globe which emitted a calming blue illumination; strong enough to allow me to see Mum from the floor but not too powerful to prevent me falling sleeping. It was 1 a.m. About three hours sleep would do, so I set the alarm for 4 a.m.

The time seemed to pass quickly. Before I knew it the clock was ringing and I got up. I put the main light on and opened Mum's pads. She was still asleep and oblivious to the mess that she was lying in. I warmed up some water on the cooker. Unfortunately, the handle on the small water heater in the kitchen was still broken. Despite many enquiries over the summer of 2007, I just couldn't find a replacement. Now that Mum was home there would be even less time to sort out problems like that. Anyway, the old fashioned method produced the same result, but it did take a bit longer.

This was the first pad change that I had to do completely on my own. I had plenty of wipes, a pair of white latex gloves and a bowl of warm water. It did feel strange poking my finger in my Mum's vagina to clean that area out along with the tube to the catheter, but it was a job that had to be done, so after mumbling the words, "Sorry, Mum," I just got on with it. When there were no more brown marks left on the wipes, I felt it was time to move on to the next part of the operation. Following exactly the same procedures observed, and even practised in the hospital, I managed to turn Mum and replace the dirty pad with a fresh one. All the rolling over was good for Mum anyway, so I didn't feel guilty if she was temporarily awoken from her slumbers. Soon she was back asleep and in a new position. I noted that at 4.30 a.m. she had been left to lie on her side but this time facing the chimney. It was recommended that she should be turned as frequently as possible but, if I was to get any sleep, it would have to be limited to about three changes a night. Besides, I can't recall a single day of her stay in hospital when she was turned as frequently as the doctors recommended.

Thank goodness for plastic bags. This was a time when the media seemed to be running a campaign against the use of such bags, but for me they were a godsend. Over the previous and forthcoming months, the volume of shit that I had to deal with meant that the bags were invaluable. Another three hours sleep and then I was up again. Mum was still clean so I was able to concentrate on washing her face and feet, while also applying some cream to help with dry skin. After breakfast, which consisted of porridge, Mum was no longer disturbed until she was given a full wash when one of the carers called round at 10 a.m. By then she did need a pad change. Mum was washed from top to bottom with a flannel and gently dried with a towel. Next, a new nightdress was put on. At first we used the ones provided by the hospital, but I soon found that cutting the backs of Mum's nightdresses made them just as easy to slip on or off as the NHS version. I covered Mum's eyes while the carer sprayed some dry shampoo and then brushed her hair. Before she left, we remembered to change Mum's position. She wasn't a nurse, but she carried out her duties very efficiently.

For lunch I warmed up some soup, adding some instant mash powder to thicken it, and fed her with a spoon. This was followed by rice pudding, ice cream and prunes. Jim, my next door neighbour, was the first of the helpers to sit with Mum. Despite being in his early eighties, he was still very alert and agile. A bit shorter than me, with white hair and glasses, he still possessed a mild Derbyshire accent, despite living in London for over fifty years. Bringing with him a book to read, he called round at 1 p.m., as arranged, and this allowed me to go to school to take the Year 11 group for football. Once the boys had finished I was able to return home. The afternoon had passed by without any problems. As soon as Jim left, I checked Mum's pads. There was no need for a change so I could concentrate on preparing the next meal. Mum was still clean by the time the nurse arrived in the evening, and so the main focus was giving her another wash and changing her position. A few more drinks later that night in order to reach her recommended target of two litres, a final check of her pads after midnight along with the catheter bag and then it was my turn to get some rest. It was not until 4:30 a.m. that I had to get up from my sleeping bag and perform another pad change.

Mum had been home for over twenty-four hours by then. No major problems. She had been washed, turned and fed. She hadn't been lying in her own mess for long, as I had been checking regularly and changed the pads when necessary. The combination of carers, nurses and neighbours sitting in, had got off to a good start and the catheter was operating well and keeping her skin dry. The next day was the turn for my sister to help out. She had agreed to come over every Thursday at about 8 a.m. and fortunately was able to keep that particular day free of any shifts from work. It was the morning when I needed the longest cover as my lesson didn't finish until nearly 1 p.m. Having my sister around for that number of hours, especially with her medical knowledge and experience, was a great relief. And for her – keeping a record of bowel movements, positions and nutrition and liquid intake – was second nature. Consequently, details in my diary were always well kept on a Thursday.

There was still Andrew, a very tall Maths teacher, to come round in the following week, and that would be preceded on Monday by a visit from another neighbour, the very pretty woman named Sara. But to my surprise, Sara called round earlier, on Friday, to check how Mum was getting on. It was a nice gesture and provided me with an opportunity to explain the routine. The last time she had seen Mum was on one of our walks, so it was just as well that Sara got used to seeing Mum's new and somewhat pitiful condition.

It was very early days but if the first week was anything to go by, it augured well for the future. It was by no means easy but I seemed to be coping well. Most importantly, Mum appeared happy to be home again. However, it did beg the following questions – how long could I keep this going – and would I cope with any unforeseen crisis?

Chapter 22 A Brush of Colour

Looking back at how frequently I had walked around the Chiswick area with my mother every single day, it was no surprise that we met so many people. Most were neighbours with whom I was already acquainted; some were colleagues from work who lived in, or were passing through, the area. But sometimes new acquaintances were made. It might be just a smile, or hello, but the regularity of the walks meant we were becoming a permanent fixture in the locality. Some waved, some even stopped to talk for a while. There was Daphne, a teacher of English and History, who was learning Italian. She owned a house like Mum's on the other side of the block that we sometimes included on our walks. In her mid to late fifties, this good-looking Scottish lady was very politely spoken. She was always keen to stop for a brief chat. Unfortunately Mum was too far gone with the dementia by then – too impatient to keep still for more than a minute – to allow Daphne any opportunity of really practising her Italian conversation. Moreover, the pavement in that street was so uneven that it was a walk I usually tried to avoid, especially after Mum tripped and badly cut her face one day.

Another woman lived on that same street. She was a young, very beautiful brunette, with two charming youngsters. My mum loved to meet children on her travels and for that reason she was always willing to spend a bit more time before moving on. In fact, meeting anybody in such circumstances was always a great help, particularly if Mum was in a bad mood or was annoyed with me for some reason. In the latter case she wouldn't even hold my hand. It was therefore always a great relief to see someone in the distance pushing a pram or walking with a toddler. My mum would greet the mother or father and then make a real fuss of their offspring. You could see real delight in my mother's face and a few minutes later she would take my hand and whatever had been annoying her a short while ago – and most of the time I didn't have a clue what had been the cause – was forgotten and I could relax as we continued on our little tour.

Sometimes the enigmatic woman who, at this stage remained nameless to me, but lived close to Daphne, would also be accompanied by a handsome man with long hair whom I assumed was her husband. At other times she might be walking with another woman who looked similar and appeared to be an elder sister, but actually turned out to be her mother. As I got to know them better, I discovered that they shared many common facial expressions – especially those displaying surprise or indignation. Both could walk incredibly fast because occasionally, when I found myself turning round to gain a sneak glance a few seconds after moving on, I could see that they had almost disappeared out of view. Every time we met, she would smile but there was never time to get into any meaningful conversation because as soon as my mum had finished making a fuss of her son and daughter, I could feel her tugging me to move on. Mum had time for children but by this stage didn't seem to care for conversations with grown-ups – particularly other women – I noticed increasingly.

These occasional meetings occurred over a period of more than a year and, apart from providing a break on the walk, didn't really seem that significant. During the summer of 2007 when Mum had her long stay in the hospital, I had a completely new routine. Consequently, I didn't see the mysterious lady at all – but to be honest – I didn't really give it any thought. Then one day on the way to the dentist, I bumped into her. She was surprised to see me without my mum. Maybe because she hadn't met us walking together for weeks, she immediately enquired about her health. She looked genuinely concerned when I told her that Mum had stopped walking towards the end of July and had already been in hospital for a few weeks while the doctors were trying to work out the cause of her anaemia. She kindly offered to help after Mum was discharged from the hospital. It was a decision that I hoped would soon be resolved. This was the first time that I had spoken to her for longer than a minute and it was then that I discovered her name was Sara.

Luckily I remembered that offer because quite a few weeks passed before I met Sara again. This was a few days after I had been given the task, as one of several conditions to secure Mum's release from the hospital, of finding a team of volunteers willing to sit with her while I was out at work. Two neighbours in the street, Jim and Andrew, had already signed up. My sister was willing to keep her Thursdays free from any shifts at the hospice so that meant only the Monday morning slot needed to be covered.

"I'll be more than happy to come round on Monday mornings, Mike." The time I suggested also fitted in quite well with Sara's need to take her children to the local Primary school because my lesson didn't start until 11 a.m. She would be able to attend to her son and daughter first, before popping round at 10 a.m. to stay about three hours while I cycled to Hounslow in order to teach at St Mark's. With her agreement everything was in place. She gave me her phone number and address, which was required by the hospital, thereby playing her part in my battle to persuade the administrators that I would be able to look after Mum at home. Christine, a friend of my neighbour June, was also prepared to assist occasionally so her name was added to the list of potential helpers.

A few days before my mum was discharged, Sara invited me around to her home, a first floor flat with a newly finished loft conversion, to discuss the arrangements. It was a warm, sunny evening. As soon as she opened the front door, she called me in. Her height was similar to mine, about 5' 8" and as I followed her up the stairs it was hard not to notice that she kept herself in good shape. She directed me to her very neat and well decorated living room. We both sat on the comfortable white settee placed against the wall facing the chimney. Although the main focus of the conversation revolved around my mum, there was also a chance to chat about other things including a sketchy picture of each other's backgrounds. I must have been there for over an hour but it wasn't just her pleasant conversation that was making it difficult for me to leave.

She must have just had a bath and was wearing a white dressing gown. Usually her hair was tied in a style where you could imagine she had just walked off the set of a period costume drama like *Pride and Prejudice*. On this particular evening, however, her wavy, dark brown and shoulder length hair, which was still damp, gave her the appearance of a seductive French actress. Although she was English, for me to conjecture such a continental link wasn't an entirely ridiculous observation. I later discovered that that she did have a French connection on her mother's side of the family, which may help to explain her fluency in the language and interest in the country. She had very attractive brown eyes and her nose, mouth and chin were all well-proportioned. She really did look beautiful and could easily have passed as a stand-in for the lead actress, Keira Knightley, in the film, *Atonement*. I almost couldn't believe my luck that she had volunteered to come over every Monday morning for the foreseeable future.

On the way out she showed me several paintings by her mother Helen, but apparently it was her uncle, Sebastian, who was the main artist in the family and who had been commissioned by several famous and wealthy people for portraits. So much talent, I thought, but an even bigger surprise was the news that Sara had divorced several years ago and that the man that I had seen her walking with was, by then, an ex-boyfriend. "Wow!" I exclaimed under my breath while punching the air, as I left her home but – after excitedly allowing my imagination to run wild for a few minutes, my thoughts came crashing down to earth. Not only was she far too pretty for me, I concluded, but I also knew I would have no time to even contemplate starting a relationship. For the last few years it had become obvious that I would have to devote most of my spare time to Mum, leaving insufficient room for anybody else. So those fleeting, speculative moments were quickly dismissed and my thoughts then turned to more practical matters like decorating the room that would be the home for Mum when she returned from the hospital in a few days' time.

The first visit to look after my mum started on Wednesday the 3rd of October with Jim. Along with Andrew, the two men proved to be very reliable and on separate days they patiently sat in the room with my mother for the two or three hours while I was out. But my sister and Sara offered other qualities. With my sister, strengthened by the bond between mother and daughter, came more than two decades' experience in nursing. Even more appropriately, quite a few of those years involved caring for patients in a hospice. This still required dealing with people of different age groups and illnesses, but a significant number were elderly and suffering from dementia. With Sara, there wasn't the medical knowledge, but she was able to tap into her experience as a mother. This proved ideal when caring for my mum as, for all intents and purposes, she had regressed back to her early childhood. Sara could be very softly spoken when necessary, as if she was dealing with a baby or very young child. I think my mum appreciated that. In fact a few weeks later there was further evidence of mum's preference for a serene ambience when she told a nurse off who was speaking too loudly. "Shhh", exclaimed my mother in annoyance. This surprised both of us, but the Irish nurse was very understanding about it. On the way out she said that it was good to see Mum was still aware of what was going on around her and, moreover, capable of expressing her feelings.

For her first visit on Monday the 8th of October, Sara arrived with her own mother, maybe because she might have wanted a little support herself. A few hours later when I returned home from teaching, I was both surprised and delighted to find my mother laughing with the two of them sitting either side of the bed. It was a good start and it was obvious that they had used the time to try to amuse her. In the last stages of dementia, people lose the ability to smile, so it was no mean achievement to see such a happy expression on her face. Before they departed, I was left with a very surprising proposition. Helen asked me if it would be possible for her brother, Sebastian, to visit in a few days' time with the intention of painting a portrait of my mother. She said that Mum had a beautiful face and I couldn't disagree with that. The idea of seeing a portrait of my mum in her early eighties sounded great, so it didn't take long for me to agree.

A few days later, Sara and her uncle, Sebastian, turned up at about 10 a.m. They were eagerly led in by Sara's Yorkshire terrier. The little dog's presence throughout the proceedings was only made noticeable by the light patter of her feet and the jingling bell around her neck whenever she left her resting place for the short trip either to the kitchen in search of a treat or outside in the garden in response to a call of nature. For the first few minutes I helped Sebastian carry in several large boxes to the dining room. Studying her uncle more closely, I was surprised to see how many facial features he shared with his elder sister, Helen. He was a tall, slim, handsome man with short dark hair and a friendly face. He typically wore a dark polo shirt and, as did his niece, a pair of jeans. The contents of the boxes were emptied to reveal a range of expensive camera equipment – signalling that Mum was about to start her belated modelling career! It all looked very professional. He showed me a portfolio of his previous portraits. I felt quite proud that Mum would be joining such an impressive collection of well-known people. Maybe over one hundred photos were taken that day as Sebastian strove to find the correct shot. Mum was sitting up in the electric bed which had been completely rotated and moved close to the French windows so that she now had her back to the garden. Her nightdress was adjusted to reveal her thin shoulders and Sebastian then carefully placed a purple sheet behind her to provide a darker, almost regal background. She often fell asleep during the photo shoot, but he did capture her with her eyes open on a few occasions. It wasn't just the stand with a bright light that altered the atmosphere. With the intermittent clicking of the camera the room had been temporarily transformed into a working studio.

Sara must have helped her uncle before because she had come well prepared with a box of delicious cakes, as if she already knew this was going to take a good few hours. Sometimes we would be asked to hold a sheet to help alter the level of light in the room until it almost felt like our arms would drop off. Her uncle was so intensely focused on taking the photos that he appeared to forget about us, as we chatted and laughed behind the screen. They stayed for most of the day, not leaving until 4 p.m., and it was nice having someone so pretty around to talk to. There were breaks for feeding and washing Mum and there was at least one interruption from a nurse who visited in the afternoon. On her arrival, I felt obliged to explain the temporary transformation of the room. While surprised, the nurse appeared completely unconcerned and with my assistance, calmly got on with changing the pads. Before leaving, Sebastian helped put the electric bed back in its former position and even found time to look at the designs I had made for the Charity Walk T-shirts. A collection that up to that point had spanned the summers between 2000 and 2007 was stored upstairs, the shirts from each year individually framed. It was nice to receive compliments from an artist and

I gave him one of the spare black shirts from 2004, which he particularly liked.

After that day, Sebastian visited on at least another five occasions. He brought a canvass and after spending some time mixing the paints, got started on the portrait. It would only be a first draft and initially that seemed a good description because her face didn't really show any distinguishable features. But Sebastian knew what he was doing; he was in no rush and wanted to get the colours right. By the time he had completed this first version, it looked impressive and to an untrained eye one would have thought this was the finished article. Sebastian explained that this was going to be the template which would enable him to continue working on the painting in his studio. Because this project was unpaid, he didn't have any planned time scale for finishing it. Essentially, it was a piece of art that he was doing for his own intrinsic interest. While it may feature as part of an exhibition at some future date, the commissioned work was his bread and butter and that had to remain the priority. Mum's portrait needed to be fitted in between, but from what I could see of his work so far, it would be left in very capable hands.

Sara turned up to some of the other sittings; it was an opportunity to see her uncle which wasn't always possible given the demands of raising a young family single handed. She had a bubbly personality and claimed that she was scatty, but over the next few months I could see that behind her excitable, impulsive and somewhat dreamlike character was an intelligent and thoughtful young woman. She had a free spirit and, given her family background, it was not unexpected that she was interested in art and literature. It was even less of a surprise that she expressed a real dislike of working in an office, something she had been trained to do, but not an experience she had found at all fulfilling. There was a contradiction. She seemed to have a refined and yet slightly untamed nature, a fascinating combination that added to her appeal. I could imagine that, apart from a few things, one of which included the lack of financial security, she probably enjoyed many of the aspects of no longer being tied down in a marriage. And maybe that appreciation of freedom was best summarised in her sharing with me what she dreamed would be her ideal holiday – roaming around Europe for several weeks in a camper van and sleeping under the stars.

It had been an interesting few days. The visits had provided an opportunity to get to know Sara and the rest of her family but, as is often the case in conversations with women, it was her questioning that was far more probing and of the two of us, she nearly always left the better informed. Nevertheless, I did glean enough information from her to form an image of a seemingly intriguing personality. Meanwhile as an added bonus, it fortuitously turned out that Sebastian was fluent in Italian. And so while photographing Mum, he was also able to communicate with her. Better still, he effectively acted as a surrogate carer during his several visits, allowing me to pop out on various errands with a temporarily lighter burden of responsibility.

With the preparatory work on the painting finished, the visits from Sara went back to the regular Mondays but, every now and again, she would pop round to see if I needed any help. If she was going to the shops she checked to see if I needed anything and occasionally returned with a gift – usually something to eat – sometimes even with an unfamiliar dish like couscous. One afternoon, before collecting her children from school, she brought over some delicious fruit yoghurts. Later that evening I opened one of the containers to feed Mum. As soon as Mum swallowed the first spoonful she reacted with a loud "Mmmm." She really enjoyed the pudding and it was such a pity that Sara hadn't been present to witness her appreciation. It was also a moment I would remember later when Mum was in hospital and one of her last pleasures would be removed when she began being fed via a tube running through one of her nostrils.

On another visit, Sara noticed that the seam on my trousers had come undone. Her offer to stitch them was gladly accepted as they were the pair that I used for going to school. A few days later she returned with them repaired. It was nice to feel that someone was looking out for me. Her face could be very expressive and she clearly looked concerned when I told her that I was sleeping on the floor. Later that evening the doorbell rang. To my surprise, Sara had turned up clutching bags of camping gear designed to ensure a more comfortable night. I did appreciate the help, but when I tried using the inflated air bed, I woke up with a sore back. I had obviously grown used to the hard surface – one that I returned to the following night.

Given her interesting background, Sara must have also felt that, culturally, I was living in a wilderness. I received texts on some days highlighting a film or drama that might be of interest on the television. She also brought round some DVDs for me to watch. *Amelie*, a quirky French film, was her favourite. I did watch it but appreciated it more at a much later date, when I no longer had the responsibility of looking after Mum. Another film, called *Cinema Paradiso*, reminded me of Mum's links to her home town, *San Damiano* – visually, in terms of the architecture and the time period in which it was set – audibly, given the Italian dialogue. I'm sure Mum would also have viewed it with interest a few years earlier, but even if watching a film was now well beyond her, at least it was filling the room with some familiar sounds associated with her past.

That autumn was a good time for costume dramas on the television. On Mondays we would catch up on the latest developments in *Cranford*, a period drama, which had been broadcast the evening before. We both thought how much fun it would be to work as an 'extra' on such programmes – and it was only a matter of time before that dream would be realised for both of us, albeit at different points in our lives. Little did I know then, but two years later I would find myself getting up very early in the morning for a cycle ride to Shepperton Film Studios. The day typically started with a substantial breakfast. Then, after changing into costume to join the other 'support artists' attired as peasants, filming for *Robin Hood* commenced on an impressive set complete with mediaeval village, castle and moat.

But for the time being, my life was dominated completely with feeding Mum and cleaning her nearly every two or three hours. As well as providing ideas for the future, Sara was a real lifeline in terms of keeping some sort of normality going, and her weekly visits became something to look forward to. She helped break the monotony of being mainly confined to the same room where my mother lay twenty-four hours a day. On some of the days I was there for all twenty-four; most days it would probably be for at least eighteen. But undoubtedly, a cheerful atmosphere followed Sara when she arrived on those Monday mornings – it felt like a fresh breeze was sweeping through the house. She added colour to the north facing room, which was especially important as another autumn slowly approached winter and the daylight hours shortened. Although we were from very different backgrounds, we still seemed to have quite a few things in common and a friendship was developing. Whether or not it would be like the wind, just transitory, or more permanent – only time would tell. But at the very least, the brush strokes applied so attentively by her uncle during that memorable fall of 2007 guaranteed to leave an enduring impression.

Chapter 23 Home Care

Just as in the hospital, caring for Mum over the weekends was conducted in a much quieter and more relaxed atmosphere. My only commitment to school over the two days involved preparation for lessons and marking, which could be carried out at home at any free moment, plus one more duty that was specific to Saturday mornings. Years ago, when Mum was totally independent, I used to help prepare teas, coffee and snacks for the teams after the rugby matches, with oranges cut up for half-time. It wasn't a bad way to spend a Saturday morning and only meant giving up about three hours. The other teachers greatly appreciated the help as it meant they could focus on preparing their teams for the forthcoming matches. It was also a way for me to make some contribution to the supportive PE department headed by Dave.

By the time Mum was at home and confined to an electric bed, the need to avoid leaving her alone for too long meant that during the autumn of 2007 I had to limit my help to delivering several bags of sliced oranges. It ensured that on arriving at the rugby pitches, there was no longer any time for a chat – as soon as the basket at the front of the bike was empty of its contents – it was straight back to Chiswick.

Each day with Mum home was slightly different, but not that much. After a few days of looking after her, I found a routine that seemed to work well. Looking back at one typical Sunday provides an idea of how things ran. There was a good chance that I was still awake at midnight of the preceding day, more than likely refreshed from an earlier short nap during *Match of the Day*. Despite my interest in football, I nearly always fell asleep after watching the first of several games being televised, only to be woken up by the signature tune at the end of the broadcast – a reflection of my tiredness rather than any failings with the commentary team. It was soon midnight, the start of another Sunday. If Mum was awake, it provided an opportunity to encourage her to take a drink or two. These would be the first of the drink entries in a diary that I kept daily, just like in the hospital. The aim was to get her to consume at least twelve glasses of liquid each day – and the more the better. It was also around that time that I usually remembered to brush her teeth. Before trying to get some sleep myself, I might wash any dirty laundry or try and tidy up the rooms. Invariably the last duties before retiring to my sleeping bag on the floor were to empty the catheter bag and check Mum's pads, making any change if necessary. At the very least, I turned her into a new position to reduce the risk of any pressure sores developing. It would usually be about 1 a.m. when I could finally set the alarm to get up for about 4 a.m. The exact times varied, depending on when I was able to 'hit the sack', but I usually hoped for about three hours of uninterrupted sleep.

As soon as the alarm went off I was up. To lie there for a few more minutes – despite the immense temptation – would have resulted in me falling straight back to sleep again. This was the time when the need for a fresh pad was almost guaranteed. After a few weeks of repeatedly carrying out these changes, which occurred anything up to a dozen times a day, I was getting quite adept at the task, even when feeling a bit drowsy at that time of the morning. I had also become completely at ease with cleaning around Mum's genitals. Because Mum was on a diet of soft food, it was probably no surprise that the shit that eventually came out was of a soup like consistency. In this condition, it was guaranteed to be pushed up the pad and completely engulf the vaginal opening. Often you could see the catheter tube poking out of a brown pool trapped within the pads. Applying an old and very distinctive spoon, one that would never ever again be used for its original, intended purpose, I scooped the mess out into either a bag or plastic container. With warm water and plenty of wipes, I then cleaned out the area but the vagina, with its various folds of skin, was not the easiest place to wash quickly. This was followed by cleaning the tube as far as Mum would allow me, but I suspect she wasn't too happy with such interference as I could only get my finger up to a certain point before feeling her muscles tightening. Performing such tasks on Mum, which could last up to ten minutes, would have been unimaginable a few months earlier, but by this stage I had become so desensitised to the whole operation, I could have just as easily been cleaning crap off the soles of my trainers. Once Mum was clean and dry, with a new pad and sleeping position, the plastic bag containing all the dirty contents could be thrown outside into the awaiting bin liner.

At last it was time to inspect the catheter bag to see if that needed to be emptied before getting ready to catch a little more rest. With that done, I gratefully clambered back into the sleeping bag and set the alarm for the next check, normally about 6 a.m. Despite it being a hard surface, I felt incredibly comfortable before drifting off to sleep again. It was naturally colder at floor level, but there was always a warm glow flowing through the whole of my body. It was a feeling of immense satisfaction that she had been spared the unpleasant and undignified experience of having to lie in her own mess overnight. And very few other experiences have left me with such an indelible and intense feeling of contentment.

The next cleaning session of Mum usually occurred between 6 a.m. to 7 a.m. On workdays it was no longer worth trying to get more sleep afterwards, but on other days, such as a Sunday, there was the opportunity for another hour's rest. By 8 a.m. I would get breakfast ready. This would consist mainly of orange juice, containing her medicines that also included the iron supplement, followed by porridge or another soft breakfast cereal. Feeding her would take at least half an hour. Soon there was a visit from one of the carers to help give Mum a thorough wash. My job was to make sure everything was ready and to help move Mum into different positions so that even her back could be washed.

Marlene, one of several young women who had been assigned to visit Mum, was the most regular carer for this important early morning slot and was very good at her job. Usually the whole operation was completed in less than thirty minutes. Mum was left clean, smelling fresh and changed into one of the comfortable and colourful nightdresses that I had adapted in order to make it easier to change while she remained bed-bound. She also reminded me to get into the habit of putting some socks on Mum's feet to keep her warmer, particularly at night. And it was Marlene who introduced me to using the sliding sheet to help move Mum around the bed almost effortlessly. In some ways it was too efficient. The first time we used the sheet I pulled it too firmly and propelled Mum forward too far, causing her to bump her head against the back of the bed. "Oops!"

Much of the remaining part of the morning was then spent trying to get Mum to drink as much as possible before she fell asleep, which invariably happened during part of the day. In the background the TV would be left running, and sometimes I would put on one of the DVDs lent by Sara. Perhaps under the circumstances it was not too surprising that it was *Mr Bean's Holiday* that I enjoyed most, and occasionally I found Mum leaning forward in frustration while reaching for another spoonful of drink or food as my attention was being distracted by the antics being performed on the screen by Rowan Atkinson.

As midday approached it was time to check if her pads needed changing again. With that task out of the way, I could then turn my attention towards preparing lunch. The range of dishes that were suitable, combined with the time constraint, meant that the cuisine was very limited. Out went any healthy salads as these would have been too chewy. Everything had to be mashed, to ease with swallowing. A blender had been a very useful purchase earlier that autumn, allowing some Italian pasta dishes to be served up. Mince, meat balls and hot dogs were all soft enough to mash and a frequently used meal consisted of a combination of cod, often in parsley sauce, with mashed potatoes and spinach all mixed up. It didn't look great, but it tasted fine and was probably quite sound nutritionally.

Puddings were less of a problem as it was easier to find a greater variety in a soft form. It was possible to select two or three to make a combination from bananas, prunes, jelly, trifle, custard, ice cream, rice pudding, yoghurts and sponge cakes – but not all together! As for drinks, Mum was encouraged to drink water, squash and particularly ones with some nutritional benefit such as Fresubin and different flavoured milk shakes. Cranberry juice was also recommended as potentially reducing the risks of another urinary tract infection, and whether or not such claims are valid, she did at least appear to enjoy the drink. She was also given a warm cup of tea but this again had to be mixed with the thickener. Although the white powder didn't really change the taste of the drink, it did alter its appearance. For the majority of beverages it looked fine. However, one day after mixing it into a glass of hot chocolate, I looked disdainfully at the end result and, without thinking that Mum was listening, murmured to myself, "This looks like absolute shit!" Suddenly I could hear Mum laughing; even more satisfying was the happy expression on her face. I soon joined in. What a lovely moment to remember. It was Sunday the 21st of October and the light was already fading by that time of the afternoon, but to see Mum laughing again – and so freely – was a joy to watch, worthy of noting down in my diary later that evening.

With lunch over and the washing-up complete, the next thought turned to the impending afternoon visit from another carer. It meant that I had to leave two saucepans of water slowly simmering on the cooker ready for the expected wash and pad change around 3 p.m. Not being able to get the handle fixed on the water heater in the kitchen was proving to be a real nuisance, but there never seemed to be the spare time in the day to sort it out. The late afternoon sometimes provided me with a bit of a break since Mum was often sleeping. But teaching often involves work outside of the classroom, and such spare time often had to be used on tasks relating to the school. Soon it was time to check Mum's bottom again, and after completing a possible pad change on my own, it was then back to preparing another meal and her prescribed medicines.

The third and final visit from a carer scheduled for about 8 p.m., was usually a repeat of the same procedure. However, on some evenings I phoned the agency to cancel the appointment when Mum was experiencing a severe bout of diarrhoea. In that case a pad change was a complete waste of time. It could just keep pouring out for anything up to an hour or even more. The best strategy, in those circumstances, was to place old bed mats under her bottom and even a few on top of her to protect the sheets, leaving her without a pad. The mats, in which she seemed to be cocooned, were then periodically replaced as they became dirty. I would just sit there by her side watching the TV, sometimes even eating a snack, and check about every ten minutes as to what was going on under the bed linen. Eventually the flow had run its full course, and it was time to wash Mum and reintroduce a fresh pad. By then it could be 10 p.m. This was followed by a gap of an hour or two, only interrupted by attempts to get Mum to take another drink, for this was a time when it was often possible to relax a bit and take stock of the day's events. It was soon midnight again. Another twenty-four hours had passed in caring for Mum. She had been fed, turned and cleaned, given her medications and finally had her teeth brushed.

Most days, as the weeks went by, were like the one described above. There was never a break – even for a single day – as days turned to weeks and then weeks turned to months. But at least for me, there was some variety because I could get out of the house a few times during the week. Admittedly they were only trips to work or the shops but they provided some contact, albeit limited, with the outside world. The rest of the time I too was imprisoned in the room with Mum. But there were visits from my sister, the various carers, nurses, representatives from Social Services and the neighbours – and even if on some days it seemed as if the house had been turned into a public thoroughfare – the interruptions did help to break up the monotony of the day.

There was the odd problem or crisis situation during her stay at home but each one was overcome. The first few weeks of looking after her were eased by the regular attendance by qualified nurses each day. This took some of the pressure off me as I knew if I spotted any change in Mum's condition there was an opportunity to get some early medical advice. When these responsibilities were handed over completely to Social Services I missed the reassurance given by the regular nursing visits, but there was still help at hand in terms of the weekly calls by one of the District Nurses, as well as my sister. The major problem that occurred, at least twice, concerned the catheter. One night I noticed that Mum's pads were wet from urine, which shouldn't have been the case. It turned out that the catheter tube had got blocked and had to be changed. On each occasion the District Nurse was quite prompt and was able to sort out the problem the following day. Counsel from the GP, late night advice from my sister on the phone, inspections from Social Care and the ample, if not always suitable supply of pads and catheter bags, all helped to make life a bit easier in terms of me trying to deliver the medical care that Mum required. But it was quite a responsibility, and it was a good job I had taken time to gain as much guidance as possible from the hospital before she had been discharged in early October.

So how was the stay at home for Mum? For such a formerly active and energetic woman, it must have been terribly boring. And I didn't have to guess that this was her opinion. She expressed such a viewpoint at least twice and quite fluently. One was "*Ché barba* (How boring)!" The other was "*Non c'é niente da fare* (There's nothing to do)!" These were rational exclamations of despair. It was quite a challenging task to entertain someone with dementia who was stuck in bed all day, especially as conversation was extremely limited. But I did have a go, in between the times when I wasn't performing the basic tasks of feeding and cleaning her. People with dementia often appreciate music right to the end. Audible in the background from the out-of-date but still functioning Hi-Fi system, I often made use of any records or cassettes that she liked. It was also relaxing for me to play the guitar and sing some songs to her. One included *Your Song* by Elton John. Fortunately Mum's side of the family have all been blessed with good voices so hopefully my singing was sufficiently melodious not to annoy her. Conversation had almost dried up, but she was still lucid in her use of words while singing. The verses appeared to be nursery rhymes learnt from her distant past, still retained despite the ravages of dementia that had weakened her brain. Sometimes she would call me from the kitchen appropriately using the command term: "*Venga* (Come)!" On other occasions she would even come out with a string of words in English, "Some people say they see...." The sentence remained incomplete and any intended meaning probably was soon forgotten. But for me it was as equally frustrating as it was fascinating to witness that thoughts were still whirling around in her head, even though I couldn't always understand their significance.

The TV was probably more of a source of entertainment for me rather than Mum, but whenever a programme was scheduled which might be of interest to her, I would switch to that particular channel. The choice was limited. It had to be colourful and musical. Anything else wouldn't attract or retain her attention. I also tried showing her old photos from her past but when she displayed no interest towards the end of 2007, I didn't bother any more. Nevertheless, it had been a very useful pastime in the earlier stages of dementia. And that was about all I could do. The key thing was that she was back in the house that she, along with Dad, had worked hard to buy. That was where she had decorated, cleaned, made dresses to earn some extra money and raised a family. I'm sure that was what she would have wished. Despite any shortcomings it was, in my view, easily the best place for her to spend the remaining days of her life.

Chapter 24 Healing Wounds

During the three and a half months that I cared for Mum at home in the autumn of 2007, I was lucky that there weren't too many extra medical problems beyond those usually associated with someone in the last stages of dementia. Nevertheless, it wasn't entirely trouble free either. There were the occasional concerns over the catheter but with some help from the District Nurses, solutions were found. Mum also had a nasty rash following a flu jab in November. This spread to both arms and also from her stomach up to her neck. It must have been very itchy for her and I had to regularly apply cream to try and reduce the discomfort. Her arms were still sufficiently mobile and the redness of her skin was probably exacerbated by her continued ability to scratch. To reduce the damage that she could have inflicted upon herself, I cut her finger nails as short as possible. Mum resisted, which meant I had to hold her arthritic hands more firmly, thereby making the whole operation unnecessarily painful. The rash first appeared a few days after the jab. I don't know if that was a coincidence, but at least it only lasted seven days. By the 18th of November it had completely disappeared and her skin was back to normal. I wasn't just pleased for her. It finally ended a week when I had been required to pay particular attention to discourage Mum from scratching herself.

However, the problems with Mum's skin were not entirely over. Generally, more care needs to be taken with the elderly as the skin gets increasingly delicate. One day I was told that, after washing Mum, it was best to dry her by gently dabbing the skin with a towel rather than rubbing it over the body. But overall, skin care was going very well. There was absolutely no redness around Mum's bottom or any sign of a pressure sore developing anywhere. The combination of catheter, regular cleaning and change of lying positions were all having a positive effect. And the skin doesn't tell lies. The nurses and carers that came round could see that I was looking after this aspect of her care conscientiously. I was therefore all the more distraught to wake up on Monday the 3rd of December and discover a small opening in her skin. Normally a cut wouldn't be too much of an issue, even for somebody in her eighties. The problem was the location. It was about 4 mm away from the opening of the anus in the crease where the two sides of the buttocks meet. This was a worrying development. How was I going to keep the wound clean and how would it heal? Would the wound go septic? These were some of my troubled thoughts as I cycled to school. After cleaning Mum's bottom before leaving, I had tried to stick a plaster, but it wouldn't hold properly, certainly not tight enough to provide a seal against any excrement that was likely to pour out all over it while I was away at work for a few hours. As an extra precaution, I applied a generous layer of antiseptic healing cream, hoping it would provide an additional barrier.

Whoever I asked seemed to be unable to offer any advice on how to treat the wound. To make matters worse, for a few minutes I suspected that the cut might have been my fault. I had recently bought some antibacterial wipes to use for cleaning Mum's bottom. That sounded great but when, after a few days of use, I checked the wrapping more carefully, I was alarmed to discover that they were designed with kitchen surfaces in mind, not bare skin. Maybe they were too strong, given her frailty, and caused a reaction? I felt that horrible feeling that you can sometimes get in the pit of your stomach when you know you have made a terrible mistake. To my relief I felt less guilty a few minutes later when I tried one of the suspect wipes on myself. True – there was a slight tingling sensation, but it didn't sting and besides, whenever the wipes had been used they had been dipped in warm water so any effects would have been diluted. No, I concluded that the tear in her skin was just a natural consequence of her weakening condition. But while that made me feel a bit better, it didn't resolve the problem.

A planned visit from the District Nurse on Tuesday looked like an opportunity to get some practical help. However, she too was just as puzzled as I was when considering how to apply any plaster or dressing to such an awkward spot. Nothing would stick since it wasn't a flat surface. In the end she concluded that the best thing for me to do was to try my best to keep the wound clean and apply antiseptic cream. But before leaving she wrote down the name of a product she felt might be helpful. Although its official name is long, she just scribbled one word, Cavilon[9], on a piece of paper. Later that day, while Jim was sitting in the room with Mum, I popped into the pharmacist on the way back from school and

---

[9] 3M™ Cavilon™ Durable Barrier Cream (3M Health Care).

bought a tube of what turned out to be a white, sticky and runny cream, with an amazingly sweet smell. The next time I had to clean Mum's bottom, I followed a procedure that I ended up repeating many times over the next few days. Having wiped her clean, I squeezed out a few drops of sterile saline on the wound from the pods that had been left by the nurses in 2006 when treating Mum's wound on the ankle. I then applied the Cavilon cream and waited a few minutes for it to dry. For good measure, I once again applied some antiseptic healing cream to act as a further barrier.

I don't know her name, but I owe the nurse a big debt of gratitude since the Cavilon product proved to be very effective. Of course I had to be very vigilant for about one week, making even more regular checks than usual. This was particularly tiring at night because, when possible, I was trying to check her bottom about every two hours. But it was a good investment of time. Each day I could see some improvement. Both the length and width of the wound seemed to be shortening fractionally. Little by little, it was closing. After about ten days of such treatment the wound had completely healed. I can scarcely express how happy and relieved I was to see such an improvement. And I also felt even more confident about looking after Mum. As for Mum – she seemed quite content and totally unaware of the problem throughout the whole worrying episode. In fact one night I was awakened at 4 a.m. not by the alarm, but by her happily singing what sounded like a nursery rhyme in Italian still remembered from her childhood.

There was another wound that was healed over the last stages of dementia but it wasn't of a physical nature – it was the relationship between my mum and sister. Both had got on very well during my sister's childhood and this continued through her teenage years, right up to adulthood. They often went shopping, or on trips together, in addition to the holidays that we all spent as a family in Felixstowe. Mum took a keen interest in my sister's education, also encouraging her to develop her talent in playing a musical instrument, notably the clarinet, as well as participating in other hobbies.

Sometime in the 1980s, Mum obtained a part-time catering job with British Rail. After years of dress-making, she turned her hand to preparing sandwiches. Indeed, if you travelled on any train in the South East during that decade, there is a reasonable chance that you may have sampled some of her work. Both types of job provided the satisfaction of seeing an end product, but increasing competition from cheap labour in the Far East meant that the more skilful trade that she had learnt from her father was no longer in such demand. Moreover, the need to work at home alongside raising a family – a major advantage of sewing – ceased to be relevant as my younger sister approached her late teens. Seeking some financial independence in a less isolated environment probably made the idea of going out to work an attractive option for Mum. If she was looking for some company, then she was lucky in her choice of job – for there was little risk of her feeling lonely at the lively catering operation at Waterloo Station.

Despite the very early starts and the odd disagreement with colleagues, I got the impression that she enjoyed working there, often sharing some humorous stories about the place when she returned home from work. Whenever a rhythmic piece of music came over the radio during the breaks, Mum was encouraged to join in with the dancing. Then there was the time when the main Chef, an Indian, was off sick for a few weeks. Mum volunteered to take over preparing staff meals. Much to her embarrassment, the rest of her workmates, perhaps relieved to have a break from the routine of an excessively spicy cuisine, organised a campaign to keep her in the post permanently! Despite appreciating the gratitude shown, Mum refused and returned to her normal, if less challenging, sandwich duties – not wishing to be the centre of any potential industrial dispute!

An additional benefit of working with British Rail was that she received a pass which allowed a certain number of free journeys per annum and, better still, the privilege was extended into retirement. Even my dad got a pass. So for a few years, Mum often travelled around the country with my sister visiting Land's End and Sandringham to name but two locations. Later when my sister bought a car, she returned the favour by taking Mum on day trips to places reasonably close by like Stonehenge, Guildford and Windsor. To me, this seemed a time when both were very close. Mum was also proud of my sister's achievements. One evening I accompanied Mum to a concert where my sister, still at school and a member of the Borough Youth Orchestra, displayed a very high degree of proficiency in playing both the clarinet and trumpet. A few years later, and despite tensions between my parents, we all still managed to attend my sister's nursing degree award ceremony together. It was held at St George's Hospital in Tooting. We arrived with very little time to spare – and might not have made it at all but for the swift and successful intervention by a mechanic attending to a broken clutch cable in Elizabeth's green car.

Despite an age gap of nearly ten years between me and my younger sister, we still shared some common experiences during childhood. Just as she had done with me, Mum took my sister to Richmond on a regular basis for swimming and ice skating lessons. Elizabeth was a very good swimmer, but she nearly always looked up to the viewing gallery, where Mum was seated, just before the end of a race. It must have cost her the winning position on a few occasions but it was a hard habit to shake off despite constant reminders from Mum as we walked back to the bus stop opposite Richmond Station on our way home.

Actually that combination of activities, in the water and on the ice, still brings back a painful memory, but also shows how well Mum coped in a stressful or embarrassing situation. I must have been about eight or nine, certainly no older because my sister had yet to be born. For a special treat Mum decided to take me to both activities in the same morning. After swimming, I had the misfortune of dropping my underpants in the gulley that ran through the changing rooms to drain the water away. Completely soaked, I just stuffed the underwear in my bag along with any other belongings. This was followed by an enjoyable session at the ice skating rink. But before leaving, I wanted to go to the toilet. Having relieved myself and in a rush to go, I quickly pulled up the zip of my trousers forgetting I had no pants on. That was almost instantaneously followed by a loud shriek. The pain was excruciating. Attempts to free myself were unsuccessful and only added to the agony. It wasn't long before I was running into the foyer in a complete panic to seek help from Mum. She calmly asked one of the employees to phone for a minicab. The third and unexpected part of the day out, ended in Richmond Hospital. Finally, and much to my relief, I was freed from the temporary, but what at that young age seemed endless, entrapment.

The early 1990s was a period of change. At the start of the decade, my sister moved out of the Chiswick house to her newly purchased home in Kingston. Two years later Mum was also on the move, but in the opposite direction as she settled into the Hammersmith property. That left Dad alone in Chiswick and from then on I began to live a nomadic lifestyle. On different days of any week, I could be sleeping in any one of three houses. The moves didn't cause any problem between Mum and my sister, but it meant that they weren't seeing each other on such a frequent basis. Of course this didn't matter too much for the remainder of the 1990s. However, it did seem to have implications for their relationship when the dementia started to have a more marked impact on Mum's ability to identify an individual's face accurately. By 2004 my mum was finding it difficult to recognise my sister and for about two years was quite unfriendly towards her. It was a difficult position for me to be in. I had already had experience of being the intermediary between Mum and Dad for about two decades – now it looked as if I might have to play a similar role once again.

Visits to my sister in Kingston never ceased but they got less frequent and the duration became shorter each time. My sister popped over to Chiswick but at best was met with indifference, while on some occasions she had to suffer undeserved hostility. The period between 2004 and 2006 was probably the worst. Even visits from Elizabeth on Christmas Day had become tense affairs. Why Mum was behaving in this way is hard to explain. Maybe she was confusing her with somebody else from her distant past – someone whom she disliked? It's quite possible that she didn't recognise her at all and just perceived her as a threat – a younger woman who was going to take away her son. That explanation might be quite realistic because I did notice that whenever I stopped to talk to women on our walks, Mum would soon get impatient and want to move on.

But at least after 2005 the relatively short rift, since it only lasted about two years, seemed to heal. Mum accepted my sister when she came round and so it was easier to leave her looking after Mum when I had a Parents' Evening, or some other commitment that required attendance at school. And by 2007, my sister was coming round every week on Thursday to sit with her as well as extra visits on other days. Thankfully, the tense atmosphere that had confronted Elizabeth over the previous two years had completely vanished. It was good to see Mum accepting my sister back into the fold, so to speak, and it certainly helped me as I needed all the assistance I could get in the latter stages of Mum's illness.

Chapter 25 Bright Lights and Fireworks

Anybody living nearby, but unaware of Mum's worsening condition, might have observed and possibly been left curious by the changing scene outside the house in Chiswick as autumn gradually gave way to another winter. The leaves from the nearby trees had once again been discarded. But unlike previous years, certainly since Mum's return in 2002, they were left unswept, concealing the pavement with a thick layer only to be occasionally disturbed by children wading through the recently shed foliage. And then, of course, there was the unprecedented stream of pretty women visiting several times a day, each day, which may have raised a few eyebrows. In the meantime, I hadn't really had much time to give the impending festivities much thought. But as Christmas 2007 approached, Sara had a surprise for both me and my mum. She brought some presents, and a card signed by her and her children, but it was something for Mum that was most touching. It was Monday the 17th of December, just a few days before the start of the holidays. Sara arrived that morning with two big carrier bags but as she didn't say anything about them, I just assumed it was something to do with her family. I set off for school as usual and, unknown to me, Sara must have got to work as soon as I left.

About three hours later I returned. As soon as I walked in, I could see that Mum's surroundings had been completely transformed. There were Christmas decorations hanging in different parts of the room. You could see that Sara, as well as her uncle, had inherited the artistic talent from her mother's side of the family because the display by the mantelpiece was arranged so stylishly. Starting from the middle, and working out to the edge on either side, each decoration was hanging in a descending order of length to form the shape of an arch. It was set out with such symmetry that obvious care had been taken while cutting out each separate length of string. But the real icing on the cake involved the Christmas lights. The opening in the wall created by my dad all those years ago, and which linked the two adjacent rooms, suddenly provided the setting for a colourful lighting display. Sara had taped the lights onto the two sides of the wall as well as the upright where the lintel spanned the opening. I eagerly switched on the power with a sense of anticipation. Mum only had a limited control over moving her head, but nevertheless she was able to glance to her right in the direction of the lights. They weren't flashing but the room containing the electric bed had suddenly become illuminated in a variety of bright colours. Exaggerated by the dim and fading winter daylight, they almost gave the place the appearance of a night club!

"Ohhh. What's that?" exclaimed Mum. Those were her exact words and in English too which, at this stage, was very unusual. It was an important moment because once again it showed that there were still some thought processes going on in her head. In fact she made a similar comment, "What on earth is that?" on Boxing Day as soon as I turned the lights on. I thanked Sara as she left. As she shut the gate, Sara turned to smile as usual before she disappeared out of view – but this time it appeared to be a resigned, sad smile.

I may have been wrong – but I still felt guilty. An uneasy thought struck me. I had probably been taking all this extra help over the last few months for granted. She had even contributed to the design for the yellow 2008 Charity Walk T-shirt by finding, on the internet, a logo of the Olympic rings that I needed. But it was difficult to show any affection towards her – all the more puzzling as I clearly liked her. I suspect it was just that by December I was left emotionally drained by the level of care given to Mum. Although Sara was often on my mind – she wasn't to know that – particularly as some of the time I must have appeared reserved and cold. My need to politely decline her invitation to join her and the rest of her family for a meal over Christmas probably added to that impression. Of course she understood, but that didn't disguise her evident disappointment. Under other circumstances it would probably have been a very pleasant evening as I had already met most of her closest relatives. I had even seen the other likely guests in a photo album that Sara had brought round one Monday, perhaps prompted by me showing her some early photos of Mum a week previously. But I didn't feel in the mood for socialising – and neither did I have the time. By December I was struggling. I was getting very little sleep and nearly three months had gone by without a break. The autumn term, which is always the toughest in the school calendar, often one of attrition, was also taking its toll. Maybe that was why I was quite comfortable with the relationship remaining platonic – at least for the time being.

The last few days of 2007 were fast approaching. It had been a remarkable year of change, but mainly for the worse. While Mum had become increasingly difficult to look after over the years, at least until the summer of that year she had still been able to walk. When New Year's Eve arrived at the end of 2006, there was no way that I could have anticipated how the forthcoming twelve months were going to turn out, particularly regarding the speed of her deterioration. And yet my sister had foreseen what would happen. On so many previous occasions she had been right in her pessimistic predictions. After all, she had witnessed this before, many times over, with countless other patients.

So what would 2008 hold? Despite the warnings of my sister, I still felt confident that while I couldn't prevent the decline caused by dementia, Mum would still have some quality of life that would make surviving worthwhile. She was getting stronger physically and I was hoping that by the summer I would be able to take her out by the river in the wheel chair that I had bought a few months earlier. This was not such an unrealistic expectation. A later blood test would reveal that her haemoglobin level, after months of taking the iron supplement, had climbed back to more normal levels. She had also regained some control over her balance. In the hospital the physiotherapists, after only two sessions, had appeared to give up on her. At that time and unable to sit up on her own without support, she wasn't allowed to be left in a chair out of her bed.

On Christmas day I felt it was time for an experiment. It had been a very peaceful morning. There had been a visit from one of the carers early on to help with washing Mum but that was the only call scheduled. For the remainder of the day we had the house to ourselves. Maybe for that reason I felt more confident about taking a chance to try something new.

I had become very used to finding ways of manoeuvring Mum's body around in a lying position on the mattress, but on this particular day I helped her to sit upright by the edge of the bed. My hands held firmly onto both her shoulders. It must have seemed like a new sensation for her as it had been nearly five months since she had last been in that position. Her eyes moved around as if she wanted to take in the new view of the room that she had not left for close to one hundred days – and yet might evoke so many memories if she still had the powers to access them. I think she did – up to a point. What to me appeared a heightened level of awareness, actually made her face look different – more like her old self – compared to the sometimes lifeless expression displayed after hours of lying on her back or side. Carefully, I removed my hands so she was completely unsupported. I kept them very close by – but I needn't have worried – she stayed upright and showed no signs of keeling over. I then put my arms under her arm pits and raised her to her feet. No words were uttered but it did provoke a surprised gasp from her. "Don't worry Mum, I'm holding you," I quickly pronounced, hoping it would reassure her. For a few minutes she was standing up. I held on tightly. There was no way that I could have let go as she wouldn't have been able to support herself on her own. That was made evident by the pressure of her weight on my arms. And even though it might have been Christmas, one couldn't expect too many miracles in one day! Nevertheless, with some prompting, guidance and continued assistance, I did manage to get her to take a few cautious steps.

Tiredness on my part – along with the knowledge that such movement was totally dependent on my continued support – prompted me to gently put her back on the bed. But I was very encouraged and felt satisfied that when the weather improved, maybe from the spring onwards, I would be able to get her in a wheel chair on my own and take her out of the house, which on some days felt like a prison. Later, well after midnight, I laid on the floor next to my mum's bed to catch a few hours sleep before getting up at 3 a.m. for the usual check, wash and change of pads, tasks that had routinely been performed since October. I was tired, but remained optimistic as I imagined the prospect of future trips along the river with Mum.

A few days later and it was New Year's Eve. That evening, I popped round to see Andrew who lived on the same street for a quick beer and chat. In addition to his wife, Louise, being present, two neighbours, Mr and Mrs North, whom I had known since I was a child, also attended.

Despite the good company, I didn't stay too long as Mum had recently taken a slight turn for the worse and was shouting a lot. It meant that I didn't feel at all relaxed and although I politely engaged in conversation, my mind was really focused on my mum. It left me wondering, was she in pain or was the shouting just part of the dementia process? I apologised to my hosts for leaving early, and soon returned home only a few houses away. When I opened the front door I could immediately hear that Mum had not stopped shouting, but still there were no visible symptoms to indicate that there was anything wrong with her.

A few minutes after midnight, I received a text from Sara wishing me a Happy New Year. She also asked me if I had seen and heard all the fireworks going off. The last time I had seen a firework display in the garden was when I was about eight years old. A misfired rocket landed in the open box containing all the other fireworks that had been set aside for the rest of the evening. My dad's reaction to hurry us all back into the house had probably been the correct call. A few seconds later, and from the safety of the conservatory, we were treated to a spectacular, but very short, display as fireworks were exploding and flying off in every direction – some vertically but most, particularly the rockets, horizontally across the lawn. It had been an unforgettable show, but guaranteed that future Guy Fawkes nights would be bereft of fireworks from that evening onwards. It also prompted Mum to tell us of a family tragedy in *San Damiano* during her childhood when a display in the square by the town hall was marred by another accident, but on this occasion with more serious consequences. A Catherine wheel had spun out of control and landed in my grandparent's home opposite the municipal building, leaving one of Mum's relatives with a nasty burn to the face.

After dwelling on these two incidents for a few moments, I soon sent a reply to Sara. It informed her that I had missed the fireworks so far but that in terms of noise level Mum was more than making up for it. From the kitchen, glancing upwards and slightly to my right, I could see Sara's house. In the winter there weren't any leaves on the trees to obscure the view. She was there, with her two children, looking out from the attic window and still enjoying the display that continued for about another ten minutes. As well as contemplating what the New Year would hold for me, I also wondered what would happen to her. I liked Sara and her family.

Yet despite her really good looks and interesting personality, my feelings towards her weren't strong enough at that time for me to abandon my safe position of sitting on the fence. But I knew that wasn't fair on her. She had expressed, on more than one occasion previously, a certain degree of dissatisfaction at not having a man in her life. Reflecting on that – and with Mum's shouting in the background reminding me exactly where my commitments rested – I then hoped that in 2008 she would meet someone nice. In my mind, but probably not my heart, I had temporarily thrown in the towel. I didn't know it at the time, but it was a wish that a few months later I would deeply regret.

Chapter 26   Some Sleepless Nights

I didn't spend too long by the kitchen window. Looking after Mum meant I didn't have much time to stop and reflect on any potential relationship, or much else for that matter. And yet at the time, I had absolutely no idea that ahead of me, the toughest week of my life awaited. Fireworks were still going off outside but, with Mum continuing to shout, there seemed to be just as much noise emanating from within the house. What amazed me was the power of her voice that night and over the previous week or two in December. During the preceding few months she had been very quiet compared to her normal vivacious personality. Some days during her summer stay in the hospital she hadn't spoken at all. When she had it wasn't much louder than a whisper. What a contrast to New Year's Eve when it was so loud and unrelenting!

From the expression on her face, she didn't appear to be in any pain. It was as if she had rediscovered the power of her vocal chords and during any waking hours, regardless of the time, was determined to flex such muscles whether through singing, which she performed very melodically on some nights, or shouting. On this occasion it was the latter, which was less pleasing on the ear. "*Etto berretto – etto berretto ....*" she kept repeating many times over for the following few hours. It rhymed but what on earth did it mean? I knew that *etto* is a weight in Italian. In fact when I checked in the dictionary, I found it to be an abbreviation for 100 grams but I couldn't find any other alternative meaning. What about *berretto*? This is a word for cap or hat. But what on earth was Mum doing shouting out the equivalent of "100 gram cap" throughout the night?

At the time it just didn't seem to make any sense. Once more I checked the dictionary. Again there was no luck even when I searched for variations on the spelling of the two words. It was more than a puzzle; it was worrying. If she had screamed out *aiuto* (help), or *male* (ill), or *dolore* (pain), then at least I would have known that she needed some medical assistance. As such it was, and still remains, a mystery. Months later I quizzed my relatives in Italy about it, since Mum could have been shouting something in her local dialect, but they just shrugged their shoulders and even the purchase of a *Piemontese* dictionary didn't provide any clues. In the end I may just have to accept the fact that I will probably never know for certain what she was trying to tell me. Of course the other possibility remains that she was just shouting out two completely random words – a pair that sounded well together but had no particular meaning implied. Or maybe she was just cold and sensibly wanted something on her head? But that night in question wasn't particularly cold and then – why specify the exact weight? One further and plausible explanation was later put forward by my friend Peter. His conjecture was that my mum may have felt some pressure or weight bearing down on her skull – maybe a throbbing headache. I wonder? After all, the term heavy head is associated with the symptom of experiencing a severe headache.

Mum remained awake and consequently noisy until about 3.30 a.m. I was finally able to grab about two hours sleep before she woke up again. But to my exasperation, the shouting resumed on that Tuesday morning. Mum hailed in the first day of 2008 by continuing to be noisy even while I was performing the usual duties of washing and then changing her pads on my own, and then later with the help of one of the carers. In fact the only thing that seemed to shut her up was when it was time to feed her or give her a drink, or when she thankfully fell asleep during part of the afternoon. That gave me some time to sort out the paperwork so that the students' coursework would be ready for posting the following day. My sister called round and was just as puzzled as myself over Mum's continual shouting. All this activity – one of the last few left which Mum still retained some control over – must have eventually sapped her energy and I was relieved when she slept well during the night. Despite peace and quiet finally descending on the house, I still had a night of interrupted sleep. The alarm had to be routinely set to get up in the middle of the night to clean her and change her pads. But at least I did get some rest, though it was only a temporary respite. The following night was a particularly bad one. I only managed to sleep between 4 a.m. and 5:30 a.m. It was at this point that I became worried as to how long the neighbours would be willing to put up with such a continuous volume of noise, particularly in a house from the late Victorian era that wasn't built with sound-proofing in mind.

With Mum still shouting during the Wednesday morning, I decided it was time to phone her GP. At last the practice was open again, since the Bank holidays were finally over. It meant there was a chance of a visit from one of the doctors. Sara called round that afternoon to check how things were going, just a few minutes before the female doctor arrived. While Mum was being examined I explained the change in Mum's behaviour since the 1st of January. I enquired if it was possible to give her some sort of sedative to calm her down as I was getting so little sleep. Unable to find any outward signs to explain such a rapid turnaround in Mum's condition, she suspected a urinary tract infection as a possible cause. With the catheter in place, taking a urine sample, this time, was a straightforward procedure. The doctor decided not to wait for the results of the test but simply wrote out a prescription for both antibiotics and a tranquillizer. Sara, who had remained present throughout the examination, kindly offered to sit with Mum while I cycled to the chemist to collect the medicines.

That evening I tried the sedative on Mum and it did seem to do the trick. It didn't knock her out straight away, but eventually she quietened down and slept well throughout the night, allowing me to enjoy the same luxury without the need to retreat upstairs to escape the noise. Instead, I was back in my sleeping bag on the floor next to the electric bed with the catheter bag in full view. I knew I would have to set the alarm for about 4 a.m. to empty the bag and possibly change Mum, but at least I felt content that I could look forward to about three hours sleep. Maybe the problem of Mum's shouting would be resolved. No such luck. It was a misplaced optimism.

The following night even the tranquillizer seemed powerless to keep her calm. The yelling had recommenced. Eventually I put my hand over Mum's mouth so that she could only breathe through her nose. Although this muffled the sound, it had no permanent effect. As soon as I released my hand the sound of her bellows – for it was a deep sound not a high-pitched scream – reverberated around the house again. I couldn't keep my hand over her mouth all night just to make life easier for my neighbours, I thought. The tone didn't vary. It was just a constant chant and her facial expression seemed to be one of stubborn defiance. She was determined to shout when she liked, regardless of any consideration for me or anyone else. This apparent thoughtlessness was completely out of character. However, her doggedness was totally in character, despite the attempt to sedate her. As a last resort, I even tried to pat her gently on the cheeks a few times, but again met with similar failure. It was time to give up. I knew that if I was to get any sleep that night, I would have to leave and retire upstairs. But even from there, I could still hear her repeating the same two words. Although it was less loud, the sound nevertheless echoed around the corridor as if intent upon following me up the staircase. Of course I was hoping that Mum wasn't experiencing any discomfort or pain, but I was also wishing that my neighbours were sleeping through it all, blissfully unaware of the noise coming from the room downstairs. Maybe they were still away on their holidays? And then I recalled being disturbed by their children crying at night when they were babies. That left me feeling a little less concerned and so I drifted off to sleep.

I had hoped to be greeted the following morning by silence. About three hours later, when I woke up before the alarm was due to ring, I was temporarily tricked into thinking that my wish had been granted. For a second there was a blissful void – nothing – but soon again I could hear her chant of "*etto – berretto*". Poor Mum, she must have been awake throughout my nap without any break from shouting or even the reassurance of an audience being present. Nevertheless, there was a reward for putting up with such a noisy Friday night. Once Mum had been washed and given some breakfast, she fell asleep and so the remainder of Saturday passed by peacefully as she woke only for meals and drinks. In fact the same applied on Sunday. However, my next main concern was that Mum seemed to be developing a chest infection, despite taking the antibiotics, as there was a gurgling sound to her breathing. But she didn't have a temperature so I felt there was no pressing need to contact the GP until Monday, especially as the option of calling NHS Direct remained if Mum's condition took a turn for the worse. With the benefit of hindsight that decision may have been a mistake.

My other worry was the possibility of a switch over in Mum's sleeping pattern. Veronica, one of the staff working in the office at school, had told me about this over a year ago. Her mother was also suffering from dementia, but the symptoms had started earlier so Veronica would sometimes pass on advice or share some of her experiences. One was that Mum could start sleeping during the day while staying awake in the night as the knowledge of what constitutes normal sleeping hours finally disappears. Maybe that was what was happening to Mum over the last few weeks, I wondered. Nevertheless, compared to the previous few days, the weekend had at least been relatively tranquil. But that was a deception. It was going to be the lull before the real storm of Monday night.

Monday started quite normally, giving absolutely no clue as to the challenges awaiting me over the next twenty-four hours. As usual on that particular day of the week, the carer came round early and helped wash Mum. Sara then arrived at 10 a.m., enabling me to set off for the bike ride to St Mark's school for the economics lesson. When I returned home Mum was taking some thickened drink from Sara, who was sitting next to her. Other than my sister, she was the only person whom I had entrusted with such a task. Mum remained sufficiently awake for most of the remaining part of the day. This helped to ensure that she ate her lunch and supper, and took sufficient liquid. She still had a slightly wheezy chest, but when I checked her temperature, it was quite normal.

Maybe the first outward sign that something was wrong on that Monday evening occurred at 8 p.m., when she opened her bowels. It was a huge amount, far more than normal, and it took some time before she was properly cleaned. Later that night while I was turning her to alter her position, I noticed that her nightdress needed changing since her back was wet from sweat. The sheet was only slightly damp so I employed the same technique that I had used over a year ago when Mum first started to wet herself. I found the hair dryer and with Mum changed and turned to the side, I managed to dry the sheet in about ten minutes. I was dreading the need to change the whole sheet unaided and so was pleased to have remembered such an easy solution. But at 11:30 p.m. my newly acquired and somewhat limited nursing skills were really going to be put to the test. There was no way of getting out of a sheet change this time. Without any warning, Mum suddenly started vomiting. There was no time to react by placing a towel or container by her mouth. Besides, the amount that Mum was bringing up would have made such intervention futile. There was vomit all over her nightdress and the sheet. Both would have to be changed.

The storage heaters in both rooms ensured that it wasn't cold even in the middle of winter. But Mum would have to remain undressed while I attended to the sheets. I put on the extra electric fan fire to the maximum setting and then took off Mum's dirty nightdress. The next task was to get rid of the soiled sheet. I turned Mum on to her side facing the chimney. I rolled up the sheet behind her and then tucked it in under her bottom just as I had been doing when carrying out the pad change. Next, I turned her back so she was facing the kitchen. I moved round to the other side of the bed and pulled out the dirty sheet. Except for the pad covering her bottom, Mum was lying completely naked on the air mattress without the comfort of a sheet underneath. It was time to act swiftly. With her back facing me, I unfolded the clean sheet and then rolled it up and tucked it under Mum's bottom again. The sheet on the side behind Mum's back was now tucked in at the side and neatly laid flat. I then rolled Mum back over to face the chimney and was able to pull the other half of the sheet from the other side. With the clean sheet correctly in place, I could then focus on putting a nightdress back on Mum. Wow! I was really pleased with myself. I had passed the bed sheet test and felt even more confident that I could look after Mum at home as long as her health held up. The final task, before she could be left undisturbed for a while, was to return the bed mat under her bottom, so that meant she had to suffer a few more turns.

Initially I felt it would be best to rinse the mess off the sheet and wash it properly the following day. That strategy changed as the night progressed when I gave up trying to get any sleep. As for the night dress, I didn't want too much laundry piling up, especially as it would be smelly, so I decided to wash it along with some other laundry there and then. As a precaution, I placed a towel near Mum's head in case she was sick again.

From my own personal experience, it is rare to get sick just once. So I was anticipating a repeat performance – but not straight after hanging up the washed laundry that had just been removed from the spin dryer. By then it was 1 a.m. and I had to go through the whole procedure again as the towel had been inadequate in saving either the nightdress or the sheet from her next bout of vomiting. Unfortunately she was sick another four times, with each one necessitating a further change of clothes and sheets. The next time was 6:30 a.m. That had followed the standard pad change around 4 a.m. By the time she was sick for the fourth time at 8:40 a.m., following a very light breakfast, it was already daylight outside so it wasn't worth trying to get any sleep. Besides, there were jobs that still had to be carried out like washing Mum. I had already phoned the school a few minutes earlier to warn them that I would probably be late for work. I then called the GP to request a visit, holding the phone close to my mum so that the receptionist could hear that Mum's breathing sounded awful. When I was told that the doctor would be able to attend, but not until later in the day, I phoned the school again and explained that I wouldn't be able to come in at all. My lesson had been planned the night before but with absolutely no sleep since then, I wouldn't have been in a particularly fit state to deliver it.

And so with the pressure of teaching at school on Tuesday the 8th of January removed, I felt relieved that I could concentrate on tending to Mum. She was sick again at 10:15 after I had tried to give her some water to drink. She just couldn't seem to hold anything down. The sixth and final vomit occurred at 12:45. By the time I had washed the last nightdress and sheet, the ground floor looked like a battlefield. There was damp but washed laundry hanging everywhere. Usually waiting for a few hours for some medical help can seem to drag on forever, but I didn't feel that frustration at all since I was far too busy. By the time the doctor arrived, it was about 2 p.m. As well as seeing that Mum was poorly she must have also observed that I looked drained. The evidence of the night's activities was all around to see. The ropes that I had put high up and across the room adjacent to where Mum slept certainly didn't look attractive, but for the last few months they had served a purpose. And on that long night they were certainly fully used. In the end, six sheets and fourteen nightdresses had been washed by hand and hung up to dry.

I really didn't want Mum to return to hospital again. Not because she had any really bad experiences on past visits, but I knew from the summer of 2007 how difficult it could be to get her home again. That largely explains my reluctance to seek medical assistance immediately. On the other hand, I was completely exhausted, like a struggling boxer on the ropes. Over the preceding three and a half months I had coped with having a very limited amount of sleep, leaving little reserves left to fight on with. The demands of the past week were stretching my body to breaking point. I had been looking after Mum on pure adrenaline, but even that was appearing to run out. When the doctor gave me the option of sending her to the hospital for a few days I snatched the opportunity despite having some misgivings. I was still ready and more than willing to continue looking after Mum, but I desperately needed to recharge the batteries. And so it was agreed. The doctor phoned the hospital directly from home and, after a short conversation, informed me that she could be admitted later that afternoon. After the doctor left I prepared a few things to be ready for when the ambulance arrived. While we were waiting, both Mum's state and breathing seemed calmer. She didn't get sick again, and for a while I began questioning myself as to whether I had made the right decision.

Chapter 27   Back in the Hospital

It must have been about 5 p.m. when the ambulance arrived. Before then I had remembered to phone the agency that supplied the carers, informing them that they wouldn't need to send anybody round for the foreseeable future. The ambulance crew, a man and a woman, efficiently transferred Mum to the vehicle but, unlike previous trips to the hospital, it didn't set off straight away. The paramedics conducted a number of tests while the ambulance remained parked in front of the house. At least ten minutes had passed, though it did seem longer, when I was informed that the readings of Mum's heart activity revealed that she might have suffered a heart attack over the previous twenty four hours. Even though he stressed it was probably a mild one and that the tests in the ambulance weren't conclusive, it still came as a shock. Nevertheless, both were sufficiently concerned that they decided to put on the blue light and siren. Soon the ambulance set off, travelling as fast as possible while still at a speed to ensure a safe and comfortable journey for Mum.

She remained quiet over the entire drive to the hospital. Although she was conscious, unlike previous trips in the ambulance, Mum was far too weak to make any fuss. This was in complete contrast to the journey in 2005 when pneumonia had made Mum delirious and probably accounted for her claiming to be the Queen. While such a pronouncement sounds ridiculous, it wasn't an entirely random comment. For some time, Mum had derived a certain degree of satisfaction from the knowledge that along with a former Prime Minister, Margaret Thatcher, all three women had been born within a few months of each other.

On our arrival at the hospital, another significant difference was that this time she wasn't kept in a holding bay at A & E. On previous visits we could be held there for hours with only periodic checks and, unless Mum was unconscious, it was very difficult to keep her still even when she was ill. Instead she was taken straight to an emergency examination room. It contained several beds but that was where any similarity with an ordinary ward ended. Vast amounts of complex equipment were close at hand. It wasn't long before Mum was wired up all over her body to obtain more accurate readings of her condition. It was a worrying sight, so it was slightly reassuring that amongst the staff examining her was the Chinese doctor who had been involved in treating Mum during the first few weeks of her previous stay over the summer of 2007.

It took a while before one of the hard pressed doctors found time to have a word with me. The X-ray revealed that Mum had a serious chest infection and the results also confirmed that she had suffered a mild heart attack. But Mum was a fighter. It would take more than that to take her and she was still holding on. With that diagnosis established, several days of treatment with antibiotics were recommended. This time the drugs could be administered intravenously as there was no danger of her pulling out the line that is attached to the veins in the arm, usually near the wrist. With the emergency seemingly over and Mum's condition stabilised, she was then transferred to a temporary ward. There was plenty of time for me to send texts to my sister and some friends, informing them that Mum had been admitted to hospital again. I stayed until 10.30 p.m. Before leaving, I reminded the nurse that Mum needed turning regularly, especially as she wasn't lying on an air mattress that night. I felt a bit uncomfortable providing such obvious advice – almost equivalent to telling your grandmother how to suck eggs – but given the choice of bedsores for Mum or upsetting a member of staff, the former was the most important to avoid that night.

Although I left the hospital still quite concerned, at least the knowledge that Mum could receive the treatment that she required – medication that I wouldn't have been able to provide at home – was some consolation. I just had to hope that she would receive the same level of care. As I walked from the hospital towards a junction, still reflecting on the recent dramatic events, I began to feel a little more sanguine. Mum had suffered chest infections before, and in both 2005 and 2007 the same hospital had helped her recover fully.

The decision to continue part of the journey home on foot was based on the logic that a ten minute walk would eventually provide me access to a wider selection of buses. It turned out to be the wrong choice. The heavens suddenly opened. I was inappropriately dressed and had no umbrella. In the meantime the bus that I could have caught, had I waited in the shelter outside the hospital, sped past. I gave chase. Remembering some of my journeys home from school about four decades earlier, I knew there was a chance the bus might get caught at the traffic lights by the junction. Within a few seconds I ran past the stationary vehicle to reach, thankfully, the next stop. With little traffic on the road at that time, it didn't take too long before I reached Kew Bridge. I soon arrived home and was relieved to get out of the soaking wet clothes. After getting changed, I made myself a hot drink. It was approaching midnight and soon it would be Wednesday.

Still taking comfort from clasping the warm mug of tea, I suddenly realised that I hadn't had any sleep since early Monday morning. It meant I had been awake for over forty hours. It was time to go to bed – and deservedly so. After all, Mum was being looked after. That responsibility had been removed temporarily. Moreover I could relax for another reason. I had no lessons in the morning, whilst the afternoon just involved organising some football matches for Year 11 along with Noel. I hoped that Mum was being turned regularly and wouldn't have to lie in any mess for too long. But for that night, her well-being was no longer in my hands. I didn't set the alarm and it wasn't long before I was fast asleep.

It was a deep sleep. I didn't wake up until 8:45 a.m. – not that late by most people's standards – but quite a lie-in for me. I had just got dressed when the doorbell suddenly rang. It was Sara looking very concerned. I invited her in and she sat down in her normal seat in the corner of the dining room, listening to my account of the events of the previous day. "Oh Mike! Why didn't you phone? I could have driven down to the hospital and collected you. There was no need to get soaked!" She probably would have done so without sparing a thought, but it would have been too late to make such a call and unfair to ask her to leave her children or wake them up to go on an unexpected trip. Suddenly the doorbell rang again and it was Marlene, the carer who came over to help wash Mum in the morning. I apologised to her for being dragged over for nothing, but clearly the message that I had left with the office the previous day had not been passed on. When she left, I phoned the office again.

Once an early lunch was over, I cycled to the school for the sports session with Year 11. As usual, Noel understandingly told me to leave as soon as the football was over. On the way to the hospital I called into a Plumbers' Merchant nearby. I was delighted when the young sales assistant didn't give up straight away. After a few enquiries he finally tracked down a supplier of the handle that was needed to work the water heater in the kitchen. I ordered the parts and made my way to the hospital, anticipating that by the time Mum returned home, I would have finally fixed the water heater. That would make life so much easier by avoiding the need to warm up saucepans of water prior to any visit from the carers. I was still clearly optimistic about Mum's prospects of leaving the hospital fully recovered from the chest infection.

My visit to the hospital on that Wednesday did nothing to dent my confidence. Mum had been moved to an unfamiliar ward but was looking comfortable when I found her. She was awake that afternoon and I was delighted to hear that a blood sample revealed that her haemoglobin level had climbed back to the more normal level of 12. I wasn't entirely surprised by the news. For a few weeks I had suspected there had been some improvement in her level of strength. All those months of running around trying to find supplies of the liquid iron supplement had paid off.

While Mum was awake I suddenly thought it would be nice to treat her to a sweet. According to the records in her folder near the bed, she hadn't eaten much earlier in the day. As a result I suspected that she must have been hungry. I popped down to the shop by the hospital entrance and a few minutes later returned with a tub of Wall's vanilla ice cream.

You could be excused for thinking that it was hardly a significant purchase – certainly under normal circumstances – but this was anything but normal. This was probably the last near-solid food that she ever took in her mouth again. It was certainly the last time I fed her. And for that reason it will always stick in my mind. Luckily she was still awake and eagerly took in each spoonful. Unfortunately an hour later she fell asleep just about fifteen minutes before the main evening meal arrived. I was unable to wake her up to eat – which was a great pity. Even though she was on a drip that ensured she had sufficient fluid, she needed some nutrition to maintain her strength and make up for all the food that had been vomited on Monday night. Nevertheless, I was sure she would have plenty of opportunity to eat the following day, especially if I brought in something that she enjoyed, like a trifle. So on balance, I left the hospital at 8:40 p.m. feeling very hopeful. She had also been put on an air mattress which was probably as much a relief to me as it was for her. However, I didn't think it was as good as the one at home or the one she had been given on the previous ward in 2007. Just before leaving I expressed my concerns and was promised that a replacement would be found. This time I cycled and arrived home dry.

Registration at school starts at 8:50 a.m., so it was a bit of a shock to wake up at 8:15. I had forgotten to set the alarm. It was a bit of a rush, but I managed to get to work just in time to start the lesson with the Upper 6th. As soon as the bell went to signify the start of lunch and the end of the school day for me, I was on the bicycle and once again bound for the hospital. My sister was off from work that day so she was able to visit as well. However, the notice that greeted us as we entered the ward was not one that I was prepared for or one that I wanted to see. Behind Mum's bed there was a small whiteboard. There, under Mum's name of Renza, were three words that completely altered my sentiments. A few minutes earlier I had approached the hospital full of optimism. But now on reading the 'NIL BY MOUTH' notice, my mood completely changed. In more ways than one, the writing really was on the wall. I suspected it; my sister probably knew it. This was definitely not a good development.

Elizabeth must have known that the end was probably near, but she kept it to herself. Even less of a surprise to her would have been the decision to feed Mum through a tube that would be inserted in her nostril to pass down her throat. A precaution against the threat of inhaling any food or drink was given as the reason. Mum would need to have an X-ray before the feeding could start to check that the tube was in the correct position. It was essential to ensure that the highly nutritional Fresubin drink would pass through to her stomach rather than her lungs. The latter possibility would obviously have disastrous consequences. My spirits slumped.

It didn't take any comment from my sister, or later discussions with Stephanie from Social Services, to appreciate the implications of this new feeding arrangement. As well as denying Mum probably her last pleasure, the taste of food, while also being potentially uncomfortable, the prospects of getting Mum home suddenly looked slim. I left the hospital that evening utterly dispirited. All my energies over the past few months had been channelled into caring for Mum. Did it mean I would now have to begin considering a nursing home? Even more worrying than the financial implications was the uncertainty that the level of care could match the attention I had given her. It was a desperate turnaround in circumstances over the space of just a few hours. My only hope was that Mum's strength would prevail, as it had always done before, and that she would soon be able to be fed normally again.

The next day was Friday. It was a day off from school and Jim, my friend next door who had looked after Mum on Tuesday afternoons, invited me round for lunch. As we tucked into the food, my mind turned back to Mum and the events of the previous day. I felt a bit guilty knowing that she would not be able to share in the simple experience of eating for a while. But at least she was being fed by tube, I tried to reassure myself. However, the concern felt the previous day, and during the meal with Jim, turned to anger later on when I arrived at the hospital early in the afternoon. It wasn't so much the 'Nil by mouth' notice that was now written on a piece of paper and stuck to the drip, but the absence of any feeding tube that really left me feeling livid. Another day had passed and apart from a tub of ice cream and some porridge for breakfast, Mum had been given hardly any food. She was being starved.

Until that point I had always been polite with the staff. They deserve respect in what is a difficult and often unappreciated job and sometimes, especially when a ward is understaffed, it must be difficult to deliver the level of care they would probably wish. But now I had to be Mum's voice. It was my turn to take a leaf out of her book and replicate a similar scene to the one that Mum had created in the Italian Consulate. Excuses weren't accepted, and I hounded different members of staff to galvanise them into action and prioritise Mum's care for a while. It worked. She was soon attended to. The tube was inserted and taped down near her nose to prevent movement. Not a pretty sight but, under the circumstances, an absolutely necessary one. She was then wheeled to X-ray with me by her side. This was to check that the tube was safely positioned. By 4:30 p.m., I could finally see the Fresubin drink travelling along the tube and being slowly pumped into her.

All the controversy over feeding had probably distracted me from attending to another potential problem. It was now time to make a fuss about the faulty air mattress which wasn't as inflated as the one at home. Worse still it had a valve that was protruding. If nurses on a new shift were unaware of the problem, there was a risk that Mum could be lying on it for a while, making the development of a pressure sore all the more likely. To my relief, a new mattress was installed on Saturday but it may have been too late. The combination of her severe illness, unsuitable mattress, possibly insufficient turning and lack of food meant that a sore was already developing on her bottom. The nurses applied dressing to the wound, but once a sore develops in a patient who is so weak, it almost always becomes irreversible.

Earlier on that Saturday, Sara had popped round to the house with a trifle that she had prepared for me, perhaps sensing I was feeling a bit down. She asked if she could visit Mum on Sunday and so I gladly gave her details of the ward. The following day she arrived in the afternoon with her two children. They had drawn a colourful 'get well' card which I placed on the cupboard next to the bed, but Mum was too sleepy to acknowledge their gift. The next two days passed by without any major problems, and the X-rays even showed some encouraging signs as the infection in her chest seemed to be clearing. The problem with the pressure sore remained, but hopefully the combination of appropriate treatment, a better mattress and regular feeding might be enough to reverse the damage. On Monday the doctors felt confident enough to take Mum off the antibiotics to see how she would cope on her own.

The next day I found that Mum had been moved from the ward into a separate room. The only reason given was that she could get more attention as it was closer to the main desk from where the doctors and nurses complete much of their administrative work. Other possible reasons for isolation didn't seem to apply because there was no notice restricting access. To me that implied Mum couldn't have caught an infection that would risk other patients or staff. Maybe the move had been prompted by her subjecting the other patients to a similar bout of shouting to the ones that I had experienced a few days earlier – but I have my doubts given her deteriorating condition.

It was a nice room, but it was too quiet and must have been incredibly boring especially for someone who could no longer read, converse or watch the television. However, such distractions may have been unimportant by that point as Mum did look weaker and the latest news from the doctors wasn't very encouraging. She hadn't responded well to the removal of the antibiotics, and there were signs that the chest infection had not been overcome. Along with the remaining problem of the worsening pressure sore and no prospects of the 'nil by mouth' notice being removed, I went home with a heavy heart – a mood that I must have carried over to the next day and was easily spotted by Noel while we were at the sports field on that Wednesday afternoon of the 16th of January.

I was right to feel apprehensive. Mum had deteriorated further by the time I reached her after the Games session. If she hadn't been in such a poor state I would have been able to look forward to an easy end to the week. My lesson with the Upper 6th on a Thursday lasted for nearly four hours – a challenge at the best of times – despite a twenty minute break in between. But on this particular week most of the students would be re-sitting an AS module exam. Even though I felt despondent about the reversal of fortunes regarding Mum's health, at least as I went to bed that Wednesday night, I had the prospect of a relatively easy Thursday morning at school. Moreover the weekend was approaching. But it still wasn't enough to lift my spirits. As I left the room downstairs, the one with the empty electric bed, and sought some solace in the anticipation of a few hours of uninterrupted sleep, it was probably no wonder that I started praying that God should spare Mum from any further misery. The whole situation was looking really grim. All the signs were unfortunately pointing to her condition getting even worse.

Chapter 28   Dying Moments

On that Thursday morning of the 17th of January, 2008, I woke up quite early, certainly before 6 a.m. The previous couple of hours of uninterrupted sleep were refreshing. For a brief moment I felt quite hopeful. Then my mind drifted back to the events of the previous night. A grey mood descended to match the gloomy weather that greeted me from outside the bedroom window. Under my bed linen I felt warm and comfortable, in complete contrast to the cold and harsh reality that was awaiting me outside. This made the thought of remaining in bed for a few more minutes, all the more desirable.

Eventually I got up and after washing, made my way downstairs where I had a light breakfast. There was plenty of spare time, so I sat down on the comfortable armchair in the corner of the dining room. For those few months from October, it had been occupied by my sister and different friends from the neighbourhood keeping a watch on Mum. In front and slightly to the right was the electric bed. The air mattress was deflated, just like my spirits. Recalling the times, a few months earlier, when my mother was still mobile, I would have been rushing around at this point in the morning. It had been important to wake up before her in order to get things ready before she could be washed. I thought back to how we often managed to fit in one, two, sometimes even three walks before I sneaked out of the house in a rush to school, invariably arriving slightly late for my first duty. It was by the school gate. Along with another two teachers, Nereida and Mirka, I was entrusted to help supervise the 6th formers responsible for recording the names of the younger students turning up after the bell – some strolling in unconcerned, others rushing past looking worried. I'm surprised that my name never got added to the list!

This particular Thursday was significant. Some of my Upper 6th students were re-sitting a modular exam. They stood a chance of picking up more marks and, combined with the high quality of coursework achieved by the end of December, were all in a position to gain one of the top grades by the summer. I was satisfied that despite all the time devoted towards looking after Mum, I had still been able to deliver lessons of a high standard.

My original intention had been to go to school a little earlier than usual, but for some strange reason I found it difficult to get out of the chair. Fortunately I didn't fall asleep again, but I must have sat there for at least another twenty minutes, looking at the clock intermittently, thinking that I really should be making a move, but at the same time feeling no real desire to leave. At that point it was already a few minutes past 8 a.m., but there was still a bit of time since the bicycle ride would be little more than ten minutes. Of course, I would have got up eventually, but the silence was abruptly interrupted by the telephone ringing. I picked up the receiver to discover it was a doctor from the hospital. Soon afterwards my heart sank. After listening to her account of what had happened over the last few hours, I was left with a terrible decision to make. Suddenly I really did feel alone. I was told that my mother's condition had dramatically worsened overnight. Her last chance was to get back on the antibiotics, but they hadn't been able to get a line into her veins. They tried her arms and elsewhere, but she was too weak by then. The last resort was described by the doctor as necessitating the use of a very large and intrusive needle to be inserted in her neck.

I couldn't answer her straight away. There was a brief pause as I imagined the traumatic scene that could be awaiting Mum. What an awful position to be put in. I suddenly had to make a decision that might determine the chances of preserving the life of the very same person who had given me life. But for her – what life did it promise – and for how long? Recalling how much she hated needles, it didn't take quite as long to reach a verdict as I had anticipated. In those last few years Mum had even been terrified of going to the GP for a flu jab; meanwhile in the hospital she had kicked up a real fuss every time the staff tried to get a blood sample, particularly when she had still been strong enough to resist. In the autumn of 2007, I had been required to assist the nurse who, until that point, had not been able to hold Mum's arm stationary to allow the doctor to carry out the procedure safely. No, there wasn't even any need to delay my answer by consulting my sister. I knew exactly what advice she would have given me. She knew the score in such situations. And yet, it seemed as if I was sentencing Mum to death. But on the other hand, I didn't feel I had much of a choice, especially when the doctor made it easier by admitting that Mum's chances of survival wouldn't be greatly enhanced by further intervention.

The charged silence on the phone was eventually broken when I gave her my decision. "Look, this is a tough call, but I can't see the point of putting her through any more suffering. Don't bother with that big needle. It sounds awful. Just try to make the last few hours for her as comfortable as possible." The doctor agreed and did her best to try to reassure me that I had made the right choice. My head felt at ease with my acquiescence to her advice, but in my heart I wasn't entirely convinced. In all those years of looking after Mum, this moment – and the previous night – were the only times I had given up on her – and it wasn't easy to accept. But there wasn't time to dwell on the issue. Before putting the phone down the doctor suggested I should come over to the hospital as soon as possible since Mum might not have long to go.

I felt guilty. I felt numb. After all, hadn't it been just a few hours earlier when I had been praying for her to pass away so that she could be spared from all this suffering? For a while, I still wasn't sure. "God, I was only joking," I thought, uncomfortably recollecting my prayers from the previous night – but on the other hand – for Mum there really wasn't any future. Her time was nearly up and I had to let go. Bit by bit, I began to conclude that I had made the right decision and could live with it. I then phoned my sister. She wasn't shocked and, as anticipated, fully supported my earlier decision. She had, after all, predicted all the declines well in advance of them occurring despite my objections and scepticism, but each time she had been proved right – eventually.

It really was time to leave, but I felt there was one more task for me to complete. A short detour to the school to see some familiar faces in this unfamiliar situation and wish the students luck wouldn't take long – and it didn't. Sometimes short visits to the school can turn out to be longer than expected, depending upon whom you bump into. Not this time. First I had a very short chat with Graham, a retired Geography teacher who still retained a mild Welsh accent, and later that morning would be in charge of administering the Economics exam. The next, of even briefer duration, was with one of the students explaining that I couldn't stay, as my mother was poorly. After that it was head down and out of the school gate on my bicycle, pedalling as fast as I could to the hospital.

Not too long afterwards I was entering the ward. Everything looked normal. Nurses, doctors and porters were all carrying out their duties as if nothing particularly out of the ordinary was happening. But for me it was anything but a normal day. You only have one mother; and today I had been told that I was very close to losing her. I wasn't sure what to expect as I approached her room. A nurse was making a few adjustments to the equipment near Mum's bed. She then gave me a sympathetic look before leaving us alone. Over a month later I would be writing a short obituary for the street newsletter describing her last moments as 'peacefully slipping away'. Maybe – but looking back at the events of that morning – I am not so sure. It may have been peaceful just at the very end – because who knows the exact second when somebody dies – but the scene in front of me was far from that. A mask had been attached over her mouth to help her breathing. Nevertheless, she was still frantically struggling for breath. It was like seeing a fish out of water – but because it was Mum – it made it a particularly distressing sight to witness. I sat in the chair beside her and held her hand. I couldn't think of any other way to help her. She had very little strength left, but I'm sure I'm not just imagining that I could feel her exert just a tiny little bit of pressure on my hand. I certainly got the feeling she had been waiting for me.

She was unable to speak, but at least the breathing started to become more relaxed. And then I noticed something extraordinary. Thankfully the mask only covered her mouth and nose, because her eyes looked truly amazing. Her head was tilted slightly to the side so that she was staring directly at me. There was no smile; she had lost the ability to do that; but it was as if all her strength, whatever little was left, was being channelled into that one area of her body. Her eyes shone brightly – fondly – lovingly, but something else very strange happened. Two years earlier when I had been filling out her application form for the renewal of the passport, I came to the section asking about colour of eyes. I hesitated for a moment. I knew they were brown when she was younger, as confirmed by the entry in her previous, out-of-date, passport. However, when I looked at her face in 2006, I could see that the tint had completely faded away. If anything, they were grey. Despite the evidence that was in front of me, I still put down 'brown'. To this day I'm not sure why, but I guess it was a reluctance to accept that the ageing process was affecting more than just her memory.

Two years later, and I was glad I had deliberated over this passport entry. Alone in the hospital with Mum, it meant that I was less likely to miss what turned out to be an amazing, if only temporary, transformation and a privilege to witness. For quite some time there had been little colour in her eyes. And yet on this day, as if to burn an indelible image in my mind, those same eyes had transformed back into such a rich brown. She appeared so surprisingly youthful. Looking at her eyes and recalling some of the photos showing her jet black wavy hair from her twenties, I then understood why it must have been hard for my dad not to fall in love with her all those years ago. Strange what thoughts can enter your head at such poignant moments!

And so the minutes passed by. I was still struck by the radiance of her eyes and, yes, they did seem to be acting as 'the window to the soul'. She was still breathing. Not much noise now, but you could just about see the rise and fall of her chest under the bed linen. It seemed like a long time, but I had only been in the hospital for about an hour. At one stage a nurse popped in to give her a dose of iron supplement. How strange? Was there any point? Earlier that morning I had been told that Mum was on the way out. It seemed even more ironic thinking back to the previous summer when the hospital had run out of the stuff and I had been cycling around to different pharmacists desperately trying to obtain a bottle. On this particular January morning it seemed in abundant supply.

There was a further visit from an Indian assistant nurse at around 10 a.m. He arrived in his light green uniform with the equipment to take measurements of blood pressure amongst other things. It was a routine that seemed to continue right to the end. He strapped the band around my mum's very thin arm and then I held her finger as he clipped a piece of equipment on. There was the very familiar buzzing noise that accompanied the inflating of the arm band and we then waited for the readings. He fiddled with some of the knobs and tapped the machine a few times. "Something appears to be wrong with this monitor. I'll get a replacement. I should be back in a few minutes." In some respects it was quite comical. This should have been a dramatic, serious moment, but amongst other things that I had inherited from my mother was her sense of humour. The nurse was young and probably not very experienced. I had guessed why he hadn't got any readings, but refrained from saying anything when he came back wheeling a new stand. We went through the same procedure but once again, no readings. I broke the silence. "I think she's dead." And that was it. All our struggles battling against dementia were over. I don't know the precise time, but when I looked at the clock and then deducted a few minutes for all the messing around with the equipment, I reckon it might have been 10:06 a.m. on Thursday the 17th of January, 2008, about one month short of what would have been her eighty-second birthday.

I didn't start crying. It was strange. I didn't really feel anything. There she lay – motionless. I sat nearby looking at her. What a journey it had been. At least six years had passed, during which time I had been required to take on more and more as her mind deteriorated. I had kept my promise and looked after her until the end. That was satisfying, but my duties were not quite over. There would be forms to fill, solicitors to deal with, a funeral to arrange and eventually one more trip to Italy to complete some unfinished business. For some odd reason, I was quite calm as I sat there witnessing her final moments. Crying uncontrollably – perhaps more accurately described as wailing from the pit of my stomach – had to wait until a few weeks later. Surprisingly, it was prompted by watching *The Notebook* being televised one evening. Towards the end of the film, one centred on a woman's battle to retain the memories of her husband that were being destroyed by dementia, I was overwhelmingly reminded of the emotional roller coaster experienced with Mum. Sitting there alone, I was able to grieve totally uninhibited, more so than at any funeral service.

My sister arrived at the hospital about ten minutes later. It was a pity she had missed those last few moments while Mum had still been alive. But at least she was present when, after popping out to answer a phone call from a concerned Head Teacher, I returned with not only some well needed warm drinks, but also a nun. I had met her on the way back and she was kindly willing to say a few prayers. How appropriate. Mum had often spoken affectionately of her school days when tuition had been mainly the responsibility of the nuns. We must have stayed for another two hours after the brief ceremony, but life must go on in a hospital and the room would soon be needed by another patient. There was nothing more that could be gained by staying.

On the way out I was given some leaflets concerning bereavement. My sister offered me a lift back to Chiswick, but as I had cycled to the hospital that morning, it made more sense to go our own separate ways and meet back at home. There we chatted for a while, but this wasn't the time to make any plans. When she left I went upstairs and had a nap. I felt exhausted and emotionally drained. I realised that I still had to phone my aunt in Italy with the bad news, but couldn't face it then. Although able to speak Italian, I wasn't perfectly fluent, and so I postponed the task for the following day. But when I eventually plucked up the courage the next evening, it was easier than I expected. Even before I struggled to say a few words, handicapped more by the emotion of the occasion than any limitations of vocabulary, she had already guessed what I was trying to tell her and she kindly kept the conversation short to spare me any further distress.

Just before it was finally time to retire on that first night, I decided that I wanted to see what it had been like for Mum sleeping in the electric bed. I turned on the machine and after a few minutes the air mattress inflated. I climbed into the bed taking in a deep breath through my nose, trying – not entirely in vain – to catch any traces of Mum's scent on the pillow. Every now and again I could feel one section of the bed deflate while another part inflated. It was designed that way to help prevent bedsores – and for the months that she had been nursed at home – it had worked remarkably well. But it was far from being comfortable! I soon concluded that sleeping on the floor had been preferable. I stuck it out for a few hours but couldn't get to sleep. It was enough, however, to prove a point to myself. I went upstairs and fell asleep on my bed reassured that at least Mum was now definitely in a better place.

Chapter 29 A Missed Opportunity?

After that short nap, which I thoroughly required on the afternoon of the 17th of January, it was time to start thinking how to tell the rest of the world, beyond my sister, about my Mum's death. It wasn't a very wide circle of people, but gradually they would be informed. On the day itself, I didn't really feel up to the task of speaking to anybody on the phone, so that meant that my aunt and a close friend from my school days, Peter, could wait one more day. I had to start somewhere and so it was Sara to whom I sent a short text message first. After all, she had been a great help over the last few months and, apart from my sister, was the only person, along with her two children, who had visited the hospital in the preceding few days before Mum's passing away. I think she had been quite surprised to see Mum's swift decline when she arrived at the ward but she had done her best to put on a brave face and look positive.

Sara responded to the text straight away, expressing shock at hearing the news and within a few minutes called round and gave me a sympathetic hug. We stood around for a while and she did her best to try and find some consoling words to say, but it was difficult. Soon it was time for her to leave and collect her children from the nearby school, but not before promising to help if I needed it, especially with anything to do with the funeral.

The next few days were awkward, but I didn't really take a break. It felt better if I was doing something, rather than sitting around the empty house just moping. I didn't have to go to work on Friday as I had no lessons at school. This allowed me time to collect the Death Certificate. Phone calls to friends and, most importantly, to my aunt in Italy, were made and whenever I visited someone, or met a neighbour in the street, I was able to break the sad news. It was never easy but, bit by bit, the announcements were accompanied with fewer tears. All this helped to prepare me for my return to school on Monday. I decided not to take time off for grieving. A school is a lively place and would provide a welcome contrast to the silence at home. Maybe the decision turned out to be a mistake, but at the time it felt the right thing to do. The first day back was, unsurprisingly, difficult. Everybody wanted to express their sympathy.

That was thoughtful but in some ways it unintentionally intensified the sadness. On the other hand what else could they have done?

Over the next few days I had to set in motion the process of dealing with probate, necessitating both correspondence and discussions with the solicitor over the will, while also obtaining property valuations. It wasn't a very pleasant time, particularly being burdened with such onerous tasks so early in bereavement. Meanwhile, Sara kept her distance for a few days, probably feeling it would be better to wait until I was ready to be contacted again. But true to her word, as soon as I did get in touch, she offered to help with the preparation for a small reception planned to follow the funeral scheduled for Friday the 1st of February. On Thursday Sara called round with her red car. After she spent a few minutes sadly admiring the photos attached to the dining room wall that displayed Mum at various points of her life, an idea borrowed from the funeral of my late friend John Kitchin, we set off for the supermarket to get some food and drink. I gratefully followed her advice as we filled up the shopping trolley. I have organised many parties and social events before, but at that moment in time I seemed to be lacking confidence and so her support was very welcome.

The next morning my sister arrived with a friend whom I had not met before. Together they soon started reorganising the furniture, but felt some preparations would be best left for after the service, particularly as far as food was concerned. Finally it was time to go to the crematorium, a short drive away. We waited outside the small chapel. It was one of those cold, crisp but sunny winter days. I remained composed until I caught a glimpse of the hearse bringing Mum's coffin. Sara was standing next to me at the time and must have sensed that I was struggling inside and reacted by gently clasping my arm for a few minutes.

The priest gave a nice service despite not knowing my mother. For some people, a funeral can provide an opportunity to pay a tribute to the person who has passed away. But not me – not on that day – I was in no position to perform that task. I had to rely on the priest making use of the short notes that I had provided and, to be fair, he did a good job. Anyway, I would eventually provide a more detailed epitaph. But it would take over a year before I was ready.

To my relief I got through the funeral service, and then it was back to Mum's house for the reception. The room where she had spent the last few months of her life had been emptied of the electric bed that had, until a week earlier, been in such a dominating position in the centre. Sara had been present at the time, having just brought round a pudding to try and cheer me up. We had both stood there watching the delivery man take apart the bed that he himself had assembled just a few months earlier back in late September. There seemed such a contrast of emotions between the two days, separated by just a relatively short space of time in Mum's life. The first day had been bright and cheerful, as if to reflect that there was still hope that Mum would soon be home from her stay in the hospital. On his return visit, however, the room was gloomy. It was as if the dismantling of the bed, and subsequent removal, was symbolic. But at least for the day of the funeral it meant that there was more space for the guests.

My sister's friend was very efficient in the kitchen, and within a few minutes a large spread of sandwiches appeared. Elizabeth and Sara also helped with the preparation of the food, while I put on the cassette that I had played to my mum over her last few months. The collection of Italian songs sung by Pavarotti seemed appropriate at the wake – though a year must have passed before I played it again.

It was an amiable gathering. Not that many were present because my mum had outlived quite a few of her friends and neighbours, while guests from Italy were too difficult to invite at such short notice. Besides, I had already made plans to bring her ashes to Italy in May so their opportunity to pay their respects would soon follow.

One of the pleasant aspects of holding the reception after the service was that it provided an opportunity to learn a bit more about the backgrounds of some of the neighbours I had been acquainted with since childhood. Mr and Mrs North had known my mother since the late 1950s. Once again the war had intervened to alter their lives permanently, just as with my parents. Beryl had been evacuated to the countryside and had then met her husband, Bernard, at the local dance. Stationed at a nearby air base, close to Cambridge, he had been a pilot flying raids over Germany at the time. While listening and also sharing some of my parent's experiences, it struck me that the generation born in the 1920s, and that went on to survive the war, nearly all had interesting stories to tell. Mr North was able to elaborate more a year later when I took him over to Café Rouge by the river in his wheel chair one beautiful sunny evening. It also provided an opportunity to make further good use of the ramp that I bought a year earlier. During a brief break in the conversation, I paused to think how nice it would have been to take Mum out at least one more time by the river, even if only in the new wheelchair that was left gathering dust in the attic. Another guest at the wake included Mrs Hogan who had been widowed a few years earlier. She was a devout Catholic and in some ways seemed to take some comfort from the fact that her husband passed away in the same year as the Pope. Jim, my next door neighbour, who had helped look after Mum, was obviously invited. He too had known her for about fifty years and, as with Mr North, was able to share some of his war time experiences, which involved serving several years in Burma.

What all four had in common, was that they had known my mother as she had been before the dementia gradually robbed her of her skills and even – though to a lesser extent – her personality. It was therefore nice to hear their recollections, one of which came from Beryl, who had received bowls of homemade ravioli from my mum when she had been left temporarily immobile from a leg injury. The other guests were more recent acquaintances. Andrew, of course, had helped look after Mum on Wednesday afternoons when I was out. In earlier years and along with his wife, Louise, they had often listened patiently to Mum's increasingly incoherent dialogue whenever we met them in the street. There was also another married couple, Michael and Marigold. They had always been friendly towards my mother during the few years that they had known her. Both had helped during the Charity Walk day of 2007 as part of the team of volunteers assembled to take shifts minding her when it became almost impossible to leave her alone all day. Mum's neighbour, Daphne, also attended and mixed well with the other guests despite only knowing Jim and Sara on arrival.

Before the end I was pleased to see my friend Peter had also managed to turn up. He had plenty of memories of the house as he used to visit weekly when, as students, we had been practising guitars with the aim of forming the band which never quite materialised. He had known my mum well and had often had meals here. I'm sure the Head Teacher would also have liked to have been present, but after the funeral service he had to return to work.[10] Nobody at the time, John included, could have anticipated that just over a year later he would be filling the large Ealing Abbey, with many mourners wishing to pay their respects to the Head Teacher, following his death from cancer in March 2009.

Most stayed for a few hours and nearly everybody commented on how helpful and polite Sara's young son had been as he carried in supplies from the kitchen. He was a bright boy and despite only being eight years old seemed quite comfortable in the company of grown-ups. The hours passed by pleasantly, but gradually people began drifting off. It had been a good day but I also felt relieved when it was over. The days running up to the funeral had been quite stressful since it had been impossible to predict how I would cope with such an emotionally charged occasion.

The funeral should have been like drawing a line in the sand, presenting some opportunity for closure. After all, I had already shed enough tears over the preceding two weeks and hoped that I could look forward to things improving over the forthcoming months. The whole episode had left me feeling very run down. When I looked in the mirror, I could see that my face was gaunt and appeared to have aged – not surprising as it felt like I had been living about six years in the same number of months. And so, with the funeral behind me, it should have been a time to start socialising more, something that friends and colleagues were trying their best to encourage. Moreover, it would have been what Mum would have wanted for me. And yet instead of feeling proud of all my efforts, I felt guilty. I bought books about caring for the elderly as if to seek assurance that I had done all I could and avoided doing things I shouldn't. Despite looking after Mum so efficiently and still maintaining good exam results, my confidence and self-esteem were suddenly at an all-time low. But I didn't have to wait long before I was shaken out of this unusual period of self-doubt. I would soon have another battle to face which would distract me from mourning for my mother.

The funeral had taken place on Friday. On Sunday morning I woke up just before 9 a.m., quite late for me, shivering and with a temperature that

---

[10] As was the case with Paul T.(PE) and Stuart A.(Economics) from St Mark's.

measured almost 40 degrees. I felt weak and had completely lost my appetite. I had to cancel the Monday lesson, the first time I had been off sick for over twelve years. This turned out to be cellulitis, that I mentioned earlier, and not the flu. By Tuesday I was able to return to work, but the next few weeks I had to have the dressing on my left leg changed regularly and hope that the antibiotics would do their job.

Slowly but surely the swelling associated with cellulitis receded and so by mid-March I felt I could look forward to the spring. Things were looking up and I had even been invited by Sara to join her family for a meal over Easter as well as planning to go to see a film, *The Other Boleyn Girl*. It wasn't exactly a date, but it seemed as if there was a growing friendship and now the trips out wouldn't just involve shopping at the local supermarket.

It was also a good time for Sara. She was getting more parts as an extra. Her first rôle was on Sunday the 9th of March when she had to turn up in formal clothes as a guest at a wedding reception. She had to leave for work before 6 a.m. However, as a precaution, she had parked her car outside my house since it had been slightly vandalised a few days earlier. As agreed, I called round half-an-hour earlier to accompany her round the block. It was all very innocent, but in the dawn light we must have appeared an odd couple – Sara looking so smartly dressed in contrast to my casual attire. After turning a corner, to my surprise, we bumped into one of my neighbours, June, who was probably going to work. As we passed by, she gave me – if I'm not mistaken – just the slightest hint of a cheeky grin. Part of me felt embarrassed, but another and less serious part, still bursting to escape from the shackles of years of worrying over Mum and, more recently, weeks of grieving – saw the funny side too.

Although Sara didn't want to be late, we continued to chat for a while even after she had got into the car. She appeared a little nervous since it was to be her first part in a TV production. Maybe wanting some reassurance, while adjusting her white fascinator in front of the mirror, she suddenly asked me how she looked. I didn't need to pause to think – it was very easy for me to pay her a genuine compliment. While talking to her, I was squatting down outside the car with my arms resting on the opened window of the car door. Before setting off, she leaned forward, maybe just expecting a kiss on the cheek, but for some reason it took me by surprise and I reacted by moving slightly back. It may have been less than an inch but it probably gave the wrong signal. If there had been an opportunity to advance the friendship in a different direction, it may have slipped through my fingers in that second. The moment was gone and as the car disappeared down the road, I had an uncomfortable feeling that so too had my chances with Sara.

Over the next few days I continued to see Sara. Her day at the wedding reception shoot had gone well and was followed by another job with her featuring in an advert. During an evening visit, I ended up having an informal meal with her family. As well as introducing me to the delights of the mango fruit, carefully cut into neat slices and passed across the table, Sara excitedly announced that she had been offered a part in a new BBC production based on Merlin. I was very pleased for her. A few days later, and almost unbelievably, I received a long email after she had returned from filming, somewhere in a castle far from London, vividly describing the costumes and scenery. It left me wondering how on earth she was able to find the time to write with so much enthusiasm and detail, particularly after coming back from a long day at work, whilst still having to look after her children. Looking back, it was a significant email in many ways because it was the last affectionate message she ever sent. True, I still received kind and polite words from her, but something changed within the space of a few days. Previously, her texts had always ended with an x. Maybe because I had been too busy looking after Mum and had been wary of giving any signals encouraging a relationship that I didn't feel I could follow through with, I had never felt comfortable reciprocating. But suddenly the kisses stopped. I didn't know if that was significant, but to my surprise I found that I started missing them.

Despite the slight cooling in the friendship, the Easter Sunday meal was still on. But a few days beforehand I received a nasty surprise. On the Thursday, with just a few days to go, my temperature soared to over 39 degrees again, signifying a most unwelcome return of cellulitis. Although the swelling wasn't as severe as the first case, it was still painful and once again I was back on the antibiotics. But this time I felt really down about it. Luckily I recovered sufficiently to make it for the meal. It turned out to be a very pleasant evening, but I didn't feel great as my leg was still hurting. I spent most of the time speaking to other members of her family and while Sara didn't ignore me, she did seem to be a bit distant, or maybe it was just that she was too busy acting as host.

Leaving for home that night was also strange. I'm sure a few weeks earlier she would have walked down the stairs and, at the least, given me a kiss on the cheek. Instead she just stood by the banister with her mother to her right and her daughter to the left and just smiled and waved goodbye with no mention of the forthcoming Boleyn film. A few days later she made an excuse about not being able to go to the cinema. My reaction was surprisingly casual, which probably made it easier for Sara. Although I was disappointed, part of me was also relieved. I still wasn't ready to go out. I didn't feel particularly well, and not having dated any women for several years meant that I wasn't feeling particularly confident about the evening anyway.

Finally the school holiday arrived and provided an opportunity to get a break from London. By then it was April and my sister drove to Felixstowe where we were able to stay a few days in the family holiday home. The roof had survived another winter and the work that I had done a few summers ago, replacing about thirty slates, had played its part in maintaining the house. It was probably the most useful skill that I had learnt from my dad. As early as about nine years old, I had been keen to follow him on the roof in the Chiswick house, despite Mum expressing her concern. But it was a good age when you have little awareness of danger. Consequently from that time onwards I never had any fear of heights. So apart from tidying up the small back garden and putting up the ladder to clear out the rain gutter, the trip was restful and gave me time to reflect.

March had been a strange month. Two nasty attacks of cellulitis and even a fungal infection on two fingernails, but at least there were signs that my leg was finally recovering, and I was able to go running again. Moreover, along with the fresh air, Felixstowe did provide some scenic routes for both walking and jogging. But quite often my mind was elsewhere. Where did I stand with Sara, I wondered? For months she had been friendly and helpful and sometimes showed moments of affection, but each time I had been unresponsive, even at times a bit cold. However, my feelings towards her seemed to be thawing as spring approached. In those weeks I seemed to be the one running round trying to be helpful, looking out for small presents or taking care of her children when she had to go out. It was as if the roles had reversed. While welcoming the help, at the same time, Sara seemed to be the one trying to keep a distance in terms of any friendship developing. I hadn't realised it at the time, but it was probably during that month that I had started to fall in love with her. An awareness of that suddenly struck me one day when I was sitting on the promenade looking out to sea at the passing ships. 'What an idiot I've been,' I thought. For all those months I had almost ignored her, and yet she was a beautiful woman with a fine figure, intelligent, along with a very interesting and charming personality. She had two lovely children. That had worried me earlier because I may have feared the prospect of taking on new and unchartered responsibilities, but I had grown to like them and they seemed to like me. No, it was time to act and snap out of this complacency, especially as she seemed to be showing signs of getting fed up with me.

That evening I decided to phone Sara, though this time I felt a bit nervous. It was a nice evening. I had left my sister by the swimming pool and sat down on a nearby bench facing the sea. The light was starting to fade, which only served to make the colourful illuminations along the promenade stand out even more. It reminded me of the Christmas decorations that Sara had put up months earlier. I was determined not to end up having some polite but mundane discussion. So fairly soon into the conversation, I asked if she would like to spend a few days in Felixstowe along with her young family. I knew that she was familiar with the area as she had once shared with me a childhood memory of a visit to the seaside town. 'Felixstowe mouse', an affectionately named toy, had been the centre of attention as she and her younger brother were escorted along the Promenade – perhaps past the very same spot where I was sitting and patiently waiting for her answer. At last, after what seemed like a pensive pause, Sara's voice continued but slowly and lacking her usual enthusiastic tone. I was slightly surprised and disappointed by her lukewarm response. Then she said, "Mike, have you read the email I sent you today?" "Not really – I don't have a computer here, but tomorrow I can check in the Library," I replied.

The next morning I popped round to the local Library wondering what on earth the communication could have been about. When I opened it, my vision seemed to blur for a few seconds. I took another more focused look and slowly read the short message. It jokingly referred to going on a date with somebody else and sharing with me her slight concern that it might be inappropriate to turn up in a 1960s hairstyle after a day's filming. "Oh bollocks!" was my immediate reaction. A few other whispered swearwords emerged from behind the screen, but I was far too engrossed in thought to be aware if such mutterings caught the attention of anybody passing by that morning. No wonder she asked me whether I had read the email the previous evening. It really showed that she must have been oblivious to my changing feelings towards her. She wouldn't have written such an insensitive comment if she had known what had been going on in my head in those last few weeks. And why should she? After all, the previous evening was the first time in a period of about six months that I had mentioned anything remotely encouraging. There were no further phone calls to Sara for the remaining few days left in Suffolk and it was hard not to feel a bit deflated on the car journey back to London with Elizabeth.

Nevertheless, my friendship with Sara continued for a few more months. I looked after her children several times and even took them ice skating over at Kew Gardens one winter evening. It was a small rink, but sufficiently illuminated to make the nearby Palm House visible enough to provide a picturesque background. In some ways it was a way of returning the favour she had bestowed on me while helping with my mum. Much earlier in the year I had mentioned the existence of a basement below the ground floor of Mum's house and one day Sara finally yielded to her son's requests to view it. He eagerly followed me down the creaking staircase with his mother trailing cautiously behind and looking slightly apprehensive. As soon as we reached the first of three large rooms, all of which were dimly lit, her son's eyes opened wide in bewilderment. For Sara, or any other adult, the sight in front of her probably appeared as vast piles of junk. But for an eight year old boy, with a still untamed imagination, my dad's hoard represented an Aladdin's cave of countless opportunities. Potential sword fights, escape tunnels, hiding places and so on must have raced through his mind. Probably fearing for his safety, Sara was reluctant for him to stay too long and we soon returned upstairs.

On a few occasions Sara was delayed at filming. Whenever her mother Helen was unavailable, or maybe to give her a break from looking after both children together, I would sometimes receive a worried text requesting some assistance. I didn't mind at all and her son seemed delighted. He accepted that the first hour involved doing some studies – but in his mind the real purpose of the visit was play. And boy, could he play! In the summer months it was down to the recreation ground for either football, throwing a Frisbee – which sometimes ended up in the adjacent allotment and then had to be retrieved, games of hide-and-seek or timed races around his devised assault course that incorporated all the available swings, slides and climbing frames. Perhaps his fondest memory may be from an autumn evening around my mum's house. There in the conservatory, he came across a bucket of apples that a few weeks earlier had been slightly bruised but, then forgotten, were now over ripe – close to rotting in fact. They had fallen from the tree that Dad had planted as a sapling many years ago and which now dominated the rest of the greenery just beyond the edge of the lawn.   Carrying the bucket outside, he proceeded to have a great time throwing each apple against the brick wall at the back of the garden. He took special delight at watching them explode, some leaving traces on the wall, whilst any remaining pieces flew off in different and unexpected directions. Each throw was followed by howls of laughter of such carefree abandon that it wasn't long before I too joined in with the fun.

Winter failed to diminish the enjoyment of such visits. One day, perhaps because he was already showing an interest in art, he asked me to draw a sketch of his face. Despite his energetic nature he sat patiently for over ten minutes and both of us were surprised with the end result of the sketch – it was a very good likeness. But soon a more active diversion had to be found. He hadn't forgotten his previous visit to the basement. As a result, several hours were passed in creating quite intricate models of battleships and tanks from some of the discarded materials found there. This included plastic pipes which, with his keen use of Sellotape, he also carefully crafted into rifles. A few minutes later this enabled a fierce battle to rage in the dining room as we fired rolled up paper pellets at each other after emerging cautiously from behind strategically placed items of furniture. Even for a few months into 2009, long after I had stopped seeing Sara and her family, I still found the odd pellet that had lain hidden, undisturbed and out of view in some of the less accessible corners of the room.

Sometimes his sister would accompany him too. She was at least two years older and was quite content to read, watch a DVD or listen to one of my music CDs. I'm sure the two children would have had great fun in the garden with snowball fights but by the time the first snowflakes started to fall and settle – for the first occasion in a number of years – Sara had already looked for alternative sources of child care. The relationship with her new boyfriend, rather than fading as I had been hoping for, was moving in the opposite direction. I'm sure it had been playing on Sara's mind and maybe to protect both me and her children's feelings, the visits ceased shortly before Christmas. This was long after the last really nice social event with Sara back in May 2008. Following a pleasant walk along the river with her and the rest of her family, we spent the remainder of the warm and sunny afternoon out shopping for clothes. She had already been casting a critical eye on the way I dressed and felt that I really needed to clear out my wardrobe! Sara had found a suitable shop near Chiswick High Road and after a cappuccino and some snacks we spent quite a bit of time in the store where I tried on different outfits. It was great fun reappearing from behind the curtains with a different outfit every few minutes to seek Sara's opinion. Although I left the shops with a much lighter wallet, I was pleased with the selection and a few weeks later it even prompted the Head Teacher to comment on the "new look Mike" during one of the staff briefings on Monday mornings.

And I guess that day out at the shops was almost it. We still met from time to time, but not really as friends any more. As the months passed I noticed that increasingly I would be introduced as a neighbour. Moreover, socialising seemed to revolve around her need for help with child care. But she was always polite and I can only think of one occasion when I was made to feel unwelcome. It was late in the morning on a Wednesday. I was on my way to school in any case, so I wouldn't have had time to go in even if invited. But I could see there was no chance of that happening when I was greeted at her front door with a stern expression. The source of her annoyance was probably the time spent helping me to sell Mum's unused tricycle. My inexperience at using the online auction site prompted me to ask far too many questions which she may have found irritating.

When it came to New Year's Eve there wasn't a text this time and shortly afterwards I learnt that she was engaged to the lawyer she had met earlier in the year. Her choice somewhat surprised me. I would have expected her to be happier with someone more creative – an artist, musician, poet or writer. That announcement of the impending marriage on a social networking internet site prompted me to send her a somewhat begrudging message of congratulations before clicking on the 'remove' icon a few days later. I knew that it was time to accept defeat and move on.

Inevitably finishing any relationship is bound to be difficult. For quite some time afterwards, I still felt that it had been a pity that things hadn't worked out better with Sara. While not really significant now, it continues to remain a bit of a mystery as to what extent she liked me. In those last few months she expressed the hope that she hadn't led me on, but the idea that she had absolutely no interest in me didn't seem to square with the frequency of her visits and texts over the first six months. But maybe that could be the answer. While travelling in the car on the day that we went clothes shopping, I can remember her saying that if she didn't get what she wanted after six months, she lost interest. Although the comment was directed at a discussion about home improvements, perhaps that timescale had a wider application. In that respect we were very different. My impression was that she could be quite impulsive and eager to move things on quickly in contrast to my tendency to deliberate, especially with relationships. Nevertheless when looking back, it had been a good friendship, even if only for a short while. I don't know if she gained anything from knowing me, but in those few months I learnt a lot about myself from her and her charming family and I'm sure it may have changed me for the better. She certainly re-awakened some neglected interests, and not just in the arts, literature and films.

A further unsolved mystery remains. There had never been enough time to see whether my sister and Sara would have got on with each other. They only met briefly about two or three times if I remember correctly. I'm sure, with time, my sister would have got to like her. However, Elizabeth appeared to be a bit uneasy when I confided with her about my growing feelings towards Sara in 2008. Her reaction made me feel uncomfortable, but any worries about the prospects of harmony between the two women proved to be premature since, well before the end of the year, any opportunity for me to advance the friendship with Sara – assuming one had existed – had already been missed.

One day, during that summer term of 2008, I popped into Tracy's office at school. Along with Debbie and Claire, she was responsible for First Aid on the Charity Walk in July and I needed to ask her something about arrangements. She was out, but a notice on the wall entitled *People who come into your life* suddenly caught my eye. With almost as many claims over authorship as there are lines in the work, it has been impossible to provide an acknowledgement, but the first part of the passage helped to put a positive perspective on that significant and yet short friendship with Sara, thereby avoiding any feelings of bitterness when it ended.

'People come into your life for a reason, a season or a lifetime. When you know which one it is, you will know what to do for that person. When someone is in your life for a REASON, it is usually to meet a need you have expressed. They come to assist you through a difficulty, to provide you with guidance and support, to aid you physically, emotionally or spiritually. They seem like a Godsend and they are. They are there for the reason you need them to be. Then, without any wrongdoing on your part or at an inconvenient time, this person will say or bring the relationship to an end. Sometimes they die. Sometimes they walk away. Sometimes they act up and force you to take a stand. What you must realise is that our need has been met, our desire fulfilled, their work is done. The prayer you sent up has been answered and now it is time to move on....'

Chapter 30   Dark Thoughts

It would be easier to leave this section out – but if this is to be a truthful account of what it can be like looking after someone with dementia – then it shouldn't be omitted.

I suppose you could look upon this as confession time. As a child I never liked being dragged to confession at church. Apart from confiding that I had forgotten to say some prayers, most of the time there wasn't anything significant to own up to. Sometimes, just to make it more interesting for the priest, I wondered if I should make something up. I never did, because even at the age of about eight I realised that such a lie would have defeated the object of going there in the first place. But many years later and after all the good work that I had done in caring for Mum, I must confess there were a few moments I am not proud of. They were just swift, passing thoughts, sometimes even wicked ones, but in no way did they result in any action on my part. However, they did enter my head, even if only for a few seconds, and I was left quite shocked.

Why on earth did I have a picture of pushing my mum into the river on one of our early morning walks? Is that why I heard her saying, "*Ho paura* (I'm afraid)!" on a few occasions, as if reading my mind? It was deserted at that time and nobody would have seen such a hideous crime. All my responsibilities suddenly over, but any freedom gained would have been so short-lived.   And when the image of my poor, helpless Mum, struggling in the dirty water of the Thames next appeared, I almost felt physically sick. 'Oh my God,' I thought, had looking after Mum for so long with hundreds of nights of sleep deprivation caused my brain to conjure up such terrible thoughts?   What made it feel even worse was that they were being directed towards my mum, whom I loved so dearly.

But there were a few days, although not many amongst the thousands of providing care, when I just wanted to be able to walk away from it all; maybe just go to Heathrow airport and escape even if only for a short while. Apart from Mum's few stays in the hospital, there just wasn't any respite. Maybe the best way for someone to appreciate the situation would be to imagine doing the same job every day of the week, with no break in the evenings and just a little during the night, but repeated every single week of the year. No breaks for week-ends or holidays – just continuous and unrelenting work.

Another terrible vision appeared – one of placing a pillow over her head while she was asleep. I could go on but such examples of dark thoughts were very infrequent and obviously were dismissed almost as instantly as they appeared. And to put it in some context, they may have amounted to only a minute or two amongst the many millions spent looking after her. But it was worrying, nonetheless, that they came into my head at all. And for a few months after Mum died and I had time to look back, it made me start to question whether I would be fit to have a relationship with anybody. For I was left wondering: had a hitherto unknown darker side to my character been allowed to surface?

Probably not was the answer. The reality of the situation was that for most of the time I remained calm during what was an extremely challenging but, nevertheless, very rewarding and satisfying experience. After all, I did have to deal with occasions when Mum could drive me to despair. Sometimes she could make totally irrational requests or demands which could be persistent and hence, became even more irritating. On other occasions she could stubbornly refuse help when to me, but maybe not to her, it would have been obviously in her best interests to accept. And although I may have had a few terrible thoughts, I think, under the circumstances, I managed to control any anger quite well. True, the pane of a cabinet unexpectedly shattered one day when I slammed it shut out of frustration, not realising that it was made of glass rather than plastic. And then there was the time when Mum was struggling with me while I was trying to wash her hair after a delay of a few months. It provoked me into tipping the whole bowl of lukewarm water over her head to rinse out the shampoo, completely soaking her along with all her clothes. Perhaps it was a positive way of channelling my anger. Her hair needed to be washed, whether she liked it or not, and at least it sped up the process. It also served to clean the kitchen floor!

On a few occasions I may also have been a bit too forceful when trying to get her to do something that she was reluctant to comply with. I can remember one night when I took her to the toilet before going to bed. As she was about to sit down on the toilet seat, she suddenly changed her mind. I should have let it go, but for some reason that night I lost my patience. This was around the time when she was already wetting the bed fairly regularly so I was determined she would at least make some attempt, even if meant waiting a few minutes. When she struggled against me, I forced her back down onto the seat but to my horror she slipped. Before I had time to react and catch her, somehow she fell. Much to my relief, she wasn't hurt but I still felt guilty about it.

Having to resort to using a tranquillizer during Mum's last few days at home was an unwelcome development but it was a response to what seemed a desperate situation. Hopefully, the doses given weren't too strong but a nagging doubt does remain. Could the attempt to sedate Mum have fatally impaired her already very weak ability to swallow safely and therefore contributed towards the onset of the chest infection that ultimately led to her pneumonia? It can give rise to an uneasy feeling when I think back to those final days but maybe any guilt should be tempered by acknowledging that I had probably been engaged in what many would have considered to be a no-win situation.

The only other regret concerns the need to pat her gently on the face a few times that night when she kept on shouting at the beginning of January 2008. How much more the neighbours would be able put up with before making an official complaint crossed my mind a few times that night. Consequently, the course of action was more of a desperate last resort rather than an indication of any hint of anger or frustration. I had already tried other ways to calm her down, but when I found that this too didn't work, I quickly gave up. And at the time, how was I to know how near it was to the end?

Well, those are the main sources of remorse that I have concerning recollections of either my thoughts or my actions towards my mum. I would prefer it if they hadn't happened, but maybe I should accept that while I feel a sense of shame, particularly about some of the visions that passed through my mind, they were very infrequent. Besides, I wonder whether other people would have been any better in such a stressful and wearying situation. But those few dark thoughts weren't just confined to Mum; there were a few times when I had suicidal thoughts.

These thoughts never occurred while I was looking after Mum. I was far too busy and, moreover, my life had a real purpose. Mum was totally dependent on me in the last few years, and apart from the odd occasion when it got me down or made me angry, I took on the challenge with enthusiasm and great affection towards her. But when Mum died in January 2008 it was followed by a few depressing months. For the first few weeks after her death, most mornings I woke up and for a few seconds I could still hear the echo of Mum's chanting of *"etto berretto"* ringing in my head. And some of the dreams I had were not very pleasant either. It probably took about two months before images associating excrement and female genitals were finally purged, but it meant that for a brief period some strange thoughts were whirling around at the back of my mind while engaged in conversation at work.

It was also a time when I felt physically run down, which wasn't helped by suffering the two bouts of cellulitis during the two months following Mum's death. I also started questioning myself in terms of the care that I had given Mum. Was it good enough? Could I have done more? Did I make any mistakes that might have contributed towards her last illness of pneumonia that finally took her? After all, every spoonful of mashed food and thickened drink that I offered Mum was equivalent to playing a game of Russian roulette, increasing the risk of pneumonia due to aspirating anything, other than air, into the respiratory tract. During February and March I was reading books on dementia and care for the elderly that I had bought after Mum passed away. They were by this stage of absolutely no benefit to her. But it seemed that I still needed to consult them for reassurance – as if to check that I done a reasonable job in looking after her.

Increasingly the setbacks experienced in the first few months of 2008 did begin to make it feel as if the year was going to be a write-off – Mum already lost – whilst prospects of any progress with Sara seemingly on the wane. Dreams, although often a kaleidoscope of many crazy visions, sometimes portray a caricature of the truth. One involved *my repeated inability to kick a football over the garden wall – frustrating because even from early on in my childhood I would have considered that to be the simplest of tasks. But it was the presence of two other people, which made this imaginary scene of incompetence feel particularly embarrassing. Standing nearby was Sara's mother, Helen. She kept handing back the ball after it rebounded off the brickwork, patiently encouraging me to have another go. Meanwhile, an increasingly disenchanted daughter, making no attempt to disguise her eagerness to leave, looked on from a short distance with disapproval stamped all over her face.* It was only a dream, but it probably reflected a greater degree of reality than I cared to acknowledge at the time.

Gradually over the summer, my self-esteem seemed to be coming back, and I was able to start going out again. But it still remained a difficult time and thoughts of taking my life did briefly cross my mind, though they were never really serious. However, there were opportunities. That summer I was working on the roof in the Chiswick house. Sometimes I would take a break by sitting on the small roof of the attic window, surveying the scenery all around. It was so peaceful. You could catch glimpses of people, looking quite small from that height, getting on with their lives and totally unaware that I was up there or what I was thinking. Occasionally I stood up very close to the edge and thought – just one more step and it would be over – but what a messy affair to crash through the glass of the conservatory that Dad had worked so hard to construct all those years ago! The other thought concerned the way the ladder was positioned on the kitchen roof. It was at the perfect angle. Given the distance from the wall, a rope of the correct length meant there would have been no turning back if I stepped off. But – just as the thoughts of harming my mum never materialised into anything – so the same applied to my own self-destruction. Just like the wind they quickly passed by, but pass by they did.

The summer holiday was a great opportunity to go out more and do different things. In August, cycling from Chiswick to Felixstowe, about one hundred miles, in just over eight hours, was some sort of achievement. I started to feel more positive about myself and about life. Continuing the journey to Norwich also provided an opportunity to revisit my old University after an absence of about thirty years. Chatting up an interesting Chinese post-graduate student in a café didn't lead to anything, but it was an indication that my confidence was returning. And why shouldn't I have felt confident after just cycling about two hundred miles over the previous few days?

This little cycling adventure, one that would have been commended by my grandfather, I'm sure, was preceded by an enjoyable day trip on the train to Brighton with my sister. It turned out to be a particularly hot day in May. After a tour around the marina, followed by a meal in a Chinese restaurant, we relaxed on the pebbled beach. Unlike Felixstowe, it remained hot until late in the evening. The weather and the view from the pier, with power boats speeding past, gave the whole seaside town a Mediterranean feel, and made it difficult to leave for the short walk back to the station and the return to Kingston. That was one of several trips organised by Elizabeth as she did her best to try and lift my spirits during 2008.

But there was at least one more test ahead. How would I feel on the anniversary of Mum's death? I fully expected to find the 17th of January, 2009, a difficult day, but to my surprise it was the day before when I got emotionally upset. It must have been because the morning was very similar to the one when Mum passed away. The weather was similar, grey and gloomy. By coincidence it was also the day when my next group of economics students were re-sitting the same AS module as a year earlier. Once again it was Graham who was in charge of supervising the exam, but this time I didn't have to rush off to the hospital. I looked into the room to check that all of my students were present, but it wasn't long before my thoughts drifted back to the events of the previous year. Graham was busy filling up the attendance sheet and my students were already writing, and with the silent corridor deserted, at least nobody could have noticed my inability to hold back a few tears. There was sadness about losing Mum, but it was also mixed with fond memories of her, including one that was probably prompted by Graham's proximity. I suddenly remembered the story that had amused the Welshman a few years earlier. I don't know why, but the day before a training day, Mum had gone into my room and inexplicably put the folder containing the new *AQA Specification for Economics* under my pillow. I can recall thinking that the pillow had felt uncomfortable but it was only in the morning that I discovered the actual reason for such discomfort. Talk about sleeping on it!

During the morning break that followed the exam I had a cup of tea with Joe, who was also sitting in the staff room. He must have noticed that my eyes were still a bit red and asked me what was wrong. I explained that it was close to the anniversary of Mum's death. The bell rang signifying the end of break, but he stayed a few more minutes to try and cheer me up. The rest of the day at school went by without any further problems so it wasn't until I got home and was on my own that I felt really depressed. I think the next few hours were the darkest of my whole life. I was completely engulfed in grief and seemed powerless to break free. It was as if a black cloud was hanging over me. Initially I sat there unable to think of one positive thought and then once again, as earlier in the summer, my mind turned back to all the rope that was lying down in the basement. But unlike previous occasions, this time these dark thoughts weren't fleeting; this time they lingered.

There was a real battle going on in my head. On the one hand there was something so appealing and calming about the prospects of no more decisions, struggles, upsets or sadness. On the other hand there were thoughts about all the people I would be letting down, and even some of the events that I could look forward to later in the year. Most importantly there was my sister. What a mess I would be leaving her to deal with. And what about my friends and all those colleagues at work? Moreover, it would be very bad timing; the students had done so well with their coursework and there were still lots of topics to complete before finishing the syllabus. Then there was the Charity Walk for 2008. I had recently finished the design for the yellow T-shirt, and it was always interesting to see the ideas on paper transferred to the material. No, it would definitely have to wait! Of course nothing actually happened. These were just thoughts running around in my head. But the mere consideration of such drastic action must have been a reflection of how unhappy I was during the year, particularly the first few months, following Mum's death.

Suddenly that evening, I thought of a very practical way of dealing with all those depressing thoughts. I don't know where the idea came from, but I decided I would sleep on the floor in exactly the same spot as I had done in those last few months of looking after Mum. And straight away I felt better. The dark cloud had lifted. The storm had passed. And as if to confirm I had got through the toughest day – and maybe to ensure that such dark thoughts weren't going to return – the phone started ringing.

It was a friend, Avion, a very pretty English teacher from the school. She was from Trinidad and a few weeks earlier had invited me over to join the rest of her delightful family for a meal on Christmas Day. Happily married with four children, the eldest of her three equally pretty daughters already in her mid-twenties, there were times when Avion looked little over thirty, especially when her black hair was styled like one of the *Supremes*. Her fine figure made the colourful combinations of clothes – that she often turned up to work in – appear even more elegant. And so, it was a welcome surprise to be talking to Avion on the phone. She called me to ask if I was all right. Joe must have spoken to her and suggested that she should have a chat with me. Replying to her I could truthfully say I was fine, because by that time I had already dealt with the demons in my head. I was happy to accept her offer to go for a meal at her sister's the following evening.

Later that night I went up to the attic and brought down the sleeping bag along with any other gear that I had used the previous year. When it was time to lie down, I even left the globe light on to re-create the atmosphere of those last few months with Mum. It was strange, but even though it was a bit cold on the floor, I felt warm inside just like I had done over a year ago when tending to Mum in the middle of the night. Maybe the warmth wasn't of the same intensity but it felt good nevertheless. I looked over to the empty space that had once been occupied by the electric bed and contentedly drifted off to sleep, sensing that on that night I was not alone. The following day I was fine and, maybe because of all the outpouring of emotions the previous day, strangely enough, I didn't give too much thought to my mum. But at least I knew I had found a way of dealing with the situation in case I felt upset on anniversaries to come.

Chapter 31 *San Damiano*

So, how to finish this story? It probably makes sense to go back to the beginning. As Mum had been born in *San Damiano d'Asti*, this seemed a fitting resting place for her ashes. Indeed, one of the original intentions of the trip to Italy in 2006 had been to fit in a visit to her birthplace; and it was only when she became so agitated and anxious, thereby forcing our earlier than expected return to London, that the idea had to be abandoned. Now I would be able to fulfil the promise made a few years earlier.

The May half-term holiday arrived and once again, exactly two years after the previous trip with my mother, we set off, but this time I was carrying her in a casket, unceremoniously placed in my rucksack along with spare clothes for the few days planned in northern Italy. It was surprising that the ashes were quite heavy – but now the journey would be lightened by not having the stress of travelling abroad accompanied by an elderly woman in the last stages of dementia.

Up at five in the morning, I didn't hang around too long. As soon as I had breakfast, I set off so that there was no danger of missing the Eurostar train that was due to depart from St Pancras at 8:30 a.m. Armed with the guide to the Paris Metro, kindly emailed to me a few days earlier by Sara, this time I made the underground journey from the *Gare du Nord* to the *Gare de Lyon*, thereby avoiding being ripped off again by one of the Parisian taxi drivers. Emerging from the labyrinth of tunnels, I was grateful to find that it was still sunny in Paris which made the hour or so waiting for the next train all the more pleasant. I stepped outside into the warmth. Close by I found a step to sit down on with a good view of the bustling activity on the platforms. While eating my packed lunch my thoughts drifted back to the scene that had been acted out two years previously – an agitated old woman being closely followed by a flustered son – in complete contrast to the relaxed journey I was now enjoying. There was even time to send Sara a text thanking her for the use of her guide, which had proved so useful. She sent me a reply wishing me well, and that the whole trip would be a 'cathartic experience'. Until that point in my life, I had never encountered or had the occasion to make use of the word, so I wasn't really sure what she was hoping for me, but a later check in a dictionary revealed it to have been an appropriate comment.

It was the last time I would see the sun for a few days. The journey from Paris to *Torino* was due to take about six hours and as the train sped southwards through the French countryside the sky clouded over. On reaching the Alps, we hit a wall of rain that apparently had been sitting over the Piedmont region, just south of France, for over a week. Even though the weather was so gloomy, travelling through the mountains provided some spectacular scenery. The journey back a few days later was even more memorable. Incredible jets of water cascaded down the mountainside to swell the churning, muddied river that had turned brown and appeared to be boiling.

I was greeted at the station that Saturday evening by my cousin Germano, and taken for a meal, along with his sister Monica. After such a long journey I was hungry, but should have stuck with their first suggestion of a pizza. Germano asked me if I would like pasta instead. "*Si*", I replied. Then I made the mistake of giving him the same answer in the affirmative when he enquired about fish. I had responded too quickly, imagining a plate of cod or plaice. A few seconds later I started to feel a bit uncomfortable realising the more likely alternative types of seafood that could complement pasta. As I feared, a few minutes later the waiter arrived and placed in front of me a massive plate of spaghetti. I would have no problem with such a generous helping had it not been artistically adorned with so many mussels, shrimps and prawns. 'Oh, no,' I thought. I didn't want to cause offence, but at the same time I didn't fancy eating it, despite my hunger. There was no escape. A quick glance around the restaurant revealed no convenient hiding place, within easy reach, for the unwanted contents on the plate to be discarded. The meal seemed to go on for hours, but eventually I did manage to finish most of it. I tried to look as appreciative as possible, but my two cousins must have realised that I had been struggling. For the remaining few days fish was definitely off the menu!

The next day involved a visit to my aunt's house. We looked through many old family photos, providing an opportunity for my aunt Maria Teresa to remind me of the names of some relatives who had passed away many years ago. In the background, the television reported on the latest developments in the *Giro d'Italia*, the bicycle race equivalent to the *Tour de France*. So it hadn't just been my mother who had inherited my grandfather's interest in his favourite sport! Finally we found a photograph of my mother, taken at her wedding in 1954, which would be suitable for the ceremony scheduled for Monday. Germano then drove us to a restaurant in the mountains just outside *Torino*. It was a lovely meal, in contrast to the previous evening, with many courses, all of which I enjoyed. After dropping off my aunt, the evening was spent at my cousin's apartment, watching the film, *A Day after Tomorrow,* on the television and dubbed in Italian. Following the news, the weather forecasts on each channel showed that Italy was split in two. Symbols for clouds and rain completely covered the north while Rome and all those regions south of the capital were caught in a heat wave. The predictions for the following day in the areas surrounding Piedmont were no better.

The forecasters were depressingly correct. The next day saw absolutely no improvement in the weather. After a large breakfast, which also served as a dinner, we set off from *Torino* for the 40 km drive to *San Damiano*. Eventually the sight of a few towers peering above the many red tiled roofs, set against the green hilly landscape, appeared in the distance, but the immediate destination was close by on the outskirts of the town. The car arrived at the cemetery with time to spare. Still clutching the box containing the casket, I was led to a small office where the paperwork was completed and the payment made. There was a little delay as the proprietor tried to explain why the charge was higher than originally indicated to my cousin. Germano made a few polite protests and looked a little embarrassed at this unexpected request for more money, but I had come prepared.

Armed with umbrellas, my aunt guided us on a tour of the cemetery and showed me a section, almost like a little house, reserved for other relatives of ours who had already been laid to rest. Gino, a cousin of my mother, had also turned up by then. I was glad to see the suave, retired banker, as my mother had spoken fondly of him on several occasions in the past. Gradually our small procession made its way to the area designated for my mother. It was not as impressive as the earlier building that I had been shown, but it was neatly arranged nonetheless. It was a long mausoleum made up of many compartments, with each front displaying a photo and information about the deceased, such as names and dates.

Oddly the final resting place for my mum was not far from the remains of Giovanna, another cousin of my mother. She had died quite young at the age of 58 about twenty five years prior to my mum. It had been Giovanna's adventurous spirit which, unintentionally but so significantly, affected both my mum's and consequently, my own life. For it was her travel to England after the war and positive comments that encouraged my mother to follow. They remained good friends for many years, evidence of which can be found in several photos of the two cousins socialising together and with other friends. One had been taken at Kew Bridge. The smiles and laughter amongst the group of seven young, single women, captured on the old print, showing Mum sitting bravely on the wall and with Giovanna standing in front, suggested that these were carefree days. And that Giovanna could hardly be described as reserved or shy – is not just picked up from those camera shots of the 1950s. Long before the term *karaoke* had ever been conceived, she was already giving a rendition of an Italian song *Mamma* to a surprised and unaccustomed clientele at a traditional English pub. Although Mum declined her cousin's invitation to join in, it was a fond memory that Mum willingly shared with me on several occasions. However, by the late 1970s they seemed to lose contact with each other. A few years later in 1983 Giovanna died, but now after all that time they would be re-united again, just a few metres apart.

The Priest then joined us. A few minutes later silence fell, just before he proceeded to conduct a short service. It would have been difficult for my aunt to attend the funeral in England a few months earlier in February so this was an opportunity for her to pay her last respects to her elder sister. This was important to her as they had been close when they were young, probably more so than with her younger sister Graziella, who strangely enough was the first to pass away in 1997. Like Giovanna, she too died relatively young. In that respect, I should consider myself privileged to have enjoyed Mum's company for so many extra years.

With the main part of the ceremony over, the casket was then placed in the small compartment that had been reserved for Mum. A worker proceeded to take one of the bricks from his wheel barrow and, with a trowel of cement, started to brick up the small entrance. He must have carried out this work many times before but I couldn't stop myself thinking that I could have done a neater job. I had to hold myself back from volunteering to take over. As each brick was placed in position, the compartment grew darker. Finally the last one shut out the light completely and at that moment I knew I had made the right decision to leave a small amount of the ashes back in England. It made the moment less final. Once the bricks were plastered over, a marble plaque was pressed on to the wet mortar, and the seal was complete. At some future date I had been assured that an inscription, along with the photo of my mum selected the previous day, would be placed on the marble cover.

It had been raining throughout the ceremony. It continued as we drove back to the town centre where we stopped for a coffee. It was a very typical old, small Italian town with a *piazza* dominated by the town hall. Virtually opposite this imposing municipal building was the home where my mother, and her two younger sisters, had been brought up before and during the Second World War. My aunt pointed towards a window with green shutters on the first floor of the yellow building. That, she told me, was the upstairs bedroom that they had shared. Memories of how cold the room could get during the winter, probably ensured that she didn't get too sentimental while telling me the story. The adjacent building, currently occupied by a bank, was the location for the tailor's shop that had been run by my grandfather Clorindo, all those years ago. I would have liked to have stayed longer, exploring the town, walking up and down the narrow streets, taking in the noise and smells and imagining what life might have been like there during the 1930s. But it was time to go back to *Torino*. 'Never mind,' I thought. I would return again one day, possibly with my sister who had been unable to travel to Italy on this occasion.

Before getting into the car that was parked in the square close to Mum's first dwellings, I shook the umbrella. At least it had stopped raining by then, but the sky was still dark and totally dominated by thick, grey clouds. Because the area surrounding *San Damiano* is hilly, the road seemed to meander as we left the town. Perhaps for my benefit so that I could capture the atmosphere of the occasion, Germano was driving quite slowly. From the back seat I turned around to take in a last glance before the town disappeared from view. And then, just for a brief moment, as if to confirm my thoughts – thoughts that sensed the presence of Mum's spirit, a small gap appeared in the clouds. From that opening, a strong, very bright ray of light shone down illuminating the valley. It only lasted a few seconds but it felt like my mum was saying *"ciao* ."

Chapter 32 On Reflection

The Italian word *ciao* means both 'hello' and 'goodbye' in equal measure. It is hard to think of an equivalent that is so completely ambiguous in the English language.

The trip to *San Damiano* had meant to provide some final closure, and when I started writing this story it was planned as the final chapter. But as I discovered over the summer of 2008, and particularly in the run up to the first anniversary of Mum's death in January, there may never be a complete end to the sense of loss. While the trip definitely helped, Mum had become too big a part of my life for a ceremony, even in her home town, to end the sorrow felt. The only hope, I suspect, is that over a sufficient length of time, new experiences will gradually fill the vacuum created by her parting. Meanwhile, memories can hopefully focus more on the numerous happier moments shared with her even in that period covering her decline. And so, instead of finishing with the transportation of her ashes to Italy, it became increasingly apparent that an alternative way to end this account might involve some reflections on how the illness affected Mum and those who really cared for her in those last few years.

Given the undisputed significance of the brain in all our lives, I would argue that any illness that affects the functioning of this organ, particularly, but not exclusively, in a physical sense, should be recognised as a medical problem and not a social one. To make a distinction between the two and exclude government support when the former case is not thought to be strong enough can have the consequence of imposing often unexpected, and consequently unplanned, financial worries and burdens to countless numbers of families around the country.

By the time Mum was ready to leave the hospital in October 2007, her dementia had deteriorated so severely that it was deemed that her requirement for care came under the umbrella of medical needs and therefore was open to public funding. An alternative judgement would have placed a heavy financial burden on top of all the other challenges that automatically accompany any attempt to care for someone with dementia, particularly in the latter stages of the illness. But as future health needs are, for the most part, unpredictable, it is probably unrealistic to expect most individuals to have either the foresight or the wherewithal to finance such commitments through private schemes. In the case of Mum, there were absolutely no warning signs of her forthcoming illness until she reached her mid-seventies. For that reason I would suggest a strong argument will always remain for a significant proportion of the costs for care to be underpinned by the State.

It has been well documented that caring for Mum involved sacrifices but one shouldn't underestimate the affection that can be returned from the person being cared for. Very often it was displayed by Mum holding my hand when we went out for a walk. At other times it would be a friendly smile or a "sorry" when Mum knew that she had annoyed me with some trying behaviour. But above all, it must have been the times when she simply said "I love you," reassuring words, though sometimes it was difficult to work out whether she knew me as her son, father, husband or boyfriend, as her mind drifted in time. The way she looked into my eyes, so intensely sometimes, when she uttered those three words, made me suspect that occasionally they were being delivered by a woman to a lover, rather than a mother to a son. If that made me feel slightly uncomfortable, it didn't matter. More importantly, Mum at least never lost one of her battles in the struggles against the effects of dementia – for that raw emotion of love – was never destroyed.

While the onset of dementia and the growing dependence by my mum for help from me definitely strengthened the bond between us, regrettably the illness seemed to have the opposite effect on the relationship between Mum and my sister – but at least that was only temporary. Elizabeth was a great support and proved a good source of medical advice, particularly during our regular chats on the phone. I also found that the experiences I gained from the last few months of nursing Mum at home meant that I had a much better appreciation of just how difficult her job at the hospital or hospice could be.

Although it only turned out to be a brief friendship of about one year, Sara's influence on me seems to have been more enduring. She certainly played a significant role at the time. Her weekly visits allowed me to go out to work, but they assisted in other ways too. My desire to look after Mum as best as I could was a sufficient driving force on its own, but Sara's praise and obvious interest in our well-being, made a further contribution to my level of motivation. Inadvertently, but in no small measure, she may also have provided the inspiration for me to write this story. It was her response to the short obituary that I had written shortly after Mum's death that probably sowed the seeds, and certainly gave me the confidence, to start such a project a year on. Her text commented on those few paragraphs as a 'lovely, beautifully written piece about your ma; it struck the perfect note.' By the time I actually started writing this story, Sara had already re-married and was no longer part of my life. Nevertheless, she had always been good company and in that way, along with the rest of her family, had already contributed towards my recovery after the sad passing away of Mum early in 2008. I even had a delightful surprise, some time later, while watching the regional news on TV to remind me of that link with Sara. Her uncle was being interviewed and there, in the background, as part of his collection, was my mother's portrait, a copy of which I gratefully received, at a later date, over the internet. However, I suppose there was a certain irony in the friendship with Sara. On reflection, it was Mum's illness that definitely had brought us together, but it was probably that same illness that also kept us apart.

A notable omission from these reflections so far has been Mum herself. What had the experience been like for her? It couldn't have been easy. Here was a feisty, independent, energetic and stubborn woman losing her powers each year and at a worrying rate. She was scared, particularly in 2004, the worst year in my opinion when her anger and frustration really emerged. But my impression was that she was happy for a large part of the time. Apart from independence, all of her other three characteristics endured in varying degrees throughout, and were only finally overcome in that last week in the hospital when she was very ill. How could the scenes in the Consulate and then on the journey to Italy not be described as feisty? At the age of eighty-one she still had the energy to walk me into the ground on some days – all the more surprising as my participation in the London Marathon in 1982 shows that I possess a reasonable degree of stamina.[11] And as for stubbornness, the only way to get her to take her medicines even when she was bed-bound was to hide them in her food or drink. But as much as she probably wanted to hold on to her independence, that was the one area where she succumbed earliest to the debilitating effects of dementia. Nevertheless, for many of the preceding years she battled with the illness and tried to maintain some degree of self-sufficiency for as long as possible – it's just that the range of activities where she could remain self-reliant diminished each year.

Nevertheless, in spite of losing so much, her cheerful side never entirely disappeared. Even in the last stages, she could be heard laughing and singing. When she voiced any complaints, notwithstanding a somewhat limited vocabulary, you could at least see that thoughts were still flashing around her, albeit, impaired brain. Perhaps most significantly for me, she still showed a strong degree of affection even right up to the end. And despite the dementia, it was good that she had been very lucky to reach the ripe old age of nearly eighty-two, well cared for by her children, neighbours, carers and the NHS because – without them – her alternative fate doesn't bear thinking about.

Over the last few years of Mum's life, there were many individuals who helped attend to her medical needs, in addition to that of social care. Whether they were doctors, nurses, carers or administrators, everybody that I dealt with seemed to have their heart in the right place and, by and large, the service was delivered well. Nevertheless, the preceding account does provide some examples where care could be improved. This is not the place for me to suggest possible reforms, especially if not backed up by adequate research, but by simply drawing on personal experience I would argue that a strong case could be made to achieve more flexibility in the system. An attempt to cater for individual needs more adequately would go a long way to improving the quality of the service. In my case, I would have preferred fewer visits from the carers each day, to be replaced by some access to respite care once in a while. Even something that might appear trivial, such as being given an opportunity to exercise some choice

---

[11] The 26 miles completed in a respectable time of 3hrs 32mins.

in the selection of pads, would have been appreciated. Notwithstanding these minor criticisms, overall I was pleased with the help offered.

Perhaps the most surprising aspect of the whole journey of caring for Mum was the length of time involved in recovering myself. Physically the wounds healed quickly. Once the cellulitis had cleared up towards the end of spring, I had the summer to look forward to and by the time the school holidays started in July, months of training to regain my fitness and getting some sun on my back were making me feel much better. Even the infection on my fingernails cleared up after a few months. But emotionally, the pace of recovery was much slower, and I still needed to get past a difficult winter before I could honestly claim that I was closer to getting over the loss.

A few weeks before writing this chapter, I had spent a Sunday afternoon at a friend's home. Older than me with long, fair, frizzy hair, Jean's pretty face and youthful appearance defied her years. Sitting opposite and surrounded by the sheets of paper already edited, her blue and very alert eyes focused on the successive pages of the next chapter, revealing her red scribbling alongside the printed lines that we were about to discuss. She had kindly spent many hours checking the early drafts for grammatical and punctuation errors. But she did more than that. She also shared her opinions and was willing to be critical as well as encouraging with praise.

One conversation with Jean, back in July 2009, particularly sticks in my mind as revealing her perceptive qualities. Originally intended to focus on Mum's feisty character and fight against the incapacitating effects of dementia, Jean put forward an unexpected slant on the story. At that stage I had only written a few chapters. After several positive comments, Jean paused. The expression on her face changed. It looked serious, as if to add some gravity to the point that she wanted to share with me. "Mike, don't think this story is mainly about your mother. It's just as much about you – probably even more so. Certainly more than you think at the moment. Don't forget that!" I didn't feel entirely comfortable with her conclusion at the time, but many chapters and several drafts later, I would be inclined to agree. Without any intention, the story became a journey of self-discovery, exploring my feelings towards my mother as well as other women. It was as much an examination of how much stress I could put up with as any previous challenges in my life – actually far greater – and I had come through the testing times probably better equipped to meet any future trials that life can present.

Time had passed by quickly and after reviewing two chapters we paused for a break; her friend, Bert, a very skilful carpenter, returned from the kitchen with a tray of tea and biscuits. Somewhere in the ensuing conversation, Jean commented on how much younger I looked since starting the project of writing Mum's story back in July 2009. She was right. I did feel much better. Although already well underway, the healing process had been sped up by tying down my whirling and uncontrolled thoughts and transferring them onto paper. Watching my account unfold and gradually become moulded into a unified story ensured that I would always be left with a lasting tribute to my mum.

Nearly two years on and finally it seems that I may have reached a point where I can look back and feel really content with the care that I had given Mum, although I guess one never can really completely recover from such a loss. Of course I didn't realise it at the time, but throughout that period of struggling to cope with Mum's illness, she was again providing me with one more final and special gift – an amazing experience and story to remember, prompting another reference to a passage from *People who come into your life*. It ends with the following appropriate quote. '*Thank you for being part of my life, whether for a reason, a season or a lifetime*'.

You see – who really cares – does matter. Obviously it had been significant for Mum. But it was and continues to be relevant to me. Maybe I was lucky that I didn't need to delegate the main part of the care to an army of well-meaning strangers. Whilst embracing such an onerous responsibility was difficult, there was a huge reward. For me, bereavement only started after her death – never while she was alive. Although each one of her skills was being lost over time, the bond between mother and son was never broken.

Postscript

"I'm thinking of writing a book about my mum." "Go for it!" was the encouraging response from Joe, one Friday morning in June 2009, probably not anticipating the regular updates that he was about to be subjected to for some time to come. The first draft only took about three months to complete – the story was already inside me. Subsequent amendments have taken much longer than expected, but the whole process has turned out to be a very satisfying and therapeutic experience nevertheless.

Now, in the spring of 2011, after much redrafting and very useful help with proof reading from family and friends, I feel that it is finally ready to submit for printing, even more so since receiving very favourable comments from my cousin, Alfred Molina. It has been a busy two years – for in addition to this most enjoyable writing project, I have been teaching at Gunnersbury, St Mark's, Gumley House and the University of Westminster, as well as making occasional appearances in TV dramas and films. And in July, I can look forward to the staging of the twelfth successive Charity Walk – an event eagerly supported by the new Head Teacher, Mr K. Burke, as did his predecessor, the late John Heffernan.

Others not previously mentioned but providing help on the Walk include: Selwyn, Sarah B, Louise W, Michael W, Louise M, Andrew K, Marilyn B, Peter C, Mrs Green, Anne C, Sabishna, Alex, Julian, Yolanda, Jeremy, Karin, Nick D, Declan L, Raj, Paul T, Hayley, Oliver B, Jay-sen, Errol H, Kay, Pam, Caroline B, Mawgan and Pietro.

Amounts raised and shirt colours between 2000 and 2011:

2000, royal blue, £1,500; **2001**, red, £1,700; **2002**, white, £2,000; **2003**, sky blue, £2,000; **2004**, black, £1,400; **2005**, grey, £1,900; **2006**, navy blue, £1,600; **2007**, green, £1,900; **2008**, yellow, £2,500; **2009**, purple, £2,700; **2010**, pink/grey, £3,100 and **2011**, royal blue, £2,400.

Typical route: Gunnersbury School-Boston Manor Park-Grand Union Canal-Brentford-Syon Park-Isleworth-Richmond Lock Bridge-Kew Gardens-Kew Bridge-Griffin Park-Gunnersbury School. Variations on the route include: Gunnersbury Park (2000), Richmond Bridge (2000-2003), Teddington Lock Bridge (2001) and Twickenham Rugby Stadium (2001 and 2005).

Allocation of Funds: Plan International, Action Aid, Cancer Research UK, Myasthenia Gravis Association, Macmillan Cancer Support, Smile Train, Dementia UK, Oxfam, Misikhu School in Kenya, Marie Curie Cancer Care and Sport Relief.

A final, but sad note remains. Since writing the first draft, two friends, mentioned in the book, passed away: Włodek Lesiecki (1947-2010) who tragically died following a diving accident while on a summer holiday in Poland, and a few weeks later, Bernard North (1920-2010) who had suffered from cancer. Such charming men will be greatly missed by family and friends alike.

KEW
PRESS

Harper
An imprint of HarperCollins*Publishers*
77–85 Fulham Palace Road,
Hammersmith, London W6 8JB

www.harpercollins.co.uk

This paperback edition 2010
1

A catalogue record for this book
is available from the British Library

ISBN: 978-0-00-729857-0

Set in Sabon by Palimpsest Book Production Limited,
Falkirk, Stirlingshire

Printed and bound in Great Britain by
Clays Ltd, St Ives plc

To my daughter Monique –
all the treasure this
father needs

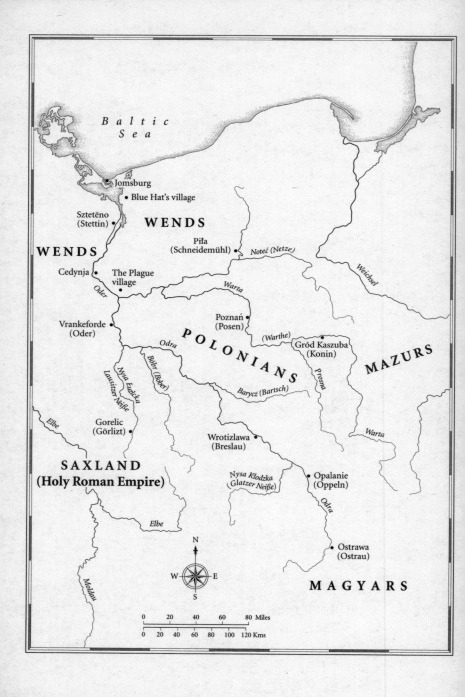

Baltic Sea

WENDS

• Jomsburg
• Blue Hat's village

Sztetëno
(Stettin) •

WENDS

Piła
(Schneidemühl) •   *Noteć (Netze)*

Cedynja •   • The Plague
village

Oder   *Warta*

Weichsel

Poznań
(Posen) •

Vrankeforde
(Oder) •

P O L O N I A N S

(Warthe)

Gród Kaszuba
(Konin) •

M A Z U R S

Odra

Bóbr (Bober)

Prosna

Nysa Łużycka
Lausitzer Neiße

Barycz (Bartsch)

Elbe

Gorelic
(Görlizt) •

Warta

Wrotizlawa
(Breslau) •

SAXLAND
(Holy Roman Empire)

Nysa Kłodzka
(Glatzer Neiße)

• Opalanie
(Oppeln)

Elbe

Odra

Moldau

N
W ✦ E
S

• Ostrawa
(Ostrau)

M A G Y A R S

0   20   40   60   80 Miles
0 20 40 60 80 100 120 Kms

The prow-beast, hostile monster of the mast
With his strength hews out a file
On ocean's even path, showing no mercy

Egil Skallagrimsson

AUSTRGOTALAND, 975AD

The sun stayed veiled behind lead clouds streaked with silver. The rain hissed and the sea heaved, black and sluggish as a walrus on a rock, while a wind dragged a fine smoke of spray into my eyes.

'Not storm enough,' Hauk Fast-Sailor declared and he had the right of it, for sure. There was not enough of a storm to stop our enemies from coming up the fjord with the wind in their favour and that great, green-bordered sail swelled out. On a ship with a snarling serpent prow that sail looked like dragon wings and gave the ship its name.

The oars on the *Fjord Elk* were dipped, but moving only to keep the prow beast snarling into the wind that drove the enemy down on us; there was no point in tiring ourselves – we were crew-light, after all – while the enemy climbed into their battle gear. When we saw their sail go down would be the time for worry, the time they were ready for war.

Instead, men kept their hands busy tightening straps and checking edges, binding back their hair as it whipped in the wind. All of Jarl Brand's lent-men from *Black Eagle* were here, save six with Ref and Bjaelfi who were herding women and weans and thralls away from Hestreng hall and up to

1

the valley, with as much food and spare sail for tentage as they could carry. Away from the wrath of Randr Sterki and the snarlers on *Dragon Wings*.

I hoped Randr Sterki would content himself with looting and burning Hestreng, would not head inland too far. I had left him wethers and cooped hens and pigs to steal, as well as a hall and the buildings to burn – and if it was the Oathsworn he wanted . . . well, here we were, waiting for him at sea.

Still, I knew what drove Randr to this attack and could not blame him for it. I had the spear in my throat and the melted bowels that always came with the prospect of facing men who wanted to cleave sharp bars of metal through me but, for once, did not wish to be elsewhere. This was where I had to be, protecting the backs of mine and all the other fledglings teetering on flight's edge, from the revenge of raiding men.

Men like us.

Gizur, swinging down from stay to stay through the ranks of men, looked like a mad little monkey I had seen once in Serkland, his weather-lined face such a perfect replica that I smiled. He was surprised at that smile, considering what we faced, then grinned back.

'We should ship oars, Jarl Orm, before they get splintered.'

I nodded; when the ships struck, the oars on that side would be a disaster to us if we left them out. There was a flurry and clatter as the oars came in and were stacked lengthways; men cursed as shafts dunted them and now I saw the great snarling prow of *Dragon Wings* clearly, heard the faint shrieks and roars, saw the weapon-waving.

I was watching them flake the sail down to the yard when two of Jarl Brand's lent-men shoved through our throng, almost to the *Fjord Elk*'s prow, nocking arrows as they went, stepping over bundled oars and shoving folk aside. They shot; distant screams made our own men roar approval – then curse as an answering flight zipped and shunked into the woodwork. One of the bowmen, Kalf Sygni, spun half round

2

and clutched his forearm where a shaft was through, side to side.

'Missed that coming,' bellowed Finn, hefting his shield as he moved to the prow, clashing ring-iron shoulders with Nes-Bjorn, who was headed the same way; they glared at each other.

'I am Jarl Brand's prow man on the *Black Eagle*,' Nes-Bjorn growled.

'You are not on the *Black Eagle*,' Finn pointed out and, reluctantly, the big man gave way, letting Finn take his place. Across on *Dragon Wings* his counterpart, hero-warrior of his boat, stepped up, mailed, helmeted and carrying a shield, but nothing better than a ship-wood axe.

They had the sail down and the oars shipped, leaving *Dragon Wings* with enough momentum to crash on us, rocking the *Elk* sideways to the waterline, staggering men who had been unprepared for it. Randr's crew howled and axes clattered over our side, causing men to duck and raise shields – the axe-owners hauled hard at the ropes ringed to the shafts, pulling the hooked heads tight to the inside of the *Elk* with their iron beards, clinching us close as lovers.

A man screamed as his leg went with such a pull, trapping him like a snared fox against the side while he beat and tugged. Holger, I remembered dully as he screamed his throat out in agony. His name was Holger.

An arrow skittered off the mast and whipped past my head; I wore no ring-coat, for I was not so sure I could wriggle out of it in time if I fell overboard. Botolf, who stood on my right, heard me curse and grinned.

'Now you know what it feels like,' he yelled and I laughed into his mad delight, for it was a long-standing joke that Botolf had never found a ring-coat big enough to fit him. Then he threw back his head and roared out his name; Randr Sterki's men shrieked and howled; the sides of the boats clashed and men flung themselves forward while the locked ships groaned and rocked.

3

The worst thing about battle, after a few bloodings drive away the first fears of it, is that it is work. The stink and the horror, the belly-wrenching terror and savage hatred of it were all things I had grown used to – but the backbreaking labour of it was what always made me blench. It was like ploughing stony ground, where the stones rise up and try to hit you and the whole affair leaves you sick and tremble-legged with exhaustion. The one good part about being jarl was that you did not sink into the grind of it, at least not all at once – but you had to stand like a tree in a boiling flood and seem unconcerned.

I stood rock-still and guarded by Botolf's shield, watching the *Dragon Wings* crew pile forward in a rush, dipping both ships almost into the water with their weight. They struggled and hacked and died on the thwart-edges, my picked men darting in to cut the ropes that bound us together, or shoot out the men on *Dragon Wings* whose task it was to haul us tight.

They were red-mouthed screamers, Randr Sterki's crew, waving spears and axes, garbed in leather and some in no more than makeshift breastplates of knotted rope. They had helms of all kinds, none of them fine craftings, and waved blades as notched as a dog's jaw – even Randr Sterki's ring-mailed prow man wielded no better than an adze-axe. Yet they had the savagery of revenge in them and that made the arm strong and the edge sharp.

Randr stood and roared out unheard curses in the middle of his ship, in the middle of a group as unlike the men round them as sheep-droppings in snow. They made my knees turn to water, those men whose eyes stared and saw nothing, who wore only thick, hairy hides over their breeks, who champed flecks of foam onto the thicket of their beards and hefted weapons with an easy skill and arms blood-marked with strength runes. Some of them, I noted, had swords, well-worn and well-earned.

'Bearcoats!' yelled Botolf in my ear. 'He has bearcoats, Orm . . .'

Even as he spoke I saw them, all twelve of them, stir like a wolf pack scenting a kill. Bearcoats – berserker – had been

no part of Randr Sterki's crew before. Where had he got them from? My mouth went dry; I saw them snarling and howling, slamming into those of their own side who did not see them in time to get out of the way.

The first of them, tow-haired, tangle-bearded, reached the side and howled out to the sky, then hurled himself over on my men before the cords of his neck had slackened; they hacked at him with the desperate fury of those too trapped to run. The rest of the pack began to follow and Randr Sterki urged them on with bellows from the middle of his ship, his face red and ugly with rage and battle.

'We shall have to kill Pig-Face,' panted Nes-Bjorn, suddenly on my other side, pointing to Randr. If he was cursing at having been left behind by Jarl Brand to serve with us on this seemingly bad-wyrded day, his cliff of a face did not show it.

'First stop the bearcoats,' I pointed out, as calmly as I could while watching Tow-Hair carve his way towards me, trailing blood and screams; Botolf hefted his shield and byrnie-biter spear and braced himself on his one good leg. I raised my own sword a little, as if only resting it lightly on one shoulder, while my throat was full of my heart at the sight of a berserker slashing a path straight to me.

'Ach,' said Nes-Bjorn with a dismissive wave of his bearded axe. 'We have our own man for that.'

At which point came a growling grunt from behind me, so like the coughing charge-roar of a boar that I half-spun in alarm. Then a half-naked figure with skin-marks of power and an axe in either hand launched straight over the heads of my own men, scattering them as he clattered into the howling bearcoat. Tow-Hair went down in a bloody eyeblink and the axes flailed on in Stygg Dusi's fists, his carefully applied skin-marks streaked with blood, as he hurled himself in a bellowing whirl of arms and legs and axes over the side and into the crowded *Dragon Wings*. Men scattered before him.

'Stygg Dusi,' Nes-Bjorn pointed out and split a feral grin

as the man by-named Shy Calm howled and chopped and died hard in the middle of the enemy ship.

'There are twelve of them,' I offered and Nes-Bjorn scowled.

'Eleven now – no, ten, for Stygg has done well. Have you a point to make, Jarl Orm of the Oathsworn, or are you just after showing your skill at tallying?'

Then he elbowed men aside to reach the prow, where Finn, gasping and exhausted, had been forced to step back, ropey strings drooling from his mouth. The *Dragon Wings* prow man was nowhere to be seen.

I listened and watched as Stygg Dusi served out the last seconds of what the Norns had woven for him from the moment he slithered wetly into the world. Everything he had done had led to this place, this moment, and I raised my sword to the life he honoured us with, almost envied him in the certainty of his place in Valholl. *Not yet, but soon*, I was thinking, the old message we gave to all the dying to take with them to those gone before. Very soon now, it seemed.

The last rope was cut; Kalf Sygni, with the arrow still through his forearm, managed to shoot the last rope-hauler and the ships drifted apart from the stern, so that the prow beasts bobbed and snarled, almost seeming to strike out at each other. Men from both crews, trapped on the wrong boat, tried to fight their way to a thwart edge and leap for it.

Everything after that became a blur to me. I remember shoulder-charging a man, sending him flying into the water and it was only when he floundered there that I saw he wore a bearcoat. Finn loomed up, shook slaver and blood from his face, then launched back into the mad struggle, roaring curses and insults.

Hauk Fast-Sailor went down under the frenzied, raving chops of a wet-mouthed trio of bearcoats; Onund Hnufa went over the side, blood streaming from a cut on his head, and a man bound in knotted rope came at me, so that I had to kill him. By the time I looked, Onund had gone and I did not know if he had surfaced or not.

Something small and dark flew at the prow and Nes-Bjorn batted it contemptuously to one side. Flame engulfed him. Just like that. One minute he was roaring invites for someone to face him, the next minute he was enveloped in flame, a pillar of fire staggering about the prow. He fell back and men shrieked; one scrambled away screaming and batting at the flames on his leg, but that only caused his hands to flare. Another flung away a flaming shield, which hit the water and sank – but the water continued to burn in a circle.

'Magic!' yelled a voice, but it was no rune-curse, this. I had seen it before and the second little pot smacked into the *Elk's* prow and burst into flames exactly as Roman Fire was supposed to. I watched the flames leap up the proud horns of Botolf's carving, saw ruin in them even as the frantic crew of *Dragon Wings* saw those same flames leap to their own ship. Then Botolf yelled out that there was a second ship.

A second ship. Roman Fire. Bearcoats. These had been no part of Randr Sterki before now. I blinked and stared, my thoughts wheeling like the embers of my burning ship while men struggled and slipped and died, raving curses.

'Orm – on your steerboard . . .'

I half-turned into a wet-red maw, where spittle skeined like spume off a wave. He had a greasy tangle of wild hair and eyes as mad as a kennel of frothing dogs, while the axe in his hand seemed as big as a wagon tree. I swung and missed, felt my sword bite into the wood of the mast, where it stuck.

I got my shield in the way a little, so that his axe splintered it and tore it sideways, out of my finger-short grasp. His whole body hit me then and there was a moment when I smelled the woodsmoke and grease stink of his pelt, the rankness of his sweat. My hand was wrenched from the hilt of my trapped sword.

Then there was only the whirl of silver sky and dark water and the great, cold plunge, like a hot nail in the quench.

ONE

Six weeks before . . .

The year cracked like a bad cauldron, just as winter unfastened its jaws a little and the cold ebbed to drip and yellow grass. Those from further south would say it was March and spring, but what did they know? It was still winter to us, who counted the seasons sensibly.

In the northlands we also know what causes the ground to move: it is the pain-writhing of Loki, when Loki's wife has to empty her bowl, leaving her bound husband in agony, his face ravaged by the dripping poison of the serpent for the time it takes her to return and catch the venom again. The gods of Asgard gave dark Loki a hard punishment for his meddlings.

His writhings that year folded the cloak of the earth to new shapes with a grinding of stones, and great scarred openings, one of which swallowed an entire field close to us, kine and all.

A sign from the Aesir, Finn said moodily, echoing what others thought – that we should be back on the whale road and not huddled on land trying to be farmers. It was hard to ignore his constant low rumbling on the matter, harder still to put my head down and shoulder into the loud unspoken stares of the rest of them, day after day.

Odin had promised us fame and fortune and, of course, it was cursed, for he had not warned us to beware of what we sought so fiercely. Now that we had it, there was no joy in it for raiding men – what point raiding, as Red Njal grumbled, if you have silver and women enough? Nor was there any joy in trying to forsake the prow beast and cleave to the land, digging it up like worms, as Hlenni pointed out.

I heard them and their talk of the crushing wyrd of Odin. Others, still claiming to be Oathsworn, had wandered off into the world, with promises to be back at my side if the need arose, the old Oath binding them – *We swear to be brothers to each other, bone, blood and steel, on Gungnir, Odin's spear, we swear, may he curse us to the Nine Realms and beyond if we break this faith, one to another.*

I accepted their promises with a nod and a clasping of hands, to keep the Oath alive and them from harm, though I did not expect to see any of them again. Those who remained struggled with the shackles that kept them from following the prow beast. They plodded grimly through winters in the hope that better weather might bring a new spark to send them coldwards and stormwards. It never seemed to flare into a fire of any fierceness, all the same.

The only ones who no longer moaned and grumbled were Botolf and Short Eldgrim, the first because he was no good on a raiding ship with one timber leg and, besides, had Ingrid and a daughter he cared more about; the second had no clear idea half the time of where he was, the inside of his head knocked out of him in a fight years before.

Finn had bairned Thordis in the fever that followed our return, silver-rich and fame-rich, and now she cradled their son, Hroald, in a sling of her looped apron. Finn looked at the boy every day with a mix of pride and misery, the one for what every father felt, the other for the forging of another link in a chain that chafed, for Thordis hourly expected a marriage offer.

On the other hand, when I looked across at Thorgunna and she let me know with her eyes that her own carrying was fine, there were no words, no mead of poetry that described how I felt at the news. It was a joy doubled, for she had lost a bairn before this and to find that it had not broken Thorgunna as a mother was worth all the silver Odin had handed us.

Yet the dull haar of disappointed men hung over Hestreng, so that the arrival of young Crowbone in a fine ship brought heads up, sniffing eagerly at his fire and arrogance like panting dogs on a bitch's arse.

Crowbone. Olaf Tryggvasson, true Prince of Norway and a boy of twelve whose fair fame went before him like a torch and was so tied in with my own that swords and axes were lowered, since no-one could believe Crowbone had come to raid and pillage his friend, Orm of Hestreng.

He sat in my hall rubbing sheep fat into his boots, the price you pay for being splendidly careless and leaping off the prow of a fine ship into the salt-rotting shallows.

I had not seen him in three years and was astounded. I had left a nine-year-old boy and now found a twelve-year-old man. He was sharp-chinned and yellow-haired, his odd-coloured eyes – one brown as a nut, the other blue-green as sea ice – were bland as always and his hair was long enough to whip in the wind, though two brow braids swung, weighted with fat silver rings woven into the ends. I was betting sure that the one thing he wanted, above all else, was to grow hair on his chin.

He wore red and blue, with a heavy silver band on each arm and another, the dragon-ended jarl torc of a chief, at his neck. He had a sword, cunningly made for his size, snugged up in a sheath worked with snake patterns and topped and tailed with bronze. He had come a long way in the three years since I had freed him from where he had been chained by the neck to the privy of a raider called Klerkon.

I said that to him, too, and he smiled a quiet smile, then answered that he had not come as far as me, since he had started as a prince and I had come to being jarl of the legendary Oathsworn from being a gawk-eyed stripling of no account. Which showed what he had learned in oiled manners and gold-browed words at the court of Vladmir.

'A fine ship,' I added as his growlers, all ringmail and swagger, filed in to argue places by the hearthfire. He swelled with pride.

'*Short Serpent* is the name,' he declared. 'Thirty oars a side and room for many more men besides.'

'*Short Serpent*?' I asked and he looked at me, serious as a wrecking.

'One day I will have one bigger than this,' he replied. 'That one I will call *Long Serpent* and it will be the finest raiding ship afloat.'

'Is Hestreng ripe for a *strandhogg*, then?' I asked dryly, for already the fame of this boy was known in halls the length of the Baltic, where he had been hit-and-run raiding – the *strandhogg* – all year.

Crowbone only grinned and shook his head so that the rings tinkled. Then I saw they were not rings at all, but coins with holes punched through them and Crowbone's grin grew wider when he saw I had spotted that. He fished in his pouch and brought out another, a whole one, which he spun at me until I made it vanish in my fist.

'I took it and its brothers and cousins from traders bound for Kiev,' Crowbone said, still grinning. 'We will choke the life from Jaropolk before we are done.'

I looked at it – a glance was all it took, for minted silver was rare enough for me to know all the coins that whirled like bright foam along the Baltic shores. It was Roman, a new-minted one they call *miliaresion* and silver-light compared with other, older cousins that spilled out of Constantinople, which we called Miklagard, the Great City. The ones Crowbone had

11

braided into the ends of his hair were gold *nomisma*, seventy-two to a Roman pound and, I saw, with the head of Nicepheros on them, which made them recent – and one-quarter light.

I said this as I spun it back to him and he grinned, suitably admiring my skill. He had skills of his own when it came to coinage, all the same – backed by the ships and men of Vladimir, Prince of the Rus in Novgorod, he had ravaged up and down the Baltic to further the cause of his friend against Vladimir's brothers, Jaropolk and Oleg. They were not quite at open war, those three Kievan brothers, but it was a matter of time only and the trade routes in their lands were ravaged and broken as a result.

That and the lack of silver from the east that made Crowbone's coin rare – and light – also made any trade trip there worthless unless you went all the way down the rivers and cataracts to the Great City. I said as much while Thorgunna and the thrall women served platters and ale and Crowbone grinned cheerfully, uncaring little wolf cub that he was.

A shadow appeared at his elbow and I turned to the mailed and helmeted figure who owned it; he stared back at me from under his Rus horse-plume and face-mail, iron-grim and stiff as old rock.

'Alyosha Buslaev,' declared little Crowbone with a grin. 'My prow man.'

Vladimir's man more like, I was thinking, as this Alyosha closed in on Crowbone like a protecting hound, sent by the fifteen-year-old Prince of Novgorod to both guard and watch his little brother-in-arms. They were snarling little cubs, the Princes Vladimir and Olaf Crowbone, and thinking on them only made me feel old.

The hall was crowded that night as we feasted young Crowbone and his crew with roast horse, pork, ale and calls to the Aesir, for Hestreng was still free of the Christ and mine was still the un-partitioned hall of a raiding jarl – despite my

best efforts to change that. Still, as I told Crowbone, the White Christ was everywhere, so that the horse trade was dying – those made Christian did not fight horses in the old way, nor eat the meat.

'Go raiding,' he replied, with the air of someone who thought I was daft for not having considered it. Then he grinned. 'I forgot – you do not need to follow the prow beast, with all the silver you have buried away under moonlight.'

I did not answer that; young Crowbone had developed a hunger for silver, ever since he had worked out that that was where ships and men came from. He needed ships and men to make himself king in Norway and I did not want him snuffling after any moonlit burials of mine – he had had his share of Atil's silver. That hoard had been hard come by and I was still not sure that it was not cursed.

I offered horn-toasts to the memory of dead Sigurd, Crowbone's silver-nosed uncle, who had been the nearest to a father the boy had had and who had been Vladimir's *druzhina* commander. Crowbone joined in, perched on the high-backed guest bench beside me, his legs too short to rest his feet like a grown man on the tall hearthstones that kept drunk and child from tumbling in the pitfire.

His men, too, appreciated the Sigurd toasts and roared it out. They were horse-eating men of Thor and Frey, big men, calloused and muscled like bull walruses from sword work and rowing, with big beards and loud voices, spilling ale down their chests and boasting. I saw Finn's nostrils flare, drinking in the salt-sea reek of them, the taste of war and wave that flowed from them like heat.

Some of them wore silk tunics and baggier breeks than others, carried curved swords rather than straight, but that was just Gardariki fashion and, apart from Alyosha, they were not the half-breed Slavs who call themselves Rus – rowers. These were all true Swedes, young oar-wolves who had crewed with Crowbone up and down the Baltic and would follow

the boy into Hel's hall itself if he went – and Alyosha was at his side to make the sensible decisions.

Crowbone saw me look them over and was pleased at what he saw in my face.

'Aye, they are hard men, right enough,' he chuckled and I shrugged as diffidently as I could, waiting for him to tell me why he and his hard men were here. All that had gone before – politeness and feasting and smiles – had been leading to this place.

'It is good of you to remember my uncle,' he said after a time of working at his boots. The hall rang with noise and the smoke-sweat fug was thicker than the bench planks. Small bones flew; roars and laughter went up when one hit a target.

He paused for effect and stroked his ringed braids, wanting moustaches so badly I almost laughed.

'He is the reason I am here,' he said, raising his voice to be heard. It piped, still, like a boy's, but I did not smile; I had long since learned that Crowbone was not the boy he seemed.

When I said nothing, he waved an impatient little hand.

'Randr Sterki sailed this way.'

I sat back at that news and the memories came welling up like reek in a blocked privy. Randr the Strong had been the right-hand of Klerkon and had taken over most of that one's crew after Klerkon died; he had sailed their ship, *Dragon Wings*, to an island off Aldeijuborg.

Klerkon. There was a harsh memory right enough. He had raided us and lived only long enough to be sorry for it, for we had wolfed down on his winter-camp on Svartey, the Black Island, finding only his thralls and the wives and weans of his crew – and Crowbone, chained to the privy.

Well, things were done on Svartey that were usual enough for red-war raids, but men too long leashed and then let loose, goaded on by a vengeful Crowbone, had guddled in blood and thrown bairns at walls. Later, Crowbone found and killed

Klerkon – but that is another tale, for nights with a good fire against the saga chill of it.

Randr Sterki had a free raiding hand while matters were resolved with Prince Vladimir over the Klerkon killing, but when all that was done, Vladimir sent Sigurd Axebitten, Crowbone's no-nose uncle and commander of his *druzhina*, to give Randr a hard dunt for his pains.

Except Sigurd had made a mess of it, or so I heard, and Crowbone had grimly followed after to find Randr Sterki and his men gone and his uncle nailed to an oak tree as a sacrifice to Perun. His famous silver nose was missing; folk said Randr wore it on a leather thong round his neck. Crowbone had been wolf-sniffing after his uncle's killer since, with no success.

'What trail did he leave, that brings you this way?' I asked, for I knew the burn for revenge was fierce in him. I knew that fire well, for the same one scorched Randr Sterki for what we had done to his kin in Klerkon's hall at Svartey; even for a time of red war, what we had done there made me uneasy.

Crowbone finished with his boots and put them on.

'Birds told me,' he answered finally and I did not doubt it; little Olaf Tryggvasson was known as Crowbone because he read the Norns' weave through the actions of birds.

'He will come here for three reasons,' he went on, growing more shrill as he raised his voice over the noise in the hall. 'You are known for your wealth and you are known for your fame.'

'And the third?'

He merely looked at me and it was enough; the memory of Klerkon's steading on Svartey, of fire and blood and madness, floated up in me like sick in a bucket.

There it was, the cursed memory, hung out like a flayed skin. Fame will always come back and hag-ride you to the grave; my own by-name, Bear Slayer, was proof of that, since

I had not slain the white bear myself, though no-one alive knew that but me. Still, the saga of it – and all the others that boasted of what the Oathsworn were supposed to have done – constantly brought men looking to join us or challenge us.

Now came Randr Sterki, for his own special reasons. The Oathsworn's fame made me easy to find and, with only a few fighting men, I was a better mark to take on than a boatload of hard Rus under the protection of the Prince of Novgorod.

'Randr Sterki is not a name that brings warriors,' Crowbone went on. 'But yours is and any man who deals you a death blow steals your wealth, your women and your fame in that stroke.'

It was said in his loud and shrill boy's voice – almost a shriek – and it was strange, looking back on it, that the hall noise should have ebbed away just then. Heads turned; silence fell like a cloak of ash.

'I am not easily felled,' I pointed out and did not have to raise my voice to be heard. Some chuckled; one drunk cheered. Red Njal added: 'Even by bears,' and got laughter for it.

Then the hall was washed with murmurs and subdued whispers; feasting flowed back to it, slow as pouring honey.

'Did you come all this way to warn me?' I asked as the noise grew again and he flushed, for I had worked out that he had not been so driven just for that.

'I would have your Sea-Finn's drum,' he answered. 'If it speaks of victory – will you join the hunt for Randr Sterki?'

Vuokko the Sea-Finn had come to us only months since, seeking the runemaster Klepp Spaki, who was chipping out the stone of our lives in the north valley. Vuokko came all the way from his Sami forests to learn the true secret of our runes from Klepp and no-one was more surprised than I when the runemaster agreed to it.

Of course, in return, Klepp had Vuokko teach him his *seidr*-magic, which was such that the little Sea-Finn was already well-known. Since *seidr* was a strange and unmanly thing,

there were whispers of what the pair of them did all alone up in a hut in the valley – but muted ones, for Klepp was a runemaster and so a man of some note.

Vuokko, of course, was an outlander Sami sorcerer and not to be trusted at all, but it seemed folk were coming over the sea to hear the beat of his rune-marked drum and watch the three gold frogs on it dance, revealing Odin's wisdom to those brave – or daft – enough to want to know it.

I saw Thorgunna, serving ale to Finn, Onund Hnufa and Red Njal, three heads close together and bobbing with argument and laughter. She smiled and the warmth of that scene, of my woman and my friends, washed me; then she gently touched her belly and moved on and the leap of that in my heart almost brought me to my feet.

'Will you hunt down Randr, Sigurd's bane, with me?'

The voice was thin with impatience, jerking me back from the warmth of wife and unborn. I turned to him and sighed, so that he saw it and frowned.

The truth was I had no belly for it. We had gained fame and wealth at a cost – too high, I often thought these days – and now the idea of sluicing sea and hard bread and stiff joints on a trip even across to Aldeijuborg made me wince. Even that was a hare-leap of joy compared to sailing off with this man-boy to hunt round the whole Baltic for the likes of Randr Sterki.

I said as much. I did not add that I thought Randr Sterki had a right to feel vengeful and that Crowbone had played a part in fuelling the fire on Svartey.

I heard the air hiss from him and there was petulance as much as disappointment in that, for young Crowbone did not like to be crossed.

'There is fame and the taste of victory,' he argued, pouting into my twist of a smile.

I already had fame, while victory, when all is said and done, tastes as blood-foul as failure – which was the other side of

the spinning coin in this matter. He scowled at that, his eyes reflecting me to myself – what I saw there was old and done, but it was the view from a boy of twelve and almost made me chuckle. Then Crowbone found himself and smiled blandly; more signs of the princely things learned from Vladimir, I saw.

'I will have the drum-frogs leap for me, all the same,' he said and I nodded.

As if he had heard, Vuokko came into the hall, so silently that one of the younger thrall girls, too fondled by these new and muscled warriors to notice, gave a scream as the Sea-Finn appeared next to her.

Men laughed, though uneasily, for Vuokko had a face like a mid-winter mummer's mask left too long in the rain, which the wind-guttered sconces did not treat kindly. The high cheekbones flared the light, making the shadows there darker still, while the eyes, slits of blackness, had no pupils that I could see and the skin of his face was soft and lined as an old walrus.

He grinned his pointed-toothed smile and sidled in, all fur and leather and bits of stolen Norse weave, hung about with feathers and bone both round his neck and wound into the straggles of his iron-grey hair.

In one hand was the drum of white reindeer skin marked with runes and signs only he knew, festooned with claws and little skulls and tufts of wool; on the surface, three frogs skittered, fastened to a ring that went round the whole circle of it. In his other hand was a tiny wooden hammer.

Men made warding signs and muttered darkly, but Crowbone smiled, for he knew the *seidr*, unmanly work of Freyja though that magic was, and a Sea-Finn's drum held no terrors for a boy who saw into the Other by the actions of birds. I wondered if he still had some more of the strange stories he had chilled us all with last year.

'This grandson of Yngling kings,' I said pointedly to the Finn, 'wants a message from your drum on an enterprise he has.'

The Sea-Finn grinned his bear-trap grin, as if he had known all along. He produced a carved runestick from his belt and then drew a large square in the hard, beaten earth of the floor – folk sidled away from him as he came near.

Then he marked off two points on all the sides and scraped lines to join them; now he had nine squares and folk shivered as if the fire had died. In the middle square, the square within a square, he folded into a cross-legged sit and cradled the drum like a child, crooning to it.

He rocked and chanted, a deep hoom in the back of his throat that raised hackles, for most knew he was calling on Lemminki, a Finnish sorcerer-god who could sing the sand into pearls for those brave enough to call on him. The square within a square was supposed to keep Vuokko safe – but folk darted uneasy looks at the flickering shadows and moved even further away from him.

Finally, he hit the drum – once only – a deep and resonating bell of sound coming from such a small thing; men winced and shifted and made Hammer signs and I saw Finn join his hands in the diamond-shape of the *ingwaz* warding rune as the gold frogs danced. No man cared for *seidr* magic, for it was a woman's thing and to see a man do it set flesh creeping.

Vuokko peered for a long time, then raised his horror of a face to Crowbone. 'You will be king,' he said simply and there was a hiss as men let out their breath all at once together, for that had not been the enterprise I had meant.

Crowbone merely smiled the smile of a man who had had the answer he expected and fished in his purse, drawing out his pilfered coin. He flicked it casually in the air towards Vuokko, who never took his eyes from Crowbone's face, ignoring the silver whirl of it.

I was astounded by the boy's arrogance and his disregard – you did not treat the likes of Vuokko like some fawning street-seer, nor did you break the safety of his square within

19

a square while he was in the Sitting-Out, half in and half out of the Other, surrounded by a swirl of dangerous strangeness.

Crowbone had half-turned away in his proud, unthinking fashion when the scorned *miliaresion* bounced on the drum, the tinkle of its final landing lost in the thunder it made. He turned, surprised.

'What was that sound, Sea-Finn?' he demanded and Vuokko smiled like a wolf closing in.

'That was the sound of your enterprise, lord,' he replied after a study of the frogs, 'falling from your hand.'

After that, the feasting was a sullen affair coloured by Crowbone's morose puzzlement, for now he did not know what the Sea-Finn had promised. Most of his followers only recalled the bit about him becoming king in Norway, so they were cheered.

I stood with Crowbone on the sand and dulse two days later, while his men hefted their sea-chests back on the splendid *Short Serpent* and got ready to sail off.

He was wrapped in his familiar white fur and a matching stare, waiting to see if terns or crows came in ones or twos, or went left or right. Only he knew what it meant.

'All the same,' he said finally, clasping my wrist and staring up into my gaze with his odd eyes, 'you would do well to join me. Randr Sterki will come for you. I hear he is sworn to Styrbjorn.'

That was no surprise; Styrbjorn was the brawling nephew of my king, Eirik Segersall. Now just come into manhood, he had designs on the high seat himself when Eirik was dead and sulked when it became clear no-one else liked the idea.

Foolishly, King Eirik had given him ships and men to go off and make a life for himself and Styrbjorn now prowled up and down off Wendland on the far Baltic shore, snarling and making his intentions known regarding what he considered his birthright. Someday soon, I was thinking, he would

need a good slap, but he was only a boy. I almost said so to Crowbone, then clenched my teeth on it and smiled instead.

I saw Alyosha hovering, a mailed and helmeted wet-nurse anxious to see his charge safely back on the boat. I widened my smile indulgently at Crowbone; I was arrogant then, believing Oathsworn fame and Odin's favour shield enough against such as Randr Sterki and having no worries about Styrbjorn, a youth with barely seventeen summers on him. I should have known better; I should have remembered myself at his age.

'Have you a tale on all this?' I asked lightly, reminding Crowbone of the biting stories he had told us, a boy holding grown freemen in thrall out on the cold empty.

'I have tales left,' he answered seriously. 'But the one I have is for later. I know birds, all the same, and they know much.'

He saw the confusion in my face and turned away, trotting towards the ship.

'An eagle told me of troubles to come,' he flung back over his shoulder. 'A threat to its young, on the flight's edge.'

The chill of that stayed with me as I watched *Short Serpent* slither off down the fjord and even the closeness of Thorgunna under my arm could not warm it, for I was aware of what she carried in her belly and of what her sister cradled in her arms.

Young eagles on the flight's edge.

TWO

The sun clawed itself higher every day; snow melted patch by patch, streams gurgled and I started to talk earnestly about joint efforts to harvest the sea, of ploughing and seeding cropland and how Finn could borrow my brace of oxen if he liked.

He looked at me as if I was a talking calf, then went back to drinking and hunting with Red Njal, while Onund Hnufa and Gizur went to make the *Fjord Elk* ready for sea and Hlenni Brimill and others fetched wood for new shields and pestered Ref to leave off tinsmithing nails against rust to put a new edge on worn blades.

After the feasting night for Crowbone, Finn had come to me and asked if the Oathsworn were going raiding after Randr Sterki, though he knew the answer before I spoke. When I confirmed it, he nodded, long, slow and thoughtful.

'I am thinking,' he said softly, as if the words were being dragged from him by oxen, 'that I might have to visit Ospak and Finnlaith in Dyfflin, or perhaps go to find Fiskr in Hedeby.'

The idea of not having Finn there made me swallow and he saw my stricken face. His own was a hammer that nailed his next words into me, even though he said them with a lopsided grin.

'It is either that or challenge for the jarl's seat.'

Well, there it was, the fracture cracked open and visible. I bowed my head to it; the curse of Odin's silver right enough.

'I will stay for one more season and, if the raiding is good, it may change my mind. If not, I am thinking it best to leave, Orm.'

This would be the third season and, I was thinking, a remarkable feat of patience for the likes of Finn. Yet I was no more certain that this raiding season, which involved a long, uncomfortable voyage up and down the Baltic and sometimes into the mouths of a few rivers, pretending to trade and looking for something to steal, would be any better than the last two. There was seldom anything worthwhile for the Oathsworn, who were choking on all they already had. Yet they trained daily, making shieldwalls and breaking them, fighting in ones and threes, showing off and honing their battle skills. The lure of the prow beast, as the skalds had it, still dragged us all back to the dark water.

Now Finn wanted more jarl-work from me and threatened either to leave or take over. I could only nod, for words were ash in my mouth. After that, the promise of summer sunshine was ominous.

The women bustled the grime and stink out of Hestreng's buildings and took clear joy in drying washing in the open air; Cormac and Helga Hiti tumbled about on sturdy legs, shouting and playing.

Into this, just after the *blot* offerings for the Feast of Vali, a ship slid up the fjord to us. I knew about it two hours before it arrived, which pleased me – I had set two thralls to watch in shifts and suffered Thorgunna's waspishness over it.

'A waste of work,' she declared, while she and Ingrid and two female thralls hurled sleeping pallets out. 'They could be beating the vermin out of these.'

'I would rather know who is coming to me,' I answered, 'than have dust-free sleeping skins.'

'Tell me that when next your backside is chewed by a flea,' she spat back, blowing a wisp of hair which had fought free of her head-cloth down onto her nose. 'And if I am doing this, I am not making butter – you will feel differently when you have to choke on dry bread.'

From this, I knew she was happy that winter was over and that she had life in her – life I would rather see grow than be burned out if Randr Sterki arrived and we did not know of it. I said as much and had her snort back at me but when word came of this ship, I saw her stiffen and turn and start chivvying thralls and Ingrid to fetch the children, gathering them to her like a hen with chicks.

I let her for a while, though I knew it was no threat; the sail was large and plainly marked with Jarl Brand's sign and unless someone had taken *Black Eagle* from him intact – as unlikely as wings on a fish – then it was himself coming up the fjord.

He came up showing off, too, the sail flaked down and the oars bending as his men made *Black Eagle* cream through the sea. Then, at a single command we all heard as we stood watching on the shore, the oars were lifted clear and taken in until only a quarter of their length was left.

Along this sprang a figure, dancing and bouncing from stem to stern; we all cheered, knowing it was probably his prow man Nes-Bjorn, called Klak – Peg – because he was shaped like one, having oar-muscled shoulders, but skinny hips and legs. He could walk the oars with those skinny legs, all the same, swinging from one side to the other on a loose line.

The crew were equally skilled and slid the thirty-oar *drakkar* neatly to the stone slipway, where the *Fjord Elk* was propped up, with scarcely a dunt on its gilded side. Men spilled ashore then, shouting greetings to those who went to meet them. Thorgunna sighed, scattered the children and roared for thralls; there were sixty new mouths to feed and precious little left in the stores.

She stopped scowling, all the same, when she found what Jarl Brand had brought. He came off smiling, as usual, bone-white as he had always been, wearing a gold-embroidered black tunic trimmed with marten, fine wool breeks that flared over kidskin boots and his neck and arms heavy with amber and silver.

At his side trotted a boy as white as Brand was and people stared for he was Cormac's double, only older, at least five; Aoife kept her head meekly down and said nothing. On Jarl Brand's other side was a strange little man dressed in a black serk to his toes, young, moon-faced and glum.

'My son,' Brand declared gruffly, indicating the sombre, white-haired boy. 'I bring him to you to foster.'

That took my breath away and I was still struggling to suck more in when he indicated the moon-face on his other side.

'This is one called Leo,' he said. 'A Greek monk of sorts, from the Great City.'

I shot Jarl Brand a look and he chuckled at it, shaking his head so that his moustaches trembled like melting icicles.

'No, I am not turned to the White Christ,' he replied. 'This Greek is sent by the Emperor to take greetings to our king. I picked him up in Jumne.'

'Like a sack of grain,' agreed the man with a slight smile. 'I have been stacked and shipped ever since.'

It took me a moment to realise he had spoken Greek and that Jarl Brand had been talking Norse, which meant this Leo knew Norse and also that both Jarl Brand and I understood Greek. Jarl Brand chuckled as I brought Thorgunna, intro-duced her and had her take Leo into the hall.

'Watch him,' Brand said, tight into my ear as the monk reeled away from us, his legs still on the sea. 'He is more than a monkish scribbler, which he does all the time. He is clever and watches constantly and knows more than he reveals.'

I agreed, but was distracted by what was now unloading

from *Black Eagle* – two women, one young and fat with child, the other older, almost as fat and fussing round her like a gull round a chick.

Jarl Brand caught my stare and grunted, the sound of a man too weighted to speak.

'Sigrith,' he said, pulling me away by the elbow. 'Fresh returned from visiting her father, Mieczyslaw, King of the Polans, and near her dropping time – which is why we are here. King Eirik wants his son born in Uppsalla.'

I blinked and gawped, despite myself. This was Sigrith, splendid as a gilded dragon-head, no more than eighteen and a queen, yet young and bright-eyed and heavy with her first bairn; she was just a frightened child of a Slav tribe from the middle of nowhere.

'The fat one is Jasna, who was her nurse when she lived with her people,' Jarl Brand went on, miserably. 'I am charged with bringing them to the king, together with whatever the queen unloads, safe and well.'

'That's a cargo I could do without,' I answered without thinking, then caught his jaundiced eye. We both smiled, though it was grim – then I noticed the girl at the back. I had taken her for a thrall, in her shapeless, colourless dress, kerchief over what I took to be a shaved head, but she walked like she had gold between her legs. Thin and small, with a face too big for her and eyes dark and liquid as the black fjord.

'She is a Mazur,' Jarl Brand said, following my gaze. 'Her name turns out in Slav to be Chernoglazov – Dark Eye – but the queen and her fat cow call her Drozdov, Blackbird.'

'A thrall?' I asked uncertainly and he shook his head.

'I was thinking that, too, when I saw her first,' he replied with a grunt of humour, 'but it is worse than that – she is a hostage, daughter of a chief of one of the tribes that Mieczyslaw the Pol wants to control to the east of him. She is proud as a queen, all the same, and worships some three-headed god. Or four, I am never sure.'

26

I looked at the bird-named woman – well, girl, in truth. A long way from home to keep her from being snatched back, held as surety for her tribe's good behaviour, she had a look half-way between scorn and a deer at the point of running. Truly, a cargo I would not wish to be carrying myself and did not relish it washing up on my beach.

However, it had an unexpected side to it; Thorgunna, presented with the honour of a queen and a jarl's *fostri* in her house, beamed with pleasure at Jarl Brand and me both, as if we had personally arranged for it. Brand saw it and patted my shoulder soothingly, smiling stiffly the while.

'This will change,' he noted, 'when Sigrith shows how a queen expects to be treated.'

His men unloaded food and drink, which was welcomed and we feasted everyone on coal-roasted horse, lamb, fine fish and good bread – though Sigrith turned her nose up at such fare, whether from sickness or disgust, and Thorgunna shot me the first of many meaningful glances across the hall and fell to muttering with her sister.

Since the women were full of bairns, one way and another, they sat and talked weans with the proud Sigrith, leaving Finn and Botolf and me with Jarl Brand and his serious-faced son, Koll.

The boy, ice-white as his da, sat stiffly at what must have been a trial for one so young – sent to the strange world of the Oathsworn's jarl, ripped from his ma's cooing, yet still eager to please. He sat, considered and careful over all he did, so as not to make a mistake and shame his father. At one and the same time it warmed and broke your heart.

There was no point in trying to talk the stiff out of him – for one thing the hall roared and fretted with feasting, so that you had to shout; it is a hard thing to be considerate and consoling when you are bellowing. For another, he was gripped with fear and saw me only as the huge stranger he was to be left with and took no comfort in that.

In the end, Thorgunna and Botolf's Ingrid swept him up and into the comfort of their mothering, which brought such relief to his face that, in the end, he managed a laugh or two. For his part, Jarl Brand smiled and drank and ate as if he did not have a care, but he had come here to leave me the boy and, like all fathers, was agonising over it even as he saw the need.

Leo the monk had seen all this, too, which did not surprise me. A scribbler of histories, he had told me earlier, wanting to know tales of the siege at Sarkel and the fight at Antioch from one who had been at both. Aye, he was young and smiling and seal-sleek, that one – but I had dealt with Great City merchants and I knew these Greek–Romans well, oiled beards and flattery both.

'I never understood about fostering,' Leo said, leaning forward to speak quietly to me, while Brand and Finn argued over, of all things, the best way to season new lamb; Brand kept shooting his son sideways glances, making sure he was not too afraid. 'It is not, as it is with us in Constantinople, a polite way of taking hostages.'

He regarded me with his olive-stone eyes and his too-ready smile, while I sought words to explain what a *fostri* was.

'Jarl Brand does me honour,' I told him. 'To be offered the rearing of a child to manhood is no light thing and usually not done outside the *aett*.'

'The . . . *aett*?'

'Clan. Family. House,' I answered in Greek and he nodded, picking at bread with the long fingers of one hand, stained black-brown from ink.

'So he has welcomed you into his house,' Leo declared, chewing with grimaces at the grit he found. 'Not, I surmise, as an equal.'

It was true, of course – accepting the fostering of another's child was also an acceptance that the father was of a higher standing than you were. But this bothered me much less than

the fact that Leo, the innocent monk from the Great City and barely out of his teens, had worked this out. Even then, with only a little more than twenty years on him, he had a mind of whirling cogs and toothed wheels, like those I had seen once driving mills and waterwheels in Serkland.

He also ate the horse, spearing greasy slivers of it on a little two-tined eating fork. This surprised me, for Christ followers considered that to be a pagan ritual and would not usually do it. He saw me follow the food to his mouth and knew what I was thinking, smiling and shrugging as he chewed.

'I shall do penance for this later. The one thing you learn swiftly about being a diplomat is not to offend.'

'Or suffer for being a Christ priest in a land of Odin,' interrupted Jarl Brand, subtle as a forge hammer. 'This is Hestreng, home of the Oathsworn, Odin's own favourites. Christ followers find no soil for their seed here, eh, Orm?

'Bone, blood and steel,' he added when I said nothing. The words were from the Odin Oath that bound what was left of my *varjazi*, my band of brothers; it made Leo raise his eyebrows, turning his eyes round and wide as if alarmed.

'I did not think I was in such danger. Am I, then, to be nailed to a tree?'

I thought about that carefully. The shaven-headed priests of the Christ could come and go as they pleased around Hestreng and say what they chose, provided they caused no trouble. Sometimes, though, the people grew tired of being ranted at and chased them away with blows. Down in the south, I had heard, the skin-wearing trolls of the *Going* folk took hold of an irritating one now and then and sacrificed him in the old way, nailed to a tree in honour of Odin. That Leo knew of this also meant he was not fresh from a cloister.

'I heard tales from travellers,' he replied, seeing me study him and looking back at me with his flat, wide-eyed gaze while he lied. 'Of course, those unfortunate monks were Franks

and Saxlanders and, though brothers in Christ – give or take an argument or two – lacking somewhat in diplomacy.'

'And weaponry,' I added and we locked eyes for a moment, like rutting elks. At the end, I felt sure there was as much steel hidden about this singular monk as there was running down his spine. I did not like him one bit and trusted him even less.

Now I had been shown the warp and weft of matters there was nothing left but to nod and smile while Cormac, Aoife's son, filled our horns. Jarl Brand frowned at the sight of him, as he always did, since the boy was as colourless as the jarl himself. White to his eyelashes, he was, with eyes of the palest blue, and it was not hard to see which tree the twig had sprouted from. When Cormac filled little Koll's horn with watered ale, their heads almost touching, I heard Brand suck in air sharply.

'The boy is growing,' he muttered. 'I must do something about him . . .'

'He needs a father, that one,' I added meaningfully and he nodded, then smiled fondly at Koll. Aoife went by, filling horns and swaying her hips just a little more, I was thinking, so that Jarl Brand grunted and stirred on his bench.

I sighed; after some nights here, the chances were strong that, this time next year, we would have another bone-haired yelper from Aoife, another ice-white bairn. As if we did not have little eagles enough at the flight's edge . . .

In the morning, buds unfolded in green mists, sunlight sparkled wetly on grass and spring sauntered across the land while the Oathsworn hauled the *Fjord Elk* off the slipway, to rock gently beside *Black Eagle*. Now was the moment when the raiding began and, on the strength of it, Finn would go or stay; that sank my stomach to my boot tops.

It was a good ship, our *Elk* – fifteen benches each side and no Slav tree trunk, but a properly straked, oak-keeled *drakkar* that had survived portage and narrow rivers on at least two trips to Gardariki.

All the same, it was a bairn next to *Black Eagle*, which had thirty oars a side and was as long as fifteen tall men laid end to end. It was tricked out in gilding, painted red and black, with the great black eagle prow and a crew of growlers who knew they had the best and fastest ship afloat. They and the Oathsworn chaffered and jeered at each other, straining muscle and sinew to get the *Elk* into the water, then demanding a race up the fjord to decide which ship and crew was better.

Into the middle of this came the queen, ponderous as an Arab slave ship, with Thordis and Ingrid and Thorgunna round her and Jasna lumbering ahead. As this woman-fleet sailed past me, heading towards Jarl Brand, Thorgunna raised weary eyebrows.

The jarl had his back to Queen Sigrith as she came up and almost leapt out of his nice coloured tunic when she spoke. Then, flustered and annoyed at having been so taken by surprise, he scowled at her, which was a mistake.

Sigrith's voice was shrill and high. Before, it might have been mistaken for girlish, but fear of childbirthing had sucked the sweetness out of it and her Polan accent was thick, so her demands to know when they were sailing from this dreadful place to one which did not smell of fish and sweaty men, had a rancid bite.

If Jarl Brand had an answer, he never gave it; one of my lookout thralls came pounding up, spraying mud and words in equal measure; a *faering* was coming up the fjord.

Such boats were too small to be feared, but the arrival of it was interesting enough to divert everyone, for which Brand was grateful. Yet, when it came heeling in, sail barely reefed and obviously badly handled, I felt an anchor-stone settle in my gut.

There were arrow shafts visible, and willing men splashed out, waist deep, to catch the little craft and help the man in it take in sail, for he was clearly hurt. They towed it in; two men were in it and blood sloshed in the scuppers; one man

was dead and the survivor gasping with pain and badly cut about.

'Skulli,' Brand said, grim as old rock, and the anchor-stone sank lower; Skulli was his steward and I looked at the man, head lolling and leaking life as the women lifted him away to be cared for.

Brand stopped them and let Skulli leak while he gasped out the saga of what had happened. It took only moments to tell – Styrbjorn had arrived, with at least five ships and the men for them, clearly bound for a slaughter against his uncle's right-hand man, to make a show of what he was capable of if things did not go his way.

Jarl Brand's hall was burning, his men dead, his thralls fled, his women taken.

The black dog of it crushed everyone for a moment, then shook itself; men bellowed and all was movement. I saw Finn's face and the mad joy on it was clear as blood on snow.

While Thorgunna and Thordis hauled Skulli off and yelled out for Bjaelfi to bring his skill and healing runes, Brand took my arm and led me a little way aside while men rushed to make *Black Eagle* ready. His face was now as bone-coloured as his hair.

'I have to go to King Eirik,' he declared. 'Add my ship to his and what men I can sweep up on the way. Styrbjorn, if he is stupid, will stay to fight us and we will kill him. If not, he will flee and I will chase him and make him pay for what he has done.'

'I can have the *Elk* ready in an hour or two,' I said, then stopped as he shook his head.

'Serve me better,' he answered. 'Call up your Oathsworn to this place. Look after the queen. I can hardly take her with me.'

That stopped my mouth, sure as a hand over it. He returned my look with a cliff of a face and eyes that said there would be no arguing; yet he cracked the stone of him an instant

32

later, when he shot a sideways glance to where Koll watched, round-eyed, as men bustled. I did not need him to say more.

'The queen and son both, then,' I replied, feeling the sick dread of what would happen if Styrbjorn sent ships here, for it would take time to send out word to the world that Hestreng needed the old Oathsworn back. Jarl Brand saw it, too, and nodded briefly.

'I will leave thirty of my crew – I wish it were more.'

It was generous, for the ones he had left would break themselves to run *Black Eagle* home, with no relief. It was also a marker of what he feared and I forced a smile.

'Who will attack the Oathsworn?' I countered, but there was no mirth in the twist of a grin he gave, turning away to bawl orders to his men.

There was a great milling of movement and words; I sent Botolf stumping off to bring the thirty of Jarl Brand's crew. They stood forlorn and grim on the shore as their oarmates sailed away – but there was none more cliff-faced and black-scowling than Finn, watching others sail away to the war he wanted. Then I gathered up Botolf's daughter, little red-haired Helga, and made her laugh, as much to make me feel better as her. Ingrid smiled.

Jasna waddled up to me, the queen moving ponderously behind her, made bulkier still by furs against the chill.

'Her Highness wishes to know what *blot* you will make for the jarl's journey,' she demanded and her tone made me angry, since she was a thrall when all was said and done. I tossed Helga in the air and made her scream.

'Laughter,' I answered brusquely. 'The gods need it sometimes.'

Jasna blinked at that, then went back to the queen, walking like a loaded pack pony; there were whispers back and forth. Out of the corner of my eye I saw Thorgunna scowling at me and in answer I carried on playing with the child.

'This is not seemly,' said an all-too familiar voice, jerking

me from Helga's gurgles. The queen stood in front of me, mittened hands folded over her swollen belly, frowning.

'Seemly?'

She waved a small hand, like a little furred paw in the mitten. Her face was sharp as a cat's and would have been pretty save for the lines at the edges of her mouth.

'You are *godi* here. This is not . . . It has no . . . *dignitas*.'

'You sound like a Christ follower,' I answered shortly, putting Helga down; she trundled off towards her mother, who gathered her up. I saw Thorgunna closing on us, fast as a racing *drakkar*.

'Christ follower!'

It was an explosion of shriek and I turned my head from it, as you would from an icy blast. Then I shrugged, for this queen, her young and beautiful face twisted with outrage, annoyed me more and more. I was annoyed, too, to have forgotten that the Christ godlet had been foisted on her father and his people; like the rest of them, she resented this.

'They also confuse misery and prayer,' I managed to answer and heard a chuckle I recognised as Leo. Thorgunna bustled up, managing to elbow me in the ribs.

'Highness,' she said to Sigrith, with a sweet smile. 'I have everything prepared – what do men know of sacrifice?'

Mollified, the queen allowed herself to be led away, followed by Jasna, who threw me a venomous glare. The ever-present, ever-silent Mazur girl followed after, but paused to shoot me a quick glance from those dark eyes; afterwards, I realised what had made me remember it. It was the first time she had looked directly at anyone at all.

At the time, I heard a little laugh which distracted me from thoughts of the girl and turned my head to where Leo watched, swathed in a cloak, hands shoved deep inside its folds.

'I thought traders of your standing had more diplomacy,' he offered and I said nothing, knowing he had the right of it and that my behaviour had been, at best, childish.

'But she galls, does she not?' he added, as if reading my mind.

'Even less soil there than here for your Christ seed,' I countered. 'Even if you get to the court. Your visit to Uppsalla is proving a failure.'

He smiled the moon-faced smile of a man who did not think anything he did was a failure, then inclined his head and moved off, leaving me with the last view of *Black Eagle*, raising sail and speeding off into the grey distance.

I felt rain spot my neck and shivered, looked up to a pewter sky and offered a prayer to bluff Thor and Aegir of the waves and Niord, god of the coasts, for a good blow and some tossing white-caps. A storm sea would keep us safe . . .

I rose in the night and left my sleeping area, mumbling to a dreamy Thorgunna about the need for a privy, which was a lie. I stepped through the hall of grunting and snores and soft stirrings in the dark, past the pitfire's grey ash, where little red eyes watched me step out of the hall.

The sharp air made me wish I had brought a cloak, made me wonder at this foolishness. There was rain in that air, yet no storm and the fear of that lack filled me. Dreams I knew – Odin's arse, I had been hag-ridden by dreams all my life – but this was strange, a formless half-life, a *draugr* of a feeling that ruined sleep and nipped my waking heels.

Never before or since have I felt the power of the prow beast on a raiding ship as it locks jaws with the spirit of the land – but I felt them both that night, muscled and snarling shadows in the dark. Even then, I knew Randr Sterki was coming.

Yet the world remained the same, etched in black and silver, misted in shreds even in the black night. A dog fox barked far out on the pasture; the great dark of Ginnungagap still held the embers of Muspelheim, flung there by Odin's brothers, Vili and Ve. Between scudding clouds, I found Aurvandill's

Toe and the Eyes of Thjazi after a search, but easily found the Wagon Star, which guides prow beasts everywhere. The one on Randr's ship would be following it like a spooring wolf.

There was a closer light from the little building that housed Ref's forge, a soft glow and I moved to it, drawn by the hope of heat. A few steps from it, the voices halted me – I have no idea why, since they were ones I knew; Ref was there and Botolf with him and the thrall boy, Toki.

Ref was nailing, which was a simple thing but a steading needed lots of them and he clearly took comfort in the easy repetitive task; he took slim lengths of worked bog-iron, flared one end and pointed the other, two taps for one, four for the other, then a plunge into the quench and a drop into a box. Even for that simple task, he kept the light in the forge dim, so that he could read the colour of the fire and the heated iron.

Toki, a doll-like silhouette with his back to me, worked the bellows and hugged his reedy arms between times, chilled despite the flames in his one-piece *kjartan* and bare feet, his near-bald head shining in the red light.

The place had the burned-hair smell of charred hooves, braided with the tang of sea-salt, charcoal and horse piss. In the dim light of the forge-fire and a small horn lantern above Botolf's head, Ref looked like a dwarf and Botolf a giant, the one forging some magical thing, the other red-dyed with light and speaking in a low rumble, like boulders grinding.

'That dog fox is out again,' he was saying. 'He's after the chickens.'

'That's why we coop them,' Ref replied, concentrating. Tap, tap. Pause. Tap, tap, tap, tap. Plunge and hiss. He picked up another length.

'He won't come near. He is afraid of the hounds,' Botolf replied, shifting his weight. He nudged Toki, who pumped the bellows a few times.

36

'Why is he afraid?' the boy asked. 'He can run.'

'Because the hounds run slower but longer and will kill him,' answered Ref. 'So would you be afraid.'

The boy shivered. 'I am afraid even in my dreams,' he answered and Botolf looked at him.

'Dreams, little Toki? What dreams? My Helga has dreams, too, which make her afraid. What do you dream?'

The boy shrugged. 'Falling from a high place, like Aoife says my da did.'

Botolf nodded soberly, remembering that Toki had been fathered by a thrall called Geitleggr, whose hairy goat legs had given him the only name he had known – but none of the animal's skill when it came to gathering eggs on narrow ledges. His mother, too, had died, of too much work, too little food and winter and now Aoife looked out for Toki, as much as anyone did.

'I like high places,' Botolf said, seeking to reassure the boy. 'They are in nearly all my dreams.'

Ref absently pinched out a flaring ember on his already scorch-marked old tunic and I doubted if his horn-skinned fingers felt it. He never took his eyes from the iron, watching the colour of the flames for the right moment, even on just a nail.

Tap, tap, tap, tap – plunge, hiss.

'What are they, then, these dreams of yours, Botolf?' Ref wanted to know, sliding another length of bog-iron into the coals and jerking his chin at Toki to start pumping.

Botolf tapped his timber foot on the side of the oak stump which held the spiked anvil.

'Since I got this, wings,' he answered. 'I dream I have wings. Big black ones, like a raven.'

'What does it feel like?' Toki asked, peering curiously. 'Is it like a real leg?'

'Mostly,' answered Botolf, 'except when it itches, for you cannot scratch it.'

'Does it itch, then?' Ref asked, pausing in wonder. 'Like a real leg?'

Botolf nodded.

'Did some magic woodworker make it so that it itched?' Toki wanted to know and Botolf chuckled.

'If he did, I wish he would come back and unmake it – or at least let me scratch. I dream of that when I am not dreaming of wings.'

'Does no-one dream of proper things any more?' Ref grumbled, turning the bog-iron length in the coals. 'Wealth and fame and women?'

'I have all three,' Botolf answered. 'I have no need of that dream.'

'I dream of food most often,' Toki admitted and the other two laughed; boys seldom had enough to eat and thralls never did.

'Sing a song,' Ref said, 'soft now, so as not to wake everyone. Pick a good one and it will go into the iron and make the nails stronger.'

So Toki sang, a child song, a soft song of the sea and being lost on it. The wave of it left me stranded at the edge of darkness, icy and empty and wondering why he had chosen that of all songs and if the hand of Odin was in it.

I had heard that song before, in another place. We had come ashore in the night, blacker than the night itself with hate and fear, unseen, unheard until we raved down on Klerkon's steading on Svartey at dawn – a steading like this, I remembered, sick and cold. Only one fighting man had been there and he had been easily killed by Kvasir and Finn.

Things had been done, as they always were in such events, made more savage because it was Klerkon we hunted and he had stolen Thorgunna's sister, Thordis. He was not there, but all his folk's women and bairns were and, prowling for him, I had heard the singing, sweet in the dawn's dim, a song to keep out the fear.

38

I heard it stop, too. I had come upon the great tangle-haired growler who had cut it out of the girl's throat with a single slash, his blade clotted with sticky darkness and strands of hair. He had turned to me, all beard and mad grin and I had known him at once – Red Njal, limping Red Njal, who now played with Botolf's Helga and carved dolls for her.

Beyond, all twisted limbs and bewildered faces, were the singer's three little siblings: blood smoked in the hearthfire coals and puddled the stones. The thrall-nurse was there, too, forearm hacked through where she had flung up her arms in a last desperate, useless attempt to ward off an axe edge. Red Njal was on his knees in the blood, rifling for plunder.

There were shouts then, and I followed them; outside lay a plough ox still dying, great head flapping and blood bubbling from its muzzle, the eyes wide and rolling. Across the heaving, weakly thrashing body of it, as if on some box-bed, three men stripped a woman to pale breasts and belly, down to the hair between her legs, while she gasped, strength almost gone but fighting still.

Her blonde braids flailed as her head thrashed back and forth and two of the men tried to hold her, while the third fought down his breeches and struggled to get between her legs. She spat crimson at him and he howled back at her and smacked her in the mouth, so that her head bounced off the twitching flank of the ox, which tried to bawl and only hissed out more blood.

They panted and struggled, like men trying to fit a new wheel on a heavy cart, calling advice, insults, curses when the ox shat itself, working steadily towards the inevitable . . . then the one between her legs, the one I knew well, lost his patience, unable to hold her and rid himself of the knee she kept wedging in his way.

He hauled a seax from his boot and slit her throat, so that she gug-gug-gugged on her own blood and started to flop like a fish. The knee dropped; the man stuck the seax in the ox

39

and his prick in the woman and started pumping while the others laughed.

The boy came from nowhere, from the dark where he had seen it all, from where he had watched his mother, Randr Sterki's wife, die. He came like a hare and snatched up the seax, while the man pumped and pumped, gone frantic and unseeing and the woman gurgled and died beneath him.

My blade took the back of the boy's skull clean off, an instant before he brought the seax down. I watched the back of his head fly in the air, the hair on it like spider legs, the gleet and brain and blood arcing out to splash the dying woman's last lover, who jerked himself away and out of her, gawping, his prick hanging like a dead chicken's neck.

'Odin's arse . . . well struck, Orm. That little hole would have had me, liver and lights, for sure.'

Grinning, Finn hauled his breeks up and grabbed his seax from the boy's gripping hand, so that, for a moment, it looked as if the lad was raising himself up. But he was dead, slumped across his mother and Finn spat on him before stumping off into the dark . . .

'Why are you standing out there?'

The voice raked me back to the night and the forge. All the heads had turned towards me and Botolf chuckled. Toki, half-turned, was bloodied by the forgelight and, for a moment, I saw the face of the boy I had killed. Toki was the same age. Too young to die. Yet Randr's boy would have killed Finn – had once laughed as he helped his mother scrape Crowbone's head raw, then chain him to the privy as punishment for running away. What the Norns weave is always intricate, but it can be as dark and ugly as it is beautiful.

'Listeners at the eaves hear no good of themselves,' Botolf intoned. Toki dropped from his perch, breaking the spell.

'Sleep comes hard,' Ref grunted, 'too many farters and snorers in the hall.'

We all knew that was not the reason I was here, but I went along with the conspiracy, grunting agreement.

Ref, seeing the flames change colour, lifted his head. 'Back to the bellows, boy,' he called, but Toki kept staring – he pointed behind me, away into the dark land where I had set watchers and fire.

'What is that light?' he asked.

I did not need to turn, felt the sick, frantic heat of that warning beacon though it was miles away. When I spoke I stared straight at Botolf, so he would know, would remember what he had been told of Klerkon's steading on Svartey.

'That light is men who kill bairns and fuck their mother on a dead ox,' I said, harsh as a crow laugh.

'Men like us.'

Men like us, following their prow beast up the fjord in a ship called *Dragon Wings*, grim with revenge, hugging a secret to them with savage glee, for they did not want a fair fight, only slaughter.

You can only wear what the Norns weave, so we sent everyone else off into the mountains and worked the *Elk* out to meet Randr Sterki. Men struggled and died screaming battle cries and bloodlust there on the raven-black, slow-shifting fjord; the prow beasts bobbed and snarled at each other as men struggled and died in the last light of a hard day – and both sides found the secret of the Roman Fire that burns even water.

THREE

The vault of his head was charred to black ruin and stank, a jarring on the nose and throat but one which had helped bring me back to coughing life. My throat burned, my chest felt tight and my ears roared with the gurgle of water. It was night, with a fitful, shrouded moon.

I blinked; his hands were gone, melted like old tallow down to the bone and his scalp had slipped like some rakish, rat-fur cap, the one remaining eye a blistered orb that bulged beneath the fused eyelids, the face a melted-tallow mass of sloughed brow and crackled-black.

'Nes-Bjorn,' said a voice and I turned to it. Finn tilted his chin at the mess; the claw of one hand still reached up as if looking for help.

'Three ladies, over the fields they crossed,' he intoned. 'One brought fire, two brought frost. Out with the fire, in with the frost. Out, fire! In, frost!'

It was an old charm, used on children who had scorched or scalded themselves, but a little late for use on the ruin that had been Nes-Bjorn.

'Came out of the sea like one of Aegir's own *draugr*,'

42

Finn added. 'Fire had seared his voice away and most of the breath in him. The gods alone know what kept him walking. I near shat myself. Then I gave him The Godi, for mercy.'

He raised the named sword in question and now I saw the raw-meat gape round the throat of the thing that had been Nes-Bjorn, while the wind hissed sand through the shroud of stiff grass, bringing the scent of salt and charred wood with it. Something shifted darkly and slid into a familiar shape that grinned at me and dragged me to sit upright with a powerful hand.

'You swallowed half the fjord,' rumbled Botolf cheerfully. 'But you have bokked most of it up now, so you should be better.'

'Better than the others,' Finn added grimly, crouched and watchful and Botolf sighed and studied the thing next to him, while the sand pattered on it and stuck. It looked like driftwood.

'Aye – poor Nes-Bjorn Klak will never run the oars again after this.'

I came back to the Now of it, realised we were somewhere in the dunes to the east of Hestreng. The charred wood smell came again, stronger on the changing wind and Finn saw my nose twitch.

'Aye,' he said, grim as weathered rock, 'the *Elk* is burned and gone and good men with her. All of them, it seems to me, save us.'

'I saw Hauk fall,' I croaked and Botolf agreed that he had also seen Hauk die.

'Gizur, too,' Finn added mournfully. 'He held on to the steerboard and told me he had made this ship and he would die with it. He did, for I saw at least two spears in him as I went over the side.'

'Red Njal? Hlenni Brimill?'

Finn shrugged and shook his head. Botolf said, brightly: 'Onund lives. I saw men drag him off up the beach.'

Finn grunted. 'He will not be long delayed to a meeting

with Hel herself then, for they will kill him for sure. That Roman Fire . . . it even spread to *Dragon Wings* and they had to beach it to throw sand on it. They tried water and that only made it worse.'

I struggled to sit up and to think, while the deaths of the Oathsworn were like turning stones, milling the sense and breath from me. Gizur and Hauk . . . ten years I had known them. And Hlenni Brimill and Red Njal, who had struggled through the Serkland deserts and the frozen steppe. All of them had sought out Atil's treasure and thought they had won fair fame and fortune . . . truly, that hoard was cursed.

'Roman Fire,' I said hoarsely and Finn spat.

'Fucking Greeks-Who-Call-Themselves-Romans,' he said bitterly. 'Who else would make a fire that burns even water?'

'Bearcoats,' I added and turned to where his eyes gleamed in the dark. My throat burned with sea water, making my voice raw.

'When did Randr Sterki get them?' I asked. 'Bearcoats don't roll up to the likes of him and announce they are his men until death – and not twelve of them. And you cannot buy pots of Roman Fire in some market, like honey, neither.'

'What are you saying, Orm?' Botolf demanded. 'My head hurts and my friends are gone, so I am no good with riddles tonight.'

'What he means is that there is more to this,' Finn growled savagely. 'More than Randr Sterki and his revenge.'

Botolf stirred, then shook his head.

'Perhaps. I am thinking only that we have become what once we raided.'

No-one spoke, but the memories slithered to us, slime-cold and unwelcome and Botolf, who had not been there but had heard some of it, let his massive shoulders slump. He looked at me, eyes white in the darkness.

'I wish you had not spoken of the woman and the dead ox. Things were clearer to me out on the whale road, when

44

we followed the prow beast and everything we owned was in a sea-chest.'

Finn's head came up at the reference to the woman and the dead ox and he looked from me to Botolf and back. Then he grunted and hunched himself against the cold memories.

'Well, we have fame, land, women and bairns,' he spat angrily. 'Odin's gifts. Should we spurn them, then, because of what we are?'

Botolf shrugged. 'What we were,' he corrected sullenly. 'Now we are the ones raided and our women are likely to be humped on a dead ox.'

'Be dumb on that,' Finn savaged. 'What do you know? Look at you. You do not even possess the thought-cage of a mouse. Where would you be without Hestreng? Without Ingrid and little Helga Hiti, eh? That is your wyrd, for sure, and running back to the whale road after the prow beast will not change what we are now, nor what we once did. Aye – and may do again, for I know myself to be a vik-Norse, until they burn me up as a good Odinsmann.'

I was astounded; Finn, above all others, had been the one muttering and raging against the shackles of land, women and bairns. Botolf sulked at Finn's rage, not knowing that it was because Finn was the humper in the story of the woman and the dead ox. Finn, for all his bluster, was aware that it was that, in part, which had brought Randr Sterki down on us – aware, also, of the threat to little Hroald, the son he did not know what to do with.

'You should not say such things to me,' Botolf muttered. 'About not having the thought-cage of a mouse.'

'Just so,' agreed Finn poisonously. 'I take it back. You do have the thought-cage of a mouse.'

'Enough,' I managed to say at last and then coughed and spat; pain lurked, dull and hot in my chest. 'I am thinking we will not have thought-cages at all, if we do not act. I am thinking Randr Sterki will not be content with claiming a

victory over the Oathsworn and stealing some chickens and pigs. Not a man who brings bearcoats and Roman Fire with him.'

'Aye, right enough,' agreed Botolf, mollified by what he saw as Finn giving in.

'What do we do, then, Orm?' Finn asked. 'It will be a sore fight whatever you decide.'

I shot him a look, for he did not even try to hide the cheerful in his voice. I did not like what we had to do. We had to find out what was happening and to do that someone had to get close. Since there was no flaring fire, the great long-house was not burned and that was because Randr and his men were using it – so someone had to sneak into the hall and find out what all this was truly about.

They looked at me in the dark, one whose idea of stealth was not to roar when he charged, the other who was half a bench; it was not hard to work out who had to be the fox.

Finn handed me his seax, as if to seal the bargain.

No starlight. A limping moon that stumbled from cloud to cloud, driven by the same wind that whipped the tops off waves and drifted sand through the grass. We moved, soft as roe deer towards the shadowed bulk of Hestreng hall and the lights scattered about.

For all his size and lack of leg, Botolf could move quietly enough and the sand muffled the thump of his timber foot, while Finn crept, shoulder-blades as hunched as a cat's. We stopped, licking dry lips and sweating like fighting stallions.

The harsh stink of burned wood hit me and I saw the looming shadow, lolling like a dead whale, slapped with soothing waves – *Dragon Wings*, beached and blackened along half its length. Botolf made a bitter laugh grunt in the back of his throat at the sight and we moved into the lee of it, where the wet char stink was worst and the shadows darkest.

Beyond, rocking at its tether near the slipway, was the second ship. I did not recognise it.

I sat down to pull off my sodden boots and handed them to Finn – then we froze at a sharp, high sound. I knew that sound well, that mating fox shriek of frantic fear; someone was being hard-used by pain.

I looked at Finn, then Botolf, then slid towards Hestreng hall, feeling the wet wool of my breeks chafe and tug, the sand sliding under my feet, sharp with shell and shingle. My ankle burned, as if it had one of Ref's hot nails through it; an old injury, like the stumps of my missing fingers, which itched maddeningly; I knew what Botolf meant about his leg.

I found what I sought and made sure no-one was in it – then I climbed on to the lean-to roof of the privy and up on to the hog-back hall roof. My soles were stabbed by wooden slates I was willing not to crack or creak as I crabbed across it to where the crossed gables with their dragon-head ends snarled blindly up into the night.

There I paused, shivering as the wind keened through my wet tunic, yet sweating. Then I grabbed one of the dragon-heads and swung over into the dark, square pit of the smokehole, just wide enough to take me in onto a beam. Voices growled up through the blue reek that told me the pitfire was still lit.

It was a strangeness, this having a smokehole at either end rather than in the middle and had been done by the previous master of the Hestreng longhouse, a Dane, before he had backed the wrong side. The twin holes had merits – sucking reek the length of the hall and high into the rafters, killing vermin and smoking hanging meats, for one – but none better than letting me slide unseen into the shadows along the roof-trees.

I slithered in, surprised at what it took to squeeze silently through; I had not realised the breadth of shoulder on me and was still a skinny boy in my head. Just as well, or I would have been too afraid to even try this.

The voices were louder, the blue reek stung my eyes; someone had opened the further door, driving the pitfire smoke up, spilling it out of the hole at this end. I touched the hilt of the seax sheathed in my lap and fought to keep my breathing shallow, while my heart pounded and my throat and eyes stung; it had been a time since I had done anything this foolish or daring.

Up in the ash-tainted dark, I perched like a raven on a branch and looked down into the fire-lit dimness, edging forward slightly, one hand on the cross-beams over my head for balance. Below me hung whalemeat and cheeses and fish, smoke-blacked and trembling on their lines; I stepped more softly still – then froze, smelling the mouth-wetting scent of roasting meat wafting in from the outside breeze.

Nithings. Odin curse them to the Nine Hells. They were spit-roasting my brace of oxen in my own cookhouse and, at last, I was bitten by the sense of loss of what was mine. I had some fifteen male thralls somewhere, most of them scattered into the night, shivering and weeping – those oxen cost more than twelve of them to buy and more than all fifteen to keep.

That was because they turned more land than harnessing fifteen thralls to a plough – and now they were greasing the chins of hard raiding men. I tried not to think of it, or of the times I had done it to others, or the dying ox in a yard on Svartey. Instead, I squinted down into the fetid dim of the hall.

I saw a huddle of men and had a heart-leap at the sight of them; two were Red Njal and Hlenni, not dead, but sitting with their arms clasped under their raised knees, wrists bound. Another was Onund, naked and strung up by the thumbs, gleaming with sweat and streaked with darker, thicker fluids. A fourth lay smiling two smiles and seeping blood through cloth wrappings; Brand's luckless steward, Skulli, whose throat had been cut in his sickbed.

There was litter scattered, what was left after men had

plundered the place, and I felt a cutting pang at the sight of eider feathers sprayed like snow; Thorgunna's favourite pillows, which she would mourn.

There was a man I did not know sitting on a bench with an axe and a sword nearby. He chewed bread, which he tore idly from a chunk, and he was smeared with black – wet charwood, I was thinking, from where he had fought a fire earlier. There was the red line of a helmet rim on his forehead and brown marks on his nose from the noseguard iron-rot.

There were two more. One was a Svear by his accent, with a striking black beard, streaked with white so that he seemed to have a badger on his face. His hair was also black and iron-grey, with a single thick brow-braid on the right side, banded in silver. He was naked from the waist and his right arm, from wrist to shoulder all round, was blue-black with skin-mark shapes and figures – a tree, I saw, and gripping beasts among others.

I knew him from the old days and he had been less salted then. Even if I had not, the skin-marks revealed him as Randr Sterki, for it was well-known that he had adopted this shield-biter perversion, which was said to be magic, for strength or protection or both. If I had been in doubt of who it was, there was the leather thong round his neck and, swinging on the end of it across the matted hair of his sweat-gleaming chest, was Sigurd's silver nose.

He strode to the pitfire and shoved a cooled length of iron back in it, then turned to the second man, who watched him with his hands on his hips and a sneer on a clean-chinned face with a neat snake moustache. His yellow hair was caught up in a thong and a braided one round his brow kept any stray wisps off his face. With his blue tunic and green breeks and silver armrings, it was clear he liked himself, this one, while the inlaid hilt of the sword at his waist told me he was probably master of the second ship. I did not know him at all, but he spoke with a Dane lilt.

'This will not serve,' he told Randr Sterki. 'We are wasting time here.'

'My time to waste,' Randr Sterki answered, sullen as rain-cloud, working the length of iron deeper into the coals of the pitfire.

'No,' said the other impatiently. 'It is not. It belongs to Styrbjorn, who has charged us both with a task.'

'You did not get your men killed and your ship all but burned to the waterline, Ljot Tokeson,' Randr Sterki bellowed, whirling on the man. 'I beat the Oathsworn in battle, not you . . . and somewhere around here is Orm Bear Slayer's silver to be dug up, his women to be taken and himself . . .'

He paused and snatched up the sword from the table; the bread-eater shied away as the careless edge whicked past his ear.

'I have his sword,' Randr hissed. 'I want the hand that wielded it.'

I did not know this Ljot Tokeson, but he was clearly one of Styrbjorn's men and one with steel in him, for few men gave Randr Sterki a hard time of it, especially when Randr had a blade in his hand – my blade, I realised, rescued from the *Elk*.

Ljot slapped his hand on the bench, with a sound like a wet drum.

'Not all your men fought and died, Randr Sterki,' he harshed out. 'Three bearcoats died. Three. My brother had those twelve with him for four fighting seasons without loss and you have lost three in a day.'

The wind seemed to suck out of Randr then and he slumped down on a bench and took up a pitcher, scorning a cup to drink; ale spilled down his chest and he wiped his beard with one slow hand.

'They fought hard, the Oathsworn,' he admitted. 'That Roman Fire did not help.'

'Then you should not have lost your head and thrown it,' Ljot growled. 'You lost more of your own men to it than the

Oathsworn did. It was given as an expensive gift, to make sure you succeeded in what Styrbjorn sent you to do.'

Randr licked his lips, his eyes filled with screaming men and burning sea.

'I did not know what it would do . . .'

'Now you do,' interrupted Ljot, sneering. 'And if you do not want the same fate for yourself, it would be better if we did what we came to do. For my brother will tie you to a pole and hurl Roman Fire at you until you melt like ice in sunshine if we fail.'

There was a long and terrible pause, broken only by the sound of Onund breathing in bubbling snores through what was clearly a broken nose. I wondered who this Ljot was and who the brother – it was not Styrbjorn, that much I did know. Then Randr stood up.

'I will send scouts out. We will find what we seek.'

The tension flowed out of the taut line that was Ljot and he forced a smile.

'There will be time enough for all this,' he said softly, waving a hand that took in the bound prisoners and the hung Onund. 'The important thing is . . .'

'Fuck yourself, Ljot Tokeson,' Randr spat back. 'When you have lost all you hold dear, come and speak to me of the important thing.'

He slammed out of the door in a blast of rainwind that swirled the blue reek of the hall, stinging my eyes. In the blur I saw the back of the boy's head shattering in a spray of blood and bone while his mother drowned in her own blood on the arse of a dying ox. All he held dear . . .

The man at the table looked up sourly from where he was idly rolling bread into little pills.

'His thought-cage is twisted, that one,' he growled at Ljot. 'Still – has Randr Sterki the right of it? About this buried silver?'

'They say the Oathsworn robbed a tomb of all the silver

51

in the world,' Ljot growled back scornfully, 'which is clearly a lie, since I myself wear silver armrings.'

'All the same,' the other said and Ljot shook his head wearily.

'Just watch them, Bjarki,' he spat. 'Fall asleep and I will gut you.'

I saw what Ljot did not as he turned to leave – the narrow-eyed hate at his back. Even before the hall door clattered shut, this guard Bjarki was on his feet and moving to the pitfire and the iron in it.

'No good will come of this,' growled Red Njal from where he sat, seeing which way the wind blew. 'Shameful deeds bring revenge, as my granny used to say.'

Bjarki ignored him and hefted the iron, wincing when it burned his fingers; he searched round for something to wrap round it, deciding on the good fur off my high seat.

'Your chance to speak will come,' Bjarki said to Red Njal, moving like a wolf towards Onund. 'Now,' he added, with a gentle sigh, 'let us hear you speak with a silver tongue, hump-back. No more screams, just a place name will do. Between us, as it were.'

He had his back to me when I gripped the beam and swung down on it, my legs slamming into his shoulder-blades. He shot forward into the upright beam to Onund's left, the crack of his forehead hitting it like the sound of a falling tree. Worse, for his part, was that he was brandishing the hot iron at the time and it was rammed between his face and the pillar.

He scarcely made a sound all the same, for the blow had laid him out and he crumpled, a great red burn welt from left eyebrow to right jawbone, across his nose and one eye, which spat angry gleet. Blood trickled from a great cut on his head and the hot iron hissed and sizzled on his chest; his tunic smoked and flames licked.

I got off my backside and kicked the iron off him into the fire, then had to rescue the wrapped fur. A good fur that,

white wolf and not cheap – I said as much as I took up my sword and turned to cut Red Njal and Hlenni Brimill loose.

'Remind me never to borrow a fur from you without asking,' Hlenni said, rubbing his wrists and standing up stiffly. He kicked Bjarki so that his head rattled back and forth.

'Little Bear,' he sneered, which was what *bjarki* meant and was a name you gave a child, not a grown man. 'A pity only that he was laid out before he felt the heat of that iron.'

'Just so,' panted Red Njal, struggling with Onund's bonds. 'Help me here instead of gloating or we will all feel the lick of that heat – pray to the gods if you must, but carry a keen blade, as my granny used to say.'

I gave Red Njal the seax and hefted the familiar weight of my sword as I opened the door cautiously, expecting at least one guard outside. There was nothing – then a bulk moved, darker than the shadows; fear griped my belly and I had to fight not to run. I smelled him then, all sweat and leather and foul breath and I knew that stink well.

Finn.

'You took so long I came to find you,' he rasped hoarsely, gleaming teeth and eyes in the dark. 'I saw folk leaving and thought to chance matters. What did you find?'

I said nothing, but heard him grunt when he saw Hlenni and Red Njal, Onund half-carried, half-dragged between them.

'This way,' he said, as if leading them to clean beds in a dry room and we shadowed into the night, from dark to dark like owls on a hunt, every muscle screaming at the expected bite of steel, every nerve waiting for the shout of discovery.

Somewhere out on the pasture, where the hall was a dim-lit bulk in the distant dark, we stopped, while I put my boots back on. We headed towards the north valley, prowling and fox-silent.

All the time, circling like wolves in my head, was what had passed between Randr Sterki and Ljot – and, when those wolves put their muzzles on weary paws, the old dead rose in their place, leering and mocking me.

FOUR

It rained, a fine mirr that blotted out the stars, so that we fumbled along, panting like dogs and stumbling. I led the way, hoping more than knowing, into the wet dark where trolls leered and *alfar* flickered at the edge of vision.

A darker shape against the black; I froze. Finn stumbled into the back of me, almost knocking me over and rain dripped off our noses as we stuck them close to each other to hiss in whispers.

'What is it?' he hoarsed out and, even as he asked, I knew.

'The stone. Our stone . . .'

Slick and rain-gleamed, the great stone, half-carved with Klepp's handiwork, half-painted by Vuokko the Sea-Finn, was as large as our relief and we hugged it close, delighting in the wet-rock smell of it, for it meant we were at the entrance to the valley.

Nearby was a hut, once the home of the horse-herder thralls, now Klepp's *hov* until it grew too cold to work stone. Dark as a cave, of course, because he would be gone, with Vuokko and Thorgunna and Thordis and all the others, heading further up the valley to the foothills of the mountains.

'Ruts,' said Finn suddenly, catching my sleeve and guiding my hand to the wet ground. The scar and the smell of new-turned

soil gave truth to it; ruts, where a cart had passed, maybe more than one.

'At least they are safe,' I muttered and we moved after the struggling figures carrying Onund into the shelter of the dark hut.

It was a rough affair, for use in the summer only and made of low split-log walls and roof-turfs and daub. Inside was the smell of leather and iron and oil, the cold-tomb smell of stone dust and the harsh throat-lick of paints.

'How is Onund?' I asked of the shadows grunting him down, panting with the effort.

'Heavy,' growled Hlenni Brimill sourly.

'Babbling,' added Red Njal and I moved closer to the wheezing bulk of Onund, wishing I had light to see how badly he was hurt.

'Bairn,' he bubbled through his broken nose. 'Bairn.'

'He's been saying that since we cut him down,' muttered Red Njal, wiping his own streaming face. Botolf stumbled over something and cursed.

'Hist, man!' Finn spat hoarsely. 'Why don't you bang on a shield, mouse-brain?'

'I was looking for a horn lantern,' came the sullen reply. 'Some light would be good.'

'Aye – set fire to the hut, why not?' Finn cursed. 'Why have our trackers fumbling in the cold and wet and dark when we can lead them right to us?'

Botolf rubbed his shin sullenly. 'Why is it always the real leg that gets hit?' he demanded. 'Why not the gods-cursed wooden one . . .?'

I wanted quiet and hissed it out, for there were sounds outside I did not like; movement, someone blowing snot and rain off their nose, the suck of hooves lifting from muddy ground.

Finn's eyes gleamed and he slid away from me, out into the night; we crouched in the hut, waiting and listening.

Three, I worked out. Maybe four. And a horse, though not ridden.

'A hut,' said a voice. 'At least we can get dry.'

'Perhaps a fire . . . butcher the horse and have a decent meal, at least,' said another.

'Oh aye – tell them all where we are, eh, Bergr?' rumbled a third. 'Before you go in that hut, Hamund, I would scout round and make sure we are alone.'

'Of course we are alone,' spat the one called Hamund. 'By the Hammer, Bruse, you are an old woman. And if we are not to eat this spavined nag, why did we bring it, eh?'

'We will eat it in good time,' Bruse answered. They were all hunkered down in the lee of the hut, no more than an arm's length and the width of a split-log wall between us.

'I will be pleased when Randr Sterki is done with this,' muttered Bergr. 'All I want is my share, enough for a farm somewhere. With cows. I like the taste of fresh milk.'

'Farm,' snorted Hamund. 'Why buy work? A good over-winter in a warm hall with a fat-arsed thrall girl and a new raid next year, that will do for me.'

'I thought you were scouting?' Bruse grunted and Hamund hawked in his throat.

'For what? They are far from here. Everyone is far from here. Only the rain is here – and us. Who are these runaways anyway? A hump-back more dead than alive, I heard, and a couple of survivors from a battle we won, no more. Hiding and running, if they have any sense. The rest of them will be half-way over the mountains and gone by now. We should take what loot we can and leave.'

'Go and scout – one of them is Finn Horsehead,' Bruse answered, straightening with a grunt. There was a pause, then the sound of splashing and a satisfied sigh as he pissed against the log wall.

'Finn Horsehead?' muttered Bergr. 'Of the Oathsworn? They say he fears nothing at all.'

56

'I can change that,' sneered Hamund.

'Pray to Odin you never meet him,' Bruse said, adjusting his stance and spurting in little grunts, his voice rising and fading – talking over his shoulder, I was thinking. 'I raided with him, so I know. I saw him rise up and walk – walk, mark you – towards a shieldwall on his own and before he got there it had split and run.'

'I know,' said the voice and I knew, as I knew my own hands, that it was right in Bruse's ear, a knell of a voice, tomb-cold and deep as a pit.

'The others said it was my ale-breath. What do you think, Bruse?'

The splashing stopped. Everything stopped. Then Bergr whimpered and Hamund yelped and everything was movement.

'The ice will not be cleaved from within,' Red Njal grunted, 'as my granny used to say.'

So we rose up and hit the door at a fast run as the screams and chopping sounds began.

By the time we got there, the work was done and Finn, flicking blood off the end of The Godi, stirred one of the three bodies with the toe of his muddy boot.

'I do not recognise him,' he said, frowning. He looked at me. 'Do you know him?'

The man – Bruse, I was thinking, because his breeks were at his knees – was bearded, the blood and rain streaking his face and running in his open, unseeing eyes. I did not know him and said so. Finn shrugged and shook his head.

'He knew me, all the same,' he grunted. 'Seems a pity that he knew me so well and I did not know him from a whore's armpit. Does not seem right to kill such a man on a wet night.'

Botolf lumbered up, clutching a rope end attached to a halter and a horse fastened to that. It limped almost in step with him and Finn laughed at the sight. Botolf, mistaking it for delight at his find, beamed.

'Well, all that talk of horse-eating made me hungry. Now that they are dead, we can have a fire and cook this beast.'

I moved to the horse's head and had it whuff at me, for it knew me well and I knew it – a young colt, a good stallion in the making, whose brothers still charged up and down the valley. I ran a hand down the offending leg, felt the heat and the lump on the pastern; not spavined at all, just ring-bone from a kick and not too badly injured at that. He was under-nourished – as they all were after the winter, rough-coated and stiff with mud – but not bound for a platter just yet. I said so and wondered why the night and Odin had brought this horse to me at all.

Botolf scrubbed his head in a spray of rain and frustration.

'He is done,' he argued. 'What – are we to wait until he drops dead?'

'He will not drop dead. Some decent grass and a little atten-tion and he will be fine,' I told him, then looked Botolf in his big, flat, sullen face. 'If he does die, all the same, it will be in this valley, when his time has come and for more reason than to provide a meal.'

'Odin's arse,' Finn growled. 'I am not usually agreeing with mouse-brain – but this is a horse. Do you think he cares much how he dies?'

Odin cared and I said so.

Botolf growled and yanked the halter harder than he needed, jerking the colt's head after him as he plootered through the rain to the hut. Finn shrugged, looked at me, looked at the horse, then at the sprawl of dead bodies, which was eloquence enough.

'Well,' he growled, 'at least we can load Onund on the beast – unless your darling pony is too poorly for that?'

I ignored the dripping sarcasm and the matching rain. Onund would not help the colt, but it would not harm him badly if it was only for a little while.

'What makes you think it will be a little while?' Finn

countered, looking up from looting the corpses. 'We cannot stay here until light – more of these may come. If we move in the dark, we will travel in half circles, even if we are careful. It could take all night.'

We would not travel in half circles and I told him so; we would easily find our way to Thorgunna and Thordis, bairns, wagons and all, in an hour or less.

'Another Odin moment, Bear Slayer?' he asked, grunting upright and wiping bloody hands on his breeks. 'Have the Norns come to you in the dark and shown you what they weave?'

'Look north,' I told him, having done so already; he did and groaned. The faint red eye of a fire, certain as a guiding star, glowed baleful in the rain-misted dark.

'What are they thinking?' Finn growled.

'I was thinking,' Thorgunna said, 'that bairns needed food and everyone else needed some dry and warm. I was thinking that thralls have run off in panic and, with nowhere to go, will be looking to find us again in the dark.'

She looked up at me, blinking. 'I was thinking,' she added, trying to keep her voice from breaking, 'that menfolk we thought dead might not be and would want to find a way home.'

I held her to me and felt her clutch hard, using her grip instead of tears. Across from me, Ingrid held Botolf and he patted her arm and rumbled like a contented cat.

'I said Thorgunna was a deep thinker,' Finn lied cheerfully, while Thordis clutched his wet tunic so tightly it bunched and squeezed water through her knuckles. 'Was I not saying that all the way here, eh, Orm?'

They swept us up and swamped us with greetings and warmth and pushed food at us. Onund Hnufa was gathered up and wrapped and cooed over, while I laid out the tale of the fight to the flame-dyed faces, grim as cliffs, who gathered to listen.

'Nes-Bjorn,' muttered Abjorn, who led the six men left out of the crew Jarl Brand had lent me. 'Someone is owed a blow for that.'

'Gizur and Hauk,' added Ref, shaking his head. 'By the Hammer, a sad day this.'

Finn went off to look at his sleeping son and Botolf went to his daughter, leaving Hlenni Brimill and Red Njal to expound the tale; the hooms and heyas and wails rose up like foul smoke as I moved from it into the lee of a *wadmal* lean-to, where Thorgunna bent over Onund. Bjaelfi sat with him.

'Can he speak?' I asked and Bjaelfi shook his head.

'Asleep, which is best. He was hard used with hot irons.'

Thorgunna saw me frown and asked why, so I told her that I thought Onund had something to say that would cast a light on all this.

'I thought it simple enough,' she replied tightly. 'Randr Sterki is come to visit on us what once we visited on him.'

I shot her a look, but she kept her head down from me, fussing pointlessly with a cowhide for Onund's bedcovering. She had been there on Svartey when we raided Klerkon, but waiting with the ship while we hewed the place to rack and ruin. We were urged on by that cursed little Crowbone, I said and she lifted her head, eyes black as sheep-droppings.

'Don't blame it all on that boy,' she spat. 'I saw then what raiders were and never wish to see it again. It was not all that boy.'

No, not all, she had the right of it there. There had been raiders too long caged, who sucked in a whiff of blood-scent started by Crowbone, and went Odin-frenzied with it. When all was said and done with it, it was a *strandhogg*, like many others – a little harsher than most, but blood and flame had been our lives for long enough and it was only, I was thinking, that we now were the victims that made the matter of it here in Hestreng so bitter.

None of which answered the mystery of why Styrbjorn's man was here alongside Randr Sterki, nor why bearcoats and Roman Fire had been given to the enterprise. I laid that out for Thorgunna, too, and watched her sit heavily, folding her hands in her lap as she turned it over in her head.

'Styrbjorn wants what he has always wanted,' she said eventually, rising to fetch spoon and platter, busying herself with the things she knew while her mind worked. She filled a bowl with milk-boiled beef and handed it to me absently, then fetched a skin of *skyr* – thick fermented cow's milk thinned down with whey – for me to drink.

'Have we brought away enough?' I asked and she shrugged.

'Anything that was ready to hand and easily lifted,' she answered. 'Food. Three wagons and the horses for them. Shelters and wood for fire. Goats for milk for the bairns. This and that.'

I nodded and ate the beef, watching her rake through her only rescued kist, picking out items to show me. Two spare over-sarks, one in glowing blue, both patched and re-hemmed with braid more than once. A walrus-ivory comb, carved with gripping beasts. A whetsone. Some small stoppered pots with her ointments and face-paints. A walrus-skin bag with a roll of good cloth in it, snugged up in the dry because it had many little pockets sewn into it, all of them stuffed with carefully wrapped spices and herbs.

I nodded and smiled and praised, knowing she mourned for what was left behind – fine bedlinen and cloaks and clothes and food stores. It would all be looted and the rest burned before things were done with; I did not mention her eider-down pillows.

'Where will we go?' she asked suddenly, her voice tight with a fear she tried hard not to show.

'Over the mountains,' I said, making it light as I could. 'Down to Arne Thorliefsson at Vitharsby. There is a *seter* of his, a summer place, just over the high point on the far side

61

– it will not be occupied this early and will give us some shelter.'

We would need it by then, for the way was thawed just enough to be a sore, hard climb at the best of times, never mind the frantic haste we would need to put distance between us and what pursued.

Arne was a good tarman and had three sons, the two youngest needing their lives sorted, since only the eldest would inherit. The younglings were tired of the filthy, backbreaking work of rendering pine root resin into tar for fresh boat planks and Arne would help on the promise of them joining me, the raiding jarl, when the time came.

'Hlenni Brimill went there last year,' Thorgunna said suddenly, remembering, 'when we bought the tar for the *Elk*.'

The *Elk*, now burned and sunk with Gizur and Hauk and all the others floating down and down to the bottom of the black water fjord. I chewed slowly, the beef all ashes in my mouth. Raiding jarl my arse; no ship, no hall and no future if Randr and his bearcoats had their way.

Thorgunna brought me flatbread and sat while I tore chunks off and stuffed it in, trying to look as if I relished eating, but glad of the *skyr* to wash down the great tasteless lumps, my throat too filled with the fear of those bearcoats. Somewhere in the questing dark they prowled, waiting for the scouts to bring them news. Then they would be unleashed on us.

'Will they stop then, when we reach the other side of the mountains?' she asked, as if reading my thoughts.

I did not know. I did not think so. I was thinking only death would stop Randr Sterki – but Styrbjorn's man, this Ljot, wanted something else and I did not know what it was and that part I mentioned to her.

Thorgunna hauled a cloak round her shoulders as the rain-chilled air smoked her breath into the night.

'Styrbjorn is King Eirik's nephew and so his heir,' she answered, slowly working it through her head. 'He was so

until he became such a ranter and raver that he was thrown out for his pains. But he still is heir and will be king if Eirik dies.'

'Aye, maybe,' I said, forcing a final swallow. 'Though more than few will not like the idea much. Anyway, he is young yet, though it seems he does not want to wait to be king.'

'He will not be at all,' Thorgunna answered meaningfully, 'if Eirik has a son.'

There it was, like a cunning picture of little tiles seen too close up; step back from it and it swam into view; Queen Sigrith. Styrbjorn wanted Sigrith – well, he wanted the child she carried and he wanted it dead.

Thorgunna watched my mouth drop like a coal-eater and then she rose, taking me by the hand. I followed her through the bodies huddled round the fire or close together under shelters, dank with misery. In one of the wagons lay a bulky, moaning figure and, squatted next to her like a bull seal, was Jasna, stroking and crooning soothing balm into the groans of the other.

'How is she?' asked Thorgunna and Jasna raised her pudding face, jowls trembling, and patted the sweat-greased cheeks of Queen Sigrith.

'Not good. No easy birth. Soon, little bird, soon. All the pain will be over and then a beautiful son, eh . . .'

I looked wildly at Thorgunna, who said nothing, but led me a little way away.

'The queen will birth, in a day, perhaps less.'

It was as good as an axe to the hull of all our hopes, that simple phrase; there would be no swift moving from here, banging her about in the back of a cart and, soon, we would have to stop entirely until the bairn was birthed. I thought I heard the bearcoats roar their triumph to the wet-shrouded moon.

Botolf added another log to the fire as Aoife collected wooden platters, Cormac locked to one hip and nodding, half-asleep.

Thorgunna came to me with dry breeks and tunic and serk, made me strip and change there and then, taking my sea-sodden boots to be rubbed with fat.

I sat next to Finn, sticking my bare feet closer to the flames as he cleaned the clotted blood from The Godi. The rain spat on the *wadmal* canopy and hissed in the fire just beyond it. Ref came up, carrying my sword; I had not even realised I had let it go, probably when Thorgunna hugged me.

'Not too bad,' he said cheerfully. 'There's a great notch out of it and I cannot grind it out, for it is all of the edge metal from that part.'

Then his face changed, like a sudden squall on a mirror fjord.

'Cannot grind it out properly anyway,' he added with a sigh. 'My forge is gone and all the tools with it.'

He handed it to me and I looked at the v-notch he pointed to. The sliver was in the mast of the *Elk*, for sure and I told him so. We all went quiet then, thinking of the black fjord and the sunken *Elk* and our oarmates, rolling in the slow, cold dark with their hair like sea-wrack.

'We should make *blot* for them,' Finn said and Abjorn came up at that moment, with little Koll at his heels.

'I have set watchers,' he told me from the grim cliff of his face, then jerked a thumb at the boy behind him. 'Like me, young Koll wishes news of his father.'

'I have none,' I answered, feeling guilty that, of all the fledg-lings who had occupied my thoughts, the one I had been charged with fostering had not been one of them. I signalled him closer and he stepped into the light and out of the rain, the firelight on his face showing up the white of him and the grit of his jaw, making a fierce light in his pale eyes.

'You are safe here,' I said, hoping it was true. 'Your father, once he has dealt with Styrbjorn, will come and help us defeat these nithings. Until then, we will get a little damp and have an adventure in the mountains.'

64

'My mother . . .' he said and I felt a stab, felt foolish. Of course . . . he had heard at the beach how Styrbjorn had dealt with all his family. Ingrid swept in then, gathering the boy into her apron and making soothing noises about honey and milk and sleep, for it was late.

I looked round the fire then, at all the expectant faces – Klepp Spaki, the blank, strange mask of Vuokko, the droop-mouthed Ref, bemoaning the loss of his forge and tools, Red Njal and Hlenni and Bjaelfi, staring at me across the flames, faces bloody with light and hoping for wisdom.

And there, in the shadows, no more than a pale blob of face, was Leo the monk.

'Roman Fire,' I called to him and he stepped forward, all the faces turning from me to him.

'So I heard,' he answered, arms folded into the sleeves of his clothing. 'Though we call it Persian Fire. Sometimes Sea Fire.'

'No matter what you call it,' I spat back into his plump smile, 'it is never let far from the Great City. Nor into the hands of such as Styrbjorn. I had heard it was a great crime to do so.'

'Indeed,' he replied sombrely. 'The ingredients of what you call Roman Fire were disclosed by an angel to the first great Constantine. It was he who ordained that there should be a curse, in writing and on the Holy Altar of the Church of God, on any who dare give the secret to another nation.'

He paused and frowned.

'Whether this is giving the secret is a matter for debate – the likes of Styrbjorn could not learn how to make it from what he has been given. However, such an event is cause for concern among many departments of the Imperium, where such weapons are strictly regulated.'

Concern? Burned ships and dead men were more than concern and I bellowed that at him. The rage gagged in my throat, both at his diffidence and the implication that the northers were barbarians too stupid to find out the secret of

65

Roman Fire from weapons handed out like toys to bairns. It did not cool me any to know he was right in it, too.

He nodded, smooth as a polished mirror and seemingly unconcerned by my glaring.

'Indeed. I would not be surprised if certain of those departments took steps to find out what has happened to their missing amounts.'

'Such as sending someone to find out?'

He inclined his head, face blank as an egg.

'I would not be in the least surprised.'

I watched him for a moment longer, but nothing flickered on it, no firm sign that he was the one sent to find out. He was young – not in the way we counted it, but certainly in the way the Great City did – but I suspected he had been sent and that made him a man to be watched. In the end, I broke the locked antlers of our eyes, turning to tell everyone that Styrbjorn had sent warriors here to end the life of Sigrith and the child she carried in her belly, so that he would remain sole heir to the high seat of the Svears and Geats.

The women grunted, while the men stayed silent. I did not say anything about why Randr Sterki had – I was sure – begged Styrbjorn to be the one to take on the task; those who remembered what we had done on Svartey did not need reminding of it. I told them all we would move north, across the mountains, as soon as it was light enough to see, trying to keep my voice easy, as if I was telling them when we would sow rye and in what field that year.

Afterwards, when others had rolled into skins and cloaks, I sat with Finn listening to Botolf snore – alone by the fire, for he had given his space beside Ingrid to Helga and Aoife and the other bairns, for better warmth. In the dark, I heard Aoife cooing softly to Cormac to soothe him – beautiful boy, she said. Where's my lovely boy, white as an egg, then?

'If it comes to it,' Finn said eventually, 'I will fight Randr Sterki.'

'Why you?' I countered and he shrugged and looked at me, half-ashamed, half-defiant. The memory of him humping away at the dying wife of Randr Sterki slunk sourly between us.

'I killed his boy,' I said sourly. 'So it should be me. Red Njal, I am remembering, killed others of his family. Perhaps we should take it in turns.'

Botolf woke himself with a particularly large snore and sat up, groaning and wiping sleep from his eyes.

'Odin's arse . . . my shoulder and back hurt. I hate sleeping on the ground in winter.'

'A hard raiding man like you?' snorted Finn. 'Surely not.'

'Shut your hole, Finn,' Botolf countered amiably, sitting up and wincing. 'The worse thing is the itch in my wooden leg.'

There was silence for a moment; a last log collapsed and whirled sparks up.

'What are we going to do?' demanded Botolf suddenly.

'About what? Your itching log-leg?' I asked and he waved his arms wildly in all directions.

'All this. The queen and weans.'

'We take them to Vitharsby and then east to Jarl Brand,' I told him.

'Just like that?' Botolf snapped. He rubbed his beard with frustration. 'Hunted by toad-licking wearers of bear and wolf skins? And at least a ship's crew of hard raiders? With a woman about to pup and half the bairns in the country?'

'One of them your own,' Finn pointed out poisonously. 'Another is mine. Do we begin throwing them over our shoulder as we run, then? We will start with Helga Hiti.'

I saw Botolf's face twist and frown as he fought to work all this out, only succeeding in fuelling more anger.

'What do you think we should do?' I asked and it was like throwing water on a sleeping drunk. He blinked. He blew out through pursed lips and surfaced with a thought, triumphant.

'We ought to leave the queen and ride off with our own,'

he declared. 'We could go to Thordis' place, which will be Finn's when he marries her. What are the fate of kings and princes to us, eh?'

It was astounding. I remembered Jarl Brand had said something of the same when we were in Serkland, only it was about the back-stabbing in high places that went on in the Great City. It never stopped amazing me, the things that stuck in Botolf's thought-cage.

'She is our queen,' Finn growled, flailing with one hand, as if trying to pluck the words he needed out of the air. 'We have to protect her. And Thordis' steading is only a short ride from Hestreng – if it was not behind the hills here, you could probably see it burn.'

I looked at him, but if the thought of everything he might one day own going up in smoke bothered him, he did not betray it by as much as a catch in his voice. Botolf flung his arms in the air.

'Protect the queen? Why? She would not give the likes of me the smell off her shit,' he grunted sourly. 'And how do we protect her? There is barely a handful of us.'

'We are Oathsworn,' Finn declared, thrusting out his chin. 'How can we do anything else but guard a queen and the heir to the throne of Eirik the Victorious?'

There was silence then, for fair fame had closed its jaws and even Botolf had no answer for the grip of them. We were Oathsworn, Odin's own, and would die before we took one step back, so the skalds had it. Not for the first time I marvelled at how fame had shackles stronger than iron to fasten you to a hopeless endeavour.

'Might be a girl,' Botolf offered sullenly and I shook my head. Thorgunna had done her hen's egg test and it had come up as a boy, no mistake. I said as much.

'Ah well,' Finn said as Botolf continued to glower. 'Perhaps you have the right of it, Botolf. I never did care much for wealth and glory; after all, we have all we need, though

rebuilding Thordis' place – if it is burned and if I wed her – will be expensive and all gold is useful.'

He stretched, winked at me where Botolf could not see and farted sonorously.

'Anyway,' he went on. 'Once I have a ship under me I am a happy man – so perhaps we should tether the queen here like a goat and head for safety.'

'Aha!' Botolf declared triumphantly, looking from me to Finn and back. Then he frowned.

'What wealth and glory?'

I shrugged, picking up from Finn as he looked wickedly at me from under his hair, pretending to wipe a scrap of fat-rich fleece carefully up and down The Godi.

'The usual stuff,' I said. 'Meaningless to the likes of us, who have silver and fame and land enough already.'

'I have no land,' Botolf growled and I felt a pang of shame, for I had known this was a fret for him, since Ingrid constantly nagged and chafed him over it, wanting him to be first in his own hall rather than just another follower in mine. That was why I had mentioned it.

'Oh, aye,' I said, as if just realising it, then shrugged. 'Still. We would have to bring the queen and bairn safe back to King Eirik before he showered us with rings and praise and odal-rights on steadings – after all, it is his first-born and the heir to his wealth and lands. What would he not give for such a safe return? But – too dangerous, as you say. Better to cut and run, pick up the pieces of our old lives once these hard raiders have gone.'

There was silence, broken only by the rain hissing in the dying fire and the snores of the sleepers nearby.

'Would they really give us land?' Botolf asked after a while.

'Aye, sadly, for we are men of the sea, after all,' Finn replied. 'Still – skalds would write whole sagas about you.'

'Fuck that,' Botolf grunted. 'I have such sagas already. You cannot graze goats on a saga. And for a man of the sea, Finn Horsearse, you are talking of steadings readily enough.'

He was silent for a moment and I decided enough was enough; somewhere, through the rain mist, dawn was racing at us. I half rose and Botolf looked up and spoke.

'Do you think we can win against *ulfhednar*?' he asked suddenly. Finn laughed, quiet and savage; I sat down again, chilled by the term, which was used for madmen in wolfskins.

'Have we ever been beaten?' Finn demanded.

Botolf considered it for a moment, then stood up, nodding and serious.

'Then you are right. We are Oathsworn. We never run from a fight and this is our queen. I am with you, for sure. Now I am off to a warm bed, if I can squeeze in between bairns.'

Finn watched him stump off into the dark beyond the fire and shook his head wearily.

'By the Hammer – there are stones with more clever than him.'

We both knew, all the same, that all Botolf had needed was an excuse to do what he already knew to be right, to have someone persuade him to it.

Then Finn turned to me, sliding The Godi back into the sheath.

'Do you think we can beat them?' he asked.

We had to. It was as simple as that. I said so and he nodded, rising and heading off for his own bed, leaving me with fire-shapes and weariness.

Thorgunna, when I went to her, was awake, sitting hunched up and wrapped in blankets and almost under the wagon in which the queen of all the Svears and Geats groaned and gasped. Nearby, Kuritsa huddled under a cloak – not his own, I fancied – under the canopy and out of the rain and his black eyes watched me arriving. He was a thrall and his name meant 'chicken' because, when I had bought him, he had a shock of hair like a cock's comb before it was cut to stubble.

'No-one sleeps tonight,' I said, trying to be light with it. Thorgunna pulled me down beside her, tenting me under her

cloak and blankets, giving me her warmth. Her head was heavy on my shoulder.

'Kuritsa just arrived,' she said. 'The two who ran off with him are still missing and Kuritsa does not know where they are. But he killed a man, he says.'

That was news and I sat up. Kuritsa sat up, too, looking warily at me from out of the cave of his face.

'You killed a man,' I said to him and he nodded uneasily; I was not surprised at his wariness, since thralls found with weapons were almost always killed outright.

'I took his little knife and killed him,' he said, almost defiantly. 'Then I took his bow and shot at his friend, but it was dark, I was hasty and I am out of the way of it. I missed.'

He produced the bow and three arrows, thrusting them towards me, his square, flat-nosed face proud. He grinned.

'I was not always a thrall,' he said. 'I hunted, in my own land.'

I looked at him; he was thin, dark-eyed, dark-haired and far from his own lands, somewhere in the Finnmark – yet he had a tilt to his close-cropped chin that would have had him beaten if matters were different. I told him to keep the bow, that he would need it sooner or later.

Kuritsa blinked at that, then smiled and held the weapon to his chest as if it warmed him.

'They hunt in fours,' he offered suddenly. 'One of the *ham-ramr* and three with him, tracking and offering him their shields. I had the favour of gods when I found two trackers and no *ham-ramr*.'

I looked at him; the word *ham-ramr* was an interesting one, for it was used on a man who changed his shape in a fit that also gave him great strength and power. Small wonder, then, that all the thralls had run off screaming – and more power to this one, who had not. Yet Thorgunna muttered under her breath, something about the direness of arming a thrall.

71

'You should sleep,' I told her and had back the familiar scorning snort.

'I am too old to enjoy cold nights and wet ground,' she replied. 'Still – this will make your son into a raiding man, for sure, since it seems that is all his lot.'

I ignored her dripping venom and put my hand on her belly then, feeling the warmth, fancying I could feel the heat of what grew in it. I thought, too, about what it would feel like to lose what was snugged up in the harbour of that belly – and the belly, too. All hopes and fears buried in the earth, given to Freyja and, with them, a part of me in that cold, worm-filled ground.

What was left, I was thinking, would be a *draugr*, a walking dead man, with only one thought left – revenge. Like Randr Sterki. I knew he would never stop until he was killed.

'Do you have a plan?' Thorgunna demanded.

'Stay alive, get to Vitharsby, then to Jarl Brand.'

'Death holds no fears for me,' she said suddenly. 'Though I am afraid of dying.'

'You will not die,' I said and felt, then, the rightness of what had to be done. She looked at me, a little surprised by the strength and depth of my voice; I was myself, for I thought a little of Odin had entered into it, even as he placed the thought in me as to what to do next.

FIVE

Dawn was whey and pewter, sullen with the promise of rain, and we were packed and moving even before it had slithered over the mountains we had to cross.

Jasna levered herself out of the wagon the queen lay in alongside bairns and supplies, for we had little room for those who could not walk or keep up; looking at the fat thrall-woman I was not sure she would manage with all that weight on her splay feet, but, if she felt the pain of trudging, nothing showed on her broad scowl of a face. The Mazur girl swayed alongside her, a skald-verse of walking, as if to show the fat woman in even worse light.

'Let us hope that Jasna can keep up,' grunted Thordis venomously, a squalling Hroald sling-wrapped round her. 'The horses will be grateful the longer we keep her out of a wagon.'

'And the walking will melt her,' added a smiling Ingrid, popping Helga into the wagon, where Cormac already sat, gurgling, Aoife looking after all of them and the soft-groaning queen. The cart lurched; the queen moaned.

'She will not suffer that long,' muttered Jasna to me in her harsh attempt at Norse. 'This first birthing time is bad for her. My little Sigrith cannot eat anything but sweet things and I have been feeding her hot milk and honey all night.'

I wondered if it had been spoon and spoon about. Precious little chance of that from now on, I thought, turning away to where Finn and Botolf stood with the limp-footed stallion. Little Toki was there, holding the head of it, for he had a way with horses – and, to my surprise, so was Abjorn and the other five men of Jarl Brand, all ringmailed and well-armed. Abjorn had his helmet cradled in the crook of one arm and a stone-grim look on his face.

'We will come with you,' he said, then looked from one man to another and back. 'There is something we must ask.'

I did not like it that they were all here and not with the struggling column, grinding a way up the mountain pass road – but what we were about to do would not take long.

There was little ceremony. We climbed a little way, to where a flat stone sprawled up above the road and into the realm of the *alfar*; whom some call Lokke; men hissed now and then when something flickered at the edge of their vision, or when the sun glimmered in a certain way on water, for they knew that it was Lokke, the Playing Man, the *alfar* no-one ever saw properly – or wanted to.

I kept my heart on my wish and my head up to the sky, away from the glitter of unnatural eyes in the moving shadows. My business was with Odin.

I drew the sword – a good blade, but not the nicked one rescued from the *Elk*. That was Kvasir's old blade and I would not be parted from that willingly, yet this was still a good sword which we had taken from the men we had killed near our rune stone and so a rich gift for Odin. I heard the men breathe out heavily, for it was known that the *alfar* did not care for iron, as I plunged it in the soft, brackened turf in front of the stone. Toki brought the limping stallion up to me.

It snuffled in the palm of my hand hopefully, but found nothing and had little time for the disappointment of it; I plunged a sharpened seax into the great pulse in its neck

and heard it squeal and jerk, the iron stink of blood adding to the fear. It kicked and reared and Toki and I hung on to it, our weight forcing it still until the pulse of blood grew weaker and the stone and the sword blade dripped and clotted with it.

Men yelled out, fierce shouts of his name to draw Odin's attention; Finn moved in and took the sharpened seax, began cutting off the rear haunches – all Odin wanted was the blood and the blade, he had little need of all the meat and the *alfar* needed none at all, nor clothing. Finn skinned it, too, waiting properly until I had made my wish aloud.

It was simple enough – a life for a life. Let everyone else survive this and take life from me, if one were needed. Men hoomed and nodded; I felt leaden at the end of it, for Odin always needed a life and there was never enough blood and steel to sate One-Eye.

'So,' Botolf said, 'that was why you did not want to eat the horse. Deep thinking, Orm. I should have known better.'

'A bad thing,' growled Finn, 'to bring your doom down on your own head.'

'Randr Sterki will not stop until he is dead or we are,' I answered; he knew why, above all the others and shrugged, unable to find the words to speak to me on it.

Abjorn stepped forward then, with a look and a nod to the men behind him.

'Jarl Orm,' he began. 'We wish to take your Oath.'

I was dumbed by this; Finn grunted and found the words which were dammed up behind my teeth.

'You are sworn already, to Jarl Brand,' he pointed out and Abjorn shifted uncomfortably, with another glance to the men behind him for reassurance.

'He gave us to Jarl Orm,' he countered stubbornly. 'And Jarl Brand is almost brother to Jarl Orm.'

'He lent you,' I offered, gentle as a horse-whisperer, not wishing to anger him. 'Not gave.'

'For all that,' Abjorn pushed, his chin jutting out. 'We have all agreed to ask – Rovald, Rorik Stari, Kaelbjorn Rog, Myrkjartan, Uddolf and myself.'

As he said their names, the men stepped forward, determined as stones rolling downhill.

'This is foolish,' Finn said, pausing in his flaying of the horse. 'Jarl Brand will be angered by it and with Jarl Orm for agreeing to it. And what if they come to quarrel, what then? Who will you fight for?'

'We will leap that stream when we reach it,' Abjorn replied. Finn threw up his hands; a gobbet of fat flew off the end of the seax and splattered on the turf.

I knew why they wanted to take the Oath. They needed it. They had heard that Odin favoured the Oathsworn, held his hand over them and with all that snapped at their heels they needed to know that hand cradled them, too.

So I nodded and, stumbling like eager colts with the words of it, with the stink of fresh blood and the gleam of *blot*-iron in their eyes, they took it.

We swear to be brothers to each other, bone, blood and steel, on Gungnir, Odin's spear we swear, may he curse us to the Nine Realms and beyond if we break this faith, one to another.

Afterwards, laden with horse meat – the head left on the stone for the birds to pick – we went back down to the path and hurried to catch up with the others.

Abjorn and the new-sworn men were cheerful, chaffering one to the other and with Botolf and even Toki, when they would not usually have looked twice at a scrawny thrall boy. They were so happy I felt sorry for them, knowing how the smell of blood and iron appeals to One-Eye even as the happy plans of men do not.

An hour later, the *ulfhednar* caught us.

I did not hear or see them at all, having my shoulder into the back of the rearmost wagon, my whole world taken up

76

by the pothole the left rear wheel had sunk into and not wanting to have to unload it to get it out again. The rest of the column was further ahead, round a bend and out of sight.

So, with Botolf alongside, Finn and Kuritsa on either rear wheel and little Toki trying to get the sagging-weary horses to pull, we strained and cursed and struggled with it. Somewhere up ahead, round the next bend, the others laboured on.

'Give them some whip!' bawled Finn.

'The fucking trail is too hard for this,' Botolf grunted out and he was right; I had no breath to argue with him anyway.

Then Toki yelled out, a high, piping screech and we all stopped and turned, sweating and panting, to see the four men come round the bend behind us in the trail. It was moot who was more surprised by it.

'Odin's arse . . .'

Finn sprang for The Godi, sheathed and in the wagon; Botolf hurled after his axe, which was in the same place, but all I had was my seax and that was handy, snugged across my lap. But Kuritsa, who had said he had been a hunter in his own land, showed that he had been a warrior, too.

Three of the men wore oatmeal clothing, carried spears and axes and shields, but the fourth was big as a bull seal and had the great, rain-sodden bearcoat that marked him. He whirled and gestured; one of the others started to run back and Kuritsa sprang up on the top of one wheel, balanced and shot – the man screamed and pitched forward.

The bearcoat roared at another, then hefted his shield in the air, caught it by one edge and slung it, whirling in a one-handed throw that sent it spinning at us, like a wooden platter hurled by a woman gone past reasonable argument. Kuritsa, nocking another arrow, did not see it until it hit him, knocking him off the wheel before he could make a sound; he hit heavily and lay gasping for breath and bleeding.

We watched the messenger vanish round the bend and the

77

bearcoat straightened slowly, hefting the bearded axe in one hand. The last man stood slightly behind him, licking his lips.

'I am Thorbrand Hrafnsson,' the bearcoat bawled out in a hoarse voice, spreading his arms wide, the great tangled mass of hair and beard matted so that his mouth was barely visible. His eyes were two beasts peering out of a wood.

'I am a slayer of men. I am a son of the wolf and the bear,' he roared.

'I,' said the man with him, 'am not eager for this.'

He backed away, shield up but sword hand held high and empty. Thorbrand never even turned round when he spat a greasy glob of disdain.

'I am known as a killer and a hard man, from Dyfflin to Skane,' he bellowed, pointing the axe at us. 'I am favoured by Thor. And you are Finn Bardisson, known as Horsehead, the one the skalds say fears no-one. And you are Orm Bear Slayer, who leads the Oathsworn and who found all the silver of the world. I see you.'

'You will not see us for long,' said Finn, hefting The Godi and stepping forward. 'And if you have heard anything of us at all, you will know you are not as god-favoured as we are.'

'What about me?' demanded Botolf angrily. 'I am Botolf, by-named Ymir. I am Oathsworn. What about me?'

'You can be last to die, One-Leg,' answered Thorbrand, 'because you are a cripple.'

Finn and I moved in swiftly then, just as Botolf bristled like an annoyed boar and we balked whatever he had intended, shouldering him to one side, then moving right and left as Thorbrand flung back his head and howled out a great frothing cry.

Then he went for Finn, but it was a feint, for he suddenly cut back and, only having a little seax and closing on him with it, I was caught flat-footed on muddy scree – so much so that I skidded on my arse, which saved me; the axe hissed at what would have been hip height, save that I was on the

ground. It thundered past my nose, big as a house and the wind of it fluttered my braids and beard.

Scrabbling away, I saw Finn dart past, slashing; Thorbrand, slavering madly, eyes red as embers, half fell, then turned like a bull elk at bay. Finn stopped and watched; Thorbrand started a run, but the leg was tendon-cut and would not work – he fell on one knee and rose up. Marvelling, I saw no blood and it was clear he felt no pain, but the leg would not work properly and Finn sauntered, thinking the man was finished. A normal man would have been.

He was *ulfhednar* and Finn should have known better, as I said later. Thorbrand simply hirpled forward in two great one-legged leaps and Finn, yelping, managed a block before Thorbrand's bearded axe hooked The Godi, trapped it and flung it out of his hand.

Now Finn was weaponless and Thorbrand, like the bear whose hide he wore, growled and lurched, dragging one leg behind him, but closing fast on the hapless Finn.

I sprang forward, was hit by what seemed to be a boulder and bounced sideways, my head whirring; Botolf stumped down on the bearcoat and was almost on him when Thorbrand heard, or sensed it and whirled round, axe up, the slaver trailing from the edge of his mouth.

'Cripple, am I?' roared Botolf and grabbed the swinging axe in both hands, tearing it free, as if ripping a stick from a wean. 'Now we are even matched.'

He flung the axe away from him. The great, stupid rock flung the axe away, then closed with Thorbrand as if it was some friendly wrestle at a handfasting. Finn scurried to find his sword and I sat up, trying to stop the world rocking and lurching as if we were all on a boat at sea.

They strained; Botolf suddenly took a step back and swung, the crack of his fist against Thorbrand's ear loud as a whip – but the man was *berserk* and felt nothing, which fact Finn roared out as he picked up The Godi.

'Feel this, then,' grunted Botolf and he gripped and wrenched, so that Thorbrand was spun sideways, the great bear hide ripping free from him and left in Botolf's hands. He flung it to one side.

'Stand clear,' yelled Finn, hefting The Godi.

'Stand back,' warned Botolf and went after Thorbrand, who had rolled over and over and now sprang up, as well as his useless leg allowed.

'No bearcoat now,' Botolf said, spitting on his palms. 'More bare arse. Now we are evenly matched, skin to skin, leg to leg.'

Thorbrand was madder than ever, a slavering wolf who howled out his rage from a corded throat and launched off his one good leg, straight at Botolf, who half knelt and took the rush of it in both hands, one at Thorbrand's crotch, the other at his throat.

Then he straightened, the muscles on him bunching so that it seemed they would split, lifted the kicking, screaming madman in the air, half-turned him like a haunch on a spit and brought him down on his knee, the one which had wood four inches below it, anchored to the ground as strong as any bone.

The crack was a tree splitting; I thought it was Botolf's leg until he levered Thorbrand off him. The man still slavered and howled, but not even his head moved, for the back of him was splintered and he was only voice now.

'I am Botolf, by-named Ymir, strongest of the Oathsworn, on one leg or two,' Botolf panted and spat on Thorbrand. 'Now you know that, so you know more.'

Finn moved in and mercifully silenced the raving screams, while I climbed wearily to my feet. The remaining man, pale and wary behind his shield, stood and said nothing, which showed that he was sensible and braver than his lack of fight seemed to suggest.

There was silence, save for panting, ragged breathing – then Finn moved to Thorbrand's axe, picked it up and handed it to Botolf.

'Your prize,' he said. 'Next time, try not to throw it away.'

Botolf reversed it, using it as a stick to lever himself upright; I saw blood on his breeks and pointed it out. He shrugged.

'His, I think. He did not hit me.'

He hirpled off to the cart, while Finn and I watched him go.

'His great heart will be the end of him,' muttered Finn softly, still breathing hard and we remembered the other times the giant had saved us. Then we looked at the last man, saying nothing until he swallowed into the silence of it, which must have been grinding his courage away.

'I am Hidhinbjorn,' he said, eventually. 'I came at the request of Ljot Tokeson, to tell this Thorbrand what has happened.'

'Tell us,' I grunted and the weight of the shield was suddenly too much for him, so that he took a knee, resting his elbow – and still behind cover, I saw, which showed cleverness.

'We had news from up the fjord. Styrbjorn fought his uncle King Eirik and Jarl Brand. Brand is sore wounded, but Styrbjorn is defeated and fled, so this enterprise is finished with, says Ljot.'

'That is news, right enough,' growled Botolf, trailing back from the cart. He looked at me and added: 'Kuritsa is dunted, so that it will hurt by morning, but he is alive and not too done up.'

I nodded; the bowman had done well, thrall or not.

'This Thorbrand,' Finn was saying, 'knew all this?'

The man nodded and shifted uncomfortably. 'The bearcoats find Randr Sterki more to their liking than Styrbjorn.'

That did not surprise me; Randr Sterki was not about to give up his revenge and the bearcoats would want something out of this mess. Hidhinbjorn saw that I understood and got wearily to his feet.

'There is one, Stenvast by name, who has said that killing the queen and the bairn in her will rescue this venture. That way, he says, they keep faith with Pallig Tokeson, who is their sworn lord.'

This Pallig was clearly Ljot's brother and one with a weight of silver to afford so many bearcoats. I did not think he would be smiling at the way they were vanishing, all the same – unless someone was handing him buckets of money to make sure Styrbjorn had his due. King Eirik would hesitate to have the troublesome boy parted from his head if he was, in fact, his only heir; but I wondered how sorely Brand was wounded, for if his eyes were in the least open, Styrbjorn would die for what he had done and Brand would apologise to the king afterwards.

Hidhinbjorn stood, taut as a strung bow, for he clearly thought he would have to fight, but I was bone-weary and blood-sick. To my surprise, it was Finn who waved The Godi casually at him to go away.

'Next time we meet, Hidhinbjorn,' he growled, 'it had better be in a friendlier setting, or I will tear off your head and piss down your neck.'

Hidhinbjorn acknowledged it with an unsmiling nod and put his back to us, which was brave and polite, rather than edge away. When he had vanished round the bend, I realised I had been holding my breath and let it out.

'Aye,' growled Finn, fishing out a rag to clean The Godi. 'It has been an awkward day – and there is light left in it yet.'

Back at the cart, Kuritsa was sitting up and wheezing, his chest bared to show a livid bruise where the shield rim had struck. He breathed in rasps and winced, so that I thought something might be broken there and told him to get in the cart, that we would take him to Bjaelfi.

'That was a good shot with the bow. We will have to promote you, from chicken to eagle,' I added and Toki chuckled.

'Well,' growled Finn, 'rooster at the very least.'

And we laughed, so shrill and brittle in the pewter day that little Toki was as deep-voiced as any of us, all bright with the relief of survival.

Yet the blood on Botolf's breeks was wet and the stain grew as we ground up the track to join the other carts. When Ingrid saw it her hand flew to her mouth and she called out for Bjaelfi, then huckled her big husband off, while little flame-haired Helga stood, solemn eyed, thumb in her mouth.

The others crowded round, wanting to know what had happened and, for a moment, the faces swam as if under-water and I wanted badly to sit. Thorgunna saw it and chided me in out of the rain and I sat down, listening to it stutter off the canvas; it came to me then that they had not progressed far and had made camp while it was still light.

I told them what had happened while Aoife and Thordis tended to Kuritsa, who was looked at with new, grudging admiration – but it was the news of Styrbjorn's defeat which occupied them most.

'At least the wee bairn is safe,' said a familiar voice and Onund Hnufa shuffled painfully forward. 'I kept trying to warn you, but all that my mouth would make was "bairn".'

I felt a flood of warmth, as if I had stepped in front of a hearthfire.

'I see you, Onund,' I told him. 'It seems you are not so easily killed, then.'

He acknowledged it with a wry smile, but you could see that they had used him hard, for he was gaunt and his face was marked from the burns, still dark, raw-red under the grease the women had salved him with; the hump that gave him his by-name seemed sharper and higher than before on his shoulder.

'They wanted to know of buried silver,' he said. 'As well you told no-one, for another lick of that hot iron and I would have told them all they needed.'

'One who sees a friend on a spit tells all he knows,' Red Njal agreed, 'as my granny used to say.'

'At least one of those who licked you with it felt the heat of it,' growled Finn and told him of the man called Bjarki.

83

'Small reward,' Onund answered, 'for the loss of Gizur and Hauk.'

I remembered them, then, as a trio, each a shadow to the other and felt Onund's loss with a sudden keen pang.

'Gizur would not leave the *Elk*,' Hlenni Brimill threw in. 'Since he had made it, he said.'

Onund grunted. 'He made some of it, but no ship is worth a death.'

That, from such a shipwright, surprised me and he saw it in my face.

'I built the *Elk*,' he said. 'There was more of me in that ship than any of the others. But I can build another.'

'Heya,' said Finn, grinning. 'Once this is done with, I shall help.'

Onund, with a flash of his old self that made me smile, raised his eyebrows at the thought and made Finn laugh out loud.

'The whole matter of this should be done with now, I am thinking,' offered Klepp Spaki hopefully, but Vuokko, his ever-present shadow, gave a little high-pitched bark and told us all that he had asked the drum and it spoke of loss, keenly felt.

That clamped lips shut, sure as a hand on the mouth; I saw Thorgunna's lips tighten and her face take on that blank look, which I knew meant that she dared not speak for fear of tears. The others, of course, tried not to look me in the eye; they all knew the *blot* I had promised Odin for their lives.

Then Abjorn stepped forward, wiping the drizzle of rain from his face; behind him, the others new-promised as Oathsworn gathered like pillars, their ring-coats dark with rain, streaked here and there with the blood of iron-rot.

'If you have it right,' he said, 'then there are eight bearcoats only.'

'And Randr Sterki and his men,' Finn pointed out, hunching down to pitch some small sticks into the guttering fire.

'Randr Sterki may be a fighter, but his men are nithings,' I said.

'Still,' said Finn, wryly, 'eight bearcoats is enough.'

Abjorn shrugged. 'These bearcoats belong to Pallig Tokeson, who is jarl in Joms these days and this Ljot we have seen is his brother, so they are thrown into the enterprise on behalf of Styrbjorn. I am thinking they may not pursue it now. I am thinking that we should be pushing on. I am thinking that the queen is still in danger and that we will stay here and guard the path – me, Rovald, Rorik Stari, Kaelbjorn Rog, Myrkjartan and Uddolf.'

'They must not have the babe,' Jasna spat and I knew who had put them up to this. They looked at her, slab-faced men with braids and eyes grey as pewter and jingling at the brim with hopelessness, for they knew they were no match for eight bearcoats.

I said as much. I said also that we would all go on, together, for there was more chance with numbers.

'We will not go on in much of a hurry,' Thorgunna said at the end of all this and jerked her head at the covered cart, where Jasna and the silent hostage-girl sat beside a lump of coverlet that moaned.

'How bad?'

Thorgunna shook her head, which was answer enough. So we were stuck here then, until the birth; I looked around at the place and found Finn doing the same. It was a fattened part of the trail, with a branch turning to the right, leading into an even more tortured scar in the mountains. There was a bridge not far along that part, raised by a mother to her sons, so said the stone by it, for once there had been fine tall pines at the top, which was the highest point overlooking the fjord.

Now there were only wind-stunted trees, twisted and useless and the trail had always ended there, dribbling out like drool from a drunk's mouth. There was a way down the other side,

but rough travelling even for a man on foot, so carts and bairns and women and fat thralls would never do it.

Finn and I looked at each other and knew what each thought – this was no great place for us to fight. I moved to him then as the gathering broke up into muttering twos and threes and he scrubbed his face furiously, a sure sign of his confusion.

'Well?' I asked.

'Well what?' he countered, scowling, his beard scrubbed into a mad fury of spikes.

'Do you think we can win?'

He stopped then, for he knew I would not voice that out loud when there was more than just him to hear it.

'Well,' he growled. 'I am no stranger to woman-killing, as you keep wanting to tell me, as if it was something to be shamed at. All the same, I have never killed a bairn that had no proper life and I am reluctant to begin.'

'Kill one to save us all?' I answered, with a wry smile, for this thought had been running like spate-water in me. He grinned, then spat.

'It is not about numbers – one or a hundred bairns, it would still be a price worth paying for such a reward as the life of wee Helga and the boy Hroald, whom I have acknowledged as mine. It is about what is right and what is not. He may be a great king, this fledgling eagle. Who can say what wonders he may bring about?'

I laughed with the sheer, surprising delight of him and pointed out the other side of the coin; that he would most likely turn out to be another Harald Bluetooth.

'If I thought that,' he growled, 'I would kill it before the head appeared between the mother's thighs.'

We were smiling, then, when Botolf limped up, towing Ingrid and Bjaelfi in his wake. Behind them, I saw the Greek, Leo, allowing Koll to lead him by the hand towards us.

'How is the leg?' I demanded and Botolf waved an answer away, hauling Helga up high in the air, so that she shrieked

with delight and bone-haired Cormac stood, wanting the same but older and so too proud to ask. When Botolf hoisted him up, he shrieked his delight all the same, but Botolf grunted with pain.

Bjaelfi gave me a look and I moved to him, so he could tell me, soft and low.

'I cut too little from the bone,' he said tersely. 'I warned him not to go back to lifting carts with the pony in them, but Botolf is Botolf.'

I remembered it well, the hot, fetid boat heading into the hard-pull of the Middle Sea up to the Great City, Botolf delirious with wound-fever, rolling great fat drops of sweat. Bjaelfi, sheened like some mad black dwarf in a cave, kept cutting and sewing, so that there was skin to wrap round and stitch for a stump, with the blood washing in the scuppers.

'I think the skin is splitting round the stump-bone,' he added bleakly. 'If it does, he will not be able to have such an end in the socket of a wooden leg, clever harness or no.'

I looked at Botolf, standing tall, Cormac held giggling and wriggling to the sky. The big man would not like being reduced to the crutch he had endured once before, while the stump healed. He would not like that at all.

Koll broke in just then, his high-pitched voice querulous and demanding.

'Tell me if what this priest says is true, Jarl Orm, for you have been to the Great City. That people live in halls set one on top of the other.'

I looked at Leo and answered his bland smile, then nodded.

'Just so,' I replied. 'And they have marvellous affairs built for no other reason than to throw water into the air, for the delight of it. And they eat lying down. Much more besides – I shall take you there when all this is done with.'

'If we live,' the boy answered, suddenly grim. 'Leo says the bearcoats are better warriors.'

Leo spread his hands in apology. 'A careless remark. I had

heard such warriors were to be feared because they had no fear of their own.'

'They will find some when they meet us,' I answered and Toki, appearing sudden as a squall, declared that Kuritsa would shoot them all with his bow. The man himself, wheezing still, but grinning, agreed from a little way away and Finn chuckled.

'By the time this is all done away with,' he declared, 'we will have to give Kuritsa a new name, I am thinking. And put Prince at the head of it.'

'Hunter will be title enough,' Kuritsa replied and I marvelled; already it was hard to tell this man from the droop-headed, silent thrall he once had been. 'I can shoot an arrow for miles and still hit true. Even round a corner. Such a thing once saved my life.'

Koll and Toki, bright-eyed and struck silent, watched him. Finn, grinning, sat down and others gathered. Kuritsa, lean-faced, shave-headed, hirpled to the wagon and sat heavily by the wheel.

'Before I was taken, in my own lands, I was set upon by the Yeks, a tribe who hated us. They were many and I was one and was, I admit it, hunting in their lands – so what do you think happened?'

'You were killed, for sure,' chuckled Botolf, leading Helga and Cormac to where they could listen, 'for there are times when you work like a dead man.'

'Not as dead as some, I am thinking,' answered Kuritsa smartly. 'I was lucky. I had my own bow with me, one I called Sure in my own tongue. Sometimes the power of that bow frightened me, for I lost many arrows and sometimes wondered whether one that vanished from my sight hit a friend in the next village, or a king in another country. It took me a time to get the grip of that bow, but after a while, I could hit a fat deer as far as I could see it – though I might have to turn half-round if it were a pair rutting, to be sure of hitting the deer and not the stag.'

88

Finn laughed out loud at that one, slapping his thigh with delight, then waved Kuritsa to go on, while the others, child and man both, listened open-mouthed.

'Well,' Kuritsa said, 'I spotted an elk far off – so far off it was no bigger than a tiny beetle and I pointed at it, so that the skin-wearing trolls of Yeks stopped and looked while I nocked an arrow in Sure and took aim. I waited until the tail twitched out of sight over the hill, then I shot – allowing for the breeze and a touch of snow in the air.'

Botolf and Finn collapsed at this point, howling and wheezing. I could make out, between the grunts and snorts, the words 'allowing for the breeze' and 'snow in the air'. Kuritsa, haughty as a jarl, ignored them.

'I persuaded those Yeks to go over the hill, with me as prisoner, on the promise that if they had elk meat at the end of it, I could go free. They agreed, for it was on their way and it took the best part of the rest of that day to walk it – but there was the elk, my arrow in him and dead. They were delighted at having the horns and the meat and so let me go.'

'A fine shot,' Finn said eventually, spluttering to halt. Kuritsa shook his head sorrowfully.

'It was that moment when I knew I was cursed – not long after, of course, the gods allowed me to be captured and taken into slavery. I have not shot such a long shot since.'

'Why?' demanded Botolf. 'Did your gods order it?'

Kuritsa sighed. 'No, my own failing eye and hand. I had aimed for the heart and there was that old bull elk, gut-shot in the worst way. I was ashamed.'

'Yet you shot today,' Toki pointed out into the chuckles following that and Kuritsa shrugged.

'Not so long. At that range I can shoot the balls off a clegg.'

'Do cleggs have balls, then?' Koll demanded, frowning and Kuritsa, serious and unsmiling, shook his head.

'No horsefly has any when I am around with a bow.'

It was good laughter, washing away the lurking horrors of

eight bearcoats and lasted well into the rattle of skillet and cauldron, while the sun staggered out from behind clouds and showed me the rain, small-dropped and fine as baby hair.

It was a good evening and you would not think we were hunted folk at all, so I thanked Freyja for that moment of goddess-peace.

Of course, it did not last until morning.

SIX

I woke to screams and fire, scrabbling for a sword and cursing the sleep out of me; then a soft voice I knew well told me to put on a tunic and stop shouting.

Thorgunna squatted by a goat, working the teats relentlessly into a bowl. It was dark, but there were fires everywhere it seemed and the place bustled with movement and purpose; somewhere, a woman moaned and then yelled aloud.

'Why are you milking a goat in the dark?' I asked, still stupid with sleep and Thorgunna, grunting with the effort of bending, jerked her head in the direction of the yelps.

'Her waters broke. I need the milk to bathe the bairn in.'

The mother-to-be appeared a second later, out from where she had been moved for more comfort, which had banished me and all the other men to find sleep and shelter where we could. She moved ponderously, splay-legged, held up by Aoife on one side and Thordis on the other.

'She has no strength,' Thordis hissed. 'She needs a birthing stool.'

'Aye, well,' grunted Thorgunna, sharp as green apples, straightening with the bowl of milk held in the crook of one arm. 'It was a thing I forgot in all the confusion of finding

things for food and shelter in a hurry, with my husband's enemies at my heels.'

I shrugged into my tunic, seeing the fires lit in a circle to keep the *alfar* at bay, for there is nothing those unseen, flickering creatures like better than stealing a newborn wean and leaving one of their own twisted wee horrors.

Ingrid appeared, dripping blood from her hands and the other women fell back a little in deference. She came up to the moaning Sigrith and clasped her rune-cut, bloodied palms on the queen's joints, to give her strength and ease. I knew Ingrid was Hestreng's *bjargrygr*, the Helping Woman for all the steading's births, which role had some *seidr* work in it, too; Thorgunna and her sister, I knew from old, had no *seidr* in them at all.

'Jasna . . .' moaned the queen.

'We cannot support her and deliver the bairn,' Thordis insisted. 'Especially at the last.'

I knew this was when the mother got on her elbows and knees, the bairn delivered from behind. Ingrid moved busily, undoing knots and loosening straps and buckles where she saw them, another spell to ease the birth. The women's hair was also unbound, tucked into their belts at the waist to keep it out of the way.

The queen moaned and sagged. 'Jasna,' she said.

'I have a birthing stool,' Ingrid said, then waved to the shadows and all heads turned as Botolf stumped into the middle of the fires, grinning. Thorgunna and Thordis looked at each other; no men were allowed at a birthing by tradition and usage.

'Oh, I am half a bench,' grunted Botolf, sitting himself on a sea-chest, 'so half of me is not here at all. The other half will close my eyes if you like.'

He hauled the queen to him, holding her in powerful arms, her legs splayed over his knees, her head resting, intimate as a lover, on his great chest.

'You'll ruin those breeks,' Thorgunna said wryly and Botolf chuckled.

'I could take them off.'

There was a chorus at that and, suddenly, the queen, sheened face raised, muttered: 'Not seemly. I will buy you a new pair, Birthing Stool.'

'That's better, my pet,' Ingrid said, sure that her palm-carved runes were working. 'A little pain and sweat and then the joy of a son.'

'Jasna . . .' whispered the queen.

'Will someone rout out that fat cow Jasna from her sleep?' bellowed Thorgunna angrily.

Ingrid looked pointedly at me. I realised I was not welcome in the circle of fires and backed off hastily, while Botolf crooned softly to the bundle in his arms and Ingrid raised her arms and started a muttered prayer-chant to Freyja.

Beyond, where men were, seemed darker away from the fires and I almost fell over Finn and Abjorn, talking urgently with each other.

'Banished, were you?' chuckled Finn. 'Just as well. No place for a man, that. I pity the stupid big arse who is now high-seat for a birthing queen.'

I told Abjorn to send out watchers and he nodded, his face grim and grey in the dark.

'Those fires . . .'

He let it trail off, for there was little need to voice it all. Those fires were a sure beacon and I could see the hunting packs of bearcoats and Randr Sterki's skin-wearing trolls slithering through the dark towards us.

'There is worse,' growled Hlenni Brimill, looming out of the dark, dragging a squirming figure by the hair; the Mazur girl yelped as he swung her into the circle of us.

'That fat cow of a thrall woman is dead,' he declared. 'When I went to get her, she was cold and stiff – and this one made a bolt out from under the wagon she was in.'

I blinked. Dead? Jasna?

We went to the wagon in a crowd, the Mazur girl dragged back with us and yelping whenever Hlenni jerked her savagely by her hair. Bjaelfi was climbing out, rubbing his chin and spreading his hands.

'She is dead, right enough,' he announced. 'Not a mark on her I can see – but it is hard enough in torchlight. Perhaps daylight will let me know more.'

'Not a mark,' muttered Red Njal from over Bjaelfi's shoulder. 'That is *seidr* work, if ever I saw it. Her hand will wag above her grave, as my granny used to say.'

Desperate eyes raked the girl, who felt them and struggled until Hlenni jerked her hard and she shrieked. An answer came from the dark, from where the fires blazed and I had had enough of it all.

'Let her go, Hlenni,' I said and he reluctantly opened his fist; the girl sank to the ground, then stood, with a visible effort. She squared her shoulders and looked at me, chin out, eyes dark and liquid as a seal. I felt a lurch in my stomach, for I had seen such looks before on women and all of them had been rich in *seidr* and had done me no good with it.

'Drozdov,' I said. 'Is that your name?'

'What they call me,' she answered, her Norse of the eastern type and further bent out of shape by her accent; those eyes were fixed on mine, swimming at the brim but not spilling over.

'Chernoglazov,' I remembered and she nodded, then said, 'Yes, lord,' before Red Njal had lifted his hand to correct her.

'Did you kill her, then?' I said, waving one hand at the dark, dead bulk in the wagon.

'No . . . lord. Someone came in the night. I heard her make little noise and then silent. I stay hidden.'

'Someone came?' demanded Finn, the scorn and suspicion reeking in his voice.

94

She turned those dark, seal eyes on him. 'A man, I think. Silent.'

'What did he do, this silent man?' I asked and she frowned and shook her head.

'Something,' she answered, then the frown disappeared and her face turned to mine like a petal to the sun. 'Lord.'

'I knew it was not good,' she added. 'So I hid.'

Yes, she would be good at hiding by now, good at staying out of the line of sight and the strong light. Finn looked at me, then at Bjaelfi and shook his head.

'Was she armed?' I asked Hlenni and he shook his own shaggy head, reluctantly.

'You looked?'

He nodded, then added sullenly: 'No blade is needed with *seidr*, Jarl Orm.'

A scream split the night and made us all start.

'Odin's hairy balls,' Finn swore, then swallowed another, for it was not good to malign the gods while the Norns were so close, weaving a new life out of the Other.

'Shave the hairs from your arm,' muttered Klepp Spaki fearfully.

I looked at the girl again, all wet eyes and defiance in the tight-strung little body. I told Hlenni to watch her the rest of the night, in turns with Red Njal. In the morning, I promised, Bjaelfi, Finn and I would look at the body and find out what had happened and that I was no stranger to *seidr* and worse.

They had heard the Oathsworn tales – some of them had been there when they were made – so they went off, muttering, to huddle in the damp dark and listen to Sigrith pant and shriek a new bairn into the world.

It took a long while; I dozed until wakened with a shake on my toe, came up with a seax in my fist – which was why Thorgunna, clever woman, had shaken only my toe and stayed clear of a swinging blade. She knew all the men were tight-wound and likely to be armed and leaping from sleep.

'Done,' she said wearily and I blinked in the light of her flickering torch; beyond it, the dawn was a thin smear.

'A boy,' she added. 'Healthy and loud. The mother is alive, too, which is good.'

It was good; too many first mothers died giving birth and, in the clearing round the dying fires, I saw the weary, gore-handed women and the blanket-wrapped bundle that was Sigrith. Botolf, a little way away, stretched stiffly and gave me a smile and a wave as I came up, the rest of the men behind me save for those on watch.

'That was a bloody affair,' he growled, moving slowly and shaking his head. 'Odin's arse, lads, I have stood in shield-walls that had less hard work in them and less blood and shit and fewer screams.'

'Take off those breeks,' Ingrid said to Botolf, bustling forward with a fur bundle which had a squashed red face nestled in it. Underneath, I knew, each limb would be linen-wrapped to keep it straight and fine, having been washed in hot milk and salt. His little mouth was a sticky bud, for the women had rubbed honey in his gums, to promote appetite.

'First,' said a waft-soft voice and we stopped, staring at Sigrith, 'since you did most to bring him into the world, Birthing Stool, you can name him. His father says he is to be Olaf.'

Botolf stopped and scrubbed his beard with confusion, pleased and embarrassed in equal measure. Ingrid handed him the bundle and he played the father, raising it to us over his head, standing proud and tall in his slathered breeks as he called us all to attend.

'Heya,' he bellowed. 'This is the son of King Eirik the Victorious. This is Olaf, Prince of the Svears and Geats.'

We stamped and cheered and there was more than duty in it, for that bairn had come to be the focus of all our lives and we watched as Ingrid handed it to Sigrith – watched, too, as she took it back moments later, when the exhausted slip of a girl fell asleep.

I was remembering that surviving the birthing was only the first step and that making it through the days that followed it were fraught for mothers. Too many of them died and I felt a stab deep in me when Thorgunna came up to stand beside me, all bright with the promise of our own child.

'It went hard with her,' she said quietly to me, as people murmured themselves into a new day. 'She needs quiet and rest and a wet-nurse, for she cannot feed the wee soul properly herself.'

'Will he die then?' I asked, alarmed, seeing the whole of our efforts crumbling. She shook her head and gave me one of her black-eyed, pitying looks.

'Of course not – the idea. We can feed him, as we do kids and calves with no mothers.'

That I knew well enough, for I had done it myself with a foal I favoured, using a sheep's bladder as a teat and a little drinking horn full of milk. It was an awkward, messy business and I said so.

'That is children all over,' she answered and clasped her belly as she leaned into me. I nestled her there for a moment or two, patting her absently while my mind raced on how there was unlikely to be a fast remove from here and my eyes scanned the lightening day for signs of bearcoats. I could feel them, like hot breath on the back of my neck.

She felt it in me and leaned away from me then, was about to speak when Toki bounded up in his breathless way, saying Bjaelfi wanted me.

I knew where he would be and there were others gathered round that wagon. Hlenni had laced the hands of the seal-eyed Mazur girl with a thong and tied it to his own wrist. Red Njal, Klepp, Vuokko and others gathered, while Bjaelfi knelt beside the corpse in the wagon bed.

'Well?' I asked, hauling myself in. Bjaelfi said nothing, simply drew back the wool cloak that covered her and pointed.

There was nothing but the blue-white dead flesh, the

grey-streaked hair . . . and the trickle, thin as a slug trail and dried so that it seemed black in the new light of a day. It had run almost to her jawline and tracked back, curling a little, to where a drop had dried and crusted on one lobe.

'The only mark on her,' Bjaelfi said, loud enough for all to hear. 'A flea-nip on an earlobe.'

The word leaped from head to head. *Seidr*. No Norse killing that. Gunnhild, Mother of Kings, was said to have been able to arrange such deaths, secret and stealthy in the night, shapeshifting to further the cause of her ambitious sons all over Norway.

I sat back on my heels, turning the coin of it over and over in my mind's fingers, testing the worth of what I worked out. A deadly fleabite? Even Gunnhild, noted shapechanger that she was, had never slipped into the body of anything so small. Or that killed so easily.

This was no *seidr*. This smacked too much of a place where poison needles settled more quarrels than blades – the Great City. I jerked up then, cursing, shouting orders that were far too late. In a moment, it was confirmed – Leo the priest had gone.

'And his sharp little needle with him,' growled Finn, when I told him what I had been thinking. He smacked an open hand on the side of the wagon, making it rock. 'Turd.'

'I am having trouble thinking this one out,' confessed Hlenni, looking from the Mazur girl to me and back again. Finn leaned over, his little eating knife flashed and cut the thongs; the girl rubbed her wrists and Hlenni scowled.

'He killed Jasna thinking it was Sigrith,' I said, working it out in my own head as I spoke. Thorgunna had moved the queen, but the little Greek had not known that and, in the dark, had felt softly along the bulked shape of what he believed to be a pregnant woman and stuck his needle in her ear, quick and sharp and away into the night, so that she scarcely made a yelp. A grunt, a scratch at another of many little bites – and

then the long sleep of death. Poor Jasna, dead of her own fat belly.

'I might as well still be in the dark,' growled Bjaelfi, confused, 'since now I know how it was done and by whom, but not why a monk from the Great City would want Queen Sigrith dead.'

Because the Great City had backed Styrbjorn and the monk had been sent, not to find out who had supplied Roman Fire, but bringing it to make sure the enterprise went off, then slithering himself to the side of the target, just in case. I had no idea why the Great City wanted Styrbjorn as king of the Svears and Geats, but that was the way they worked and I knew it well.

Once, I had been at the sacking of the Khazar city of Sarkel by Sviatoslav, Prince of Kiev, and he had been given engineers by the Great City. He needed them to help him knock that fortress down because it had been built for the Khazars by engineers of the Great City. They were a snake-knot of plots, were the Greeks who called themselves Romans in Constantinople.

Now Styrbjorn had failed, so the whole enterprise seemed doomed and the leader of it fled – but not to ruin if he was still the only heir to the high-seat. His uncle would think twice about having him killed in that case and where bearcoats seemed to be stumbling, a silent, grim little Greek with poison thought he could do better. Thankfully, he had not.

'Aye, well, you would know, for sure, Orm,' Onund Hnufa said, lumbering out of the sour-milk dawn to hear me lay out the length of this for folk to measure. 'I have seen and heard you dealing with the Great City and it is a marvellous thing how you can fathom the way their minds work, right enough.'

Everyone agreed with it, with nods and hooms.

'So perhaps you can be after telling me this, then,' Onund added. 'Why has this Greek taken little Koll with him?'

SEVEN

It was a fine bridge, as long as two tall men, wide enough for a wagon to pass over and made of good stone. Beneath it, the river that had cut the gorge burbled and sang to itself, while the green-mossed stones of the mountain flashed with quartz and trickled with silver water. Jewels of the Mountain King, Finn said, in a skald moment.

We were like that, standing there waiting, for I was thinking that this was where the Norns' weave came to an end for me. I had offered a life to Odin and I knew One-Eye would take his sacrifice. Provided he kept to his part of the bargain, I told myself, it was worth it.

Still, life was sweet and seemed sweeter still, standing there, waiting for the bearcoats to come, with the clouds piled up like snow and a sea-swallow, ragged by the wind and yet swooping for the sheer joy of it, grating a shriek that scoured a sky as blue as a newborn's eye.

That, too, made my heart leap painfully into my throat; I would never live to see the son Thorgunna carried. Yet, if Odin held to his part, another babe would find a life, the bairn Botolf carried in the crook of his arm, stumping his unseen way up to the headland overlooking the fjord.

A scramble down the other side and he was safe. A hard

scramble for a man with two good legs, as Finn pointed out when we made this plan, never mind one who was half a bench, with the thought-cage of a mouse and a wean under one arm. He said this where Botolf could not hear it, all the same.

'And a boy with him, too, dragging a goat,' I added, trying to make light of it. Toki, hearing the word 'goat', looked up, beaming, and gave his charge a pat between the thick horns.

Finn grunted his answer to that, then Botolf himself came up, his broad face braided in a smile, the babe wrapped up so warm it looked no more than a bundled old cloak held against his chest.

'Here,' said Thordis, shoving a bag at Finn. It was a good waterproofed walrus-hide bag and he peered in it, thinking to find food and warm clothing. Instead, he found linen squares and moss.

'Am I expected to eat this, woman?' he grumbled and she slapped him smartly on the arm.

'No,' she answered, but less tartly than she might have, since she was afraid for him. 'You are expected to use it on the bairn's arse, to keep it clean. From the state of your own breeks, it is a lesson you should learn for yourself, too, before we are wed.'

Finn grunted as if hit at this last and those closest laughed, the too-hearty laughs of those straining to find humour. Botolf slung a similar bag over one shoulder, with all that was needed to feed the sleeping prince, then turned and grinned at Toki and his goat.

'Ready, wee man?' he demanded and Toki, trembling with the excitement of it all, nodded furiously, then scowled as Aoife, winking on the brink of tears, dragged him into an embrace.

'Look after my little hero,' she demanded of Botolf and he patted her shoulder. Then he turned to the wagon and the figure in it, propped up on pillows and pale as winter wolfskin.

'Take care of my son, Birthing Stool,' said the queen in a voice with no more in it than wind.

'He will be safely delivered,' Botolf promised and Finn, hearing the firm resolve in his voice, shook his head at the memory of the man who had so recently wanted to leave queen and wean both and run for the hills.

It had seemed a fair plan in the cold light of dawn; take the bairn, leave the queen, confuse the enemy and split them. It was the queen's bairn they wanted, so the rest of the women and weans might be left alone, considering there were men willing to fight and nothing to be gained taking them on. Well – only for those who wanted bloody revenge and I was hoping the bearcoats would not think fit to join in with that. Meanwhile, we could take the little prince to safety, getting a headstart and travelling fast and light.

'With a goat?' demanded Finn.

'What milk will you find to feed a bairn?' countered Thorgunna. 'And Toki is to goats what Botolf seems to be to that wee prince.'

At which the big man grinned, for it was a strange sort of almost-*seidr* he had and he was not ashamed of it at all. The newborn prince wailed, no matter who cooed or shushed or rocked him – even his too-weak mother – until he was placed in the fat-biceped crook of Botolf's arm, where he closed his eyes and went silently to sleep.

Red Njal and Hlenni Brimill came up and we clasped, wrist to wrist. I had already made them swear to do all in their power to recover little Koll from wherever he had gone and told them I suspected the one called Ljot Tokeson would get him, for he was Styrbjorn's man.

The only reason for the Greek to have taken Jarl Brand's son was to use him as a hostage against Brand and so against King Eirik.

Randr Sterki would not give the snap of his fingers for Koll, or the new little prince of the Svears and Geats; it was vengeance he wanted and he would keep after Thorgunna and the others with what was left of his men – but the bearcoats would not,

or so I hoped. The bearcoats would come after us and the bairn, in the hope of rescuing the whole endeavour at the last.

That's what I told them and they nodded, millstone-grim and silent. I did not tell them of the vicious gnawing in my heart and belly at what I had done to Koll. Too taken up with everything else, I had been happy to have him cared for by the women – and grateful for the soft, consoling words that the priest seemed to be offering him. My words, they should have been – but I was too busy with the work of protecting him to notice how he had strayed into danger.

Some foster-father me, and now I was thinking I would never find out if I might have improved on the task, for him or me, or both, would be dead soon.

Others came up and said their farewells, so that I was glad to leave in the end, away from the weight of their sadness. Their faces, pale blobs of concern in the whey-light of dawn, looked at me with that hard, miserable stare I had given others I knew I would never see again.

But it was only Thorgunna's face, stricken and *skyr*-pale, that stayed with me all the way to the bridge.

It was a fine bridge – Finn said so. Narrow enough for two men to hold against many.

So Botolf looked at us, from one to the other, the babe crooked in his arm and one hand on the head of Toki.

'Bone, blood and steel,' Finn said and gave him the bag of arse-wrappings. Nothing more was said, just a nod and a clasp for each of us, wrist to wrist, then Botolf turned abruptly and hirpled over the bridge, Toki and the unwilling goat trotting behind him.

Botolf did not look back, yet I knew he was seeing us there and would see us for the rest of his life, standing on that bridge and not dead. Like Pinleg, long ago, dying under a shrieking pack of swords on a beach, allowing us to sail safely away – if we did not see his death happen, then perhaps he was fighting there still.

103

'That is that, then,' Finn said, when the big man and the boy and the goat had vanished. He peered over the side of the bridge, as if checking for trolls, then hauled out The Godi and inspected the edge.

'Your doom is not on you,' I said to him, though my bowels were water as I spoke it. 'You should go with him.'

Finn cocked one eyebrow, looking at me from under the tangle of his hair, which he refused to tie back – it revealed that he only had one good ear, the other mangled in a fight.

'Who knows what the Norns weave?' he replied with a shrug. 'This could be my day or not – but you cannot hold this bridge alone.'

He grinned.

'Bone, blood . . .' he began.

'. . . and steel,' I finished.

He took off his sheath and shed his cloak, for he did not want them tangling his legs in the fight. He checked the straps on his helmet and put it on, hunched his shoulders a few times to settle the rust-streaked ring-coat he wore, for it was not his own, then sat, leaning back against the stone of the bridge, while the water splashed and sang.

I envied him and hated him in equal measure; Finn, the man who feared nothing. How could he not tremble and find a great spear in his throat that made it impossible to swallow? Frothing madmen in skins would come after us and he had the wit to imagine what would happen. But all he did was open a lazy eye and wonder who Assur had been.

It was the inscription, weathered and lichen-streaked, on the grey stone by the bridge – *Helga, ThorgæiRs dottir, systir SygrøðaR auk þæiRa Gauts, hun let giæra bro þæssa auk ræisa stæin þænna æftir Assur bonda sinn. SaR waR wikinga warðr mæð Gæiti. Siþi sa manr is þusi kubl ub biruti.*

'Helga, daughter of Thorgar, sister of Sygrida and Gauts and others, she had this bridge made and this stone raised after Assur, her husband. He was an oathsworn guard with

Gauts. Let him practise *seidr*, the man who this monument destroys.'

'A good curse, that last – see, it is written as if in warning to anyone who desecrates the monument, but also that the monument itself will destroy. A good runesman, that.'

'A well-thought-of man, this Assur,' I noted, seeing the power of the runes there. Only his name survived, but this Assur would be remembered for as long as stone and we knew he had a loving wife and sisters, who thought enough of him to make runes for him.

'A sworn man, like us,' Finn noted and grinned. 'Good place to die, then, under a monument to a sword-brother.'

I was not so sure – a silly stone bridge leading to nowhere. Fitting, all the same, for the life we had led. Finn scowled when I blurted this out.

'Once it led to the best trees for miles around,' he pointed out. 'Good pine for ship planks and resin. No matter the place – we stand defending the back of a prince and what could be more fitting for the famed Oathsworn of Orm Bear Slayer than that? Besides, even now, it is a place of beauty.'

Once, I wanted to point out to him gloomily, it had been the famed Oathsworn of Einar the Black, save he was now dead – so where did it get him? But Finn had the right of it about the place and I raised my head to the sun and the joyous sea-swallow and the clouds like snow. Below, life bubbled in a stream, which started with the melting of snow in the mountains, flowing and merging out to the warm sea, where the sun sucked it up and dragged it back over the mountains to fall as snow again.

The Norns' loom of life; I drank it in, sucked it in like a parched man with water.

Then Finn slid to his feet and said: 'They are here.'

They came loping up the rough path to the bridge and stopped; two men, spear-armed and without armour or helmets, though they had shields and I saw knives at their

belts. They stopped, wolf-wary at the sight of two ringmailed warriors, well-armed and shielded.

Randr's trackers, I was thinking, and Finn agreed, with a derisive spit in their direction. I would have added one of my own if I had had any water in my mouth.

They crouched a little, the two men, and one looked over his shoulder. In a moment, three other men appeared and I felt Finn shift a little, settling himself behind his shield; the bearcoats were here. Three only – I wondered where the others were.

One was tawny-haired, with a massive beard plaited in at least four braids, heavy with fat iron rings. Over stained clothing that had once been fine, he had a stiff-furred cloak – a boar skin it looked like to me – and he carried a sword with a deal of silver on it, but a blade notched as a dog's jaw.

A second wore the pelt of a wolf, the head and top jaw over his leather helmet, the paws tied on his chest, so that when he lowered his head and loped up, it raised the hairs on my arms, for he looked like a wolf on its hind legs – but the two swords he carried, one in either fist, were his true fangs.

The third wore ringmail and a bearcoat, had a dark beard cut short and his hair braided tight and coiled – a careful man, then, who did not want anything for an enemy to grab. He carried a long axe and I did not like the look of this one at all, knew him for their leader by the way the other two glanced at him, looking for instruction.

He stopped then and rested one hand casually on the top haft of the long axe, resting his chin lightly on the inch or so of wood above the bitt. It was as if he was meeting old friends.

'Stenvast, they call me,' he called out. 'I see you.'

'Ingimund,' bellowed the tawny one, slapping his sword on his shield. 'Son of Tosti, son of Ulfkel, son of Floki Hooknose of Oppland. I fear no man.'

Finn sighed, as if weary.

106

'I am Finn Bardisson of Skane,' he replied, just loud enough to carry the distance between them, 'and I can change that.'

'Randr had the right of it, then,' Stenvast said. 'Three men, a boy and a goat – milk for the bairn, was it?'

'Aye,' agreed Finn easily. 'He is a sharp one, that Randr. He will cut himself one day – or someone will. He should have sent more of you, all the same. This is not a little insulting.'

'Best if you stand aside,' Stenvast said, 'but I see you will not do that.'

'I am Guthrum,' the wolfskin said to me. 'You are Orm, leader of the Oathsworn. I see you and have come to take your life.'

'Three men guard my life,' I answered, hoping my voice did not sound hoarse with fear, 'Odin, Thor and Frey. None may harm me, unless he is greater than they.'

He made a sign against that old charm and I laughed at him, but my top lip stuck to my teeth and I hoped he had not seen that.

We stood and waited and that was part of what little plan we had; they were *beserker* and so a strange breed, having a power that made folk afraid, which fear fed the power. Some, like Pinleg, could summon it in an eyeblink and others needed time, needed to pace like trapped animals and growl and work up to it, believing they were sucking up the strength and speed of the skins they wore. It was said that others licked the strange slime off the backs of toads, or drank bog myrtle brews, but I had not seen any of that myself.

Let them do what they will, we had agreed, for every minute we held them at the bridge was a stride or two more for Botolf and Toki.

'I say the boar will get to it first,' Finn growled at me, without looking away from his man. 'An ounce of silver says he will go piggy-eyed and charge before any of the others.'

I should have taken his bet, for it was the wolf-skin who reached his power first, throwing back his head and howling

it out – then he came at me, all blinding hand-speed and fast shuffle, so that I fell back a little and heard the blades score down my shield and shriek off the boss. All I could manage in return was a half-hearted wave of my blade, then he was bounding back, crouching and boring in again.

Like a wolf, I thought. He attacks, low and fast, trying for the soft spots, trying to disable and bring me down like a bull elk . . . but you needed a pack for that. One was not enough and I cut him badly on his third attack and he bounced back, looked at his forearm and shook his head, grinning with foam-smoked lips. There was no blood and no pain – and no focus in his mad eyes when he came at me again.

There were clangs and grunts and yells from my left but I dared not look – but a flicker on my right made me half-turn my head; Stenvast slid past me and, for a moment, I thought he was going to take me from behind and felt a shriek of terror at the thought of two of them. Then Guthrum slithered in again, blades whirling and I had to block and cut and dance with him.

'Finn . . .'

It was a stupid, desperate call and might have been the death of Finn if he had been a lesser fighter – but he did not turn his head, simply cursed and yelled back that he was a little busy at the moment. Stenvast vanished over the bridge and up the trail.

Guthrum howled and leaped and bounced and I cut back at him when I could, but knew the best I could do was hang on and not let him kill me. My breath rasped and wheezed loud in my ears under the helmet; a blade scored the ring-mail sleeve of my sword-arm, another spanged off the hilt of my sword.

He bored in again, a high cut that I barely blocked with the shield; it sliced slivers off the edge and scored along under the rim of my helmet above one eye, so that I saw, for a glimmering moment, the pits in the blade-metal and the change

108

in colour where core met cutting edge. I stumbled back, felt the coping stones of the parapet on the backs of my thighs and twisted desperately to one side, not wanting to go over.

There was a great, soft roaring in my ears and the world went black, then red. I felt a blow on my belly, thought to myself, well, there is the soup-wound, no pain yet but here it comes, the death and the offering to Odin, make it quick, One-Eye . . .

Light flashed, red-smeared. A great, filthy finger poked me in the eye and Finn's face loomed, streaked with sweated rust from under his helmet. The hand came again, with a rag in it, and he wiped my face.

'Nasty wee cut, Bear Slayer. Lots of blood, but no real damage. Good scar, though, which will make women swoon and men back off.'

I struggled upright. Finn handed me the blood-soaked rag and sank down on one knee; one sleeve was bloody at the forearm and three men were dead behind him.

'What?' I said, shaking the red mist from my eyes and the inside of my head.

'Aye, all dead,' Finn answered cheerfully. 'That wolf man included, unless he can survive a long drop and a dookin in the river below us. Neat trick that, Bear Slayer – I thought he had you until you turned him off the bridge.'

I blinked and got up on shaky legs, looking round.

'I did not turn him,' I said. 'At least, I did not mean to. At least, I do not think I meant to.'

'Do not fash,' Finn replied, getting off his knee and wincing as he did so, holding his ribs.

'He got you one then,' I noted and Finn snorted.

'Not that bladder Ingimund – I killed him in a heartbeat, but then had to knock his legs out from under him, which is the way of these mouth-frothers. No, it was those goat-fucking spearmen who caused me trouble.'

I did not doubt it; two spearmen who knew the work,

acting together on a single enemy, was the worst thing a warrior could face – other than an archer in a place too high to reach.

'Aye,' Finn agreed, scowling. 'I took a poke which would have burst me if it had not been for that ringmail. Battle-luck that I was the same size as Red Njal – but, look you, I will have to pay him for it now.'

He stuck fingers in the shredded hole and waggled them; we grinned and then laughed and clasped each other.

Alive. Enemies dead and us alive – Odin had not claimed me yet. I had forgotten that he liked to play with his prey, like a cat does. I felt my legs shake then and had to sit; I did not know how Finn felt no fear and said so.

'I was too afraid even to run,' I added, half-ashamed, half-defiant, but Finn grinned and clapped me on the shoulder.

'There,' he grunted. 'Now you have the secret of it.'

Too afraid even to run. I looked at him, wondering if it was true, or just Finn being Finn. Then the memory of what had happened on the bridge flooded in, leaping me to my feet.

'Stenvast,' I said and Finn scowled.

'Aye.'

We hirpled off up the trail, leaving the bridge and the dead and the gathering crows. The cut started to bleed again, running with the sweat into my eye and stinging it, so that I had to shake it away in fat, scarlet drops.

It started to rain.

Toki told us what had happened, half-awed by it, half-shaking. We found him right at the top of the headland, where the trail ended on a scarp of rock, like the scalp of a bald man. Once, there had been trees here, but overcutting had taken them and the rain, without the bind of root, had washed away the top soil; what trees were left clung here like stray hairs, gnarled and stunted by the wind.

Beyond, the trail to safety led down into the last stands of thick pine on a slope too steep to cut trees, but it was clear that Botolf and Toki had just started down it when Stenvast came up on them. The way Toki told it, in his wide-eyed child's way, this giant had appeared, waving a big axe and bellowed at Botolf to stop.

Botolf had handed the bairn to Toki, telling the boy to be fast on his way down. The giant, said Toki, made to cut him off, but Botolf moved to block it.

'He only had a seax,' Toki said, then half-sobbed. 'It was not fair.'

'What happened then?' asked Finn, looking round; I knew he searched for bodies, but there were none, which was a puzzle. The rain fell, shroud-soft and silent and the slate-blue fjord was white-capped in the background. The bairn squalled in Toki's arms and I took it from him.

'I wanted to go,' Toki said with a sniff. 'But I could not move and the goat would not move and the wean was greetin' fit to burst . . .'

'What happened with Botolf and the giant?' I asked gently, settling down beside him. I pulled the hood of his *kjartan* up against the rain and the goat nuzzled, trying to get under his armpit, so that he took it and stroked its muzzle, absently.

'The giant told Botolf to stand aside and that his name was Stenvast and that he had come for the bairn. Botolf said his name was Botolf and he would not get the bairn and then the giant looked at Botolf a little, sideways, the way Thorgunna looks at Finn sometimes when he has done something unexpected, like fetch the milk unasked. Then he asked if this was the same Botolf, the cripple who had broken the back of Thorbrand Hrafnsson and Botolf said he had snapped the spine of a man, but that Stenvast must be mistaken, for he was no cripple and then the giant . . .'

He stopped, hiccuped and shivered and I patted him while

111

Finn prowled, scrubbing his beard furiously, which he did when things did not tally up for him.

'What then?'

Toki scrubbed his red eyes.

'The Giant Stenvast said to Botolf that he was a man who had come up leg short and blade short against a better one and that he had the brain of a beetle if he had the idea he was going to win this fight. But Botolf grinned and wagged one finger and said that was your first mistake, I have the thought-cage of a mouse, not a beetle, for a good friend said so.'

Toki stopped and looked at me, brow furrowed, face streaked with tears and snot.

'I did not understand this,' he went on and I told him it did not matter. He hiccuped.

'The giant did not understand it either,' he went on. 'He whirled his axe and cut and Botolf stopped it with his seax, but he could not leap out of the way and the giant cut the other way and it hit Botolf in the leg, his wooden one, so that it snapped and he pitched on the ground. The giant said now you are a cripple and Botolf got on one good leg and he turned and winked at me.'

My heart froze, for I knew that wink. Toki blinked and tears spilled.

'He said I was to watch out for wee Helga and when she was older, tell her he was sorry her da was not there, but a prince got in the way. Then he said to the giant, you have the bettering of me right enough, for you have a longer blade and a stronger leg, but there is something I am betting sure I can still do that you cannot.'

Toki stopped then and the tears spilled to the brim of his wide, bright little eyes.

'What was it that Botolf could do, then?' demanded Finn, still scouring everywhere with his eyes, looking for blood or bodies and finding none.

'Fly,' said Toki and I felt the world fall away from me in a dizzying rush, as if I had been carried up on wings myself. I heard a groan, which was me, found myself blinking at the ground.

'He leaped off his good leg,' Toki said, 'and took the giant in the belly with his head and they both went over the edge. I saw Botolf spread his arms. He had wings. Black ones.'

Toki stopped and bowed his head and the tears fell, soft as rain.

'I was sure he had wings.'

My belly had dropped away, leaving a black void filled with loss – I remembered Vuokko saying it: 'a loss, keenly felt'. I had thought, in my arrogance, that it would be me.

Finn, his eyes desperate, looked from me to Toki and then out over the headland to the fjord. He made a half move, no more than a step, towards it, as if to hurl himself over.

'Arse,' he said, in a voice thick with grief. 'Stupid, stupid, stupid great arse.'

'He will come back,' Toki said, but his voice was uncertain. 'He dreamed sometimes he had big black wings, like a raven he said and I saw them. I am sure I saw them.'

Finn peered out over the headland, as if to find Botolf hanging grimly by a fingernail a few feet down, which is how the skalds would have it. Instead, he shaded his eyes with a hand and then half-turned to me.

'A ship is leaving the fjord,' he called and I moved to his side; it was Ljot and his crew, rowing hard for the open water. That meant only Randr Sterki was left.

'Why is he leaving, I wonder?' Finn asked. I did not care, it was what he had on board that worried me – one Greek monk and my *fostri*.

'He will fly back,' said Toki, dragging us back to why we stood at the edge of the cliff in the first place, so that the loss crashed in like a huge wave. I handed him the squalling bairn

and gathered the pair of them to me as the sun burst out like a wash of honey, turning the fine rain to a mist of gold.

We all saw it, then, the great arch of Bifrost, the rainbow bridge which only appears when a hero is crossing to Valholl. So we knew Botolf was not flying back.

EIGHT

The way of it, as Randr Sterki told everyone, was like this: you throw your weapons in the dirt and Orm Bear Slayer does not get hurt. Of course, what he did not add were the words 'for the moment', but everyone knew that – knew, also, that throwing down their weapons would not be the end of the matter, only the beginning.

So, rightly, Red Njal and Hlenni shook their heads and shot glances of misery at me, tied up and held by a savage snarler whose face was a great stone cliff set against me.

'The wolf and the dog,' Red Njal shouted hoarsely, 'do not play together, as my granny used to say.'

True though it was, I had been hoping his granny had something useful on my predicament. Finn and Toki and me had surfaced from our grief on the bald mountain and it was clear to both Finn and me what had to be done next, so it it did not take much talk. He and Toki, goat and precious-as-gold bairn went one way, to safety. I turned back, for I could not leave the women and weans to bear the brunt of Randr Sterki and the remaining bearcoats alone – anyway, I had made my promise to Odin.

Perhaps it was he, then, who walked me past the fly-buzzing heaps on the bridge, back up the water-runnelled trail a way,

round a bend, round another – and into the scores of heads, turning in amazement.

Like a nithing into the middle of Randr's men, where I was grabbed and trussed like a stupid sheep.

Beyond stood a line of ringmail pillars, shields up and ready – Rovald, Rorik Stari, Kaelbjorn Rog, Myrkjartan and Uddolf, with Abjorn in their middle, while Red Njal and Hlenni, with only shield and helmet, hovered behind them. Two bodies lay at their feet and a third a little way off, an arrow in one eye showing that Kuritsa had not boasted about his prowess idly.

'Heya,' I called out. 'The child is safe – Finn is with him and Toki. The bearcoats they sent are dead . . .'

The blow whirled stars into me and I half-fell; someone yelped out a scream and I found the legs of the man who had hit me, followed them upwards to the face, a braided twist of hate.

'Another peep, Bear Slayer,' the man growled, 'and I will fill your mouth with your own teeth.'

'Where is Botolf?'

I heard the half-scream and knew, without looking, that it was Ingrid. I never took my eyes from that face of hate.

'Crossing Bifrost,' I bellowed and he hit me. Even ready for it, I managed only to deflect the blow a little and felt my nose crunch, the pain shrieking in so that I found myself, blind with tears and snot and blood, open-mouthed and gasping for air on my hands and knees. The wailing that went up from the women at the news of Botolf was more painful still.

'Leave that, Tov,' snarled a voice. 'I want him undamaged.'

Gradually, I blinked back into the blurred world and the noise of keening women. Now all that remained was to stand like a decent sacrifice and die well, so I hauled myself into the pain, spitting out the blood that flowed down the back of my tortured nose. The cut on my forehead had opened, too, and I had to flick the blood out of my eyes, which caused my nose to throb.

116

'The Giant Ymir is gone, then? One less,' bellowed Randr Sterki, at his own men as much as mine, I realised.

'The cost was high,' growled a voice – one of the remaining *ulfhednar*, I realised. 'Stenvast now is dead.'

It came to me then that half his crew were too new for this, had not been on Svartey and were not driven by the revenge of the others. Half was half a chance . . .

'Still many of us left,' I called out hoarsely, the force of the words inside my head making my nose scream with new pain. Randr whirled and thrust a sword – my sword – under it.

'You have the right of it, for sure,' he said and viciously tapped upwards so that my head burst with the red light of pain and new tears sprang to blind me.

'Tell them to throw down their weapons.'

'So you can slaughter them?' I managed to cough out and shook my head, which was a painful mistake. 'No bargain for them there.'

'No bargain anywhere,' howled Tov, trying to fist the side of my head and missing. 'You took my woman and my wealth, you hole – I will rip off your balls . . .'

There was a slap of sound and Tov yelped; Randr lowered the sword, scowling.

'Think yourself lucky I used the flat,' he spat. 'I told you to leave off with all that.'

Tov glowered back, barely held by the last shreds of a leash of fear; soon, I thought, it will part and he will spring at Randr like a ship down a slipway. All it took was that last push . . .

'There is a bargain, all the same,' I yelled out, trying to ignore the stabs of pain each word lanced in my head. 'Moonlit-buried silver, blood-price enough to end this feud.'

That brought heads up; everyone there knew the Oathsworn tales, particularly the one about finding all the silver of the world. Even allowing for the lies of skalds, that left silver enough for any man's dreams.

'There is not enough silver to end this,' Randr bellowed

back, then heard the mutterings that ran through the wolf pack behind him and whirled to face it. In an eyeblink, he saw them fracture, into those who thought there was enough silver and those who wanted blood only.

'Stenvast is dead,' growled the same bearcoat who had spoken before. 'There is little left for us here and some of the Oathsworn's famed silver seems a fair price.'

'I will tell you where you can find it,' I offered, driving the wedges deeper. 'If you agree that it is finished and we each go our ways.'

'You bitch-licking turd!'

The shriek came from Tov and he launched himself at me, all screaming and clawed fingers, seeing his revenge tremble on the brink of failure.

It was reflex from Randr, no more than that, the savage, sudden burst of anger from a jarl with too many problems all at once and disobeyed once too often; my sword whicked past my own ear and cut Tov's throat out of him in a vomit of blood that splashed me as he thumped on the road.

There was a frozen moment of stillness, broken only by the sound of Tov's blood trickling to a whisper and sliding in tendrils through the rain-water.

Then uproar and yells and argument. Fights started and Randr bellowed and laid about him with the sword. I saw Abjorn and the others look at each other, sizing up the chance of taking the fight to the enemy while they were so fractured and, for a moment, was frantic they would do it.

In the end, the bearcoats, bristling and growling in a group tight as a fist, brought order where Randr failed – and faster than the Oathsworn could make their minds up; I heaved a sigh of relief.

There was a brief, muttered argument, then Randr stalked angrily at me, badger-beard trembling. Two men were with him, one of them a wild-bearded giant of a bearcoat who announced himself as Skeggi Ogmundsson.

'Tell where the hoard is,' Randr said, jerking his head at the men. 'They will go to it. If it is not there, you will die when the news is brought back.'

'If it is?' I countered, my voice thick with blood and pain, sounding strange and faraway in my ears.

He looked into my tear- and blood-streaked face and sneered.

'We will take it and sail away. You and your whelps may have your lives for now.'

The 'for now' did not escape me. I knew he would not agree to forever, so I nodded and told what I knew.

Standing there for the time it took the men to go all the way to it and back was a long, long day. No-one spoke much, nor gave up their positions, nor rested their arms save in shifts. Randr's men lit a couple of fires, but they had precious little fuel and they soon went out while, from the direction of the carts, I smelled smoke and soup, heard the grumbles from Randr's hungry men and would have smiled, save that the muscles would not work for the trembling in them.

Then it rained again and the shadows slid and darkened. Men broke out what cloaks they had, or pulled their clothing tighter round them as the cold gnawed them. My nose throbbed and I had to stand open-mouthed as a coal-eater, because I could not breathe through it.

Then, suddenly, one of the men was back, lurching up the trail. Men stood; excitement drove out hunger and cold and they waited.

'Well, Hallgeir?' demanded a cold-eyed Randr.

'Silver,' said the man, scarcely able to speak. 'Great piles of it – look.'

He thrust out a hand and men crowded to it; in the char-coal dim, the soft glow of coin and silver torc sucked the breath from them with a hiss. They looked at the handful, seeing it in dragon heaps.

'Well,' said Randr, straightening. 'Now we have the silver.'

'Untie me,' I said and he laughed, a crow-snarl laugh that let me know it was not about to happen.

'There is another matter . . .' Hallgeir said, trying to thrust himself through the crowd that wanted to see, to touch, part of the fabled hoard of the Oathsworn.

Scowling, Randr turned, impatient at being thwarted from killing me, which was his next act, I knew. Odin was about to get his sacrifice. Make it quick, AllFather, I was thinking, while part of me was gibbering and wanting to flee rather than stand there like an ox at a *blot*.

'Where is Skeggi Ogmundsson?' demanded a voice.

Before anyone could speak, something flew out of the shadows, whirling like a stone. It smacked wetly on the ground and rolled towards Randr, who stepped back from it; all hackles were up when they saw it was the bloody ruin of a wild-bearded head.

'There was a grey gull.'

The voice came out of the darkness, down the trail from where the head of Skeggi the bearcoat had come. A piping voice, not yet broken.

A boy's voice.

Heads turned and voices stilled; I saw Randr Sterki's face just then and it was white round eyes which flicked briefly with fear, like Hati the moon goddess hearing the howl of the devouring wolf which pursued her.

'That is the other matter,' Hallgeir sighed, wearied with resignation. His hand fell to his side and the silver in it dropped, unregarded by anyone, to the rain and the mud.

Crowbone stepped to where men could see him. He wore a ringmail coat made for his size and carried a spear in either hand, was bareheaded so that his coin-weighted braids swung, and he did not look like a mere boy. Alyosha, as ever, was at his shoulder and, behind, the creak and shink and breathing of ringmailed men, gleaming faint and grey in the twilight, was a cliff at Crowbone's back.

My legs sagged; now I knew why Ljot had been rowing so hard for the open water – to avoid Crowbone coming up. That Ljot had not informed Randr Sterki of it told a great deal.

'There was a grey gull,' Crowbone said, stepping closer and shouting less. 'A raiding gull, who lived high on a cliff, on the flight's edge. A king of gulls, whom men called Sterki – Strong – and who laughed at those same men and stole their fish and shat on them for fun.'

There were nervous sniggers, for they had all suffered that. Meaningful looks were shot at Randr Sterki, who shared the same name as this gull and at whom the tale was clearly aimed. I saw men sidle sideways, away from the rest; the last of the bearcoats, I was thinking.

'I need no talk of gulls,' Randr began, but Alyosha, only eyes showing in the helmet of his face, made a little gesture with a big axe that spoke loudly. The bearcoats stopped moving.

'Better listen,' I offered. 'Better one of little Prince Crowbone's sharp stories than the sharper alternative.'

Randr licked his lips; the alternative stared back at him from all the faint faces behind Crowbone's back. Yet here was the boy who had turned his hate on all Randr had held dear. Here were all his enemies, all those he wanted revenge on and he hovered on the sheer cliff of wanting to hurl himself at them. He also knew, in the little part of him not blinded with red mist, that he would fail and that leash held him a little yet.

'This king of gulls had an egg, a fine egg,' Crowbone said, after a pause during which the silence became painful as my nose. 'He knew it would hatch to be a fine son to replace him in his time and he left his fine gull-wife to sit on it while he flew away in search of food.

'When he returned, he found his gull-wife with her neck broken and the fine egg gone and he knew, at once, that it

121

was the blacksmith who had done it. He had shat on the smith many a time, stolen the fish right from the fingers of his children – and he knew the smith could climb any cliff.'

'Speak up,' yelled Ref from where the fire burned. 'I think I know this man.'

There were soft laughs, but they had no mirth in them and Crowbone went on, level and firm and slow, in his rill-clear voice.

'The gull-king knew at once that the blacksmith must have taken it. So he went to the man and demanded that he give the egg back. But the smith pretended it was just a shrieking bird flying round his head and waved the gull-king away.

'The gull-king was heartbroken and flew about looking for help. On the way he met a pig, and asked him to root up the carrots of the smith who had stolen his egg, to make him give it back.

'The pig grunted once or twice. "No, not I," he said and walked away.

'The gull-king then met a hunter, who bowed politely and asked why the mighty lord of gannets was so distressed. The bird said: "Will you shoot an arrow at the pig who would not root up the carrots of the smith and make him give me back my stolen egg?"

'But the hunter shook his head. "Why should I? Leave me out of this."

'The gull-king wept tears of pure bile and flew on till he met a rat, who also asked why he was in tears. The gull-king said: "Will you gnaw and cut the bowstring of the hunter who would not shoot the pig who would not root up the carrots of the smith and make him give back my egg?"

'The rat squeaked once, then twice, then promised to do it – but ran away instead.'

'Heya,' yelled a voice from the dark. 'I know that rat.'

'I wed her,' yelled another, which brought grim laughter

and calls for silence equally. Crowbone waited until the silence again became painful, then continued.

'Next, the gull-king met a cat and asked her to catch the rat who would not cut the bowstring of the hunter who would not shoot the pig who would not root up the carrots of the smith and force him to give back the egg he had stolen.

'The cat licked her whiskers once, then twice, then said she would rather mind her own business and ran off.

'The poor gull-king was beside himself with anger and grief. His wails attracted the attention of a passing dog, who asked what was bothering the mighty gannet. He asked: "Will you bite the cat who would not catch the rat who would not cut the bowstring of the hunter who would not shoot the pig who would not dig up the carrots of the smith who stole my egg?"

'The dog barked once. "No, not I," he said and ran away.

'The gull-king's wails grew louder and louder. An old man with a long white beard came that way and asked the screaming bird what the matter was. He said: "Grandfather, will you beat the dog who would not bite the cat who would not catch the rat who would not cut the bowstring of the hunter who would not shoot the pig who would not root up the carrots of the smith who has stolen my egg and will not give it back?"

'This greybeard shook his head at such foolishness and went his way. The gull-king, in desperation, next went to the fire for help and asked it to burn the white beard of the old man, but the fire would not do it. Next the gull-king went to the water and asked it to put out the fire which would not burn the beard of the old man who refused to beat the dog who would not bite the cat who would not catch the rat who would not cut the bowstring of the hunter who would not shoot the pig who would not root up the carrots of the smith who had stolen his egg and would not give it back.

'But the water just gurgled and refused to help Sterki the gull-king.

'Frantic and furious, the gull-king swooped down on an

ox, demanding that it stir up the water which would not put out the fire which refused to burn the beard of the old man who would not . . .

'But the ox did not even wait for the explanation; it lowered its massive head and went back to chewing.'

Crowbone paused, as if to take a longer breath and those who knew the way of it stirred, for here was the closure of the tale; no-one moved or spoke.

'Then,' said little Crowbone, 'the gull-king spotted a flea on the arse of the ox, who also asked what was troubling the mighty Sterki, king of gulls.

'The gull-king, who would never have even noticed such a creature before, sprang eagerly up and bowed. "O flea! I know you can help me. Will you bite the arse of the ox for not stirring up the water which would not put out the fire which would not burn the beard of the old man who would not beat the dog who would not bite the cat who would not catch the rat who would not cut the bowstring of the hunter who would not shoot the pig who would not root up the carrots of the smith who stole my egg and will not give it back?"'

At which point there were admiring noises about Crowbone's feat of memory, from those who did not realise he was not the boy he appeared.

'The flea,' said Crowbone, ignoring them, 'thought about it for a moment, then said: "Why not? Here I go." And he crawled right up the arse of the ox and bit, which made the beast dash into the pool of water and stir it up. The water splashed and began to put out the fire, which went mad and burned the white beard of the old man, who beat the dog, who ran after the cat and bit her. The cat caught the rat, who had to gnaw the string of the hunter's bow before she was freed. The hunter tied on a new one and shot an arrow at the pig, who went and rooted up the carrots of the smith.

'"Aha, aha!" shrieked the gull-king in triumph and the

smith, looking ruefully at the remains of his carrot patch, shrugged and said: "You have succeeded, right enough, Sterki."

'The gull-king swooped and laughed. "Then hand back my egg," he screamed. The smith blinked once and blinked twice.

'"Is that what this is all about?" he asked and shook his head. "I ate that egg for breakfast days ago."'

There was silence as the story echoed to a close. Men shifted, not liking the ending much.

'Take the silver,' Crowbone said softly. 'Your egg is gone, Randr Sterki, and all your long revenge will not bring it back.'

There was silence, broken only by the hissing wind and the sibilance of shifting feet.

'I should have killed you when I caught you running off,' Randr said bitterly and Crowbone stepped closer, a spear in each hand and his voice sharper than either of them.

'Instead,' he said, his voice suddenly deeper than before, 'you gave me to Klerkon's woman, to beat and chain like a dog outside the privy. Instead, you had your woman and boy shave me with an edgeless seax. You let Kveldulf put his wean in my ma's belly and then kick the life out of both of them when it suited him. And laughed.'

Randr blinked and shook his head, as if trying to drive that away like an irrelevant fly – but it would not quit him and he had no answer to it. Slowly, he nodded once, then twice. Behind him, men shifted and muttered and then a bearcoat threw back his head, howled and lurched at Crowbone. The gods alone know why, for there was no profit or sense in it, but those skin-wearing droolers seldom fight for either, though fighting is all they know.

It was like watching a cliff fall on a mouse – yet Crowbone did not even flinch, merely looked up, half-spun and threw with both hands. Two spears smacked the man, one in his chest, the other in his right thigh and he went pitching forward on his nose. Alyosha stepped forward smartly and axed his

throat open, knowing a pelt-wearer was not dead until he was really dead.

Someone – from Randr's own men – gave an admiring 'heya' even as the victim curled and writhed round the spears, like a hooked worm; the last trio of bearcoats, trembling on the brink of summoning power, looked at each other – and all their skin-magic soaked away, so that they seemed to wrinkle and sag like empty *skyr*-bags.

'Courage is not hacksilver, to be shut always in a purse,' Red Njal growled, seeing this. 'It needs to be taken out and shown the sun, as my granny used to say.'

'Finish this,' Hlenni called out, but I saw Crowbone's warning eye and held up a stopping hand.

'Enough has been done, one to the other,' I said. 'Take the silver you have dug up and let that be blood-price for any loss. Let this be an end.'

Randr's face was smeared with twisted hate, yet he backed away then, into the maw of his men, hauling Hallgeir with him; one by one at first, then in groups, they sidled round the half-hidden men of Crowbone and slithered into the shadows, heading for my silver and safety.

Alyosha let out his breath with a sharp sound as the last one vanished and my own men rushed forward to free me.

'Good throwing,' Alyosha declared, but Crowbone frowned, looking at the dying man with disdain.

'Too weak in the left hand,' he answered. 'Both spears were meant to go in his chest.'

In later life, Crowbone perfected throwing spears with both hands at the same time and it served him well, but this first attempt was timely enough for me, I thought, as eager hands untied me. I managed to get that out to him before Thorgunna's embrace drove the air from me entirely.

Crowbone's scowl vanished.

'Aye, it was timely at that,' he answered brightly, as if realising it for the first time.

'You should have finished Randr Sterki,' Hlenni pointed out and, even washed by the safe and loving press of friends and those who held me dear, I could feel Randr's hate and wondered why the boy had not pressed the fight.

'He still has Sigurd's nose,' I said to him.

'Your sword also,' he replied, then lost the grin and sighed. 'I would have, but . . .'

Right there and then I heard the crack as his voice broke to manhood. He cleared his throat and looked bewildered for a moment or two, then spoke on, his voice breaking on every second or third word, to his annoyance.

'I came short-handed to the feast. Alyosha was concerned.' Then he motioned, so that a mere ten men stepped forward from the shadows behind him. If Randr had decided to fight, Crowbone and his men would almost certainly have gone under. Alyosha peeled off his gilded, face-mailed helmet, puffing out sweat-sheened cheeks and grinning from behind a damp beard.

'We left too many men with *Short Serpent*,' he declared and shot Crowbone a sharp, sideways look that made it clear whose fault that had been; the boy loved his ship too much. Crowbone ignored him and held out his small fist; I clasped him, wrist to wrist and heard his voice, rising and falling like a ship on a bad sea.

'I will take back Sigurd's nose one day, from off the stump of Randr Sterki's neck,' he said, trying to growl and only half succeeding. 'But all is done with for now.'

The grin returned, making it clear who I had to thank for it. Somehow, I knew there would be a price to pay for that – if Odin let me live that long.

'Will he be done with this now that he has your silver?' Red Njal asked and I remembered Randr's hate-mask of a face. My look told him all he needed to know.

Still, we were free of danger for now, so that people clapped each other on the shoulder, or hugged one another, smiling

127

and the children, caught up in the moment, laughed and danced. But the joy of it was soured by the weeping for Botolf – and, later, the great red glow which I knew was Hestreng hall burning, a last spiteful act that told me Randr had not finished yet with his hate.

'That and your silver loss,' Crowbone mused, watching the red glow, 'must be a sore dunt – but I saw the state *Dragon Wings* was in and it comes to me that those burned strakes will maybe leak him all the way to the bottom of the Baltic, *weregild* silver and all.'

I said nothing. The one child not laughing was red-faced, flame-haired Helga Hiti, wailing because her mother wailed for Botolf – yet it was still birdsong to me, as was every other voice I heard, for they were alive and safe and I said as much, so that the new man that was Crowbone nodded soberly.

'Fitting, then, for that old tale,' he said and, through the pain of Thorgunna spooning the blood clots from my tortured nose, I managed to tell him that I owed him for the telling of it, which made him grin. The grin broadened as Thorgunna and her sister told me to be still and to weesht and stop behaving like a bairn while they tortured my neb further.

Through the tears I saw Crowbone, too pleased to take the news of it blandly, as an older prince would do. He managed to stammer out that nothing was owed between friends and I am sure he meant it, seeing the baleful red eye turning Hestreng to ashes and Randr Sterki running off with my wealth.

Well, that was one moonlit burial and, though it was the largest amount of Atil's cursed silver, it was not the only hoard of it; only a careless man piles all his wealth in one hole. I kept my teeth shut on that matter around Crowbone, all the same, for it is a doubly-careless man who boasts of such cleverness.

Anyway, if I had opened my mouth at all, only foul curses would have come from it at what Thorgunna and her sister

were doing to my nose, which would have left me with cold oatmeal and a turned back for weeks. With everything else, that would have been a mountain weight on my shoulders.

The air was a sharp breath of ash and snow around Hestreng hall on the day we trundled back to it. A ribcage of wet, black timbers it was, collapsed on itself like a dead beast and a light rain sifting down like tears to turn the ground round it to black mud.

'I am sorry for it,' said the queen, coming up behind Thorgunna and Aoife and me as we stood, stilled by the loss, while the others poked about and cried out when they recognised the remains of something they had once known well.

'Aye,' agreed Crowbone, though too young to make his pretended sombre look work. He had seen too much of this – done a deal of this himself – up and down the Baltic to be truly moved by a tragedy that was not his to bear. It came to me then that I had done the same, in my time.

'I shall have men and timber sent,' the queen said, 'when I am home.'

I remembered Finn telling Botolf about what a king such as Eirik would do for those who saved his little prince and hoped the big man heard this now in Odin's hall, enough to nod and smile at it all, standing proud and tall on two good legs.

Thorgunna and Thordis embraced, then bustled off to choke their tears in ordering folk about, to set up what shelters and cooking fires we could; Ingrid, red-eyed, chivvied Helga away from the ruins of Hestreng hall, too late to prevent black streaking her dress and face.

'At least the bairns are safe,' Red Njal offered, trying to be bright. 'And if you need silver . . . well, I have most of my share in a secret hole. Hlenni Brimill, too.'

I felt the warmth of them then, felt the other side of that cold Oath we had sworn when we had followed the prow beast and owned no more than could be safely stowed in a

sea-chest. I told him I still had my own secret hole, at which he nodded as if he had known it all along. Then he clapped me on the shoulder and went off to help sort matters out; the old yard of Hestreng rang with noise and bustle, just as if it was not burned.

Yet not all the bairns were safe. Somewhere, out on the slow-heaving grey-green water of the whale road, Jarl Brand's son shivered and hoped.

NINE

It was an island humped like Onund's shoulder, where green slopes ran down to meet sand, then water; on a day of bright sunshine and birdsong it would have been a pretty place to be, but on this day, with what we had come for and the rain in our faces, it had no charm.

On the shore were buildings, mean as sties most of them, but others large and prosperous-looking, with carved wooden doorways and thatched roofs. In the quiet curve of this cluster of houses lay a series of wharves, like spokes on a half-wheel, where ships were tied up; more vessels were run up on the beach not far away and most were the solid, heavy riverboats the Slavs call *strugs*, carved from a single tree. The others were fat trading *knarrer*, but the only raiding ship other than the one I stood on was hauled up for careening; I knew it at once as Ljot's ship.

'Look at them run,' laughed Ospak, pointing and a few others joined in, harsh with the excitement of it all. They were all the newer crew, who had never been anywhere; the old hands hardly looked up.

There was a clanging noise from the solid fortress, a square of fat timber piles, their sharpened points softened by age and moss, with square towers at each corner and flanking the

gate. I had taken the prow beasts off, but the settlement swarmed like an anthill and the alarm was sounding in the fortress which glowered over it.

'Send a man to the prow,' I said to Crowbone. 'Unarmed and without byrnie. Let him stand there with his arms out and weapon-free, to show we mean no harm.'

He acknowledged it with a small nod and passed it on to Alyosha, who cut a man from the pack and sent him. So far, so good – but having Crowbone and his crew as Oathsworn was like walking on the edge of a seax; I would not have done it had it not been for Jarl Brand and Koll.

Jarl Brand had been the only one not at the feast King Eirik gave for the safe return of his queen and his son. As Finn had said, once we had done with our greetings, that was not because Brand was lacking the strength or grit for it, but just because he had a wounded face that would put folk off their eating.

Not that everyone at the feast, where King Eirik presented his son, had an appetite; too many of the guests were strange company for that.

There were Christ priests, a gaggle of them from the West Franks and the Saxlanders of Hammaburg, all gabbling about baptisms and chrism-loosenings while glaring at each other and trying to make sure they had no horse meat in their bowls.

Then there was Haakon of Hladir, ruler of Norway which he had from the hand of Denmark's King Harald Bluetooth and which hand he was now trying to bite. Bluetooth, not quite a broken-fanged dog, was snarling back and so Haakon was seated at King Eirik's left, looking for help and smiling politely through the teeth he had to grit every time he heard Crowbone called 'Prince of Norway'.

Eirik himself, though crowned king of the Svears and Geats, still had troubles up and down his lands and Bluetooth had designs on them that he was not about to give up, so any

enemy of Bluetooth was a friend of King Eirik and Haakon had been handy for the fight against Styrbjorn.

Then, astoundingly perched in the guest bench, was Svein, Bluetooth's son, who had also helped against Styrbjorn, though he was scarce older than that cursed youth. Young enough, in fact, not have fleeced up the chin-hair that would give him his famed by-name in later life – Forkbeard – he was here to annoy his da, for he wanted more say in Danish matters and Bluetooth had no liking to let him.

Then there was Crowbone, fresh broken to manhood and following Queen Sigrith with his dog-eyes. For her part, she was dressed in a blue so dark it was almost black, trimmed with white wolf and dripping with amber and silver, every inch the queen she wanted to appear, pleased with herself for presenting a son to her king, rich and ripe with life because she and the boy had survived the affair. Better still, of course, was her man's acceptance of little Olaf, for he had not been near the birth himself as was proper and that was a matter doubled when kings were involved.

So she knew the effect she had on the new man that was Crowbone and revelled in the power of it while spurning him, as you would a little boy, with witty flytings wherever possible.

Some trader had brought a talking-bird all the way from Serkland, a green affair with a crown of blood and Haakon had bought it for show. It sat, hunched, with its feathers falling out and miserable from the cold and dark of the north as well as the lack of proper food – the thrall weans kept trying to feed it flakes of fish, as if it was a gull.

'It speaks,' Svein called, trying to make himself a presence, 'in that tongue they use in Serkland.'

Then he turned to me, a twisted little smile smeared on his face and called out the length of the table: 'Orm Bear Slayer, you speak some of that. What does it say?'

It gave the proper response to a greeting in the Mussulmann tongue, as well as phrases such as 'God is great' and 'There

is no god but Allah and Muhammad is his prophet' and so people oohed and aahed when it seemed that I chatted amiably to the bird. My standing, fame-rich already, was confirmed and it was clear from his scowl that Svein had not meant that to happen. Nor, it seemed, was Haakon any happier and he did not like me to begin with because of my closeness with young Crowbone. I could not blame him for that – he was king in Norway and sitting a few careful benches down from a boy claiming to be the true prince of that land.

'Perhaps the Bear Slayer can use this gift to command the return of his *fostri*, Koll Brandsson,' he said nastily and smiled a sharp-toothed grin. I marked it, pretended disinterest and continued to tell the thralls charged with caring for the bird that it needed berries and nuts, should be kept out of the cold and put in the sun, when it actually shone.

Then, eventually, I turned into his smile and ignored it, looking at King Eirik instead.

'A marvellous bird,' I told him. 'Seldom seen in these parts and so doubly strange that Jarl Haakon here has come into possession of it.'

'Strange?' Eirik asked.

'Aye,' I mused. 'I know Gunnhild is old and fled from Norway – but her *seidr* is still strong enough.'

The smile died on Haakon's face; panic and fear chased over it like cat and dog and he looked wildly from me to the bird and back again. He had ousted Gunnhild, and the last of Bloodaxe's sons, from Norway five years ago – they had fled to Orkney and were causing trouble there – but he feared the witch Mother of Kings still. She was reputed to be able to take the shape of any bird and fly through the Other, far and wide, to perch and listen to plots and plans.

'Such *seidr*,' I added, lightly vicious as the kiss of a fang, 'has no effect on me.'

Which, because they had heard all the skald tales of the witches I had supposedly killed and the scaled trolls and all

134

the rest, was a boast accepted easily by the company and they laughed, though shakily.

As a result King Eirik had the bird removed from the feasting hall and Haakon watched it all the way out of the room; later, I heard he had it thrown to his deerhounds and felt sorry for that, even though I knew the bird would have died soon anyway.

One other watched that bird leave the room. I had forgotten that Crowbone had developed his way with birds because of Gunnhild's reputation; she, of course, had hunted the young Crowbone after killing his father to get the throne Haakon now sat on. It was that which prompted Crowbone to do what he did next, I am sure of it, for he always acted on the signs birds offered up to him and there was no more singular bird than that blood-headed talking one from Serkland.

'If you go after Koll Brandsson,' he whispered to me, ashen-faced, 'I will take your Odin Oath and follow you.'

I blinked at that; the idea of Crowbone as one of the Oathsworn was one I did not wish to think about at all for the dangers in it – but there was no easy way to refuse it, especially when it became clear that I needed him.

That was after the feasting was done and the real business commenced. King Eirik promised thralls and timber and men who knew how to build, as well as fat ships to transport all of this and supplies enough to see Hestreng through the lean time of summer to the first harvest.

'I cannot spare fighting men,' he added, frowning, 'nor raiding ships, for I am battle-light in both and my right arm is felled for now.'

Eye to eye and alone in his closed room in the prow of the hall, he leaned closer, blood-dyed by torch glow. His neat-trimmed beard was faded red-gold and under the hat he wore for vanity he was bald save for a fringe round his ears. His feasting horn of mead was elsewhere; now he toyed with a blue glass goblet of wine and had offered me some, but I stuck

with an iron-banded horn of nutty ale. Clear heads are best when dealing with kings – besides, my head hurt enough from the scar on my forehead and my blood-clotted nose to add wine fumes to it.

'The Greek monk, Leo, has taken Koll as hostage and sailed with Ljot Tokeson,' he said, pinching salt on bread to rid himself of the cloy of mead in his mouth. 'Ljot is brother to Pallig Tokeson and Styrbjorn is with them both.'

Pallig, Lord of Joms. King Eirik looked at me with rheumy eyes and saw I knew the name, then waved a hand and sighed.

'I know, I know – Styrbjorn is a young fool and will need to be punished – but he is my nephew and still has uses. I want him returned to me.'

I did not think Styrbjorn would want to return until he was sure of mercy rather than wrath and I said so.

'Just so,' Eirik said, looking at me. 'So when you go to get your *fostri*, you may like to carry my mercy with you and let him know of it.'

'Jarl Brand, lord?' I asked, as bland and polite as I could make it. King Eirik stroked the neat trim of his beard and scowled.

'It will sit hard with him, but he has placed his hands in mine and I will pay any blood-price for his losses at the hand of Styrbjorn, who is kin, after all.'

So there it was – King Eirik wanted Styrbjorn around, for his son was a bairn and bairns are fragile wee things; Styrbjorn was the only other heir he had. It came to me that Brand might not suffer it as lightly as King Eirik thought – what was the blood-price for a dead wife and the hostaged son of someone as powerful as Jarl Brand? Not enough if it was my wife and bairn.

He saw something of that in my face and, to my surprise, laid a friendly hand on the length of my forearm.

'You are a good man, Orm Bear Slayer,' he said slowly, as if picking his words from a chest of coins and wanting all the

136

whole ones. 'You have silver-luck and fame-luck and men follow you for it, for all that your birthing was awkward. You have served me well these past years.'

He paused and I said nothing, though it smacked me like a blow, the fact that a king thought my birthing awkward; if he did, then others thought the same.

The fact of it is that, in the north, knowing who fathered a child to an unmarried woman was important enough to have its own law. According to it, the old Bogarthing Law, a woman was asked the father's name at the point of labour and, if she stayed silent, the child was considered a thrall from birth. If she named a man, he became 'half-father' and had responsibilities to the child.

My mother, of course, had married Rurik while filled full with me and he had claimed fatherhood. The truth was that another, Gunnar Raudi, had been the seed of me and was thought dead. By the time he returned, I was born and my mother dead of the strain of it – so I had avoided thralldom by the merest whisper of Rurik's breath. All of which made the awkward matter the king spoke of.

He looked at me and took a breath; I braced for more daggers to come.

'I would not do you offence,' he went on, 'but for those reasons and some others you will never be more than a little jarl and, for all your women and weans and sheep and horses, never a landsman farmer.'

He stopped, studying me carefully to see my reaction and the air in the room became as still and thick as a curtain. I kept my face bland and my hands on the table where he could see them; the truth was that he had the right of it, for sure, and though the blood was in my face, I could not do anything other than admit it by a silence like the stillness of rock.

'You follow the prow beast,' Eirik went on, 'taking the Aesir with you out onto the whale road. Here on the land . . .'

He paused again and waved his glass to encompass his

kingdom, slopping wine on his knuckles. 'Here on the land, matters are differently done. Like the Christ priests at my table.'

'I saw them,' I gritted out.

The king nodded, sucked wine from his hand and sighed.

'They come from the Franks and Otto's Saxlanders and snarl at each other,' he said. 'Do you know why, Jarl Orm?'

'They like to argue about their Tortured God,' I answered and he blinked and smiled gently.

'Aye, just so – and not so. What think you of the Christ Jesus?'

I gave him the answer I gave all who asked me that – I have never met the man. Then I added that I would say nothing more, for it was not a good thing to malign the Tortured God in a place thick with his priests and Eirik shifted a little on his bench at that.

'They come and snarl at each other and smile at me because there is more to this White Christ matter than worship,' he said eventually, then leaned forward a little, as if imparting some great secret.

'They are always the first men to come. What follows is a binding among kings. Alliances, wealth and power,' he hissed. 'There are Frank priests and Saxland priests and even ones from the Englisc, all looking to bring their White Christ to my lands rather than suffer someone else to bring the White Christ here. They offer much in return for a dip in water. That is kingship.'

'They offer a white underkirtle,' I answered flatly, 'or so I had heard.'

Eirik's smile was lopsided and wry. 'Kings do a little better – though sometimes I am thinking the prizes glitter well, but are not worth all the kneeling and praying they say has to go with it.'

'So much the better for kicking them all out and offering a sacrifice to Odin for having the clever to do it,' I answered

138

stubbornly, more sharply than I had intended, but Eirik simply squeezed my forearm and shook his head sorrowfully.

'Out on the whale road that may seem clear,' he answered and, in that moment I saw he envied the thought of that and realised the true burden of the crown he wore.

'So – you have Christ priests looking to prise you away from the Aesir,' I growled, irritated with the maudlin king, more so because he was right in what he said. 'What has this to do with the matter of Styrbjorn?'

King Eirik blinked and drank some wine.

'You are a clever man,' he said. 'You know it was this Leo who brought the silver that let Styrbjorn buy Pallig, Ljot and their bearcoats. You have yet to ask yourself the why of it.'

I blinked, for he had it right and I felt the blood flush to my cheeks at this, as sure a sign of being a little jarl as he had claimed. King Eirik nodded.

'All the Christ priests here are from the West,' he said. 'No Greek ones, the ones who cross their chests the opposite way. Vladimir of Novgorod has no Greek ones at his court either, which makes us friends. His brothers do, which makes them my enemies.'

I saw it then, in a sudden churn of belly and mind. Vladimir of Novgorod, facing off against his brothers Oleg and Jaropolk, was for the old gods of the Slavs, though he tolerated Christ worshippers for his grandmother had been one. His brothers had priests of the Greek type swarming all over them, but Vladimir did not care for those monks much.

This was the Great City at work. Vladimir stood in the way of their turning all the Rus to the Greek Christ – and so to the will of Constantinople – so it would try to oust him using his brothers. King Eirik, of course, had sent warriors to help Vladimir, so the Great City would prefer it if that changed. Enter Styrbjorn.

He saw I had worked it out at last and sighed.

'I am thinking Styrbjorn's failure makes him useless to

them now. They will try another way. I may even have to accept that monk Leo back at my court, offering me rich gifts to turn my eyes away from Vladimir. Or a secret death in my wine or food. What they cannot force they will try to buy or kill.'

I felt pity for him then, this man who would be king, who had to bend and twist himself into unnatural shapes to make his arse fit the seat of it. I drank to take the taste away, but that only made it worse.

'Go to Pallig Tokeson, where the monk Leo has fled,' Eirik said. 'If Pallig sees there is no trade to be had other than my friendship for the boy's return, he will give your *fostri* back,' King Eirik said. 'If he has any clever in him at all.'

There was much said about Pallig Tokeson but excessive clever was not part of it. He controlled Joms, which the Saxlanders called Jumne and the Wends, Wolin. There were other names for it, but the skalds – gold-fed by Pallig, no doubt – sang silly tales of the warriors of Joms, who never took a step back in battle and who all lived in a great fortress, where no women were allowed. For all that his men were no Northmen at all, but Wends, he had enough of them to be a dangerous man – and still had some bearcoats, which I mentioned.

'Styrbjorn himself will help,' King Eirik declared, 'for he will want me to know how sorry he is for all that has been done and so will put himself at some risk to make Pallig see sense.'

The fact that I was putting myself at risk, of course, was neither here nor there, it seemed. I still did not think Brand would be so amiable about matters and was surer still after Finn and I went to see him, later in the night.

Brand had taken an arrow in the face, to the right of his nose and just below the eye. It had been a hunting arrow, which was wound-luck for him, for the shaft sprang free and left the head, which was not barbed. Normally, a hunter would cut the valuable arrowhead out of the animal and use it again

– but now it was driven six inches deep through the cheek and into the back of Jarl Brand's skull.

Ofegh, they called Jarl Brand. It was a good by-name for him and meant 'one whose doom is not upon him', though a man with four eyes would be hard put to see that in the face that turned to Finn and me. His main wife, Koll's mother, was dead and his own life was down to a single strand of Norn-weave, it seemed to me.

In the light of a fat, guttering tallow his bone-white hair was lank and stuck to his yellowed face by sweat, but his eyes were still hot and fierce and his wrist-clasp strong. He had what seemed to be a tree growing from his face, though it turned out to be thin, stripped withies of elder, dried and stitched into silk marked with suitable runes, though they were not our own sort.

This was to widen the wound down to where the arrow-head was and, once the healer – a Khazar Jew – was certain it was deep enough, he would insert some narrow-point smithing tongs and take the thing out. Until then, there was only the great, raw-wet lipless mouth of the widened wound and endless agony, which had carved itself on Brand's face, shaved clean for the first time I had known him.

'Bad business,' Brand said in a voice mushed with pain; the withies waggled as he spoke and the Khazar fussed with cleaning probes made from flax soaked in barley, honey and what looked like the pine resin tar we used on fresh ship planks. It stank.

'Aye – it looks a sore one, right enough,' I answered, which seemed inadequate when I could see Brand's back teeth and his tongue waggle as he spoke. He waved one hand as if chasing a fly.

'My son,' he said. 'That priest.'

'I will get him back,' I answered and he closed his eyes briefly, which was a nod, I worked out, the real thing being too painful for him. So was talking, but he did it.

'The king will help. Styrbjorn.'

He meant he was owed by the king for what Styrbjorn had done. I told him what the king had said about him helping to free Koll and being brought back as if nothing had happened at all.

Jarl Brand blinked his blink.

'Kingship,' he mushed, which was answer enough, I now knew.

Men appeared suddenly, quiet and shuffling, bareheaded and twisting their hands – Rovald, Rorik Stari, Kaelbjorn Rog, Myrkjartan and Uddolf, with Abjorn at their head.

'Nithings,' Jarl Brand hissed and would have said a lot more if it had not been agony for him to speak at all. Instead, he waved a hand and sent them off, droop-headed and shamed, dismissed from his service – and into mine, of course.

'Take care of them,' he growled at me and twisted his face in what tried to be a smile, but failed for the pain of it. Then he flapped his hand again and a man appeared holding a sheathed sword. Brand took it and handed it to me.

'I hear,' he said, pain gritting his teeth between the words, 'Randr Sterki took yours. Take this. Get your *fostri* back.'

Then he looked at me, pale eyes lambent with meaning.

'Use the blade well, as I would,' he forced out and gripped my hand like a raven's claw.

It was his own blade and so a rich offering doubled. The hilt was worked with carved antler horn and silver, the sheath whorled and snaked with gripping beasts in fine leather. The gift-price of it did not go by me – I knew he wanted me to bury it in Styrbjorn – nor did his phrase: 'Get your *fostri* back.'

Not his son. My *fostri*. My responsibility, my shame for losing him and my shame doubled if I did not get him back unharmed. I had known that and knew also that Brand was just cutting the runes of it clearly, like a prudent father, so I allowed no offence, bowed politely, took the sword and left,

142

thinking to myself that it did not matter, that nothing mattered to a man as wyrded with doom as myself.

I hoped Odin might hold off enough to let me save Koll, all the same – and kill Styrbjorn, if possible. I brooded on that, sitting under the prow beast as it carved across the slate-water to the mouth of the Odra, saying nothing much and aware that folk were looking at me. I remembered, years before, we had all looked at the Oathsworn's old leader Einar the Black in much the same way, when we were sure his doom was on him and so on all of us, too.

I spoke with Finn on it all, partly because I had to charge him with some of the task if Odin decided to take his sacrifice sooner rather than later. I wanted to mark it out clearly for him to follow – but this was Finn.

'Get the boy back. Kill Styrbjorn. I need no tally stick for that,' he growled.

I sighed. 'Get the boy back, but kill Styrbjorn carefully. Remember – Jarl Brand wants him dead. King Eirik wants him alive. Both have power over the ones we leave behind us.'

Finn scrubbed his beard with frustration, but he nodded, blinking furiously. I spent the rest of the time trying not to pick the itching scar on my forehead, blow bloody snot out of my aching nose and brood on how Finn, a man who thought a quiet, subtle killing was not screaming a warcry and leaving your named sword in the corpse, would carry off the death of Styrbjorn if it fell to him. Or, for that matter, how I would.

Heading into the maw of Pallig Tokeson and his Jomsvikings did not help. The Joms *borg* was feted far and wide as a powerful fortress of sworn brothers, the best fighting men around, but that was all skald-puffed mummery; the reality was a moss-pointed square of timbers with a clanging alarm and a mad scramble of ragged-arsed Wends.

We backed water beyond long arrow range and waited,

143

me standing in the beastless prow with my arms held out, until I was sure they had seen us and the peace-signs we made. Then I had the ship rowed beyond the main wharves, where Hoskuld, called Trollaskegg – Trollbeard – brought us to the beach with almost as neat a movement as Gizur or Hauk might have done.

The mar on it was a hard bang against the shingle, but Crowbone beamed, for the ship was *Short Serpent* and most of the sailing crew was his. They had all sworn the Oath, of course, but I knew the braiding of us together was a loose affair so far.

'Is it not the finest ship afloat?' he yelled, bright with the excitement of it all and his men, used to his ways, laughed with him.

Onund Hnufa snorted.

'You do not think so, Onund Hnufa?' demanded Crowbone sharply – then took an involuntary step backwards as the great bear-bulk of the shipwright loomed over him, the hump on his back like a mountain. Onund did not have to use the word 'boy', for his whole body and voice did that for him.

'You had this ship from Vladimir in Novgorod,' he rumbled and Crowbone managed to squeak that he had the right of it. Onund grunted. Men paused in spilling over the side, armed and ready.

'It was not a question,' he went on. 'It is an old ship, left there long ago, when Novgorod was more known as Holmgard – in my grandfather's day, I am thinking. Maybe the crew sold it, for it was damaged and it is certain Slavs repaired it – look there. The original ribs of it are good oak, but several have been replaced and the oak is poor quality and cut too thick. Where those have been placed makes the ship less of a snake in the water, too stiff, like a wounded old bull.'

We looked; Crowbone gawped.

'Planks were also replaced – see there?' Onund growled. 'The original rivet holes were burned all the same size – good

work, from folk who knew and had pride in their skill – and so the rivets fit tight. The new ones were badly done and some of the holes are too big, so they leak. You need to pine resin it fresh, inside and out. Not oak resin, which will crack when the ship moves. You need to replace the oar-strap – it is loose and the steer-oar does not answer quick enough to the helmsman's hand. That's why we dunted the beach so hard.'

He paused. No-one spoke, but Hoskuld was nodding.

'Anything else?' Crowbone demanded bitterly, recovering himself.

'Teach your crew and your helmsman better,' Onund said and there were growls at that from the men formed up on the shingle, so he rounded on them like some angered boar and they all shrank back a little.

'Who is it that keeps dragging the boat out of the water on rocks and gravel? The keel is no doubt scarred and there is no avoiding that – but any sailor with the least clever in him knows to lift the steer-oar off. It is worn nubbed and splintered from such dragging – my teeth look better.'

And he snarled blackly at them to prove the point, while Abjorn and Uddolf and the others who had sailed *Black Eagle* nodded agreement, which did not endear them to the men of *Short Serpent*. With the few old Oathsworn, there were three crews here, not one; that would have to change, I was thinking.

There was shamefaced silence, then Crowbone opened his mouth to speak – and I used the moment. I may not have had what King Eirik thought of as jarl-greatness in me, but I had enough to know the timing of such a thing.

'While we are talking with Pallig here,' I said to Onund, 'replace the oar-strap. The rest will have to wait until we can beach her and sort it out – at which time the crew, I am thinking, will be carrying the steer-oar as if it was their own bairn.'

There were wry chuckles at that and Crowbone, furious at

being interrupted, opened and closed his mouth; I was aware, somewhere behind me, of Alyosha, watching and listening. He said nothing, for I was leader here, even if Crowbone had not realised it yet.

'I am sure Crowbone here will want you to build his next ship, Onund,' I added with a light laugh. 'When he is king in Norway. He plans to call it *Long Serpent* and make it the biggest boat in the world.'

'I will be long dead by then,' grumbled Onund and that raised a louder laugh; Crowbone's mouth was working like a dying fish, but I was spared mentioning it by the arrivals from the fortress, moving along the shingle in an ungainly half-trot.

They were ring-coated, helmed and armed with shield and spear, about a dozen led by Ljot, who wore only coloured clothing and a green, fur-trimmed cloak, so I relaxed a little, for this arrival had been the awkward moment and it seemed to have passed off well enough.

'Olaf, son of Tryggve,' he said politely, bowing to Crowbone, for he had fixed his eyes on the boy and the rest of us were just well-armed retainers, he thought. 'Welcome to Jomsburg.'

'Olaf Tryggvasson thanks you,' I said, before Crowbone could get his mouth working. 'Jarl Orm of Hestreng is come to the Joms *borg*.'

Ljot finally saw me and jerked his head to me and back to Crowbone, confused; he had seen and recognised the ship and made assumptions from that. I nodded and grinned a wolf grin at him. Finn slung his shield on his mailed back and gave a bark of laughter.

'Aye – here is your worst nightmare, Ljot,' he snarled. 'Crowbone is now one of the Oathsworn of Jarl Orm of Hestreng. We have come for our property.'

Ljot gaped and stuttered a bit, then looked at me with narrowed eyes.

'If you plan trouble here,' he began and I waved a silencing hand. Finn chuckled.

'No trouble,' I answered, 'but this is for Pallig's ears, not all these.'

Ljot glanced round at the ringmailed and gawping growlers he had at his back, Wends mostly, with a scattering of those tribal trolls who always gather round trade places. He nodded and led the way up to the *borg* proper, off the beach and tussocked grass and on to the raised half-log walkways.

I called Finnlaith over, just before I fell in behind them all.

'Keep these thieves off the ship,' I told him. 'And keep the girl hidden.'

He nodded, then scowled. 'Why we have her is not clear to me, sure,' he grunted. 'She is a strange one and no mistake.'

I had no quarrel with him on that and said so, which made him grin. Then he called up his Irishers, Ospak among them and I heard them chaffer and bang shields together, as if they had won a good fight, as we went off after Ljot.

I was glad of Finnlaith and Ospak, old Oathsworn who had arrived at Hestreng while Finn and I were with Jarl Brand. They had come 'for the raiding' and heard in Hedeby that there was trouble at Hestreng.

They had left Dyfflin some time ago and arrived on a trading *knarr* owned by someone who knew me and trusted that the half-a-dozen mad Irishers with their bearded axes and strange gabble were unlikely to cause harm to him or his cargo.

'A timely arrival,' Finnlaith had said, once beams and wrist-grips had been exchanged, 'for sure. It is a sad thing, so it is, to see Hestreng reduced to ashes.'

Then he had brightened a little and said that now that the Ui Neill had arrived, the war against those who had done it could commence and made out that he had come all the way from Dyfflin just for that.

The truth, of course, was that the Irisher lands were in flame – again – and the Ui Neill were not getting the best of it.

147

Meanwhile, the Norse in Dyfflin laughed at the Irishers quarrelling over who was king of the dungheap, when they controlled the trade and so the wealth.

'But sure,' Finnlaith had added, when he had finished bewildering me with all their names, 'we will go back presently and sort this Brian Boru lad out.'

Meanwhile, he was back with his old oarmates, enjoying the *craic* at the entrance to the Odra and thinking it a good day, even with the rain sifting down on him, because he had friends, a bearded axe slung on one shoulder, a handful of silver in a pouch under his armpit and the prow beast telling him where to go.

I envied him as we clattered over the slick walkways through the town, all smells and curious people, to where the buildings thinned until there were only a few scattered round the meadow. Mounded above it, the Joms *borg* itself squatted like a troll moody over his lost bridge.

Finn nudged me as we went, pointing out the forge and the mill – and the Christ church, where a priest, his brown robe caught up between his legs to make short, baggy breeks, worked a patch of vegetables, looking up only once at us. Most of the folk we saw, including the leather-clad guards on the gates, were Wends.

Pallig waited at the threshold of the hall, surrounded by three women; the youngest – barely a woman at all – he presented as his wife and a thumb-sucking boy he proudly announced was Toke, his son.

'No women allowed at all,' Finn whispered scornfully to me and then laughed at the lies of skalds.

I had expected a different look to Pallig, for his brother was of a good height with no belly on him and reasonable in his looks, making the most of them with his neatness. All of which made his name – Ugly – a joke. Pallig, on the other hand, was sow-snouted, bald save for a straggling fringe of dirty flax and had a paunch that trembled like a new-shelled egg yolk.

Ale was brought and bread and cheese. Crowbone sat apart, chatting animatedly to Pallig's wife and, after a scowl or two, Pallig decided that he was too young to bother with. We sat on benches and Pallig, beaming and jovial, hooked one knee over the arm of a high seat and spread his hands expansively. No-one was fooled; he and the cat-wary Ljot were ruffled by the arrival of the Oathsworn and, for all his bluster, Pallig was not sure he could handle such trouble if it came to a fight.

Still, he played a tafl game of being unconcerned.

'Welcome to my hall, Orm of Hestreng,' he announced. 'The Oathsworn fame has travelled far and wide and is almost as great as my own. It is an honour to have you here.'

Then, unable to resist it, he peered at me and gave a little laugh. 'You look a little battered – was it a rough crossing?'

I said nothing, for the high seat he was on, like a perilously perched pig, had the familiar carving on the back, of Thor arrogantly fishing for the World Serpent. He saw me look and smiled, for it had all been planned that way.

'You admire my high seat? It is very fine.'

'I know it well,' I answered. 'It belonged to Ivar Weatherhat until recently. Then my arse was on it until Ljot came to Hestreng.'

Pallig feigned surprise.

'Then you must have it back,' he declared expansively.

I shook my head and his smile wavered a little, for refusal had not been in his design. But I knew how the game was played and had shoved words around the board with better men than him.

'Keep it,' I countered. 'For Ivar had it and was burned out of all he had and I had it and enjoyed the same luck. The Norns, as they say, weave in threes. I can always get another seat.'

'Once you get another hall,' Ljot offered, with a dangerous sneer that made Pallig shoot him a hard look. I felt Finn shift a little beside me, to ease his hilt nearer his hand.

149

'Oh, that is being built,' I said lightly. 'It will be finished by the time we return to Jarl Brand with his *fostri*, the boy Koll whom your man Leo took.'

The brothers exchanged looks then, no doubt remembering – as I had intended – the Oathsworn tales of unlimited silver. Then Pallig, in an attempt to counter this unexpected move, slathered a vicious smile on his face and waved one hand. Men came forward – two of the bearcoats I had last seen sidling away to burn Hestreng, I noticed – and Styrbjorn between them. He was pale, but smiling and wore good coloured clothing and his hands were unbound, though he had no more than an eating knife on him.

'Orm Bear Slayer,' he acknowledged with a nod. Pallig watched my face and, finally, I turned into his pouched gaze.

'King Eirik would like Styrbjorn returned to him,' I said. 'He is confident you will not oppose him in this.'

Styrbjorn laughed, showing too many white teeth.

'I am sure my uncle would like me to walk into his mouth and be eaten,' he replied, 'but, as you see, I am among friends.'

Pallig said nothing and even Styrbjorn was not convinced by what he said so confidently.

'The king speaks of mercy and forgiveness,' I said. 'He will pay *weregild* to Jarl Brand for what was lost. He swears no harm will come to you.'

Styrbjorn's whole body seemed to sag a little, then he straightened, beaming.

'Well – so it is, then,' he declared to Pallig. 'A king swears it, so it must be true.'

There was silence and Styrbjorn blundered on into it, like a ram in a thicket. 'I will put myself at the mercy of my uncle and king, so bringing this affair to an end. You have my thanks, Pallig, for your hospitality.'

There was a heartbeat of silence, then Pallig broke contact with my eyes and looked at Styrbjorn, as if just noticing that he was there at all.

'I can see that you have served your purpose,' he growled. 'So now you have, it would be best if you stayed silent. Better still if you waited somewhere else for the grown men to finish their business.'

Crowbone could not stifle a snort of delight at Styrbjorn's look, which was ugly and red, tight around the eyes and mouth. He drove to his feet, clattering over the bench; the ringmailed men on either side of his shoulders clamped him with hands hard as wolf bites, so that Pallig waved them to be still.

'You forget who I am, Pallig,' Styrbjorn said, his mouth twisted and wet. 'You would do well to remember it.'

'Who are you?' Pallig challenged. 'Nephew to King Eirik, no more than that. If he wishes you back and swears not to kill you, then he is a fool – and a fool is easily parted from money. Will he pay to have you back, do you think?'

He looked at me as he spoke, but I made my face a cliff and, with a scowl, he turned back to Styrbjorn.

'You are a nithing boy, with no men and less ships and such battle luck as to attract none. Besides, the Great City has disowned you.'

Everyone was too occupied in marvelling at the colours Styrbjorn was turning in his rage to notice the real import of that last bit, but I did. While the bearcoats hauled the youth off, I pilled some bread idly and thought matters through.

Leo the monk was gone.

It came to me then that perhaps King Eirik and I and everyone else had woven the tapestry of this in the wrong colours. After a while, I asked: 'So, where did the Greek monk go, then?'

Pallig frowned for a moment, then glanced at Crowbone. He was wondering, no doubt, if tales of little Olaf's bird-magic were true and that, somehow, the monk's arrival and departure had been seen by some *seidr*-possessed crow on a branch. Crowbone grinned at him and I saw the realisation

flash in Pallig that he had been the one to give it away, like a bad move in a game of tafl.

'Gone back to the Great City,' he said, scowling. 'Down to Ostrawa and into the Magyar and Bulgar lands.'

The old Amber Road; I had not thought that trail still existed and Ljot, while his brother fumed at his slip and poured ale to cover his annoyance, explained that it was not much of one, not for boats unless they flew, nor carts. Pack horses could make it and men with small loads, so it was usually little stuff that got carried that way – amber and furs, or the cargo that carried itself, slaves.

'Small boys and monks?' asked Crowbone. Pallig managed a laugh.

'Aye, probably slaves by now, or dead. They went together and the monk hired some men – Sorbs – as guards.'

So there it was. Pallig had not been the final destination of the fleeing Leo. The little turd of a monk was heading for home, though it was unlikely he would ever reach it, as Finn pointed out.

'Sorbs,' he said and would have spat if there had been anywhere to do it without offending. Pallig cocked an un-apologetic eyebrow.

'What is this monk to me now?' he said. 'He came, he invited us to fight for Styrbjorn and he came back when all had failed. I do not expect him to return in a hurry to invite us again. He took the boy with him, thinking to use him to control Jarl Brand and through him influence King Eirik since Brand is his right arm, as everyone knows.'

He stopped and laced his hands across the trembling belly, frowning.

'This Styrbjorn business was ill-paid. It is not good to have such a stain on your fame,' he grumbled and looked at me. 'You know how it is, Jarl Orm – this is just red war and the way such matters are done. Having poor battle luck is bad for the fame at Joms.'

152

'Perhaps you will think differently, when such red war visits you one day,' I told him and watched his eyes narrow.

'Perhaps,' he said. 'I am sorry you were caught up in this and for your losses. I want no trouble from you. I will pay blood-price for what was done at Hestreng and it is this – I will permit you to leave and tell King Eirik that he can have that useless lump Styrbjorn if he offers me a fair price. Then you should go back to Hestreng, fasten the peace-strings on your hilt and be grateful the Northmen of Joms are not turning out on you.'

This was enough for Finn, who leaned forward with his face as hard and ugly and grim as a hidden rock in a sound.

'You wobbling nithing,' he began. 'All your Northmen are Wendish trolls and never saw a decent vik . . .'

Before I could act, Crowbone laid a quiet hand on Finn's arm, which made the man blink from his rage and look round. The boy shook his head and smiled; Finn subsided like a scrap-fed hound, to my amazement.

The spell of it broken, I stood up and nodded.

'As to Styrbjorn,' I said with a shrug, 'you may do as you see fit – but when we leave we will go upriver, not down.'

Ljot shook his head and Pallig made a pig-grunt of sound.

'Not good,' Ljot said, then smiled a rueful, apologetic smile. 'Look you – I know Jarl Brand's boy was taken and that he was your *fostri*, so it will sit hard with both of you. The boy is gone, all the same – almost certain dead or a slave of the Sorbs or the Wends or the Pols, which is all the same thing. That monk was a chief of the *gestir* of the Great City's emperor, but it will make no difference – those skin-wearing trolls along the river are all supposed to be Christ men, but they will kill him, just the same.'

Gestir, he had said. Well, it had been obvious enough, but it was good to have it said out loud. There are two kinds of oathed men in a king's hall. The first are the great louts, like those standing guard at Pallig's door. The second are the *gestir*,

153

clever men who can spy and make trade agreements and treaties and more. Leo the monk, it seemed, was one of them, working for the emperor in Constantinople and so a man of considerable skills – among them, I was sure, the ability to deal with skin-wearing trolls along the Odra.

'Besides,' Pallig grumbled. 'I do not want you going upriver. You will cause upset in a boat like that and interrupt the trading.'

He dipped one finger in his ale and drew a wet, wiggly line on the table.

'Here is the Odra, flowing south from the mountains beyond Ostrawa to us in the north. It is a frontier land. Here we are at the mouth of it, where are the Wends, who you call trolls and the Saxlanders call Wilzi and others call Sorbs. There are many small tribes of them, on both banks of the river, but most are subject to the Saxlanders on the west.'

He stopped and sucked his wet finger while we all peered at the wiggly line as if it were about to come alive on the table and snake along it.

'On the east bank are more Wends and Sorbs and such, but also the Pols of Miesko, who are coming north pretty fast – only last year they beat the Saxlanders at Cidini which is very close to us. Now the Saxlanders and Pols glare at each other across the river and the trade on it is a *fud*-hair away from being ruined.'

He frowned and wiped the wiggly snake away with a sweep of one hand, breaking the spell on us.

'No-one will want to see a raiding boat such as yours on the river,' he added. 'Otto's Saxlander forts on the west bank will think I sent you up to cause trouble. The east bank has Pol forts who will think the same.'

'Not that you will get that far,' added Ljot, almost beaming with the finality of it, 'for there are other tribes, who will eat you.'

No-one spoke for a long heartbeat, then Pallig cleared his throat and spread expansive arms.

'Well, there is the way of it,' he said, then beamed. 'I would not wish you to sail away from here feeling less than well-treated so I invite you and the young Prince Olaf here to be feasted in my hall tonight.'

I agreed and smiled, which was hard work on the cheek muscles since I was working against a lot of scowl. There was the arrogance of these brothers, the problem of Styrbjorn and how to free him and, worst of all, the thought of what the Polanians – the ones the brothers scornfully called 'Pols' – would do if they found the Mazur girl they thought safely hostaged in a foreign land with the daughter of their king.

Not for the first time, I wondered what Vuokko had seen in his drum later on that feast night for the return of Eirik's bairn. The Sea Finn had appeared out of the shadows like some nightmare, just as Finn and I were picking our way in the salt-tanged dark to see Jarl Brand.

'I have called it and the drum has spoken,' he told us in his rheum-thick accent. 'It says to take the Mazur girl.'

With three runes to speak with it might have said more, but I had gone to Sigrith in the night, half-ashamed at doing it just because of the Sea Finn's drum, and asked her to let me have Blackbird, whose real name was Dark Eye. She, even knowing the worth of the girl to her father and where I was headed, did so, as she said, 'for the loss of her Birthing Stool'.

Now Blackbird was stowed like baggage on *Short Serpent* and as nagging as a broken nail in my mind as we clumped back down to the ship, where Finnlaith and Alyosha were growling at men to get them loading supplies.

They crowded round, wanting to hear what had been said and by whom, so I laid it out for them.

'Take these Joms bladders now,' growled a big Swede called Asfast when I finished.

'Burn them,' snarled Abjorn, 'as Ljot burned Hestreng.'

155

'Ljot did not burn Hestreng,' Rorik Stari pointed out. 'It was Randr Sterki who did that.'

There were rumbles for and against charging up and cutting them down, calls for blood and fire. There were also growls about going upriver at all, for there was little in it that raiding men could see.

So I put them on the straight course of that simply enough.

'There are two matters that must be done,' I told them. 'One is to free Styrbjorn, for King Eirik's sake.'

Finn grunted, but said nothing, for only he and I knew that it was also to kill him, for Jarl Brand's sake, though neither he nor I had worked out a way to make a square out of that circle.

'I am also going after my *fostri*,' I added, 'for it is my honour and good name here. You may follow if you choose, but will break your Oath if you do not. The only other way is for one of you to become jarl.'

That silenced them, so much so that I was sure they could all hear the bird-fluttering beating of my heart at the idea of one of them challenging me for the dragon-torc of jarl. Fame, that double-edged sword, held them at arm's length, for this was Orm, single-handed slayer of white bears, killer of scaled trolls, who had once won a *holmgang* with a single stroke and only recently had fought and killed berserkers, two at a time.

Yet they were sullen about it and a broad-faced growler called Gudmund could not let the bone of it loose.

'Pallig does not want us to go upriver,' he offered moodily.

'So?' spat Red Njal, fanning the flames of it. 'Who is Pallig Tokeson to tell the Oathsworn of Orm Bear Slayer where they can go or not?'

'He is kin to Harald Bluetooth,' Crowbone offered brightly. 'The wife he took pains to introduce us to is Bluetooth's daughter and the sister of the Svein who was at King Eirik's feast.'

He stared into the astonished faces, then innocently up into mine and I knew now what he had been doing, while seeming to play the eyelash-batting boy with the womenfolk.

Bluetooth was not a name you ignored lightly, as Gudmund persisted. Finn spat and pointed out that we had been ignoring Bluetooth for years, had stolen his ships and killed his men and were none the worse for it, which cheered everyone, for they knew we were going upriver, no matter what.

Then Onund cleared his throat, which he always did before he said something important and we all stopped, thinking it would be ship talk and being as wrong as a two-headed cow.

'If it is such a bad thing to be going upriver, for the trouble it will cause the brothers of Joms,' he rumbled thoughtfully, 'I am wondering why they let Randr Sterki and his dogs go up?'

TEN

Having hurled the axe of that into the middle of us, the hunchback laid out the saga of how he had found out about Randr. While we spoke with Pallig, he had gone off to find decent wood to fix the steerboard and quickly found an entire steerboard, in good condition, which he thought was ship-luck.

A few traders further on, as he looked for just the right cut of ash wood to make an elk prow for the ship – Crowbone shifted and scowled at that part of his tale – he had found good nails and ready-cut ship planks, far better quality than he would have expected in a place such as Joms. Then a trader said it would be better to have a whole prow rather than go the trouble of carving one and showed Onund one he had.

'So I asked him where he had it from,' Onund told us. 'I had to be firm with him, too, for he was reluctant. I picked him up by the heel and hung him for a while until he spoke and we concluded the business. I was pleased to have done it with no violence.'

That got him chuckles and I wished there was no feasting that night, for I wanted to be away as fast as supplies could be loaded, if for no other reason than to avoid the results of Onund's firmness with a trader.

In the end, Onund was shown the source of the snarling dragon prow he knew well – we all knew well. On the far side from the settlement, wallowing half-in, half-out of the weak Baltic tideline, stripped to the ribs and the keel and the charred strakes no-one wanted, was what was left of *Dragon Wings*.

'We should go to Pallig and his brother,' Finn growled after this news was out, 'and use your little truth knife on them.'

Those who knew of the truth knife, which whittled off body parts until the victim stopped lying, agreed with relish and I felt the little, worn-handled blade burn where it nested in the small of my back. It had belonged to Einar the Black once and had served me as well as it had him, but there was no need for it now.

'Randr Sterki had ship-luck to make it this far,' I pointed out. 'He would be coming to have it out with Ljot for leaving him and I bet he had more men bailing than rowing by the time he ran *Dragon Wings* ashore here.'

They nodded and growled assent to that.

'What of the hoard they had from you?' demanded Finn of Onund and the hunchback shrugged, a frightening affair

'If he did not take it with him, then it is scattered through the settlement,' he answered. 'And so lost to you, Orm – these *rann-sack* pigs took every last rivet from the wreck.'

There would be no hoard found, I was bitter-sure, for Randr would have used some of it to buy supplies and one of those tree-carved riverboats. The rest would be either with him or buried secretly and I had no doubt a deal of it went to Pallig, for no balm soothes like silver.

'Why is he going upriver at all?' Finn had asked. That one was easier still; to get Koll and the monk. The monk, in Randr Sterki's hate-splintered eye, either owed money or blood or both and the boy was my *fostri*. He would want the boy alive, would know I was coming after him with Crowbone. All his enemies, sailing straight towards the revenge he was not yet done with.

'He did not take the lesson from your last story,' I said to Crowbone and he shrugged.

'I will tell him a harder one, then,' he growled back and everyone laughed at his new, deep voice, so that his cheeks flushed. He looked at me, those odd eyes glittering like agate.

'I have a thought on how to get Styrbjorn away,' he said, then inclined his head in a gracious little bow.

'If my lord is pleased to hear it,' he added and folk chuckled. I heard Finn mutter, though, and did not need to hear it clearly to know what he was saying: that boy is older than stones.

'A prince's wisdom is always welcome,' I said and he grinned his sharp-toothed mouse grin and then laid it out. It was a good plan, put him at the centre of matters and at no little risk – which was what the fame-hungry little wolf cub wanted – and gave the skill and strength of it to Finn. I looked at Finn after Crowbone had finished.

'Can you do this?'

Finn's grin was the same one seen an instant before fangs closed on a kill and folk chuckled at so eloquent an answer with not a word spoken.

It seemed less of a good plan in the flickering red roar of Pallig's feasting. He sat on my high seat flanked by two big men in ringmail and helms who scowled at having to miss the best of the feast because of this duty. Pallig beamed greasily while his men growled and gorged and threw bones at one another, or grabbed the female thralls who stumbled in with platters of mutton boiled outside in a stone-lined pit heated by rocks.

I sat on a bench directly across the pitfire from Pallig, horn-paired with Crowbone for the feasting. None of my own men were here and Pallig knew why – they were with the ship, pointedly kept there because I did not trust him. I had already noted that, while Pallig's women were clustered round him, there was no sign of Ljot, nor of the two bearcoats, last of the beasts, it seemed. Styrbjorn, his mouth in a thin, tight

160

line, sat clenched in on himself on a lower bench and far enough away from the door that he could not make a run for it if he chose.

A skald had been wintering here, a man with a lean face and a body thin as gruel. His name was Helgi and he claimed the by-name of Mannvitsbrekka – Wisdom-Slope – though it was clear any deep thinking he had was long since slid away, for he persisted in trotting out the same old stuff he had most likely been giving them for months. Even the commands of Pallig failed to stop men deep in their ale from flinging bread and bone at him.

Crowbone looked at me with his odd eyes and grinned his mouse grin. Then he stood up.

'I have a tale or two,' he said.

Silence fell almost at once, for the marvellous tales of this man-boy were fame-richer than my own supposed heroics. Graciously, Pallig waved a hand for him to continue.

Crowbone told tales of Dyl U'la-Spegill, which was perfect for the audience he had. They were old tales and still told today, for the laughter in them. Dyl U'la-Spegill is sometimes a youth, sometimes an old man and his very name is as much a whispered mystery as runes; there were those present, I saw, who fancied Crowbone was Dyl U'la-Spegill himself and I could not have refuted it if asked, for he held them as if enchanted.

'Once,' Crowbone said into the silence, 'there was a man down on his luck – we shall call him Ljot – who was given a piece of bread. Hoping this was a sign from Asgard's finest, he went to the market stalls and begged, thinking some meat or a little fish would go well with his bread. They all turned him away with nothing, but Ljot saw a large kettle of soup cooking over the fire. He held his piece of bread over the steaming pot, hoping to thus capture a bit of flavour from the good-smelling vapour.'

Folk chuckled – those, I was thinking, who knew how it felt to be that hungry. Pallig glared them to silence.

'Suddenly the owner of the soup – let us call him Brand – seized the unhappy Ljot by the arm and accused him of stealing soup,' Crowbone continued. 'Poor Ljot was afraid at this. "I took no soup," he said. "I was only smelling it." "Then you must pay for the smell," answered Brand. Poor Ljot had no money, so the angry Brand dragged him before his jarl.'

'Is that where Ljot has gone, then?' shouted someone and I knew Finn's voice when I heard it. Pallig snarled a smile into the laughter that followed and Crowbone went on with his tale.

'Now,' he said, 'it so happened that Dyl U'la-Spegill was visiting with this jarl at the time and he heard Brand's accusation and Ljot's explanation. "So you demand payment for the smell of your soup?" he asked as the jarl struggled to come to a decision on the matter.

'"I do," insisted Brand.

'"Then I myself will pay you," said Dyl and he drew two silver rings from his arm and juggled them in his hand so that they rang – then he put them back, much to Brand's annoyance.

'"You are paid," Dyl told the man. "The sound of silver for the smell of soup."'

They laughed and thumped the tables at that one and, hidden by the noise and uproar, Finn slid to my side briefly and nodded, then rolled his shoulders.

'They will choose the bearcoat called Stammkel, the one they call Hilditonn – War Tooth,' he said quietly to me. I did not ask him if this would be a problem.

'Once,' Crowbone began again, 'Dyl U'la-Spegill lay in the shade of an ancient oak tree, thinking as he always did, on the greatness of the gods and the mightiness of Odin.'

There was a loud throat-clearing sound from down the table, where the Christ priest sat and, for a moment, all heads turned to him, so that he flushed at being the centre of such attention.

162

'God will not be mocked,' he offered and Crowbone shrugged.

'Then let him sit elsewhere,' he replied, which brought laughter – though muted, for there were more than a few Christ men here. Pallig craned a little to look down the benches at the priest, who drew in his neck a little and, after a pause, the jarl turned his poached-egg eyes back to Crowbone and beamed.

'Go on, little man,' he said expansively, 'for this is better stuff than we have had for some time.'

At which the skald scowled.

'Dyl,' Crowbone began, 'considered the wisdom of Odin – and then questioned whether it was indeed wise that such a great tree as this be created to bear only tiny acorns. Look at the stout stem and strong limbs, which could easily carry, say, fat marrows that sprout from spindly stems along the ground. Should the mighty oak not bear such as a marrow and the acorn creep in the mud?'

'I have often thought so myself,' the skald interrupted desperately, but voices howled him down.

'So thinking,' Crowbone continued, 'Dyl went to sleep – only to be awakened by an acorn that fell from the tree, striking him on his forehead. "Aha," he cried. "Now I see the wisdom of One-Eye – if the world had been created according to Dyl U'la-Spegill, I would have been marrow-killed for sure."'

Crowbone paused and stared at the priest.

'Never again did Dyl U'la-Spegill question the wisdom of Odin,' he finished and the hall banged tables and hooted; a few bones flew at the priest – in a good-natured way and Pallig stood and held up his hands for silence, planning no doubt to lay into them for treating the priest so poorly. Just as the wobbling-bellied jarl opened his mouth to the silence, he broke wind noisily.

Folk sniggered and Pallig went white, then red. Crowbone cleared his throat a little and spoke into the embarrassment.

'There was once a jarl who farted dishonour to himself forever,' he began and Pallig's face had thunder on it – but there were enough drunks in the hall to cheer stupidly at another Crowbone tale, so he sat back down, silent and dangerously black-browed.

'It was at his own wedding,' Crowbone went on. 'The bride was displayed in all her gold to the women, who could not take their eyes off her for the jealousy. At last the bridegroom was summoned to stand by her side, while the *godi* stood ready with his blessing hammer.'

At this point, the priest stood up and made the sign of the cross and there were as many who joined in as those who hooted. Say what you like about Christ priests, say they are as annoying as a cleg-bite in summer, say they have minds so narrow it is a wonder anything can live there – but never say they are afraid. I seldom encountered one who had no courage.

Crowbone favoured him with a look until the priest had finished and was sitting. Then he cleared his throat and went on with his tale.

'The jarl rose slowly and with dignity from his bench,' he said and then paused, looking round the breathless company.

'In so doing,' he went on portentously, 'he let fly a great and terrible fart, for he was overfull of meat and drink. It was a Thor-wind, that one, a mighty cracking.'

'I think I know this jarl,' shouted someone, anonymous in the dark and Pallig shifted in his seat a little, then braided his scowl into an uneasy smile. Crowbone waited a little, then went on.

'Of course, it was a great insult to the bride and her kin and, in fear of blood-feud and the ruin of a good day and dowry, all the guests immediately turned to their neighbours and talked aloud, pretending to have heard nothing.

'The mortified jarl, in that instant, was so overcome by shame that he turned away from the bridal chamber and as if to answer a call of nature. He went down to the courtyard,

164

saddled his mare and rode off, weeping bitterly through the night. In time he reached Dovrefell, went on across it to the very snows, where he sacrificed the horse and lived among the Sami for years.'

'Safe enough there,' observed a growler morosely, 'since they are all expert breakers of wind in that country.'

He was hissed to silence and Crowbone went on with his tale.

'Finally, this unlucky jarl was overcome with longing for his native land – like that of a lover pining for his beloved it would not be denied, though it nearly cost him his life. He sneaked away from the Sami without taking leave and made his way alone and dressed in the rags of a seer, enduring a thousand hardships of hunger, thirst and fatigue, braving a thousand dangers from trolls and wyrm and *draugr*. He eventually came to his old home and, eyes brimming with tears, walked among the houses of it, unknown, pretending to be an old seer of no account.'

Crowbone paused; there was not a breath of sound.

'He was delighted with being home,' he went on, 'thought of announcing himself and abjectly grovelling in apology for his foolishness in running away for so trivial a reason, no doubt forgotten a day or two after it had happened. Just as he had made up his mind to do just that, he passed a hut and heard the voice of a young girl saying, "Mother, tell me what day was I born on, for there is an old seer outside and I want him to tell my fortune."

'The mother did not hesitate. "My daughter," she said, "you were born on the very night the old jarl farted." No sooner had the jarl heard these words than he rose up from the bench and fled for the last time, for his fart was now a date that would be remembered for ever and ever.'

The laughter was long, though Pallig had to force his out. For all that, he peeled off an armring and tossed it regally to the young Crowbone, who caught it deftly. The skald's

165

head drooped like a wilting stalk, seeing his own riches melt from him.

'Good tales, well told,' he announced. 'If you continue the same way, I will give you the one off my other arm.'

Crowbone laughed, then looked sideways at me a moment and I nodded.

'I have no more tales of momentous farts,' he said to the assembled company; a few of them groaned in mock disappointment and Crowbone held up one hand with the ring in it.

'I could tell of Thor fishing for the World Serpent,' he said slowly, looking pointedly at Pallig, whose back rested on that very carving. He shifted nervously and caught my eye – I hoped my old high seat dug splinters in him.

'On the other hand,' Crowbone went on slowly, 'tales of strength like that are best witnessed at first hand. Happily, we have one of the Oathsworn here with such Thor strength.'

On cue, Finn stood up and spread his arms wide as if to embrace them all, turning left and right and into as many jeers as cheers – though the jeers were muted, for most had heard of Finn's fame.

'I am Finn Horsehead from Skane,' he declared, jutting out his badger-beard. 'When I fart, walls tumble. Dragons use my pizzle to perch like birds on a branch.'

I watched Pallig, saw his eyes slide to one side and jerk his chin at a thrall, who immediately got up and went outside. Now comes the hard bit, I thought.

'So – a feat of strength, then, Finn Horsehead,' Pallig declared, grinning in a twisted way, vicious as a rat in a barrel. 'Arm wrestling perhaps?'

'With you, Jarl Pallig?' Finn asked and managed to put enough sneer in that to make Pallig flush and start half out of his seat. Then he subsided and worked a smile back to his face.

'My champion,' he announced and, as if magicked up, the man himself came into the hall, bringing all the heads round. Breath hung, suspended and frozen.

He was ring-coated, of course, with a helm worked in silver and he had to duck coming under the lintel. With him came a long axe, mark of a Chosen Man of the jarl's retinue and he carried it as easily as a child does a stick.

'Stammkel War Tooth,' Pallig announced and the hall rang with cheers from all his oarmates. Pallig looked at the great flat, stolid face of Stammkel, framed by a wild tangle of ribbon-tied beard like flame and the fancy helmet he wore, all silver and dented iron.

'This is Finn Horsehead of the Oathsworn,' Pallig went on. 'He wishes to arm wrestle you.'

Stammkel grunted and peeled off his helmet, so that a great shock of red hair sprang up like a bush. Finn regarded him up and down, then turned back to Pallig.

'Some mistake, surely,' he said. 'Is the father not available?'

The hall liked that and showed it with catcalls and table thumping. Stammkel may have glowered and narrowed his eyes, but it was hard to tell in that face. His voice was clear enough, all the same.

'Arm wrestling is hardly a fair contest with this one,' he rumbled, then stared straight at Finn out of the red tangle of his face. 'I would kiss one of Odin's Daughters with him, but I fancy he would be afraid of her lip.'

I felt my bowels drop, for this had not been the plan; Finn did not so much as blink. Into the silence that followed came the sound of Pallig clearing his throat.

'So be it,' he said – then I forced myself to stand, for it was always best to keep moving forward, even if your plan was askew. Pallig looked at me in some confusion.

'A wager,' I said lightly, 'to make matters more entertaining.'

The hall growled and hoomed and thumped tables in agreement, so that Pallig had to agree, though he did not like it

much, beginning to see a trap and not yet sure where to put his feet to avoid it. Too late, I was thinking – and sprang it.

'Him,' I said, pointing to Styrbjorn, 'when Finn wins.'

Pallig, too late to back out of it, looked from the sullen youth to me and back again. Then he stared at Stammkel, the great long axe clutched like a honeycomb in a bear's paw. Finally, he smiled and settled back in my old high seat.

'What will be my reward, then, when your man loses?' he demanded and I tried not to hesitate, or draw in a breath as I laid a hand on the jarl torc round my neck. Scarred, notched, it was a mere twelve ounces of braided silver – burned silver, which meant that it had been skimmed of impurities when molten – yet it was the mark of a jarl and, moreover, of Jarl Orm of the Oathsworn. A prize I knew Pallig could not resist; I was right, for he licked his lips and demanded that they bring Odin's Daughter into the hall.

A Chosen Man carried it in, after a moment or two of delay which, I worked out, was involved in blowing the dust and cobwebs off her for she had not been used in a time and the reason for that sat in a brown robe, scowling disapproval from under his tonsure.

The Chosen Man laid her on a bench; folk drew back in a ring and Odin's Daughter lay there, smiling, gleaming, naked and ornate.

It was a *blot* axe, a great heavy single-bit, worked with intricate knot-patterns, skeined with silver and gold. Such axes are never used for fighting – they are over heavy and ornamented for that work – only in sacrifices to Odin, hence the name. You can put such an axe head on any shaft you prefer and most are the length of a man's arm from fingertip to elbow, easy for a *godi* to handle without making a mess of the work.

Odin's Daughters, they call them, only half in jest, for Odin's daughters are the Valkyrii, which translates as Choosers of the Slain and so also were these axes, some of them named. This had no name, but was a slender and tall daughter of

168

Odin lying on the table for all that. Four times the length of a man's arm from fingertip to elbow and thick as a boy's wrist, this long axe was seldom used for sacrifice work in these Christ days, but was still the mark of the Jomsviking jarls and carried by a Chosen Man, to be raised aloft in the heat and dust of battle to show that the jarl still stood fast. There was only one other more powerful than this and that had belonged to Eirik Bloodaxe of Jorvik – but that was lost when he went under treacherous enemy blades.

Pallig wobbled out of his chair, holding up a length of red silk ribbon for everyone to see, then fastened it round the rune-skeined shaft, a forearm's length from the bottom. He stood back and raised his arms.

'Who wishes the first kiss?' he demanded and Finn, rolling his neck and shoulders, looked at the impassive Stammkel, grunted and moved forward to take up the smooth, polished ash length in both hands.

Men drew further back as Finn then stepped up onto a bench and moved to the end of the table. It shifted slightly and Crowbone, being nearest, leaned forward on the other end, to keep it from tilting – a brave move, since it put him danger-close to the affair. Everyone else, I saw, had drawn far back and Pallig had moved swiftly back to the high seat.

Perched on the edge of the table like a bird – to add balance to strength and prevent any excessive bending to compensate for lack of wrist power – Finn took a breath or two and hefted the axe to feel the weight of it. I caught his eye, then, across the heads and down the length of the table and he flicked a grin through the great beard of his face.

He took the shaft, just below where the ribbon was tied and raised it in both hands, arms outstretched and locked at the elbow. Then he raised it higher and began tilting it down to his upturned face, blade first, until, with hardly a tremor at all, the power of his wrists lowered the razor edge of it to his lips.

There were a few cheers as he did so, then he leaped off the table and offered the shaft to Stammkel. He took it, climbed onto the creaking table and did the same; men roared and thumped on wood as Pallig stepped forward and, careful to let everyone see, lowered the ribbon by a hand-span.

That is kissing Odin's Daughter. Each time the ribbon creeps to the end of the shaft, the axehead grows heavier and harder to control. Drunks or fools do this at feasts with ordinary long axes and rarely come out of it without scars, or bits of nose and lip missing.

The silence grew with each soft slither of the ribbon down the shaft until, at last, there was no room to grip with both hands and everyone held their breath, for this was where it started to get interesting and desperate. I was sweating, now, for I had seen Stammkel at work and he and Finn were like a pair of plough oxen, perfectly matched and moving in step. I was no longer as sure as I had been when we had made this plan based on Finn's arm-wrestling skills.

Finn took the axe in his right hand and, with a look left and right at the pale, upturned faces gleaming in the red-dyed dark, he raised the one arm and slowly, slowly, tilted the axe head down. Sweat gleamed on his forehead, I saw – but the blade touched his lips, no more. There were no cheers, simply the exhaling of held breath, like a wind through trees.

Stammkel stepped up, hefted the axe and the flame-beard of him split in a grin that curdled the bowels in me. I knew he would do it and with ease – the great roar that went up when he did made the rafters shake and I saw Pallig settle back in my high seat, stroking his thin beard and smiling.

The way it worked now, of course, was that the pair kept doing it until exhaustion set in and a wrist failed. Finn had other ideas and he winked at me, that old Botolf wink that dried all the spit in my mouth.

Then he climbed on to the table and took Odin's Daughter in his hand. His left hand; folk made soft mutterings, like

moths searching in the dark. A fighting man was almost always right-handed and that was his strong hand – Finn had raised the stakes.

He lifted the long shaft until the pitfire gleam slid carefully along the winking edge of it, then slowly lowered it to his face, turned like a petal to rain, like a child to a mother. I saw it waver, just once and had to clench hard to keep my bladder in check. Then he kissed it – a harder kiss than before, perhaps, but not hard enough to draw blood.

There were a few cheers at this, for even Pallig's men knew skill and strength when they saw it and Finn dropped to the beaten-earth floor of the hall and offered the axe back to Stammkel, his face impassive as a wrecking reef.

The big warrior took it, scowling – was that uncertainty in his eye? I grasped at that straw as I watched him climb on to the table edge and take the axe in his left hand. He hefted it for a moment or two and frowned – my heart gave a great leap at that. He was unsure; he did not have the strength of wrist in his left!

Finn thought so and grinned up at him, trying to add to the pressure. Hesitant, uneasy, Stammkel raised the axe high – and it wavered. Folk who saw it groaned and Finn's grin widened, so that Stammkel saw it.

Then, to my horror, the red beard opened in a laugh. Stammkel raised the axe higher still, tilted it and brought it smoothly down, kissed it lingering and gentle, then straightened and lowered it to the floor.

'You should know, wee man,' he said to Finn, 'that I fight with two bearded axes, one in either hand, for the fun in it.'

The roars and howls and thumping took a long time to subside, by which time I was slumped like an empty winebag; I saw Pallig look at me and the triumph was greasy on his face.

I saw Finn's face, too and was more afraid of that, for it had turned granite hard, with all the laughing in it that a

cliff has. He took the axe from Stammkel and paused. Then he swept up the other one, Stammkel's own long-axe, and leaped onto the table end.

My heart was hammering so hard I was sure those nearest could hear it. Finn stretched his arms out, an axe in both hands – and one heavier than the other, which made matters nigh impossible, I was thinking – then looked down at Stammkel, whose face showed only mild interest and appreciation.

'A good kiss needs two lips,' he said and raised the axes high.

I hoped the skald was watching, for if anything the Oathsworn ever did deserved a good saga-tale then Finn's kissing of both Daughters at once was one. He brought them down and I had to grind my teeth to keep from crying out when the left one – Stammkel's own axe – wavered left and right. Then it settled and both Odin's Daughters, delicate as maidens should be, kissed Finn's lips.

Now there was uproar. I found myself bawling out myself, all dignity lost as Finn dropped lightly to the floor and grounded the butts of both axes.

Stammkel – give that warrior his due – nodded once or twice as the uproar subsided, for folk knew legend-making when they witnessed it and none wanted to miss the word-play in it.

'You kiss well,' Stammkel said, 'for a boy. Here – let me show you how such matters are done when a man is involved.'

He was bordering on arrogance, so much so that I fretted. He could not match this, surely? No sane man would try.

Yet I knew, from the moment he measured the different weights with little bounces of his wrists, that he would do it. The cold stone of that settled like ballast in my belly – where did we go from here?

Crowbone knew it, too. I only realised that when I saw his blond head come up as Stammkel raised the axes high and the hall began to ring with the rhythmic thumping of fist

and ale cup to the sound of his soft-shouted name – Stamm-kel, Stamm-kel, Stamm-kel.

It was at the point where he started to shift the axes to his face that Crowbone sat up a little straighter – no more than that, as if to see better, as if craning in a boy's eagerness to witness this supreme feat of strength and skill.

The weight came off the table and it trembled a little, dipped slightly under Stammkel's bulk. Stammkel wobbled. The right-hand axe, the true Odin's Daughter, wavered. He almost recovered it, but it was lost – the harsh, unforgiving, ornate weight dragged it down and, with a sharp cry, Stammkel jerked his head to one side and sprang down in a clatter of falling axes. Blood showed on his face.

Finn was at his side in a blink, looked, raised a hand and smeared the blood from the man's stricken cheek. Then he grinned and clapped Stammkel on the shoulder.

'Aye,' he said. 'A nice cheek scar. A name-wound, that.'

Stammkel looked at Pallig's thunderous scowl. Then he looked across at Crowbone and my heart fluttered like a mad, trapped bird. Finally, he looked into Finn's beaming face and I waited for the accusations, the fury, the blood that would flow. I groaned – this was not how it was supposed to be.

Instead, to my shock, I saw Stammkel nod once or twice, as if settling something to himself.

'Next time, Finn Horsehead,' he said and I saw Finn's eyes narrow – then realised he had not seen what Crowbone had done, saw also that Stammkel knew this, too.

I wiped it from me as I stepped forward and looked hard at Pallig, then at the hunched figure of Styrbjorn, blinking stupidly.

'Mine,' I said and waved the youth to my side. He came, rat-swift and too stunned to even offer pretence of dignity.

'Good contest,' I said to Stammkel and dared not look him in the eye – but Crowbone, the cursed little monster, smiled so sweetly at him I felt I had to bundle him away before even Stammkel cracked.

Outside, in the cool of a night-wind washed with the promise of rain and the smell of wrack and salt, we moved steadily away from the hall, down towards the shore and the rest of the crew. My back creeped; I could hear the mutterings and feel the heat of hate on it from the hall we left, but I would not turn round to see.

'That went well,' Crowbone offered, his voice moon-bright in the dim.

'Shut your hole,' I growled at him, which brought me a puzzled look from Finn, but he was too occupied in carrying the torch that lit our way and herding the stumbling Styrbjorn, who had recovered himself a little and was beginning to make whining noises about his treatment and who he was.

'Did you think simply to leave here?'

The voice was a thin sliver out of the dark and we came to a halt at the sound of it. Then Ljot loomed and, behind him, a handful of figures, dark with ringmail and intent. One, I recognised with sag of my knees, was the last bearcoat.

'I have imposed on your hospitality too much,' I managed and Ljot's smile was a stain on his face.

'I was told not to allow you to go upriver,' he went on gently and the soft snake-hiss of his sword coming out of the sheath was sibilant in the shadows. 'Now I will also relieve you of the burden of Styrbjorn. I am surprised that you thought you could get away so easily, Orm of the Oathsworn. There is too much arrogance in that.'

I nodded to Finn, who raised the torch even higher, as if to see better.

'Not arrogance,' I answered into the planes and shadows of his flickering face and jerked my chin. 'Planning.'

The shink-shink sound of ringmail made him half-whirl, then back to me.

'Is that an escort you are having there, Jarl Orm?' called a familiar voice. 'Or do we have to axe off their heads and piss down their necks?'

174

I looked at Ljot, his lip-licking face pale under the ornate helm and horsehair plume.

'Your choice,' I said easily. 'What answer do I give Ospak and the rest of the Oathsworn?'

I was so sure of Ljot I was already starting to move round him, sure that he did not have the balls to do this. Bearcoats, though – you should never depend on those mouth-frothers for anything sane.

This one had a head full of fire and howling wolves, for he brought them all out in a hoiking mourn of sound that made me jerk back. Then he flew at the pack of us.

Out of the side of one eye I spotted Finn, hauling his Roman nail from his boot with a wide-mouthed snarling curse while, beyond him, Styrbjorn dived for the shadows and rolled away. Out of the other, I saw Crowbone leaping sideways, fumbling for the only weapon he had, an eating knife.

Ahead, though, was only the great descending darkness of the bulked bearcoat, rank with the stink of sweat and ale and badly-cured wolfpelt. Too slow to move, or reach for the eating knife at my belt, I was caught by him, but his wolf-mad eagerness undid him, for he crashed into me, too close to swing the great notched blade he had.

I clutched at him and we went over, crashing to the ground hard enough to make us both grunt and to drive the wind from me. He scrabbled like a mad beast to get away and stand, find room to start swinging, but I was remembering the fight between Hring and the berserker Pinleg, when the latter had gone frothing mad and chopped the luckless Hring into bloody pats; I clung to this bearcoat's skin like a sliding cat on a tree trunk.

He roared and beat me with the pommel end, each blow wild, so that I felt the crash of it on my shoulder, then one that rang stars into me and scraped the skin down my face. I tasted blood and knew the end was on me, for I could not hang on any longer.

Light burst in me at the next blow and my head seemed far away and filled with fire and ice. Then something rose up from the depths, a dark and cold and slimed something; for all I knew it well, Brother John's dark Abyss, I opened myself like lovers' legs to it, licked the fear and fire of it. Polite, that feral snarl of a place, it asked me at the last, winking on the brim of dark madness.

'Yes,' I heard myself say and opened my eyes to where the pallid pulse of the bearcoat's throbbing throat nestled against my chin. I felt the harsh kiss of his beard on my lips.

Then I opened my mouth and savaged him.

They peeled me from the dead man not long after, but I knew nothing of it. Ljot was dead, with Finn's Roman nail in his eye and the rest of his men were slashed bloody and pillaged swiftly, for the uproar had caused the rest of the hall to spill out like disturbed bees.

It was the sight of me chewing the throat out of a berserker that had done it, Finn claimed later to the awe-struck Oathsworn. Ljot and his men had hesitated on the spot at seeing that, so killing them had been simple. Then we had all run for the ship and the river, Styrbjorn included.

I knew nothing of it for a long time, only that my body ached and my head thundered and I felt sick and slathered inside. I had felt the toad-lick of the berserk once before, when I had fought Gudlief's son after he had killed Rurik at Sarkel; I had lost the fingers off my left hand without even knowing it.

At least then I had fought decently with sword and shield and put the madness of it down to excessive grief, for I had thought Rurik my father until he told me the truth two heart-beats before he went to Valholl.

This time, though, there had only been the dark madness and the small-bird pulse of his throat, the taste of his blood in my mouth and the flood of his fear when he knew he would die.

I had enjoyed it.

ELEVEN

Perched as high as he could get, arms wrapped lovingly round the prow beast, Red Njal peered out ahead, looking for the ripple of water that told of hidden snags. He did not try and speak, for the wind took words and shredded them, as it flattened his clothes to his ribs and whipped his hair and beard, so that it looked as if it grew out of one side of his head only.

The oars bowed, the crew grunted with effort, eyes fixed on the stroke men – no-one beat time, like they did on Arab and Greek ships; what would be the point in sneaking up on a *strandhogg* raid while hammering a drum?

We were not silent, all the same. *Short Serpent* crabbed, rattling and creaking, up the wide river, which was stippled by that chill lout of a wind, bulling over the floodplain like a rutting elk, sweeping and swirling down the river, crashing through the fringing of trees on both banks.

I stood on the mastfish and smiled and grinned at the rowers, who had stowed their ringmail; half of them were naked to the waist and sweating hard despite that wind and because of it, too – it circled and beat sometimes on the steerboard, sometimes running into the teeth of the prow beast. The wind and the current meant hard work at the oars.

'We should lay up and wait for the wind to change,'

Crowbone said in his cracked bell of a voice, hunched into his white cloak. I had no doubt that was what he would have done and had the men thank him for it and toast his name in the ale he would no doubt have broken out. Truth was, I would have done it myself if he had not mentioned it, but now he had and so I ignored it – and that made me irritated at myself.

'We stop when I say,' I answered shortly and, after a pause, the white-swathed figure stumbled to where he could sit and brood. I glanced at him briefly as he went and caught the eye of Alyosha, watching as always; he irritated me also.

'Something to say, Alyosha?'

He raised his hands in mock surrender and grinned.

'Not me,' he said. 'I am charged by Prince Vladimir to watch the little man and see he comes to no harm. There is no part in that which tells me to interfere when he is being taught the ways of the real world. He took the Oath like everyone else, save me and Styrbjorn, and now he must settle with it.'

I eased a little, half-ashamed at myself for being twitched as a flea-bitten dog. Crowbone had held to his promise at King Eirik's feast and the whole crew with him, not a few bewildered to be taking such a binding Oath, but all of them awed by the fact that, having done so, they were now part of the fame that was the Oathsworn.

As *godi*, I did what was expected with an expensive ram and the whole business was done properly and drenched in blood – much to the annoyance of the competing Christ priests and King Eirik's embarrassment at having such a ritual done in front of them.

We swear to be brothers to each other, bone, blood and steel, on Gungnir, Odin's spear we swear, may he curse us to the Nine Realms and beyond if we break this faith, one to another.

Simple enough for a mouse-brain to remember and harder to break than any chains, even the one that bound Loki's cursed

son, the devouring wolf Fenrir. Yet two handfuls of Odin oath-words were stronger.

At the time, Finn growled and grumbled at the business, certain that Crowbone would get someone from his crew to challenge me for jarlship of the Oathsworn and try to take over. He and Hlenni Brimill, Red Njal and others started taking bets on who it would be, the favourites being Alyosha and the half-sized, black-haired Yan, by-named Alf because, it was said, he was so fast in his movements that you only ever saw him flicker out of the corner of your eye, like one of the *alfir*.

Yet, that day, the day I thrust the challenge into all their faces, the memory of my mouth clotted with the throat of a berserker was still young and no-one had stepped forward; now the bets were all off.

Alyosha had told me straight away that he would not take the Oath, for he was service-bound to Vladimir and, besides, his gods were proper Slav ones. Yet he would come with us, for he was charged with looking after Crowbone – and, truth was, half the crew who sailed with Crowbone only did so because they knew Alyosha guided Crowbone.

Crowbone's men were all free Svears who had fought for King Eirik until released to find blade work with Vladimir. They had followed Crowbone for the plunder in it – and because Alyosha was there to make the sensible decisions – and thought there would be buckets of silver now that they were in the famed Oathsworn of Orm Bear Slayer.

Styrbjorn, of course, had not been given the offer to take the Oath – and was now dragged along with us whether he liked it or not; it was clear he did not like it at all.

'You can stay in Joms,' I had said to his scowl, 'but Pallig may not be as friendly as before and may work out that keeping you as a hostage is a waste of food and ale; Eirik might be daft enough to pay to have you back, but Pallig may not have the patience for it. You are safer with us – unless, of course, you trip over that petted lip and fall in the water.'

Finn, of course, had not been able to suppress a look and laugh at that, for he knew the truth of why we had rescued Styrbjorn and only wondered why the youth was still alive at all. So, I suspected, did Styrbjorn – and the truth of it was that the bearcoat's throat was still so uppermost in my mind that it stole any stomach I had for red-murdering the boy.

He came with us all the same, wary as a wet cat and dragging his heels, a hand on the hilt of his eating knife – Eirik had sent him a fine sword, as proof of his forgiveness, but I had it snugged up in secret – and nursing all his grievances to him until he could pay everyone back.

I was thinking he would run for it first chance he got and was in two minds whether to let him or not, for if some skin-wearing tribesman killed him along the Odra, I could hold up my hands to the king and honestly say it was no fault of mine.

It was clear now that any who had designs on jarl matters were still stunned by what I had done and, taken with all the other legends that swirled round me, were too afraid to speak up – even Crowbone, who might have tried it, for all his size and lack of years.

The truth of it all was clear to me and worse, of course, than Finn thought. Crowbone did not need to challenge me for the jarl torc. He knew the Oath bound us all, as it said, one to another; if it meant he had to sulk in the stern now and behave himself, one day he would call on us and we would be reeled in like fish in the net of that Oath, to go and help win him a throne in Norway. That I had stuck myself in that net was what irritated me, for I needed Crowbone's ship and his crew.

All day we rowed and I took my turn at the oar like everyone else, so that I ached by the end of the day, a hot bar from shoulder to shoulder and my arse rubbed raw on my own sea-chest. Yan Alf saw it when I squatted over the lee side for relief and laughed.

'Orm is truly a great jarl,' he yelled. 'Look – he even prepared for a coming fog by making a beacon.'

They hooted and slapped thighs at the sight of my arse which, if it glowed like it felt, was indeed a fair light in a mist.

'I went into a red forest,' Bjaelfi intoned, waving a wax-sealed little pot. 'In the red forest was a red house and in the house was a red table, and on the table was a red knife. Take the red knife and cut red bread.'

But I refused Bjaelfi's potent charm against the rash on my cheeks, since it was accompanied by an offer to smear salve on the affected part. The men, enjoying the sight of their jarl so put out, hooted and guffawed and slapped themselves and each other, which was, I knew, as good a way as any of braiding them together. Unlike them, though, I could not put the bearcoat's throat behind me.

I caught sight of Crowbone watching me, appraising and not the least put out. Another lesson learned for him, I thought, for I was no more than one of the spears he practised with each time we made landfall, throwing them with either hand and getting better all the while.

At night we lit fires and ate horse beans and bread, the bought stuff first before it got too moulded. After a week of this there were moans, which did not surprise me. Those with the skill wanted to hunt, Kuritsa among them.

'If I eat any more horse beans,' he grumbled, 'I will blow the boat up the mountains to where this river begins.'

I said anyone who fancied it could hunt and saw the delighted looks among those who saw a way out of rowing; folk were even doing it in their sleep and elbowing their neighbours on the cramped boat.

Then I reminded everyone of the Redars and Czrezpienians, the Wengrians, Glomacze, Milczians and Sorbs, all of whom would be pleased to find Northlanders hunting their lands and would surely offer proper hospitality.

181

'With a stake up the arse,' Finn added and Red Njal flung back his head and laughed, the cords of his neck standing out.

'*Gefender heilir,*' he intoned a moment later, '*gestr er inn kominn.* Greetings to the host, a guest is come.'

'*Hvar skal sitja sja? Mjok er bradr, sa er brondum skal, sins um freista framr* – Where must this one sit? He is very impatient, the one who must sit on the firewood to test his luck,' Styrbjorn finished and those who knew the old Sayings Of Odin howled with laughter at their own cleverness.

That was the night I tried to talk sensibly with the Mazur girl. She was sitting, quiet as a hare and her eyes, those dark, seal eyes, were never still. They looked large and brimmed with fluid in her thin face, too big for it, too big for the small shoulders over which she had drawn a cloak given to her by Queen Sigrith, too large certainly for the legs that came out of the oatmeal-coloured shift and ended in small, clumpy turn-shoes, another gift.

For all that, the great hairy Svears and Irishers raised their brows and rolled their eyes at her, watching her when they could while she stared at nothing, like a little carving of wood. At night, I had men I could trust guard her, Finnlaith and Ospak usually; she was young and small but these were vik men and if some had not humped a dying woman on a dead ox it was only from lack of opportunity. They would hump a knothole if the mood took them.

I sat beside her and smiled. Her eyes flicked to my face and she said nothing; I saw the heads of the rowers we sat behind twisting themselves off to try and see what the jarl was up to.

They knew the girl was no thrall, was highly prized and that I had told them all to keep away, no talking to her, no hands on her or, by the Hammer, I would tie those who did to a tree with their pricks hanging and leave them for the Sorb women.

182

'I hope you have some comfort and are not afraid,' I said slowly, knowing her Norse was poor; I could speak neither Wend, nor Polanian, which she might know and certainly not Mazur. 'You are worried about why I have brought you, no?'

'No.'

The reply was flat and soft, surprising enough to make me blink, but her face did not change and the eyes, those eyes, were deep as a fjord. I felt there was some old wisdom gliding in the dark water of them; for a stabbing moment I was reminded of Hild, the mad woman who led us all to Attila's hoard and, at the same time, caught sight of Crowbone, a shadowed shape looking at me, though his face was all dark-ness and I could not see his eyes.

Something about that disturbed me – but, then, I was all disturbance, like a cat in a high wind, fur-ruffled this way and that and made uneasy and twitched. Having your doom laid on you will do that. Ripping the throat from a man with your teeth will do that.

'You are not worried?' I managed and she shook her head.

'No. You brought me because the flatfaced one with the drum told you to. You brought me because the Polanians will want me and you might have to bargain with them. It is dangerous; they will certainly try and take me by force when they find out.'

She had not missed the mark of it, right enough and spoke it in a detached way, as though it concerned someone else. The other fact of it was that, no matter what, she would not get back to her people, far to the east of the Polanians. Yet I was sure she clutched the hope of that tight to her.

She looked at me with her wood-carved look, then dropped those swimming eyes, saying nothing more.

'Well,' I said, though it was like pushing boulders uphill, 'you have listened and watched, I am thinking. Now I need you to talk.'

I needed her to tell me of the river, for we had no guide.

183

I needed to know where it narrowed, or shallowed, what settlements of size were on it and whether they could be trusted and where the Saxlander and Wend forts were. Further up still, I needed to know of the Polanians and what lay even beyond them, up to where the river stopped being navigable by a boat such as *Short Serpent*.

'The river runs for days,' she answered, 'it runs for weeks. Forever. Here, where it is wide and slow are Wends, on both sides, but they do not live near the river unless there is high ground. They keep sheep and cattle and do not farm much, because the river floods.'

She paused and her mouth twisted.

'They are sheep and cattle themselves, who do not fight.'

That was good to know, but beyond it Dark Eye was not much use. There was a Wendish settlement called Szteteno further up, where two rivers met and made almost a lake, with islands in the middle. Saxlanders were there, too.

Beyond that – and by the time you could just shoot an arrow from a good bow to reach the far bank – there would be thicker woods and higher ground on either side. The river shallowed once that she could remember, at a place the Slavs called Sliwitz and the Saxlanders Vrankeforde – Free Ford – and there they had built a big log fort.

There were fur and amber traders there, she remembered, but mostly slavers, for both the Wends and the Polanians raided each other and sold the captives as slaves. Beyond that, further into the mountains, was a place called Wrotizlawa but Dark Eye had never been there. The only settlement either of us knew north of that was the end of the Amber Road, Ostrawa.

'I was young when they took me down this river,' she added defiantly, seeing my look of disappointment and I nodded and acknowledged it with a rueful smile.

'This ford – is it passable upriver by boats?'

She frowned. 'The riverboats are hauled over it by long lines from the bank, but they take everything out to make

184

them lighter. It is hard work and they can do it only because the boats are made from a single trunk. It is stony beneath the water, which comes up over the hub of a cart wheel. Another river comes to it here and there are islands in the middle, where it joins the Odra.'

If we took the steerboard up, Onund said later when I mentioned it, we could also haul *Short Serpent* over it, though there was a chance we would break its back and the keel would take bad damage.

'Since we are not bringing it back on to a real sea,' he added, with a sideways look at me, 'that does not make much difference.'

I had not mentioned such a matter, of course, but should have known Onund would have spotted it. We would never get *Short Serpent* all the way upriver and I was prepared to follow this Leo through the Bulgar lands to the Great City if he took Koll there. I said as much and Onund nodded, with no sign of remorse for all his wood-skill.

'Why all this, then?' I added, nodding at the half-carved elk-head prow.

'If we burn this ship,' he rumbled, 'I thought to burn her as the *Fjord Elk*. It is fitting – besides, I am trying to have the fame of being the shipbuilder who has lost more vessels of that name than any other.'

We laughed, though grimly; the tally of lost *Elks* was growing fearsome. I told him not to say anything to Crowbone and he grunted. That boy, however, had other matters on his mind and came up to me to air them.

'She will run,' he said, perched at my elbow like a white squirrel. 'The first chance she can take.'

I did not need to ask who and he perhaps had the right of it. I asked if his birds had told him what Dark Eye was planning, but he scowled at that, though I had not meant it as a sneer. Still, I told Finnlaith and Ospak to watch as much for the girl escaping as for visitors with their pricks in their hands

185

as we snagged up for the night. There was some daylight left under the pewter sky, so that those who wanted to hunt could do it.

By the time darkness came we were eating duck with the horse beans, with some fresh-caught river fish and wild onions. I broached the ale, enough to put some flame in the mouth but not enough to cause trouble; by the fireglow, men laughed and sang filthy songs, arm wrestled and watched admiringly as Onund Hnufa brought an elk to life out of the ash-wood with each careful paring of his knife.

The night sang with freshening life and Bjaelfi unwrapped a harp. It was really Klepp Spaki's instrument, but he had given it to Bjaelfi before we left; neither he nor Vuokko came with us, for they had the memory stone to finish and I had no quarrel with that. So Bjaelfi bowed us a tune, which even Finnlaith and his Irishers nodded and smiled at.

'Though it has to be said,' Finnlaith added seriously, 'that while your instrument is like a harp, it is only as like a harp as a chicken is a duck.'

'For a true harp,' added one of the Irishers, a great lump of a red-haired giant who, like all of those rich-named folk, was called Murrough mac Mael, mac Buadhach, mac Cearbhall, 'is a dream of sound which comes from being strung with fine deer gut and plucked, not hung with horsehair strings and scraped, like a sharp edge on the chin.'

'They are braiding together well,' Finn noted quietly while the argument and laughter rolled on, his face blooded by firelight and his loose hair ragging in the wind.

'Save for Crowbone,' he added, nodding to where the boy sat, scowling at the clever work Onund was making; he did not want to see a new prow on his ship, nor it renamed *Fjord Elk*.

'We will pay his price for all this by and by,' I answered and Finn nodded, then sighed as Bjaelfi bowed his harp and sang on.

> *Eager and ready, the weeping lone-flyer,*
> *Frets for the whale-path, the heart lured*
> *Over tracks of ocean. Better that from Odin,*
> *Than the dead life he loans me on land.*

Those close enough to hear grunted low appreciation and Finn's soft 'heya' was a world of praise all on its own. It came to me then that he was the most content I had seen him in a long time and the moon-shadow of the prow beast that rose suddenly behind him was no accident; Finn was where he was happiest.

Worse was, it came to me with a stab of guilt for all those I imagined labouring away in Hestreng, that I shared the feeling, if only because the Oathsworn were the only family who would not shrink from me completely on learning what I had done.

TWELVE

The wind went to the stern, or died to a whisper and let us make better time over the next few days, though it rained soft and hard, stippling the skin of the water. As Dark Eye had said, we saw no sign of life beyond the tree-fringed banks save in the far distance, but I thought it likely our presence was now well-known. I wanted to find peaceful folk to ask about a monk, a boy and a boat full of hard-faced men.

The ship, powered by all the oars, slid along so that the water creamed under the prow beast's neck and the crew had an easy pull of it. Trollaskegg would not put up the sail, for the wind was twitchy and we did not have enough sea room for mistakes; the sky veered from a faded blue to a mottled grey, where harsh clouds piled up and looked like the face of a great, grim cliff.

The men, serene as swans on this water, sang their rowing songs, where each line was repeated by the opposite side, a pulling chant that helped keep time out on the open sea, where we did not need stealth. Here, the thinking was, everyone knew we were on the river and being loud would make folk realise we meant no harm.

> *What do we care, how white the minch is?*
> *Who here bothers about wind and weather?*
> *Pull the harder lads, for every inch is,*
> *Taking us on to gold and fame.*

This last was always boomed out, rolling over the water like the wind, which whined now, a hound too long tied up. It came in strange gusts, leaping and whirling round like an eager pup, then vanishing, so that I wondered where it went. Did it bowl on and on across the long floodplain, endlessly blowing?

'Perhaps it is another type of *djinn*,' Red Njal put in when I voiced this aloud. 'Like the circling sand ones we saw in Serkland.'

'Or the snow ones we had out on the Great White,' added Crowbone, 'the ones which always came before those *buran* storms.'

The Svears, who had sailed up and down the Baltic a few times and thought themselves far-farers, looked at the old Oathsworn differently after that, realising now just where we had been and nudged into remembering the tales of what we had done. That a boy of twelve had seen and done more than them, with their tangle of beard and growling, was to be considered; like all who knew Crowbone for a length, they were coming to realise that he was not the stripling he appeared.

The thought of all these clever far-farers as oarmates cheered them, all the same, so that they sang until their throats burned.

> *Skanish women have no combs.*
> *Pull, swords, pull,*
> *They fix their hair with herring bones.*
> *Pull, swords, pull away.*

The song floated out across the water, rippling past the tree-fringed shore, out across the meadowland of the floodplain,

to where deer heard it, or, I thought aloud, perhaps a herdsman who hid himself and watched, unseen by us.

'Deer,' snorted Kuritsa when he heard this. 'Not enough brush for deer.'

So far the hunters had shot five ducks, three geese and, once, a half-a-dozen fat wood pigeons, but nothing else. Further along, Kuritsa said, if the woods thicken like the girl said, we would find deer and maybe elk, too.

'We need a *strandhogg*,' Finn grunted. 'Fuck your deer – let us find a place with flour and smoked meat and ale that we can raid. Aye, and women, too, else we *will* be fucking your deer.'

> *The Varmland men have no sleds.*
> *Pull, swords, pull.*
> *They slide downhill on old cod heads.*
> *Pull swords, pull away.*

The singing stopped late on in that day, when the wind came skittering down on the prow beast again and stole our breath away with the effort of rowing against it. The sky grew too dark for it to be night and then, across the front of us like a herd of black bulls, stormclouds rolled, spitting white stabs at the earth; rain lanced the river.

We took the sail over and used some awning canvas as well, but it was a miserable wet night, despite hot coals on the ballast stones near the mastfish which gave us grilled fish and soggy bread. We drank the last of the ale and hunched into ourselves listening to the rain hiss and the night bang; the blue-white flashes left us blinking and the air was thick and heavy with a strange, blood tang.

Red Njal said that it was a pity Finn had not worked out the use of his hat and Finn told the tale of it, of how he had taken Ivar Weatherhat's famed headgear in a raid. Those who had laughed at the crumpled, stained object with the wide, notched brim now looked at it with more respect.

'Keep away from your ring-coats and helms, lads,' warned Alyosha, 'for when the night smells of a hot forge, Perun is hurling his axe at any byrnied warrior he can see.'

'Is that true?' demanded Bjaelfi and men hummed and hemmed about it.

'It is true, bonesmith,' Alyosha declared, 'for I have seen it and Perun is as like your Thor as to be a parted birth-brother. Once I saw a *druzhina* horseman in an autumn storm such as this near Lord Novgorod the Great. A proud man and brave, too, all splendid in brass and iron and he rode with his tall spear sticking into the rain and wind as if he did not care. Then there was a flash and Perun's axe smacked him.

'There was nothing much left but twisted metal and a black affair that might have been him. The horse had been turned inside out and we found one of its shoes in the summer, when we went to the wood a good walk away. It was stuck in a birch, half-way up the tree.'

Another flash and bang showed the white-eyed stares of the listeners and everyone hunkered deeper into their own shoulders, shifted a little away from stowed weapons.

The storm wore itself to weary grumbles eventually and I drifted to sleep, listening to the water hiss and gurgle and comforted by the faint glow of the dying coals. Men were curled and twisted into odd shapes, round sea-chests and oars, squeezed in corners and all of them sleeping as if the places they touched leached rest into them. They snored and whistled and wheezed and that was as comforting to me as the glow of coals.

I saw Finnlaith, on watch, shift slightly, a vague silhouette against the faint blood-glow of the coals; as I watched, I saw him settle and tip, like a bag of grain not set down square and I knew he was asleep. That made me annoyed, for I had just got myself comfortable and was enjoying the fire and the men snoring and the river talking quietly to itself about

191

the storm that had blown out. Now I was going to have to lever myself up and kick his Irisher arse awake.

Somewhere a wolf ached, sharp and sorrowful, threading its cry through the night like a bone needle and I struggled and grunted out of my space, feeling the chill as the cloak spilled warmth out – then I froze, astonished.

At first I thought it was a mangy bear, waddling slow and quiet towards the boat, for they do sometimes on the travelled routes of Gardariki, seeking meat or a lick of sweetness after their winter sleep. Then I saw it was a man, working slowly, easily, down towards the ship; a shift of brief moonlight slid along the blade he held.

I almost let out a yell, then, for all the while I had been thinking it one of the crew deciding to try his luck with Dark Eye while her guard slept – but this man was coming from the shore, from further down. Besides, the naked blade told the truth of it.

Moving slowly, rolling each foot along from heel to toe as old Bagnose had taught me, placing each one carefully between sleepers and stacked oars, I crept towards Finnlaith. Beyond him, the shadowed figure with the long knife paused, then came on again.

I snapped Finnlaith's axe from his hand and flung it, even as the Irisher sprang awake with a yell. The long, heavy bearded axe spun through the air and I heard the crack and the grunt as it hit the creeping man; I leaped, hoping he was stunned at least and scrabbled for the place he had fallen, hearing Finnlaith bellowing behind me.

I landed on the man's back, driving more air out of him, sprang a forearm under his neck and gripped his other shoulder, levering his chin up until I heard the neck bones creak. He swung wildly behind him and I saw he still had the knife, flickering like a wolf fang in the watered moonlit dark.

He grunted when I grabbed for the hand, spilled me off him and we rolled now, me desperate not to let go of his

knife-hand. I banged my nose and the pain of it made my whole head explode in red.

Men were yelling and the world was a whirl of grass and cracking twigs, heavy with the fetid stink of sweat and fear and fresh-scabbed muddy earth. I heard shouts, felt the thump that hit the man I struggled with; he fell away from me then.

'That will tame him,' growled a voice.

'After the other one . . . quick now. Move yourselves.'

A hand hauled me up and light flared as someone lit a torch from the coals and brought it. Finn looked me over with narrowed eyes as men thronged around, then he relaxed.

'That neb of yours is not lucky,' he pointed out, but I did not need him to tell me that, for it throbbed blindingly. Someone held the torch over a little and, as Finnlaith fetched his axe, grinning, I saw what I had been fighting.

'Sure and that was a fine throw,' he said cheerfully, 'though you are lucky it is not so balanced and only the shaft hit him, else he would be dead.'

'Sure and it is a fine thing,' I answered, mimicking his tone, 'that I did it when I did, else you would be dead and we would have to wake you to let you know of it.'

Finnlaith's grin slipped a little and he nodded wryly, scrubbing his head with embarrassment. The giant red-head, Murrough, reached down and plucked a limp figure from the bruised grass.

He was a small man, dressed in a stained tunic that might have been white once and wearing bits of fur here and there, which is why I took him for a mangy bear. His face was mole-sharp and shaved clean, though he had greasy hair the colour of old iron worked in three braids, two from his brow and one behind him. He half-hung in Murrough's grip looking one way then another with small, narrow eyes, as if to find something he could bite.

'Is this a Wend or a Sorb?' I asked. 'Does anyone speak enough to ask him?'

193

'Only the girl,' growled Alyosha and Crowbone appeared then, his cheeks flushed and eyes bright from running.

'The second man ran for it and we lost him in the dark – who is this one?'

'A Sorb,' grunted someone.

'Or a Wend.'

Mole-Face said nothing, but tried a smile with more gap than tooth and spread his hands, moving them to his mouth.

'Came to steal food, I am thinking,' Finn growled. I picked up the man's long knife; it was a good one, ground down from what had once been a decent sword, so that the hilt and fittings were all there and they were Norse. The likes of Mole-Face would have sold it long ago if he was so starving and I said so.

I handed it to Finn and added: 'Well, I have my truth knife and it has never failed, no matter whether we speak the same tongue or not. So string him up and we will start with his fingers, until they are all gone. Then we will move to his toes . . .'

'Until they are all gone,' chorused those who knew the way of it, laughing like tongue-lolling wolves.

'Then I will start on his prick and balls,' I added.

'Until they are all gone,' came the chorus.

'Ah, no, wait – Christ's bones, no.' The man's tongue flicked like an adder and he stared wildly from one to the other.

'That truth knife,' Finn grunted, 'seldom fails to impress me. Already we know he speaks good Norse and is a Christmann and we have not even drawn blood.'

'I know who he is,' Styrbjorn declared, bursting through the throng. 'His name is Visbur, by-named Krok, but most know him as Pall, which name he took when he was baptised and chrism-loosened. He is one of Ljot's men.'

'You may not have any food,' Finnlaith said to the mole-faced man, 'but you are rich in names.'

'Bind him,' I said and men sprang to obey; the man panted and struggled briefly, but he stayed silent, stumbling back to

194

the ship with the press of men at his back. Once there I had them loop a cord round his ankles and then hauled him a little way up the mast, where he hung and swung like a spider's prey. I brought the truth knife out, feeling the cold sick settle in me, for I never liked this.

'Now,' I said, 'I know you are called Hook and named after a Christ-saint called Paul and that you are no Wend or Sorb.'

'True, true,' he panted. 'Let me down – I will tell you everything. Anything.'

'Who was the other man?'

'What other man? I was . . .'

He broke off, for I had grabbed one bound hand and whicked the little finger off him; the knife was so keenly sharp that he felt it as no more than a tug – then he saw the blood spurt and the pain hit him and he shrieked, high and thin, sounding like Sigrith when she was birthing her son.

'Yes, yes,' he screamed. 'Two of us. We were sent by Pallig.'

'I remember now,' Styrbjorn spat out suddenly. 'He was always at the elbow of another called Frey . . . something.' He frowned, then brightened. 'Freystein, that is it.'

The hanging man moaned and blubbered and Finn, with a scornful look, thanked Styrbjorn for his part, while wishing he had been a little quicker.

'I am sure Pall here will forgive you for the loss of his finger,' he added, 'it being just a little one.'

Styrbjorn scowled and the pair of them bristled at each other for a moment – but this was Finn, who made stones tremble and Styrbjorn wisely slunk off. I was aware of them only at the edge of my mind, for Visbur/Pall had started to babble.

It all spilled out like blood from his finger-stump, while the torch guttered in a rising wind and he turned and swung and bumped against the mast.

Pallig had sent him and three others. This Pall and the one

195

called Freystein had been dropped off when they spotted the boat; the other two had rowed their little faering silently past, the idea being to pick Pall and his oarmate up once they had done their task. They had planned to set the boat adrift, maybe even fire it if the occasion presented itself.

I sent men off down the bank and we waited moody as wet cats, while Pall swung and moaned.

'Cut him down,' said a small, light voice and Dark Eye stepped into the torchlight.

'This is no matter for you,' growled Finn. 'Go and lie down somewhere warm.'

Dark Eye studied him and most would have said she did it as cool as a calved berg, but I saw the tremble in her and, suddenly, stepped away from myself to her side and saw it as she did – a band of savage-eyed, grim men, tangle-haired beasts gathered round a pole to poke and taunt a hapless victim. She looked at me with those seal eyes and I felt shame.

'Take him down,' I said and, after a pause, Red Njal and Hlenni did so. Pall collapsed on the deck in a heap and Bjaelfi, who never liked this business, came forward and thrust a scrap of cloth at him, one of the many he had rune-marked for healing.

'Here,' he said gruffly. 'Bind the wound with this and keep it clean. Do not take it off, for the rune on it is Ul, a *limrune,* which is to say a healing rune, in case you have Christianed yourself away from even that knowledge. It invokes Waldh, who is an old healing-god of the Frisians.'

Dark Eye smiled, a small sun that flared for a moment and was gone as she moved off back to her place in the lee of the stern. Finn hawked and spat over the side.

'So thralls rule us now,' he growled and I felt a surge of anger; any less a man would have had my fist on him.

'She is no thrall,' I answered, stung. 'A princess in her own lands and as valuable to us as a queen. And no-one rules us, not even me and, for sure, not you.'

He saw the thunder in my face and realised he had gone too far. Unable to row back from what he had said, he simply turned and rolled off down the ship to the prow, pulling off his crumpled hat and scrubbing his head with confusion.

The men I had sent out came back when the birds had finished yelling at the dawn.

'They saw us,' Kuritsa said, 'just as the sky got light. We managed a shot or two, but they rowed off. There were only two.'

'My fault,' added another of the trackers wryly, a lanky Svear called Koghe. 'I am not as skilled as Kuritsa here and let them see me.'

Kuritsa waggled his head from side to side, a gesture that meant the matter was neither here nor there. He also voiced an opinion that had been in my head, too.

'It means the second man from tonight is still somewhere around.'

He had done more than well, what with this and other matters and I looked at him and knew what I had to do. Gripping him by one shoulder I bellowed it out so that everyone could hear.

'I see you.'

Men turned; a few 'heyas' went up, for they liked Kuritsa and had long since stopped treating him as a thrall – which meant not noticing him at all. Now I had declared him as noticed and had Red Njal bring my drinking horn, filled with the last scum of the ale. Grinning, he handed it to Kuritsa, who then handed it to me. I drank and gave it back to him. He drank and everyone cheered, for Kuritsa was now a free man.

In some places there is more to it, involving six ounces of silver – if the thrall is buying his freedom – and him brewing ale from three measures, which is a powerful drink to present to his former owner, but all that is colouring the cloth of it.

'Well,' Crowbone said brightly, 'now that we have no more thralls, we will have to rely on Finn Horsehead's cooking.'

Which, of course, was what we had been doing already, for Finn was known for his excellent meals, but it raised a laugh as men clattered about, sorting themselves, trying to find sleep again and mostly failing. When the light was enough to see by, the ship was shoved off from the bank, the rowers settled on to their sea-chests, slid out the oars and bedded themselves into the rhythm of it, helped by Trollaskegg's loving curses.

Dogs, he called them one minute and *maeki saurgan* the next, which strangers take as an insult, since it means 'dirty sword'. They miss the part of how such a sword came to be so stained, by proving its worth and not breaking.

I took Pall by the scruff of the neck and hauled him to where Finn sat.

'Here,' I said. 'Aim your scowls at this instead of me, Finn. This Pall might be useful yet, even if only in one of your stews.'

Finn managed a twist of his mouth, for he did not want a quarrel any more than I; Pall hunkered miserably, but I saw his thin face turn this way and that, cunning as a rat. A thought struck me and I cursed myself for a nithing fool.

'Where were you going?' I demanded. 'Before you thought to be clever with our boat.'

He flicked his adder tongue over dry lips and I reached round into the small of my back, under the cloak, which made him flinch and cup his finger-short hand in the other.

'Upriver,' he answered in a voice as whiny as the wind, then, seeing me produce the truth knife, added hastily: 'To warn the Saxlanders you are coming. Pallig wants you dead for killing his brother.'

'Dare not do it himself, all the same,' I pointed out scornfully.

'Crucify him,' Finn advised, then, remembering the Rus punishment for Christ-worshipping criminals, added: 'Upside down.'

'Christ Jesus,' moaned Pall and collapsed to the deck, no doubt believing he was on his knees to his White Christ while the reality was he babbled with his nose in Finn's boots; Finn

198

laughed and prodded his face with a toe, while I added this latest bad cess to the growing heap of problems.

The rain started again and the wind swirled and circled, sometimes strong enough to catch the prow or the steerboard and lurch the ship sideways, like a balked horse. The current was strong, too and, in the end, I had us back at the east bank with the rowers drooling and panting. It had thicker woods nearby, so we stayed the rest of that day, sending men hunting or fetching firewood and fretting at having little food and less ale.

It gave me too much time to think, about when Odin would take me as his sacrifice, about what Thorgunna and the others at Hestreng would be doing and about the night-sneak by Pall and his oarmate.

When I had spotted it, I was thinking it one of the crew stealing up on Dark Eye, and tried to tell myself the feelings I had had were because she was valuable to us. Since then, she only took those eyes from me when she scanned the banks, as if hoping to see a face she knew. Even with my back to her I could feel the heat of those eyes.

She was young, yet old enough to grip the interest of all the crew, but she seemed like some animal fresh from a burrow in the woods, thrown into somewhere strange; I saw a hunger in those eyes, which I took to be for the woods and hills of her own place. I knew that hunger. Mine was for a fjord and misted cliffs and a distant blue line of mountain, like something seen on the inside of your eyelids when first you close them at night. I tried hard not to think of hers as another hunger and mostly failed.

That night we had a bigger blaze, just to cheer us and the glow of it fired the river and drowned the dark with blood red. I saw her, when everyone had gone to snores and grunts, a sharp profile against a sudden unveiled moon.

She turned and the firelight caught the shadow of a smile on a mouth that was neat as a hem, yet full enough for me to wonder if she knew how to kiss.

THIRTEEN

The woods seemed still until you were in them, when things moved and made noises; a brown bird flickering in a bush of berries, a fox picking delicately through the sodden edge of the meadow, rooks arguing in a tangle of trees, their new-hatched joining in with an uncertain clamour of young voices as broken as Crowbone's.

I was enjoying this, a hunt and a scout both and free of the ship and the grumbling, quarrelsome crew, even if my bow-skill was likely to shoot my own foot as something tasty for the pot.

The scouting was more important – the day before we had spotted smoke, a thread in the weak, faded blue, no more – but it spoke of fresh food and ale and perhaps even women, so here we were, Kuritsa and me, plootering as quietly as we could through the damp woods in a sudden burst of warmth which brought out the insects in stinging swarms.

For all that I was bitten and had to keep spitting them out, felt them in my hair and trying for my eyes and nose, the pests could not make me unhappy. At times, a silence fell so that I thought I could hear the new buds straining to be free on all the branches, that I could hear the grass hiss and rustle out of the ground. It was during one of these

moments that I caught the movement, like *alfar* at the edge of my eye.

I froze and turned, but Kuritsa had already seen it, no more than a shadow sliding in shadows – then I lost it. A curlew called, sharp and two-toned and I saw it, wings curved and gliding, so that just the tips of them fluttered; a mallard hen bow-waved out of nearby reeds, fluffing in anger and followed by a string of ducklings; the river swirled in fat, slow eddies.

Kuritsa placed his fingers on his lips and it was clear he did not like even that much shifting, so I stayed where I was in the willows and peered, feeling the sweat trickle and the insects nip; their whine became the loudest noise.

Somewhere behind, coming up with long, slow, easy strokes, was *Short Serpent*, looking to us for warning, for they were close to the east bank, the west being where the sharpest current swung downriver. And I was sure now that we were not alone here, even if only Kuritsa seemed to know that other men were about. Pallig's men? Perhaps the two who had escaped in the boat, or the one who had fled on foot.

I was offering prayers to Odin that it be them when I saw the man, no more than an arm's length away through the screen of new brush.

He was bareheaded and had dark hair done in braids, with soot-stripes down his cheeks and across his forehead, to break his face up in the brush, like the dapple of a deer. That alone marked him as no friend, for only someone trying to remain hidden from sharp-eyed men would do that, but the bow, nocked and ready with a big, barbed battle arrow, was a clear sign of what he hunted.

The curlew called again, hovering over the nest the man had gone too near and he glanced up towards the sound, knowing he had given himself away to anyone who could read the sign. Then the stripes on his cheeks dropped away as his eyes widened at the sight of me.

There was no time for a bowshot. I dropped it and leaped

ahead, crashing through the willows and trying to haul the seax out of the sheath across my front. The man grunted and tried to back off, give himself some room to shoot, but it was too late for that; I felt branches whip my face and try to snag my tunic.

He dropped the bow, flailed a wild slash at me with the arrow and I crashed on him, grabbing his hand as he grabbed mine; face to face we heaved and grunted and I tasted the onion breath and fear-stink coming off him in waves, saw the bursting beads of sweat roll darkly through the charcoal streaks.

He brought his knee up and almost caught me in the nads, but I had half-turned and he hit my thigh instead which dead-legged me. I knew I should call out, but that would bring his friends as well as mine and he had clearly worked out the same, for we fought in grunting, panting silence, straining like lovers.

I stumbled on the numbed leg, twisted myself and dragged him over on me; we crashed through the willow twigs and shrubs and my knee was up between his legs when he landed on me and I heard him cough out a grunt that turned into a thin, high whine when he lost my knife hand and knew his doom was on him.

I got the seax round then, got it right around and slid it into him, feeling the slight give and the skidding on ribs before it found the gap between and sank all the way. He freed my other hand then and I clamped it across his mouth. His eyes, inches from mine, went big and round with desperation, almost pleading, as if to beg me to take back the knife, the moment of it going in. I saw a tear pearl along the lower lashes of his right eye, then I rolled him off and scrambled back, panting.

He flopped on his back, eyes open, and kicked once or twice. The fingers of one hand moved, almost like a farewell wave from a child.

Kuritsa came up then and I whirled, panicked as a deer, so

202

that he held up both hands and stopped where he was until I saw him. I spat a sour taste in my mouth, blinking the rivers of sweat that poured in my eyes, while the insects whined and pinged, joyous with the iron stink of fresh blood welling and soaking through the rough undyed wool tunic he wore.

'Men ahead,' Kuritsa whispered, his mouth so close to my ear that the hot breath scalded. 'Hiding in the reeds in those wood and skin boats they have.'

He had eyes like a dog, the dead man, like a sad, whipped, gods-cursed dog. I should have rifled him, armpits to boots, for what he carried, though I was betting-certain he had less than an empty bag. Finn would have searched him, or Red Njal, or Hlenni, puddling in the blood and his last shit to find his riches, but I was not that good a raiding-man at this moment.

I stumbled away, dragging my bow and his war arrows, Kuritsa leading the way.

There were seven or eight boats, long fishing efforts made of hide stretched over a wood frame and each crammed with at least ten men. If we had not found them, they would have shot out of the reeds and been on *Short Serpent* in seconds and, though these folk did not look much and had no helmets or armour, they had bows and short spears and desperation enough. They might even have succeeded.

Instead, as they crouched and sweated and batted insects as silently as they could, they suddenly discovered themselves ambushed. My first shot took a man just below his rough-chopped hair, almost in his ear; his scream was as shattering as a stone in the quiet, slow-eddying river. Seconds later, he was in the river and it thrashed with bloody foam.

We shot all the big battle arrows, about ten, one after another, fast as we could and if we missed a mark, I did not see it. Then, as the men howled and scrambled and dived into the water from their boats to escape, we slid away, then ran and ran until, laughing and sobbing, we burst free of the bush

and trees and saw *Short Serpent*, swan-serene, walking down the river to us on all its oarlegs.

Heads bobbed up from behind racked shields and stared in astonishment at Kuritsa and me, hanging on to each other, panting drool and spraying sweat and laughter at getting away unharmed.

Not long after, when we all came up to the place, we found one boat upturned and four or five bodies, turning and bobbing in the current. Another man lay on the bank, half-in, half-out. I did not want to splinter through the willows to find the one I had knifed.

'Well,' said Finn, 'we have found the source of the smoke we saw.'

'We have found that they are not friendly,' Alyosha pointed out. 'Even after taking the prow beast off.'

I had agreed to that, though I did not think it would matter much – *Short Serpent* was no little *hafskip*, or river *strug*. It was a *drakkar*, a raiding ship and looked as friendly as a fox in a hen coop, but the men wanted to try and appease the spirit of this land and so the prow beast came off and was stowed gently away.

'Why would they want to attack us?' Yan Alf asked Pall and that one's mole-face split in a twisted grin.

'Perhaps they think you are the sort who would string a man up and cut off his fingers,' he answered bitterly and Trollaskegg smacked him hard on the back of his head, so that he pounded forward three steps.

'Perhaps,' I added, while Pall sullenly rubbed the back of his scalp and scowled, 'someone has been telling them how bad we are. Your friends, I am thinking.'

Finn blinked as the idea took root in him, then he growled, so that Pall scurried a few steps away from him.

'No, no – they are in as much danger here as we are,' he whined.

'They think you are slave-takers,' said a soft voice and we

204

all turned to where Dark Eye stood, wrapped like a little Greek ikon in my cloak. 'In a ship like this, coming upriver, they will think you come to raid early.'

She had the right of it, sure enough, though raiding men with a *drakkar* would not usually come up this far – it was easier to buy such slaves cheap in Joms, having left it to the Wends to raid Polanians and the Polanians to raid Wends. Sometimes, I had heard, their respective chiefs even raided their own villages and took folk to sell if they were silver-short that year.

I was anxious for news, of Randr Sterki and of a monk with a band of Sorbs and a boy. Even so, there was more sense in rowing on and leaving the whole matter, as I pointed out. Other voices, hungry for cheese and meat and ale, wanted to see if this misunderstanding could not be put right. And one of my names was Trader . . .

Since there were scowls that made it clear this was all my fault, I did not think it clever to refuse. I dropped thirty of us, about half the crew, on the east bank, then had Trollaskegg move the ship to the opposite side, out of immediate harm.

'If you see us running like the dragon Fafnir was breathing flame on our arses,' Hlenni said, scowling at Trollaskegg, 'you had better be within leaping distance of this bank before I get to it, or matters will be bad for you.'

'If I am not, you will be dead, I am thinking,' chuckled Trollaskegg good-naturedly, 'and so no danger to me.'

'Even dead,' Hlenni yelled back as we moved off, 'I am a danger to you. Black-faced and with my head under my arm, I am a danger to you.'

Which was not, considering matters, a good thing to let the gods hear you say, as Red Njal pointed out.

It was not hard to find them, these lurkers in reeds – there were tracks everywhere and signs, like sheepfolds and marked tillage, that a settlement was close. Not that we needed them, as Finn said.

'Just follow the screamers,' he growled, trying to cuff Pall, who was dragging on the end of a rope leash like an awkward dog.

It was not surprising, I was thinking, that folk fled from us, yelling and waving their arms and leaving kine and sheep behind. One man, with scarcely a backward glance, even left a toddler, all fat limbs and wailing; Hlenni scooped him into the crook of one arm and jogged him, though the red-cheeked, yellow-haired boy only started to gurgle and grin when Hlenni took his helmet off.

'Lucky it was Hlenni and not Finn,' Red Njal chuckled, sticking out a dirt-stained finger for the boy to grab. 'To win over bairns and maids takes a gentle lure, as my granny used to say. That wean would have shat himself if Finn had taken his helmet off.'

'I think he has anyway,' mourned Hlenni, sniffing suspiciously at the boy's breeks.

'Na,' said Finn, seeing his chance. 'I am thinking that is just how Hlenni always smells.'

There was laughter and no-one thought Orm Trader could not gold-tongue and silver-gift his way out of this matter and into the smiles of the settlement. I was not so sure; we were all byrnied, helmeted, shielded and armed, moving with a shink-shink of metal, cutting a scar across their pasture and ploughland to where they perched on a mound behind a log stockade. Besides – we had just killed a lot of them; even before we had come within hailing distance, I heard the gates boom shut.

That brought us to a ragged, uncertain halt. It was a small settlement and the stockade was dark with age, yet it looked solid and the gate had a big, square tower with a solid hat of wood to cover it. Men appeared, just their heads and shoulders showing above the rampart edge. So did the points of spears.

'You are the jarl and so should speak to them,' Crowbone said and winced a little at the withering look I gave him.

'Just so,' I said. 'Hold a little. I will learn their tongue while we make a fire. Perhaps Finn can make us a stew while we wait?'

'I can,' said Finn, 'if I had water and someone found some roots and Kuritsa shot something tasty.'

'I thought we brought Pall for talking to them?' Crowbone persisted.

'Aye,' growled Finnlaith, giving the answer before I could speak, 'but can you trust what the little rat tells you is being said?'

'We brought Pall because I like him where I can see him,' I pointed out and Crowbone, seeing it now, frowned a little and nodded. It did not diminish the truth of what he said, all the same. There was nothing else to be done, otherwise we had come all this way for no reason – but I did not have to like it.

Hlenni, Red Njal, me, Finn and the leashed Pall and Styrbjorn all moved out – the latter because I did not want him out of my sight – with Finnlaith and Ospak as shieldmen in case matters turned uglier than Hel's daughters. Every step into the place where arrows might reach made my arse pucker and my belly contract. When I thought we had come close enough to be heard without bellowing at the edge of voice, I stopped and hailed them.

A head appeared, this one wearing a blue hat with a fringe of fur round it, probably what passed for the rank of riches in this place – everyone else I had seen was bareheaded. The iron-grey beard beneath that blue hat hid a mouth I knew would be a thin line.

He was hard, this headman, a nub of a man worn by toil even if he had managed to work himself up to a blue hat with fur round it; even at a distance I saw the lines on his face, etched deep by wind and worry.

'We come to trade,' I yelled, hearing the stupidity of it in my own voice, for we had just killed a half-dozen of his people, a hard dunt of menfolk loss in a settlement this size. He was not slow to point this out and I was surprised to hear him say it in halting Norse.

'It seems we will not need you today, Christ-rat,' growled Styrbjorn nastily and gave Pall a kick so that he yelped.

'Go away, slavers,' Blue Hat added, his voice carrying clearly with the faint wind that drove from him to us. 'Nothing easy is here for you today.'

'I seek a monk,' I yelled back. 'A Greek one in black. He had a boy with him.'

There was silence for a moment, while the damp warmth seeped and the insects annoyed us.

'Escape you?' came the reply. 'Good.'

I sighed; this was going to be a long, hard day.

'We can trade,' I began, trying to keep the weary desperation out of my voice . . . but Hlenni stepped forward suddenly and held up the yellow-haired boy, swung him up and into the air at the end of both of his hands so that he could be clearly seen. The boy chuckled and laughed, enjoying it.

'See?' he bellowed. 'We mean no harm.'

A woman screamed – probably the mother; I wondered how her man had explained how he had run off and left the lad.

Hlenni moved forward and someone – Red Njal, when I thought on matters later – called his name uncertainly, but Hlenni strode forward with the boy in his arms and set him down almost under the gate.

'Growl not at guests, nor drive them from the gate,' Hlenni said, grinning back at Red Njal. 'As your granny used to say.'

The boy toddled a bit, lost his balance, fell forward, crawled a bit, then rose up, wobbling. Abandoned, uncertain, he began to bawl.

'Cautious and silent let him enter a dwelling,' Red Njal muttered. 'To the heedful seldom comes harm.'

There was an argument above and a woman's voice sounded shrill, so it was not hard to work matters out.

'Your granny,' Hlenni said, turning to grin at Red Njal, 'was . . .'

Then someone hurled the rock at him from the ramparts.

A big one it was, big as Hlenni's stupid head and the crack of it hitting in the curve of his neck and shoulder was loud; louder yet was the roar of disbelief and rage that went up from us. Hlenni pitched forward on his face and Red Njal howled and leaped forward.

Arrows came over with a hiss and shunk, some skittering through the wet grass. Finnlaith caught Red Njal as he hirpled past, caught and held him, though Njal raved and struggled and frothed and Ospak stepped in front of them both, shield up against the shafts.

Eventually we dragged Red Njal away out of range, where he subsided, gnawing a knuckle and trembling, his eyes fixed on the fallen Hlenni.

The gate opened and men darted out, grabbed the bairn and took Hlenni by the heels and dragged him in, which set all the men off again until Finn and I had to crack heads and draw blood.

Sweating, we crouched like wolves after a failed hunt, panting with our mouths open, sick with loss.

'Perhaps he is alive,' Styrbjorn ventured, thoughtful as only a man who did not really care could be. 'They may regret what they have done and bind his wound.'

No-one spoke. I blinked the sting of sweat from my eyes and tried to think. In the end, though it wove itself around like a knot of mating snakes, matters came out the same way. I rose up and went back to the stockade to hail them.

I had barely bellowed when something arced over the stockade wall, smacked into the wet earth with a crunch and then rolled almost to my feet. I did not have to look to know what it was; none of us did.

Red Njal howled until the cords on his neck stood out and spittle flew, roared until he burst something in his throat and coughed blood. The rest of us did not speak for a long time and I only had to nod to send long-legged Koghe loping back to fetch the rest of the crew, for the sight of Hlenni's bloody, battered head, the rough-hacked neck trailing tatters of skin, had sealed the wyrd of this place.

Hlenni. Gone and gone. One of the original Oathsworn from long before my time, who had survived everything the gods could hurl, save a stone from some dirty-handed, skin-wearing troll of a farmer.

'I do not think,' Finn said bitterly to Styrbjorn, 'that they have bound his wounds. Or regret what they have done.'

Red Njal lifted his face then, a stream of misery and hate poured up at the stockade, his eyes cold as blue ice.

'They will,' he rasped.

I found Blue Hat, eventually. He was in the Christ hall, for these folk were followers of the White Christ and had built his temple partly in stone, thinking it a refuge for times of trouble. But they had never come on trouble like the Oathsworn, wolf-woken to revenge.

We took our time on it, too, cold as old vomit, while the rain drizzled. We took all but ten men from the boat and stood behind shields, beyond arrow range of the wooden walls, the rain dripping off the nasals of our helmets and seeping through the rings of iron to the tunics beneath.

We were howe-silent, too, which unnerved the defenders and when I sent others to cut wood, that steady rhythm of sound must have seemed, in the end, like a death drum to those in the stockade, for they stopped their taunts.

'Well,' growled Finn as men came back lugging a solid trunk, trimmed and sharpened. 'What is the plan, Jarl Orm?'

Most of the others looked surprised, for it seemed clear to them – under cover of our shields we would knock the gates

in with this ram then storm the place. Apart from deciding what insults to bellow, that was usually the way and surely the way the famed Oathsworn would do it.

Finn knew me better than that and even Crowbone, stroking his beardless chin like some ancient jarl considering the problem, knew more than older heads.

'You do not care for that way, fame or not,' he said while men gathered to listen.

I admitted it then and have done since. I am like other men and desire proper respect and esteem, when it is due. In the end, though, Odin taught me about fair fame – it was a tool, an edged one that can cut the user unless it is properly used. I said so and Abjorn grunted a little.

'You do not agree?' Finn challenged and Alyosha chuckled, one jarl-hound to another, it seemed to me.

'It does not seem quite right,' admitted Abjorn, but it was Styrbjorn, all fire and movement, like a colt new to the bridle, who hoiked it up for us all to look at.

'A man's reputation is everything,' he spluttered. 'Fair fame is all we have.'

'Once I thought so,' I answered. 'Like the Oath we swear, it binds us. It weakens us, too, for it makes us act in ways we would not usually do.'

'Like charging through the gates of that place like mad bulls,' Crowbone added brightly. Styrbjorn subsided, muttering, but Abjorn nodded slowly as the idea rooted itself.

In the end, it was simple enough. I had men run forward, shields up and shouting, so that heads popped up on the ramparts and a flurry of shafts came over. No-one was hurt and we collected some.

'Hunting arrows,' Finn said with satisfaction. It was what I had been thinking; Kuritsa and me had shot off what war arrows these people possessed. Hunting arrows we could protect ourselves from.

*   *   *

211

The sky lowered itself like a gull on eggs, all grey and fat and ugly. Twenty men, led by Finn, went into the woods carrying bundles and axes and more chopping sounds came. This time, though, they were making ladders and the bundles held all the spare tunics folk had, which they put on under their mail, up to four of them. Then they circled, unseen, to the far side of the stockade.

I sent men with the ram against the gates, moving up under shields where there was only pant and grunt and fear. Rocks clattered on us, shafts whumped into shields, or struck and bounced, skittering like mad snakes through the wet grass.

On the far side, while the gate thundered like a deep bell, Finn slapped ladders against the almost undefended rear wall and led the others up and over. There were only twenty of them, but they were skilled men, mailed, shielded and moving as fast as their bulk would let them, fast as a shuffling trot, hacking at anything that came near and heading for the bar on the gate.

The folk in the settlement panicked when they saw such a group, iron men slicing through their meeting square, toppling the cross-pillar, scattering chickens, splintering carts, kicking buckets, some of them stuck with arrows which went through byrnie and one layer, perhaps two – but would not go through ring-coats and the padding of four tunics.

Hedgepigs in steel, they were and that broke the will of the defenders, so that they ran, screaming and throwing away their hayforks and hunting spears.

When the gate broke open, then, all I saw was a shrieking, milling crowd running this way and that and it was like mice to cats – the very act of them running in fear brought what they dreaded on them, launched the howling Oathsworn at them, flaming for vengeance over Hlenni Brimill.

Arrows flicked at the edge of vision and I ducked, for I wore no helmet, thanks to the still healing scar across my forehead and my tender nose and I could hear my father,

Gunnar, snort in my ear at that – if you have the choice of only one piece of armour, take a helm, he had dinned into me. Never go bareheaded in a fight.

Well, it did Koghe no good, for the arrow that flew past me hit him and there was a wet, deep sound. I half-turned; tall Koghe staggered past with the force of his own rush, the arrow through his mouth, a *fud*-hair below the nasal of his helmet. Choking on his own blood and teeth, pawing the shaft, he was dead even as he gurgled and fell.

I saw the bowman then, ran at him as another arrow was fitted to the nock, held my sword – Brand's splendid blade – in front of my body until the last moment before I got to him, for I knew what the archer would have to do.

He snapped the arrow into one hand and stabbed with it and I took it round in an arc down and right, smashed in with my shoulder and knocked him flying, arse over tip. He was still struggling like a beetle on his back when I chopped him between neck and shoulder.

Shouts and screams soaked the air, almost drowning out the high, thin sound of a bell; I sensed a shadow and stepped back sharply. A body struck the ground, the wood axe meant for my head spilling from one hand and then Styrbjorn stepped up, grinning, the seax and the hand that held it thick with gore.

'The Christ place,' he said, nodding towards the building and I realised that someone was calling the last defenders to him there. Still grinning, he let me lead the way and I realised he had probably saved my life with his handy backstab.

Blue Hat was the bellringer and he was dead by the time I got to him, through a madness that was as like Svartey as to have been its crazed brother. Men moved like grim shadows, killing. There was no plunder, no tupping women in the dust. Only killing.

I walked through it as if in a dream; Uddolf ran across my path, chasing a fear-babbling youngster up to a wall, where he ran at him with his spear, so hard that it broke and the

boy, pinned, screamed and writhed like a worm on a hook. Uddolf, shrieking, beat the boy's face bloody with the broken haft.

Ospak kicked away a young woman, begging on her knees with her hands clasped round his calves, then split the head from her mother with two strokes; yellow marrow oozed from the bone of her neck.

The Christ place was dim and silent and I slumped against the painted wall, feeling the shadows and the quiet like a balm. Then my eyes grew used to the light.

Under the cross with its Tortured God, Red Njal stood on splayed legs, head bowed, panting like a bull after mating. At his feet was Blue Hat and I would not have known the man had it not been for his headgear, for Red Njal had not been kind.

'Hlenni . . .'

I followed Red Njal's glazed look and saw the body, strange with no head, but linen-wrapped neat enough. Nearby was a dead Shaven Priest in his brown robe, killed kneeling in prayer.

They had bound Hlenni's wounds after all, it seemed. Just a little late.

It was all too late. Dull-eyed men staggered, too exhausted to kill now but it did not matter for everyone was dead. No, that was not right, I saw. Every *thing* was dead, even the dogs and the goats and the hens. Everything.

I found myself in a long hall, a meeting place perhaps, for these folk did not do chieftain's *hovs*. Yet it was like one as to bring a rush of memories and I ran to them with my arms out, to try and wrap myself from what went on outside.

There was a pitfire, cold ash now, but the smell of it and the seasoned wood of the pillars flooded Hestreng back on me, a Hestreng unburned. This was the time of year when the sap shifted in everything and the sun came back, so that you could peg out furs and bedclothes and let the sun drive out the lice and fleas. Men would work half-naked, though it was

this side of too cool to be comfortable; there was enough food, but most of the ale was finished, so fights were few.

Summer was the lean time between harvests, so that the unlucky could starve to death eating grass while the sun poured down like honey.

There were sheep and goats to be taken to upland pastures, but not the ones reserved for the horses; sheep and goats ate the grass down to the soil, leaving nothing – but they gave wool for *wadmal*, and milk for curd and cheese and this was the time when *skyr* was made. I remembered it, thickened whey, white as a virgin's skin, lush off the wooden spoon.

But Hestreng was black timber and ash. With luck, a new hall would be up and giving shelter, the wood reeking of newness and tar, but there would be no time for *skyr* and few furs or bedclothes to peg out.

The outside noise yelled me back to a strange, cold, dead hall; someone burst in, saw me and backed out. I rose, feeling as if my legs had turned to wood, but having to move before the tale went round that Orm, White Bear Slayer, leader of the famed Oathsworn, slayer of were-dragons, tamer of the half-women, half-horse steppe creatures was sitting by himself staring at fire ash and near weeping.

Outside, those with life left in their legs and arms had started to look for plunder, moving as if the air was thick as honey; I picked my way through the litter of corpses, feeling the suck of bloody mud on my boots.

I stopped only once, in the act of stepping over a corpse, at first just one more among so many. It was smaller by far, though, with fat little limbs and yellow hair, though there was a lot of blood in it now and the little, budded, thumb-sucking mouth that had smiled at Hlenni Brimill was slack and already had a fly in it.

FOURTEEN

There were hills on either side of us, easy rolling and wooded with willow and elm and the flash of birch, thick with berry bushes and game, while the river hardly flowed against *Short Serpent* at all. But there was no singing from the oarsmen now and no joy in the stacked plunder, for all that they had snarled at the lack of it before.

We had beaver and squirrel and marten skins, *wadmal* cloth baled with grease-rich fleeces against the rain – the work of winter looms – and carded wool waiting to be woven.

Now there was mutton and lamb and beef, for we had slaughtered every breathing creature in that place. We had winter roots pickled in barrels and sweetness wax-sealed in pots. Ale, too, though old and a little bitter. There was even hard drink, like the green wine of far-away Holmgard, a clear spirit made from rye – but not enough of it to chase the sick taste of what we had done to that nameless place.

We loaded it all, stuffing it into *Short Serpent* until it wobbled precariously, as if the more we took the better the excuse for what had been done. For some of us, the only excuse was the laying out of Hlenni on a cross-stack of timbers ripped from the houses, with Koghe next to him and Blue Hat at both their feet.

Then we scattered all the lamp oil we could find, sprayed that expensive stuff like water, for this was not a howing-up, dedicated to Frey – this was a blaze that sped Hlenni and Koghe straight up to Odin, as was proper. A beacon, one or two muttered uneasily, that could be seen for days.

They had been our only deaths. The morose Gudmund had taken the prong of a hayfork in his belly and Yan Alf had taken the flat of a wooden spade on the side of his head – wielded by a woman, too, to add to his annoyance and shame – but he had only a rich, purple bruise to show for it.

We had slaughtered one hundred and seventy-four of them, women and bairns among them. Now there was a sickness on us, like the aftermath of a *jul* feast that had gone on too long, one where folk told you what a time you had because you could not quite recall it for yourself. One where, for days after, everything tasted of ash and your mind was too dull to work.

Worse than that, at least for me, was the feeling that there had been too much blood spilled, as if it poured into a deep, black hole in the earth, the Abyss that Brother John always warned me I was destined to descend. The same Abyss which had flowed out and into me the night I had ripped out the throat of a berserker.

I felt like the prow beast, carved in an endless snarl, unable to change my expression, only capable of nodding approval at what was done. I looked at that beast now, back where it had been taken from and rearing proudly up; there seemed small point now in appeasing the spirits of this land. I would rather have them afraid of us.

We came round the bend and into the sight and sound and smell of a big settlement, this one on the west bank of the river.

It was, said Pall, the Wend *borg* of Sztetëno. He was still leashed, tied to one or other of us, or the mast when all were busy, yet he had recovered a measure of his sleekit smoothness

and grinned at the sight of the place, picking the beef from his gapped teeth with a sliver of bone.

'They have no love for those on the east side of the river,' he told us. 'They will, perhaps, thank us warmly for burning those trolls out.'

'Do you believe this ferret?' sneered Styrbjorn and I looked from one to the other.

'I have a little knife that finds out the truth,' I answered, which made Pall glance at his bound hand, scowling. Styrbjorn laughed and I turned and handed him a long bundle wrapped in a square of sun-faded silk which had once been blue. He looked at it, bewildered, then took it, feeling the weight and knowing what it was. Yet he whistled through pursed lips at the silk.

'They say worms make this,' he grinned. 'I have seen worms and all they make is dung and good bait for fishing. It is something when a man hands me my sword and the wrapping on it is half the worth of the sheath.'

'The silk is something to trade, the blade will help you keep what you get. Take both, use them to go home,' I said with a growl and more gruffly than I had intended. 'Take Pall with you, for he is no more use to me than a hole in a bucket. I am thinking that what you do with him and how much you trust him is your affair.'

It was reward enough for his seax-skill at the settlement and we both knew it. When the ship slid with a gentle kissing dunt against one of the spray of wooden piers, he sprang over the side with a laugh and a wave. Pall, less skilled and more eager, scrambled after and darted away, throwing the leash off him with a last curse.

'Is that jarl-cleverness I am seeing, then?' asked Finn, appearing at my elbow as the oars were clattered down and men milled, sorting themselves out and tying *Short Serpent* to the wharf. 'Is there a plan to it? Am I follow and finish it?'

There had been enough blood over all of this to slake even Odin's thirst and I said as much. He shrugged.

218

'Well, there is always the Loki-luck that will see them throat-cut before they reach King Eirik again. By then, of course, you will have come up with some gold-browed words to appease Jarl Brand.'

Returning his son would be enough, I was thinking. I watched until the figure of Styrbjorn had vanished in the throng on the wooden walkways. Tall and lithe and still raw with youth, he had the look of greatness, yet something was lacking in him – I was thinking that he knew it, too, and it scorched him sullen. Still, I did not think it was his wyrd to be throat-cut.

The men spilled out of the boat and had no trouble stepping easily onto the planks of the wharf, which I noted; usually we had to scramble up half the height of a man to a planked pier such as this, but the river had risen.

'Aye,' grunted Trollaskegg, seeing me look at the rain-sodden sky. 'I can smell storm, me. Over behind the mist are those mountains and I am betting sure Thor is stamping up and down and throwing Mjollnir for all he is worth.'

'No matter,' Crowbone broke in, bright with excitement, 'for we will be snug and safe here, at least for one night.'

Those nearest agreed with hooms and heyas, looking forward to a chance to dry out cloaks and tunics and boots by a real fire, with milk-cooked food and ale enough to chase away the blood-cloud which had settled on all of us like a cloak of black flies.

I was more fretting than I showed; Pall's oarmates had escaped and he had told us they were coming upriver to alert the Saxlanders.

I had been thinking that, if we proved empty-handed with weapons and full-fisted with silver, the Saxlanders would not care overly much – yet we were alone on that wharf, the men turning this way and that, wary as kitchen dogs hunting scraps, hunched under the stares of dark doorways and the sightless eyes of shuttered windholes. Beyond that, I saw big men in

leather armour and spears, with a man in front holding a staff.

'Should we prepare war gear, Orm?' Alyosha asked and I shook my head; no-one had approached us at all, neither trader nor soldier and I had the notion matters were held, like an insect in amber.

I told them to unload and stack the furs and *wadmal*, so that the sight of such a mundane task – and the profit it promised – might allay some fears. For all that, the sweat was greasy on my face and slid a cold finger down between my shoulders.

For a little while we sat and shivered in the rain of that place, the men growing more and more restive, hunched and miserable and leashed by me, for I wanted some acknowledgement that we were welcome before I let these growlers loose to scatter through the settlement.

It did not help that they could smell the roasting ribs and boiling cauldron snakes and hear the fishermen inviting customers to choose an eel and have it sliced and cooked there and then. The gulls wheeled and screeched – better fed, muttered Bjaelfi, than the Oathsworn.

A man started down the walkway, not looking up until he saw us and realised he was alone, having crossed some invisible line which held everyone back; he was so startled that he took a step off the walkway into the muck and lost his shoe jerking his foot back. Cursing, he fished it out and half-hopped away.

A child ran out, laughing, hands out and mouth open; his mother raced after him, snatched him up and glared at us as if it was our fault. Even the dogs slunk, tails curled and growling.

We waited, driven mad by the smells of what we had not had in a long time, so thick we could taste them; cooking fish and hot ovens and brewing beer – and shite pits and middens. One or two grumbles went up and Murrough, in

a loud voice, proclaimed that if he didn't get some fish and bread and ale soon he would eat the next dog that presented itself, skin and all.

Then the man with the staff suddenly appeared, striding down to us; men burst out laughing, nudging Murrough and telling him his meal had arrived. The man, a grey-beard dressed in embroidered red, half-shrouded in a blue cloak fastened on one shoulder with a large pin, was bewildered and bristling, so that he paused and glared.

'Welcome,' he said eventually. Up close, I saw the staff was impressively carved and had a large yellow stone set in the bulbous end.

'There will be no berthing fees for you,' he added, chewing the Norse like a dog does a wasp.

'Fees? What fees?' demanded Trollaskegg, chin bristling.

'Berthing fees,' I told him and he spat, only just missing the staff, while the messenger stared down his long nose.

'I do not pay berthing fees,' Trollaskegg declared, folding his arms.

'That is what he said,' I answered wearily and Trollaskegg, uncertain now whether he had won something or not, grunted and nodded, deciding he had the victory.

The messenger inclined his head in a curt bow and swaggered off, almost knocked over in the rush of traders who arrived in a sudden, unleashed mob, hucksters all of them, crowding round and spreading their wares out on linen or felt, dark coloured for the gem and trinket sellers.

They had combs and pins and brooches of bone and ivory, some pieces of Serkland silver set with amber and flashing stones; the Oathsworn gathered round and fished out barter-stuff and even hacksilver, for these hard, tangle-haired growlers were magpies for glitter.

The traders were good, too, I noted, even if all their gems were glass, for they had stories for all the pieces and, if they forgot which story went with which from customer to customer,

221

it did not matter much. If all the stories were true, though, each had some potent magic from somewhere which would create sure sons in the most barren womb and make men hard as keel-trees if their women wore it when they wore nothing else.

Men believe what they wish to believe, a weakness that can be used, like any other. The gods know this; Odin especially knows this.

The men milled and slowly scattered, looking for food and ale and women. I spent some time haggling a price for the *wadmal* and furs and knew I was robbed; it was too early to be this far upriver. Since we had raided all the goods, though, it hardly mattered and was all profit – anyway, I was glad to be quit of the bundles and what they made me remember.

I had just finished handseling a deal with a spit and slap when Abjorn forced his way through the throng, chewing meat on a wooden skewer. He jerked his head backwards as he spoke.

'There is someone wants a word,' he said, spraying food and I looked behind him; the grey-beard with the staff had returned. The trader I had been talking to took a sideways sidle to avoid him and clamped his lips on what he had been telling me. I had asked this trader, as I had asked others, about a Greek priest and a north boy and had nothing worth noting – they had been here, for sure, yet folk seemed reluctant to admit it.

'The merchant Kasperick wishes words with you,' the grey-beard intoned.

'Who is this Kasperick?' I asked and the messenger raised one irritated eyebrow.

'He is the one who wishes to see you,' he replied smartly and Finn growled like a warning dog.

'Then I must make myself worthy of visiting such an eminence,' I replied, before Finn decided to pitch the messenger into the river. I turned to Trollaskegg.

'Fetch my blue cloak from my sea-chest and the pin that goes with it,' I told him loudly and watched the scowl thunder onto his brow as he did it, slow and stiff with annoyance. He thrust them truculently at me and, before he could also tell me to fuck off and die and that he was no thrall to me, I drew him closer.

'Get everyone on board and stay there,' I hissed. 'Loosen off the lines. I will take Finn, Crowbone and Red Njal with me and if all is well, I will send Crowbone back. If not, Red Njal. If you see Red Njal, pole off to the river and row for it – upriver. Make sure the girl is safe and kept on board.'

Trollaskegg blinked a bit, then nodded. The water was up and it would be hard pull against the narrowed spate.

'Can I go ashore?' asked a voice and we all turned to where Dark Eye stood. She wore a tunic, one of Yan's for he was smallest, yet it suited her for a dress down to her calves.

I shook my head. 'Later perhaps,' I added and she drowned me with those seal eyes, making me ashamed of even that friendly lie.

'We should go armed,' growled Finn and again I shook my head, never taking my eyes off her. No sense in inviting trouble. A sword, as was proper, but no byrnie or helms or shields or great bearded axes. Finn grunted, unconvinced.

'I see no trouble,' Onund argued, looking around, while the messenger waited, tapping his staff impatiently.

We had come upriver on a raiding boat with the prows up, smoke from a burning staining the sky behind us and the warning whispers of enemies in every ear. Even allowing for the folk on the west bank not liking those on the east, traders in geegaws, along with everyone else, would have vanished like snow off a sun-warmed dyke at the sight of us. Yet here they were, lying and haggling, not in the least afraid – but it had taken them two hours and more to be so friendly.

Onund thought about it, frowning, but it was Dark Eye who dunted him gently to the centre of it.

'They have been told not to be afraid, to make us welcome,' she said, soft as the lisp of rain. 'They have been told that either we are no danger – or will be made to be no danger.'

'Heya,' Finn said, grasping it. 'It is a trap then.'

'And you walk into it like a bairn?' Bjaelfi accused, but Finn clapped him on the shoulder, grinning.

'It is only a trap if there is no escape from it,' he said.

'There is only escape if others come for us,' Crowbone added. 'What are Onund and Trollaskegg and Abjorn and the others to do?'

I looked at him and them and shrugged.

'I am thinking you may have to hold a *Thing* on that for yourselves,' I said, 'once the girl and the ship both are safe.'

'Quickly,' added Finn meaningfully to Trollaskegg. 'So you reach that part where you come to rescue us.'

The place was more than *thorp*, less than town, a fetid cluster of little log houses with steep roofs that came almost to the ground, with a shop or a workplace in an open part and sleeping benches in an attached, closed space.

Tight-herded about split-pine walkways, the houses teemed with life and smells – but the messenger who led us seemed well-known and folk moved out of our path, even those who struggled with heavy loads of fish, or barrels. In any trade town further north, the haughty messenger, stick or no, would have been kicked into the side muck, as Finn pointed out.

I was only vaguely aware of it. As we left, she had whispered, 'Come back alive,' and my arm and my cheek burned – the one where her hand had laid, the other where her lips had touched. Finn had growled like a guard hound and shaken his head. I was still swimming up from the depths of her seal eyes as we traipsed after the messenger.

The houses straggled out, became more withy and less wood, until they stopped entirely. Then there was the fortress, the approach to it lined with cages on poles and, in most of them,

a dessicated, rot-blackened affair that had once been human. A few of them, I saw, were fresher dead than that.

It was a good, solid affair, ditched and stockaded, with a solid half-timber, half-stone keep on a mound – what the Rus-Slavs call *kreml* and *detinets*, though there were no Rus-Slavs here. No Wends, either, I saw and we all exchanged meaningful glances, for the leather-armoured spearholders at the gates were big, ox-shouldered Saxlanders, who stared straight ahead. The wind hissed through the cages, played teasingly with the lank straggles of remaining hair.

This Kasperick was also Saxlander, I was thinking, when we were eventually ushered into the hall, a place drifting with a mist of smoke, where people in the dim light seemed transparent as ghosts.

There was heat, but it came from a clay stove, which I had seen before in *izbas* in Novgorod. There was light, too, from sconces stuck on the pillars, metal-backed to keep the wood from scorching and most of them were clustered round a high seat, on which was this Kasperick.

He did not rise to greet us, which got a growl from Crowbone; his voice had broken completely now and our amusement with his testing of it had ebbed. The rest of us had been to the Great City and were used to these sorts of manners – but Kasperick was no Greek nor, I was thinking, was he Wend.

Saxlander then, I decided, watching his white hands flutter over documents. A ring caught the sconce light on a carved surface and played with it as I watched his square face, handsome once but running to jowl even under the red-gold beard, as neat-trimmed as his hair. I watched his eyes, too, which were watching us and not the documents he held.

I did not think he could read at all and, if he did, it was birchbark he read on and had probably brought out the parchment – and the seal-ring, the expensive, fur-trimmed robe he wore and the Christ cross round his neck – to impress us with

225

his riches and power and learning. All of it, of course, a mummer's play.

'I am here, merchant,' I said, like an iron bar dropped on a stone floor. He looked up languidly and I nodded at the document in his hands. Since parchment was too expensive to waste, both sides had been written on and the one I saw was in Latin and I could read it easily save that it was upside down. I took a chance that the side he was supposed to be reading was the same way.

'You may find that more interesting if you turn it the right way up,' I added and he fluttered his hands and scowled, a look as nasty as a black storm on the Baltic, when he realised he had given himself away. Then, in an instant, he was all smiles.

'Of course,' he said in smooth Norse, with only a slight accent. 'Forgive me . . . I am so used to overawing these Wendish folk that I forget, sometimes, who I am dealing with.'

'You are dealing with Orm Ruriksson,' I said. 'A Norse trader from Hestreng who can read runes and Latin, speaks Latin and Greek and some few other tongues and knows every sort of coin folk use in the world. Who am I dealing with?'

'Kasperick,' he answered, then chuckled, waving forward a thrall with a fat silver pitcher. 'Sit, sit,' he added, waving expansively at the benches, so we did so and the thrall poured – wine, I saw, rich and red and unwatered. Crowbone barely sipped his; Red Njal guzzled down half of his before he realised it was in a cup of expensive blue glass and fell to examining it. Finn never touched his at all and neither did I.

'Trader?' Kasperick went on, lacing his white fingers together and smiling. 'You are, I suspect, no more a trader than I am a merchant.'

'So – what are you?'

'Slenzanie,' he replied lightly. 'Saxlander to you, but I am of the Slenzanie tribe and charged with holding this place as a concern by the Margrave Hodo. You may call me lord.'

'Is that the same Hodo who got his arse kicked by the Pols at Cidini?' Finn demanded scornfully, for he had listened carefully to the talk back in Joms. Kasperick pursed his mouth like a cat's arse but, just then, Red Njal, engrossed in the lights within the blue glass cup, turned it up to look at the bottom; wine spashed on his knees and he looked up guiltily.

'There was such a ... setback,' Kasperick replied stiffly. 'We shall make the Pols pay for that and no-one should make the mistake of thinking we are weakened because of that battle. Especially you *Ascomanni*, who think yourselves lords of the rivers because your king, Bluemouth, is humping a Wendish princess.'

'Well, now we are off to a fine beginning for two folk who are not merchants,' I answered, 'for we are trading insults well enough. It is not Bluemouth, but Bluetooth, though I am thinking you know this.'

His eyes flicked a little, but he kept his lips tight as a line of stitching.

'You are right to call us *Ascomanni* – Ashmen – for we are northers with good ash spears,' I went on into the stone of his face, 'but we are not Bluetooth's Danes. At least, not the ones you know of, from Joms, for they are mostly Wends of no account, but I am thinking you know this, too. We are mostly Svears and a few Slavs from further east and north, whom the Serkland Arabs call Rus, but I am not expecting you to know that. Perhaps a Dzhadoshanie or an Opolanie would have known that – even one of the Lupiglaa – but I make allowances for the wit-lack of the Slenzanie.'

I had been listening well at Joms, too. Two red spots appeared on Kasperick's cheeks at this and there was a sucking in of breath from the ghosts who listened and watched in the dimness at the mention of the other, rival, tribes of the Silesians.

Kasperick controlled himself with an effort, though the smile started to tremble a little. He drank to cover himself and took a breath or two.

227

'No matter who you are,' he said after a moment or two and waved a dismissive hand, 'you all appear the same to me, you Northmen. It is what you carry on your ship that matters.'

'Ah, you still have your merchant hat on, I see,' I replied and then spread my hands in apology. 'I suspect some folk from downriver have tried to mire our good name, but they are mean-mouthed nithings. We have nothing much more than some *wadmal* and a few furs. Hardly worth your time. Besides – I have handseled a deal on that.'

'You have the Mazur girl,' he answered, his voice like a slap.

Finn growled and I took a breath. How had he known that? My thoughts whirled up like leaves in a *djinn* of wind.

'Slaves?' I managed to answer. 'One slave? She is thin and you have, I am thinking, plumper girls closer to hand.'

'I like Mazur ones,' he replied, enjoying himself now he had set us back on our heels. Oiled smooth as a Greek beard he was now and Finn's scowl revealed how he did not care for it much.

'To a man used to Slenzanie women, I suppose she would be sweet,' he grunted. 'They all smell of fish, though they are never near the sea.'

The red spots reappeared and Kasperick leaned forward, his eyes narrowed and his fingers steepled.

'You are the one called Finn,' he said, 'who fears nothing. We will see about that.'

Now how had he known that? A suspicion trailed fingers across my thoughts, but Finn was curling his lip in a sneer, which distracted me.

'The Mazur girl,' I said hastily, before Finn spat out a curse at him, 'is not a slave and good Christmenn do not enslave the free, or so I had heard.'

I nodded at the cross peeping shyly out from above the neck of his tunic and he glanced down and frowned.

'This? I took this from a Sorb, one of a band I had to deal

with. You probably saw them on the way in, safely caged. I am a Christ follower but not one of these Greeks, who can all argue that God does not exist save in Constantinople.'

I stopped, chilled, as he brought it out and waved it scornfully – the Christ cross was a fat Greek one, plain dark wood with a cunning design of the Tortured God on it worked in little coloured tiles; I had seen it before, but not round Kasperick's plump neck.

'You are Christ-sworn yourself,' he went on, smirking, 'and I suspect this Mazur girl is not. So passing her to me is no sin.'

It was my turn to look down and frown. He had seen the little cross on a thong hanging on my breastbone.

'This? I had this from the first man I ever killed,' I told him, which was the truth – though it was truer to say the man had been a boy. I had been fifteen when I did it.

'That other trinket that looks like a cross is a good Thor Hammer,' I added. 'There is another, the *valknut*, which is an Odin sign.'

Kasperick frowned. 'I had heard you were baptised.'

I shook my head and smiled apologetically, more sure than ever about who had been whispering in Kasperick's ear.

'If your God is willing to prevent evil but not able then he is not all-wise and all-seeing, as gods are supposed to be,' I told him. 'If he is able but not willing, then he is more vicious than a rat in a barrel. If he is both able and willing, then from where comes all the evil your priests rave about? If he is neither able nor willing, then why call him a god?'

'So,' he said thoughtfully. 'A follower of Thor? Odin? Some other dirty-handed little farmer god of the Wends, one with four faces? No matter – they will help you here no better than the Sorbs I caged outside, no matter how clever your words.'

'I thought those Sorbs were good Christmenn,' I answered, trying to think clearly as I spoke. 'Like you.'

'I took this cross from them, as they took it from a Greek

priest they sold. They used the money to get drunk and once drunk they killed a man. So there is the Lord at work – even if it was only a Greek priest he worked through.'

I blinked with the thunderbolt of it, a strike as hard as Thor's own Hammer. I had been right about the cross, then.

'Did this Greek priest have a boy with him?' I asked. 'A Northerner – a Dane.'

Kasperick, bewildered at the way this conversation had suddenly darted off the path, waved an irritated hand.

'They sold them both to another of your sort. He was going upriver.'

Upriver. A slave dealer going upriver and buying a Greek monk and a boy. The chill in me settled like winter haar.

'The dealer,' I asked. 'Did he have marks on him, blue marks? A beard like a badger's arse?'

The conversation was now a little dog which would not come to heel and Kasperick was scowling a leash at it.

'There was such a man,' he hissed, 'but enough of this. Fetch the girl and be done with it, for you have no choice in the matter.'

Randr Sterki had Leo and Koll and one swift glance sideways let me know that Finn and Crowbone had realised it, too. So did Red Njal, who had been strange since Hlenni's death and was now starting to tremble at the edges, the way wolf-coats do when the killing rage comes on.

'Red Njal,' I said sharply and he blinked and shook himself like a dog coming out of water. Kasperick, wary and angry as a wet cat, lifted a hand and men appeared, leather-armoured, carrying spears and bulking out the light. Finn, who hated Saxlanders, curled his lip at them.

'Step out and go and fetch the Mazur girl,' I told Red Njal and he looked at me, then at Kasperick and grinned, nodded and hirpled away on his bad leg. I settled on the bench, waiting and Crowbone cocked his head sideways, like a bird and stared curiously at Kasperick.

'What?' demanded Kasperick, suspicious and scowling, but Crowbone merely shrugged.

'Once,' he said, 'a long time gone – don't ask me when – up in Dovrefell in the north of Norway, there was a troll.'

'This will pass the time until folk return with my Mazur girl,' Kasperick announced pointedly and there was a dutiful murmur of laughter from the dim figures behind him. Crowbone waggled his head from side to side.

'Perhaps,' he said, 'perhaps not. This is not a long tale, for this troll was famous for two things – he was noted for his ugliness, even by other trolls and that fame was outstripped only by his stupidity. One day, he found a piece of bread in a cleft in the rock and was delighted, for food is scarce for trolls in Dovrefell. So he gripped it tight – then found he could not get his fist out unless he let the crust go. He thought about it a long time, but there was no way round it – he had to let go, or stay where he was and he could not make up his mind. For all I know, he is there yet, with a fistful of stale crumbs, but determined never to let go.'

'Trolls are notorious fools,' Kasperick agreed sourly.

'A man should always know when to let go of something he cannot hang on to,' Crowbone countered blankly.

In only minutes, it seemed, someone pounded breathlessly in and hurled himself to the ear of Kasperick, whispering furiously. The red spots flared and Kasperick leaped up.

'Only a troll tries to hang on to what is beyond his grasp,' Crowbone announced and Kasperick bellowed as the ox-shouldered guards dragged Red Njal back in and flung him to us; there was blood on his beard and on his teeth, but his grin let us know *Short Serpent* was safe away.

'The bigger the bairn, the bigger the burden,' he said, then spat blood at Kasperick.

'As my granny used to say,' he added.

Kasperick, his face a snarl, snapped an order and the oxen Saxlander guards lumbered towards us. From the dimness,

231

one of the ghosts gained shape, sliding forward onto the bench opposite and grinning at me as hands ripped our weapons from us.

Now I knew how Kasperick had heard so much of us. That face, with no grin on it at all, I had last seen on the hard-packed floor of Hestreng, where the hot iron that had seared the ugly scar across it and blistered one eye to a puckered hole, had started a fire on his chest. I had put it out and left him.

'Bjarki,' I said into his weasel smile. 'I should have let you burn.'

FIFTEEN

The place stank like a *blot* stone, all offal and roasted meat and was not much of a prison, just a large cage in an old storeroom strewn with stinking straw, the bars made from thick balks of timber reinforced with iron.

The cage was up against one wall of this stone room, part of the lower foundations of the keep and once an underground store for the kitchens, for the stone walls were cold. Now the place was hung with chains and metal cuffs, dark with stains and leprous from the heat of the brazier. There were two thick-barred squares to let in light and circling air but they did not do much work on either.

The Saxlanders flung us into the cage and one locked the door with a huge key, his tongue between his teeth as he concentrated on getting it right. They had taken away everything of value and left our weapons on a nearby table where we could see them, but not get to them.

When they were gone, leaving us alone in the half-light, a grinning Finn fished in one boot and brought out his long, black Roman nail.

'If those Saxlanders had any clever in them,' he said, grinning, 'it was well hidden. Unlike my nail, which they should

233

have found even if they were looking for my money – boots, balls and armpits, as any raiding man knows.'

He went to the lock and discovered, in short order and at the cost of a bloody finger, that this prison was no little chest of treasures with a dainty lock that could be snapped. The one penning us in was huge and solid and would not be cracked open with a Roman nail, which was also too thick to use as a pick.

'That Bjarki,' Finn growled, sucking the grimy, bleeding finger as if that man had done it to him personally. He shoved the nail back in his boot.

'This is not much of a prison,' Crowbone mused, looking round. It was not, as I agreed, but it was enough of one for me; what bothered me most were the wall chains and cuffs, the glowing brazier and the thick, scarred wooden table littered with tools I did not think belonged to a forge-man, though some of them were similar.

'I did not like the look of that Kasperick at all,' Red Njal grunted. 'He has the eyes of one who likes to see blood spilled, provided it is not his own and there is no danger in it. A man who, as my granny used to say, prefers to build the lowest fences, since it is easiest for him to cross.'

'Well,' said Finn, settling down with his back to one wall, 'we will find out soon enough.'

I did not like the idea and was envious – not for the first time – of how he could sit with his eyes half-closed, as if he dozed on a bench near a warm fire after a good meal and some ale. I said as much and he grinned.

'The smell, I am thinking,' he answered wistfully. 'It reminds me of the feast we had at Vladimir's hall, the one just before we all went out on to the Grass Sea to hunt down Atil's treasure.'

'Is that the one where you threw someone in the pitfire?' Red Njal demanded, though he grinned when he said it and I was pleased to see that; the death of Hlenni had been sitting heavy on him.

'Not someone – the son of the advisor to Prince Yaropolk, Vladimir's brother,' Crowbone pointed out and both he and Finn laughed.

'One side of his face now looks like Finn's left bollock,' Crowbone added, 'wrinkled and ugly.'

'You never saw my bollocks, boy,' Finn countered, 'for you are not struck blind and dumb with amazement and admiration – besides, it was not for quarrels that I remember that feast night. It was for the blood sausage. I ate one as long as my arm.'

'You were as sick as a mangy dog,' Red Njal reminded him and Finn waved a dismissive hand.

'That was a swallow or two of bad ale,' he corrected. 'Anyway – I ate another arm-length after, to make up for what had been lost.'

That feast had seen great cakes of bread and fried turnips and stewed meat, fished out of pots on the end of long spits, I remembered, for Vladimir held to the old ways of his great-grandfather. But the smell of a man's face and hair burning in the fire had soured much of it for me and left us with a lasting enemy – another one, as if we did not have enough of them.

Boiled blood and spew, that's what this place reminded me of and I said as much.

Finn shrugged.

'I recall it now only because we were all in prison there, too,' he added. 'You, me and Crowbone at least. And we got out of that.'

True enough. We had been flung in Vladimir's pit-prison when Crowbone put his little axe in Klerkon's forehead, which was not a bad thing in our eyes. However, he did it in the main square of Holmgard, Vladimir's Novgorod, which had not been clever. That time, we faced a stake up our arses; now we faced a hanging-cage until we starved or were stoned to death.

'Any tales that might help?' I asked Crowbone and he frowned; it was one of his better stories that had made us all laugh and got us hauled out of the pit-prison, since laughter was not usually the sound that came from such a place.

'It would be better if I stopped telling such tales,' he answered moodily. 'They are child's matters and I am a man now.'

'Your voice has snapped,' Finn pointed out, 'which is not the same thing. Let me know when your own bollocks drop like wrinkled walnuts and then I may consider calling you a man.

'Anyway,' he added, 'I like your tales.'

Which was an astounding lie from the man who had once rattled Crowbone into the thwarts of a boat at the announcement 'Once there was a man . . .'. Crowbone merely looked at Finn with his odd eyes narrowed.

'So we die here,' Red Njal grunted, in the same voice he would have used deciding on where to curl up and sleep for a while. 'Well, not the place I would have chosen, but we wear what the Norns weave for us. Better ask for too little than offer too much, as my granny used to say.'

I was thinking we would not die, for this Kasperick wanted the Mazur girl and the profit that could be had selling her to the Pols – or her own folk, whichever paid most – but he had to lay hands on her first. He would use us to trade with the crew of *Short Serpent*.

'He is a belly-crawler,' Finn pointed out when I mused on this. 'He will not hold to such a trade and will kill us anyway.'

Then Bjarki came in, sliding round the storeroom door like rancid seal oil, his grin stretched to a leer by the ruined side of his mouth.

'Kill me now,' Finn growled when he saw him, 'rather than have to suffer the gloat of a little turd like this.'

Bjarki, who was alone, came and sat carefully out of reach beyond the bars.

'No easy death for you, Finn Horsehead,' he slurred through his twisted mouth. 'Nor, especially, for you, Orm Bear Slayer. I owe you an eye and a scar.'

'When you meet Onund,' I warned him, 'be ready to pay more than that.'

'Expecting a rescue, Bear Slayer?' Bjarki jeered.

'You should be afraid,' answered Crowbone, 'for the Oathsworn are coming.'

Bjarki curled his lip.

'You are a little diminished,' he pointed out. 'A king with no crown, a prince with no *hird*. A shadow of what you were, boy. Soon even that will be gone.'

'A shadow is still a powerful thing,' Crowbone said. 'Once there existed somewhere in the world – do not ask me when, do not ask me where – a place where the Sami learned to be workers of powerful *seidr* magic. Wherever this place was, it was somewhere below ground, eternally dark and changeless. There was no teacher either, but everything was learned from fiery runes, which could be read quite easily in the dark. Never were the pupils allowed to go out into the open air or see the daylight during the whole time they stayed there, which was from five to seven years. By then they had gained all they needed of the Sami art.'

'Ha,' scowled Bjarki. 'What a poor tale. How did they eat in all this time, then?'

'A shaggy grey hand came through the wall every day with meals,' answered Crowbone without as much as a breath of hesitation. 'When they had finished eating and drinking the same hand took back the horns and platters.

'They saw no-one but each other and that only in the dim light of the fiery runes,' he went on and Bjarki, scowling, was fixed by it. 'Those same runes told them the only rule of the place, which was that the Master should keep for himself the student who was last to leave the school every year. Considering that most folk who knew of the place thought

Loki himself was the Master, you may fancy what a scramble there was at each year's end, everybody doing his best to avoid being last to leave.

'It happened once that three Icelanders went to this school, by the name of Sæmundur the Learned, Kálfur Arnason, and one called, simply, Orm; and as they all arrived at the same time, they were all supposed to leave at the same time. Seven years later, when it came to taking the bit of it in their teeth, Orm declared himself willing to be the last of them, at which the others were much lightened in mind. So he threw over himself a large cloak, leaving the pin loose.

'A staircase led to the upper world, and when Orm was about to mount this Loki grasped at him and said, "You are mine!" But Orm ducked his head, slipped free and made off with all speed, leaving Loki the empty cloak. However, just as he reached the heavy iron yett beyond the door, it slammed shut. "Did you imagine that the Father of Tricksters would be fooled by that?" said a dark voice from the blackness.

'A great hand reached out to drag Orm back just as he saw the sun for the first time in seven years, a great blaze of light which fell on him, throwing his shadow onto the wall behind him. Orm said: "I am not the last. Do you not see who follows me?"

'So Loki, mistaking the shadow for a man, raised the yett and grabbed at the shadow, allowing Orm to escape – but from that hour Orm was always shadowless, for whatever Loki took, he never gave back again.'

There was silence and then Bjarki gave an uneasy laugh, while Finn beamed like a happy uncle and clapped Crowbone on the back.

'As I said – I like your tales. They seldom miss the mark.'

'A boy's tale,' Bjarki scowled back. 'There will be no shadow-escape for you and the Oathsworn are unlikely to be storming this fortress.'

238

He broke off and smeared a grin on his face, ugly as a hunchbacked rat.

'Well – here is one of your saviours coming now, fresh from this hero-saga,' he added as sounds clattered at the door. It swung open and two huge Saxlanders dragged in a slumped, dangle-headed figure. Two more men scowled their way in after them.

Bjarki moved to the prisoner and lifted his head by the hair; it was Styrbjorn and the surprise of it must have showed in all our faces, for Bjarki frowned; he had not been expecting that. His face twisted even more when one of the Saxlander guards slapped his hand free with a short, phlegm-thick curse. The other fetched the key, opened the door and slung Styrbjorn in, so that he crashed to the floor and bounced.

Bjarki sniggered, hovering by the door and the irritated guard shoved him back, so that he staggered and almost fell; one hand flew to the dagger at his belt and the guard, ring-mailed and helmed and armed with a great stave of spear looked inquiringly at him, then laughed when Bjarki saw what he was about to do and took his hand away.

'You are not as welcome here as you make it seem, little bear,' Finn said with a dry laugh. One of the men who had followed Styrbjorn into the room, bald-headed and stubbled on a sharp chin, spat at him then, which narrowed Finn's eyes.

'Your welcome is worse,' Stubble-Chin said. 'This Styrbjorn killed Pall, which is red murder. No matter what happens, he will swing in a cage for it.'

'Which one are you?' asked Crowbone. 'Freystein? I did not ever hear the name of the fourth man.'

'I am Freystein,' said the second man and jerked a thumb at the bald-headed one. 'He is Thorstein, Pall's brother.'

'Ah,' said Finn knowingly. 'Same litter – I thought I saw it, but was not sure. All rats look the same to me.'

The door opened again and the Saxlander guards straightened a little as Kasperick came in, lifting the trailing hem of his

239

robe from the floor of the place. He surveyed the scene with a satisfied smile and moved to the table where our possessions had been left, lifting Crowbone's sword admiringly.

'A fine and cunning weapon,' he said, drawing it out and swinging it once or twice. 'A little light, but perfect for a boy.'

Then he drew mine, which was Jarl Brand's and he smiled like a cream-fed cat over that one. Then there was Styrbjorn's; the silk wrapping was gone. When he drew The Godi, Finn growled, hackled like a hound on a boar scent.

'Four swords of price,' he declared. 'Not a bad day – you three can take the rest of their possessions as reward. Get out.'

Bjarki and the others blinked and Bjarki looked as if he would argue, but the two huge guards leaned forward a little and the three of them left, summoning up as much swagger as they could, which was not much.

'They expected more,' I said, 'for whispering in your ear about the Mazur girl.'

Kasperick waved a languid hand. 'They are little yaps, from that large dog Pallig Tokeson. One day, we will deal with Pallig, but his little pups are useful and of small account to me when they have barked. To each other, too, I am thinking – the death of Pall will not concern them much, save that they can now split the reward I gave them into thirds instead of fourths.'

He settled his rump on the edge of the table and looked us over.

'You will send word to release the Mazur girl,' he declared. 'In return, I will release all of you – except the one they call Styrbjorn, for he is guilty of murder.'

'Styrbjorn? What does one of Pallig's little yappers matter to you?' I countered and he nodded, a nasty smile on his face.

'Nothing,' he agreed, 'save that justice must be seen to be done – anyway, I have gone to all the trouble of lighting a brazier and started heating up instruments. I will not have all my enjoyment removed.'

The threat was plain enough and he saw it had hit home as he slid his arse off the table.

'You have until first light to think,' he added flatly. Then he swept out, followed by the two guards; the door banged shut behind them, leaving us alone in the fetid half-dark.

'One who sees a friend roasting on a spit tells all he knows,' Red Njal noted. 'My granny said so and it remains true.'

'Spit-luck for us, then, that Styrbjorn is a few wrist-clasps short of a friend to any of us,' Finn answered and prodded the luckless subject with one toe. Styrbjorn groaned and Red Njal bent briefly to look at him.

'Lump like a gull's egg and a bruise, nothing much more,' he growled, straightening. Finn took the pisspot and emptied the contents on Styrbjorn, who surfaced, wheezing and blowing.

'Better?' Finn inquired as Styrbjorn blinked into the Now of it all. The enormity of where he was crashed on him like creaming surf and he subsided.

'I thought it was a dream,' he groaned.

'If it is,' Red Njal told him, 'dream me out of it.'

'No dream,' I told him harshly. 'What did you do to Pall?'

Styrbjorn shifted, rolled over and sat up slowly, like a sobering drunk after a feast. He touched the lump on his forehead and winced.

'Pall made straight for his three friends,' Styrbjorn explained. 'We just looked for the cheapest, noisiest drinking place in the settlement and, sure enough, there they were, having already poured Pallig's poison in the ear of this Kasperick about us. Pall told them of the value of the Mazur girl, said we should tell Kasperick and he would surely reward us.'

'I said he was a rat and that releasing him was a bad idea. And you went with them,' Finn growled meaningfully. Styrbjorn held his head and groaned.

'Aye, well, I was not all that welcome there, since they

241

blamed me for much that had happened, especially the one called Bjarki – silly name for a grown man, is it not?'

No-one argued with that, so he sat up a little more and then began sniffing suspiciously at the damp on him.

'The other three went off, saying that Pall and me should watch the ship – what did you just pour on me, Finn Horsehead?'

'Healing balm,' I said, wanting him to keep to the sharp of his tale. 'What happened then?'

He blinked and made himself more comfortable, closing his eyes. I remembered a time when I had taken a dunt to the head and almost felt sorry for him. Almost.

'Then we waited in the rain for a while,' Styrbjorn went on after a moment. 'We saw the crew coming back, not all at once, but in ones and twos and seeming to be easy and light about it until they were aboard. Pall said the ship was getting ready to leave, which was clear to any sailing man; he said he was off to warn Bjarki that the prize was slipping away.'

He paused and frowned, then sniffed again.

'This is piss,' he declared accusingly.

'What happened?' I snarled and he raised an eyebrow at me, then shrugged, which act made him wince. This time I felt no sympathy.

'I thought it best not to let him,' he said. 'So I slit his throat and dropped him in the river.'

'Heya,' growled Finn admiringly and Styrbjorn smiled. I looked at the youth with some new and grudging respect; he had decided to save us and killed a man without so much as a blink – yet it was a throat-cut in the dark.

I was thinking that was what kept Styrbjorn from being the hero-king he wanted to be. He could kill, right enough, but would rather be sleekit about it than face a man in a fair fight; even his saving of me was a stab to my enemy's back.

Nor had he been sleekit enough about the killing of Pall, either, since he got caught.

242

'Aye,' he agreed wryly when I pointed this last fact out to him. 'I was making for the ship, for it was now the safest place for me to be after dropping the little turd in the water, when Bjarki and the others turned up with some armed men. They grabbed me and Bjarki asked where Pall was, so the whole matter came out in the open soon after.'

He paused, defiantly.

'If it had not been for them being so bothered with me,' he added, 'the ship might not have pulled safely away at all.'

I let him think it, even if I doubted it to be true. Not that any of that helped us here, as I whispered to Finn, drawing him a little apart from the others.

'Aye,' he answered, then grinned. 'Though there may yet be a way out of this cage. Best if we wait for dark. Best also if I keep it to myself, just in case this Kasperick grows impatient for spit-roasts and questioning.'

The thought that he had a plan when I did not was nagging enough, but the idea that he did not want to share it made matters worse. As the faint light from the barred squares in the wall faded we sat in silence; I did not know what the others were thinking, but home swam up in the maelstrom of my thoughts.

I dreamed up a new Hestreng, with soaring roof and many high rooms, grand as any king's and rich with cunning carvings. I summoned up Thorgunna in it and a fine-limbed boy and thralls and a forge and sturdy wharves where all my ships swung gently.

It was a good dream, save for some annoyances; the face of the fine-limbed son was always Koll and accusing. Nor could I place myself anywhere in this neatly-crafted hall.

Worst of all, I could not put a remembered face on Thorgunna at all and summoning up the night moments, hip to hip and thigh to thigh, languorous and loving, only brought a small, tight-muscled body and a sharp face with those huge, seal eyes.

'Well,' said a voice, cracking Hestreng apart; I was almost grateful to see Red Njal hunkered near.

'Well?' I countered and he gave me a look as glassed and grey as a Baltic swell.

'I am thinking we will not get out of this.'

'A man's life is never finished until Skuld snips the last thread of it,' I said.

'Aye, right enough – but best to search while a trail is new, as my granny told me. I can feel the edge of that Norn's shears and wish only to make it known to you and the gods that I bear no malice, for we are oathed to each other and I took it freely. I would not want to come as a *draugr* to bother your family.'

It took me a moment to realise he meant he would die because of my wyrd, which I had brought on myself with my sacrifice-promise to Odin. I swallowed any venom I had to spit at him for it all the same and thanked him nicely, though I could not help but add that it was only my wyrd to die and not his. Perhaps the gods would be content with just the one death, I told him, just to watch him brighten like a bairn who had been promised a new seax for his name-day.

'Ah, well,' he answered. 'I thought to mention it, all the same. Care gnaws the heart when a man cannot tell all his mind to another.'

'Your granny was a singular woman,' I told him, straight-faced into his delighted grins.

And all the while I felt Einar at my back, the old leader who had brought his own wyrd down on himself and whom we had cursed for it, sure he was leading all the Oathsworn of that time into their doom. Not for the first time, I knew how Einar the Black had felt.

'I do not think it is my wyrd to die here,' frowned Crowbone and that did not surprise me either; the arrogance of youth was doubled and re-doubled in that odd-eyed man-boy.

'Then you can be the one to rescue Koll,' Finn decreed.

Styrbjorn sniffed and tentatively marked out the edges of pain on his lumped forehead.

'Jarl Brand is a good man,' he agreed, 'and a generous ring-giver, it is true – but would we be plootering through the rain after him if Orm did not owe him it as foster-father to his son?'

Again my fault and I let some anger slip the leash into my voice.

'Would you not go after the boy only to save him, then?' I demanded. 'It is all your wyrd that he is taken and we are in this mire.'

Styrbjorn thought about it, frowning and serious.

'You have the truth of it being as a result of my quarrel with my uncle,' he admitted, then waved one hand to dismiss it. 'That is the way of such matters and folk cannot go putting all the blame of it on me – war is war, after all.

'As to the boy,' he went on, 'if the reward was good for me, I would go after him. For you it is losing the stain on your fame and regaining the friendship of the jarl who gave you land and a steading. Good reasons – the fame and the friendship of great men is half the secret to ships and men, as you know, Jarl Orm. The other half is silver. But there is too little fame here for me, while Jarl Brand is too small a friendship for a man of my standing.'

He was a nasty twist of a youth, this one, and his arrogance sucked the breath from you. I saw it then, clear as Iceland's Silfra water – Styrbjorn would die from his unthinking attitude, one day or the next.

'You would not try for rescue at all, then?' Finn growled, a twisted grin on his face. 'From where I look, wee man with a lot to say for yourself, you have no standing. You are sitting in piss, with a dunted head and no good fame at all.'

Styrbjorn did not answer, but Crowbone fixed him with that odd-eyed stare.

'You would go if you knew what the lad felt,' he said, in

a voice which had deepened considerably since it had snapped free of boyhood. 'If you were far from home, among enemies, treated as a thrall, thrashed and bound and starved, all that would keep you taking one breath after another was the hope that someone was coming to get you.'

We all remembered, then, the saga of Crowbone's life to this point – a fugitive from the womb, his father dead. A thrall at six, his foster-father slain, his mother the usage of Klerkon's camp, bairned by Kveldulf and then kicked to death by him. At nine, he had been freed by me into the world of the Oathsworn, which was no gentle place for a growing boy.

He looked at me and acknowledged that rescue with only his eyes. Now, at twelve, Crowbone's last foster-father, his Uncle Sigurd, was also dead and, though he had sisters and kin somewhere too dangerous still to visit, he was more alone than the moon. It came to me that this was the reason, more than any, which had made him take our Oath – any family, even the Odin-hagged Oathsworn, was better than none.

'Aye, such a wyrd would be a sore one to swallow,' Styrbjorn agreed, then beamed and slapped Crowbone's shoulder. 'Skalds would make a fair tale about someone so rescued. You have convinced me that there is, after all, enough fame in it – we will hunt down the little bairn and bring him safe home, even if Orm ends up swinging in a cage here.'

'A comfort, for sure,' I muttered darkly and he laughed.

'Where is Randr Sterki going, I am wondering?' Finn asked, frowning. 'I thought he wanted us to come to him, so why is he running?'

For the lack of men, I was thinking. He would want to find a place where there were shiftless swords for hire, for I was betting sure he was crew-light now. I said so and Styrbjorn chuckled.

'Well,' he said brightly, 'in a way you have me to thank for that.'

I could not speak at all, but Red Njal always had a ready tongue.

'The jarl would favour you,' he pointed out, his mildness only adding to the venom of it, 'save that it is unlikely you will survive, even if this Saxlander lord does release us for the Mazur girl. You he wants to keep and play with.'

Styrbjorn's fear slid under the clear surface of his face and he swallowed.

I could scarcely see their features now; their faces were white blobs in the dim and the glow of the brazier coals seemed brighter now that the dark had raced in like Sleipnir, One-Eye's eight-legged stallion.

'If you have a spell to snap this lock, Finn Horsehead,' I grunted, annoyed by their talk of my Odin-wyrd – and, I confess it, belly-clenching afraid of it, too. Finn chuckled and drew out his iron nail, a slash of black in the grey.

'No spell, but *duergar*-magic, all the same,' he said. 'I need your leg bindings, Red Njal.'

Slowly, Red Njal unwound one leg. Once they had been fine, green wool bindings, embroidered in red and with silver clasp-ends – but the ends had gone on dice or drink long since and the frayed ends of wool, now stained to a mud-dark with only the memory of embroidery, were tucked roughly in the bind itself.

For all that, he passed an unravel of them over sullenly, one breeks leg flapping loosely over his shoes. We all watched Finn tie one end of the wool length to his nail and swing it like a depth-line, testing weight and knot – then, sudden as a spark, the whole room lit up in blue-white light.

For an instant, everything stood out, stark and eldritch and the barred squares were etched on the far wall. I saw the faces of the others in that eyeblink, flares of fright and bewilderment and knew my own was no different.

In the utter dark that followed, we heard the millstone grind of thunder, slow and low and then a hiss of rain, faint

through the high, barred squares. A storm; the darkness had indeed raced like Sleipnir for it was not proper night, this.

'I came to knowing of this thanks to the rot,' Finn said calmly, ignoring the light and noise as he adjusted the knot. 'I like this iron nail, for it has served me well from the day I picked it up. On Cyprus, as you will remember, Orm and Njal, when Orm fought the leader of some Danes in a *holmgang*. We used nails like this as *tjosnur*, to properly mark out the fighting boundary.'

The light flared again, flicking him in an instant, frozen image, as he draped the dangling nail through the bars, swung it backwards and forwards a few times, then lobbed it out, trailing the wool binding behind it. The nail whispered through the darkness and slammed on the table, hard enough to leap everything upwards; a wooden beaker fell over on its side and rolled.

The great, rolling rumble of thunder swallowed all sounds of it, seemed to tremble the backs of my teeth and come up through my feet from the floor. Red Njal looked up, just a pale blob of face in the darkness, blooded on one side by the brazier. The brightest thing in that face was the white of his eyes.

'Thor is racing his chariot hard tonight,' he muttered. 'Plead all you please with the gods, but learn a good healing spell, as my granny used to say.'

Thor could race his goats until their hooves fell off, I was thinking, for it hid the noise of Finn's nail-madness – he hauled it off the table onto the flags of the floor and what should have been a bell-loud clatter went unheard in the grinding of the Thunder-God. Finn pulled it back to him and might just as well have been dragging it over eiderdown.

'Being iron,' he said into the silence between thunders, 'it needed careful attention, but I saw that it did not get the same rot as other things of iron. Swords, for example, and axe-heads.'

'Different rot?' muttered Red Njal, with the voice of a man who thought Finn addled. The light flared; Thor's iron-wheeled chariot ground out another teeth-aching rumble.

Finn swung the nail back and forth and launched it again; one more crash on the table set the cup bouncing off with a clatter. Once more the nail hit the floor with a clang and was dragged back.

'If your plan was to alarm the guards,' Styrbjorn muttered, 'it may yet succeed, despite Thor.'

'The rot,' Finn went on, as if Styrbjorn had not spoken at all, 'on most swords and every axe-head I have seen, is the colour of old blood. Everyone knows that and even the best of swords gets it. It leaches from the metal like sap from a tree.'

Thor hurled his hammer in another blue-white flare. The nail trailed its wool tail through the air and slammed into the table-top again. My bone-handled seax fell off this time – together with the key to the cell lock.

'Aha,' said Crowbone. 'Careful when you pull it off the table . . .'

He fell silent when Finn jerked the nail off the table and made no attempt to try and hook the key with it – which, I was thinking, would have been a clever trick if he could have managed it, for he would have to somehow get the nail through the ring of the key, if it was large enough even to take it . . .

'So,' Finn went on, winding his nail back to him, 'I am watching my nail for signs of blood rot and seeing none. Instead, I am finding grit on my fingers, black as charcoal.'

A cold wind through one of the barred squares set the brazier glowing enough to send up some sparks, then trailed fingers through our beards, with the smell of rain and turned earth and escape. Finn bent low and slithered the nail out, underhand, towards the key. It overshot by a few finger-lengths. Again the thunder rumbled and the blue-white scarred our faces into the dark.

'This, I thought, was also rot, so I scraped it all off first time I found it, then laid the nail down to fetch some fat to grease it with,' Finn went on, tentatively tugging the nail this way and that with the wool. 'Yet, when I came back to it, all the grit I had scraped off was back on the nail again.'

He looked up into our silent, gawping faces and grinned at the sight of them.

'It was Ref who put me right on it,' he said, giving a last tug, 'for he knows iron as a farmer knows rye. The iron that leaches red rot is made from bloodstone, which is the most common iron, the stuff you fish out as a bloom on bog-grass. The iron that made my nail is rare, from a dug-out stone, where it is found in little black studs, like pips in an apple.'

He moved the nail a last nudge; the key slid towards it, stopped, slid again and then snugged up next to it. No-one could breathe for the wonder of it and even the thunder did not seem as loud.

'Ref says,' Finn went on, half to himself as he slowly dragged his nail, the key stuck to it as tight as a resin-trapped fly, 'that this iron embraces all the other iron it sees.'

He scooped the nail and key up and grinned at us, dangling it, swinging it gently back and forth.

'Be happy this key is not made of gold.'

The lightning seared the image of us staring at him, fixed by the sight of that key, sucked firmly to the side of the nail. The Thunder-God boomed out a laugh.

'There is clever for you,' muttered Red Njal, sullenly splintering the silence that followed. 'Can I have my binding back? There is a cold wind blowing right up the sheuch of my arse.'

Thor-light flicked us when we wraithed through the door of the storeroom; an eyeblink of stark, white light showed us the long, gentle slope up to the surface, a ramp where once barrels of salted meat and ale had been rolled. That was before

Kasperick had taken the place over for his own sick-slathered pleasures.

At the top should have been a pair of double-doors, shut and barred on the outside and only fixed with chains and a lock when something of true value was inside. And guards, always guards, at least one against the pilferers when it was a store, two, I was thinking, now that it was something else. Yet they were more to prevent folk coming across what Kasperick did in his pleasure room rather than keep his prisoners getting out.

But the rain snaked in hissing waves and the two guards Kasperick had left had opened the doors and crept inside a little way for shelter; the startling flash showed them, crouched, draped in iron and rightly afraid of attracting Perun's eye, fixed as rabbits on the stoat of Thor-lights.

No-one had to speak; Finn and Red Njal moved up like a pair of boarhounds, almost in step with one another. Red Njal's seax gleamed briefly and one guard went sagging against him, scarcely making more than a sigh as his throat was cut.

Finn made a mess of it. Though he had done this before, his Roman nail was no edged weapon and relied on his brute strength and placing skill to tear out the voice of the guard as well as rip through the heart-in-the-throat, where life pulsed.

The guard half-turned when he saw his oarmate go down to Red Njal, a movement that put Finn's perfect thrust off by a hair; the Roman nail ripped in and blood spurted straight back in Finn's eyes. Blinded and cursing, he let the nail and the man go to sweep the gore away.

The nail clattered to the stone flags and the guard, his mouth opening and closing like a dying fish, staggered out into the hissing downpour, his hands clamped to his throat and blood spraying through his fingers. He could not yell and the air hissed and bubbled from his torn throat as he tried, but he reeled in circles in the rain – and someone saw him.

The yell went through me like one of Thor's ragged blue-white bolts. Finn scooped up his nail, still cursing and sprang forward; one thrust took the nail into the gasping guard's eye, an in-out movement that sent him backwards like a felled oak.

Too late, I was thinking as someone started smacking the alarm-iron, far too late . . .

'Row for it, lads!' roared Finn.

Make for the main gate. I heard myself screaming it like a chant and sprinted into the rain, sword out. It was not proper night and the main gate would still be open, for folk came and went on all sorts of business in a fortress such as this.

The confusion helped us. The alarm was beating, but no-one knew why, or who they were looking for and we were most of the way across the yard before I heard someone bellowing out to close the gates. I spun in a half-circle, blinking rain out of my face and saw the others closing on me. A lancing fern of blue-white fretted the dark and, in the flicker of its life, showed us to each other; the great crash that followed was a mountain falling, drowning all other sound and leaving my mouth fizzing with each ragged breath.

'Keep Crowbone in the middle,' I yelled and did not have to add the why of it; he was too small and light in a fight. Finn came to my shieldless side, Styrbjorn on the other and we splattered through the muddy yard – so close now, I could hear the creak and groan of bad hinging and wood as men put shoulders to the gates.

We passed them, slashing left and right and they scattered, unarmed for the most part. Styrbjorn gave a yelp as someone snarled out at him with a fistful of steel, but he took the blow on his blade well enough and back-slashed, hardly pausing at all and not bothering to see if he had done damage. Shouts went up behind us. Arrows whicked by my head and one shunked into the back of a fleeing gateman, so that Crowbone had to hurdle him.

We were through the gate, skittering on the slick, uneven log walkway and the yells were different behind us, fewer and more commanding as the garrison sorted itself out; the stark, white, flash of Thor-light sent the luckless caged leering at us as we sprinted down their avenue.

We passed two side streets; folk scattered and screamed. At the third, I yelled for everyone to go right, but I was guessing. The dark rumbled and spat white fire, while a wind sprayed rain and flattened a dying, discarded torch flame; a lantern swung and rattled.

I could not be sure and spun in a half-circle, almost falling off the walkway and the others panted up to me.

'Which way?' Styrbjorn wanted to know, jerking this way and that, brimming on the edge of panic. I chose one, a left turn which sloped down. Down was good. Down led to water.

There were screams and the distant clanging of the alarm; Finn growled at a head which stuck out of a doorway and the owner jerked it back again. I stepped off the walkway by accident, a long drop that jarred my foot and pitched me on my face in the clotted mat of rot, split by a running stream. Spitting and coughing, I clawed my way up and back onto the walkway.

'They are closing,' spat Red Njal, which made us all turn to see the dark figures moving down through the buildings. Moving fast, too.

'Fuck,' said Finn, disgustedly. 'I am running from Saxlanders.'

'Good,' snarled Styrbjorn, shoving past him and skidding on the slick logs, 'keep running.'

Finn smile was twisted, his face flared by another flickering message from Thor.

'Take the boy,' he said over his shoulder. 'I am tired of running.'

'Boy . . .' began Crowbone, shrilling it in his anger; Red Njal grabbed him by the shoulder and shoved him after the retreating Styrbjorn.

253

'It is not seemly,' he yelled as he pushed, 'to interrupt a man when he is dying to save you. That is not my granny's saying, but one of my own.'

The dark shapes bobbed and lumbered down the darkness towards us and Finn glanced sideways at me.

'This walkway is narrow enough for one,' he grunted. 'And high enough.'

'Just another bridge,' I answered and his teeth were white in the shadow of his face.

'Bone, blood and steel,' he grunted.

The thunder grumbled and, in the next fern of white light, I saw the Saxlanders, uneasy in their ring-coats and spears with Himself banging around the sky, throwing anger about. They milled uncertainly when the light showed two men with bright blades waiting for them.

'Get them,' shrieked a familiar voice. 'Take them alive.'

Kasperick. I hoped he would come within reach but if I knew that man he would lead from the back. I wiped rain from my face and squinted into the shadows of a day gone night. There were splashes.

'They are off the walkway,' I warned – then a dark shape was on me, panting out of the dark, slick with rain and fear. He was below me, in the mud and filth, glittering with old fishscales and stuck with feathers and hair. He sliced at my ankles with the spear, for he could not see me clearly and thought a scything blow would sweep me off my feet if it failed to cut me.

I hopped up awkwardly, landed badly and on my weak ankle, which shot fire through me. On one knee and cursing, I heard him suck in a triumphant breath and lurch forward; the spearhead, trailing droplets of water, slid past my eye and I slashed wildly, felt the edge hit and heard him scream and the splashing of him stumbling away.

'If you have rested enough,' Finn panted from above me, 'I would be glad of some help.'

254

Two Saxlanders were at him, one on the logs and one off, slithering to keep his balance, ankle-deep in clinging mud.

Finn turned from the one on the walkway, took two steps, swung The Godi up as if for a great downward cut and then kicked the Saxlander spearman in the face as he followed the arc of it, his mouth slightly open. The man hurled backwards with a strangled choking sound; one boot was left stuck in the mud.

During this, I scrambled up and took on the other man, who crabbed and stabbed and huddled behind his shield, so that the best I could do was fend him off. Then he saw Finn was coming for him and backed off into the frustrated bellows of Kasperick, urging his men on.

They were wary, but circling, dropping off one walkway, slogging through the mud and on to another; the flash of white light showed them, dark as hunting wolves and almost behind us.

That same flash showed them stop, almost in mid-step. The darkness that followed was blacker still, but Finn had seen them and stood up straight, throwing out his arms, scattering water droplets like bright pearls.

'I am Finn Bardisson, known as Horsehead, from Skane,' he roared. 'You want me? Here I come, you nithing, chicken-fucking, Saxlander whoresons.'

He hurled himself forward roaring, nail in one hand, The Godi in the other and I tried to snag him before he went, but failed. I half-stumbled on that cursed ankle, feeling the fire-ache of it and the sick, belly-dropping certainty that this was the moment Odin took his sacrifice and that I had doomed Finn with me.

The white light split the darkness again – and they fled.

The Saxlanders turned and ran, stumbling, away from the mad, wild-haired Finn and Kasperick stopped bellowing at them to get us and ran with them. I knelt, panting, bewildered, heard a noise and staggered up on one good foot, whirling round to face the dark shapes behind.

They loomed up, silent and grey-grim against the black. Then the lightning flashed again and I saw them, as the Saxlanders must have seen them, ring-coated and helmed, sharp with edges and grins, their faces streaked black with charcoal and sheep-fat.

Familiar faces – Alyosha, Finnlaith, Abjorn and the others.

'That was a good trick of Finn's,' Styrbjorn said, pushing through to the front, 'waiting until he saw us come up and then charging them. That set them running, for sure.'

Finn strolled back, The Godi over one shoulder, his nail in his teeth. He took it out and shoved it down one boot, then shouldered into the stone-grey ranks of men as we all backed off, heading for the river. I stood, trembling with reprieve.

'You are a fool,' I said to the grinning Styrbjorn, as Abjorn and Ospak helped me hirple away, 'if you think Finn noticed any of you were there at all before he ran at them.'

SIXTEEN

The Odra roared and spat like a boiling cauldron, brimmed over into the woods and growled among the trees. It slashed the higher bank, so that sections of it slithered and sighed in slow splashes and turned the water black-brown. Trees came down, too, teetering slowly with a noise like ripping linen, clawed roots tangling so that they chained to the broken shore and made dams against which other drifts piled.

We watched it all warily, for the current in the river slithered like a coil of mating snakes, first one way, then the other, breaking round *Short Serpent* and fattening out into the floodplain so that we had no idea now where the old shore had been.

The rain fell, too. It had caused all this on the slopes of the distant mountains, now unseen through the fine, misted water that lisped on us and filled the very air so that every breath came as if we held linen cloths over our mouths and noses.

'This is no time to be sitting on this river, I am thinking,' Onund observed mournfully, 'for we can neither use oars nor sail in this and if we sit here, a floater will get us, for sure.'

It was no time to be moving, either, for though we all feared the current and the clutch of water, we feared the floaters

257

most and had seen three or four already, looming out of the boil like whales with great thrashing root-limbs. Hovering for a moment in the current, they would sink from sight again and, like the bergs of the north, most of the dangerous part was unseen. One of those great earth-clogged claws would swipe in the planks of *Short Serpent*.

There was no possibility of stopping, all the same; we had to put distance between us and Kasperick, keeping to the east bank and trusting that the spate prevented him crossing. I was sure, all the same, that I had seen horsemen, faded as fetches through the rain-mist, splashing a miserable way up the west bank, appearing and disappearing as the swollen river widened and narrowed.

'Time to haul away,' Trollaskegg said cheerfully and the men groaned, for this was almost too much when added to the lack of food and ale and the soaked cloaks and blankets on a boat filmed with water.

Little Yan went up the mast with the rope and fastened it, then it was paid out and men leaped overboard, to the places where the water was shallow, or had not yet reached. Then they pulled, so that *Short Serpent*, balking like a stubborn goat on a tether, slowly moved forward; the linden-bast rope hummed and water spurted out of it, while the mast curved.

Everyone lent a hand, the strong ones pulling and staggering through the shallows or over the brush of the bank, the weaker ones using the oars as poles to fend off the drift. Even Dark Eye bailed and I did not care for that, though I told myself, and everyone else who saw my unease, that it was because it would not do for her to get sick or injured, for we might need her yet. I had already provided my good sealskin cloak for her as a makeshift shelter.

Finn, squeezing the water from his beard so that it squirted through his knuckles, had squinted from under the drooped, sodden brim of his weather-hat and smiled, a quizzical, knowing

smile I tried to ignore, all the while feeling it nag me as badly as the ache in my ankle.

She had clasped me tight when we lumbered, sodden and uneasy, spilling hurriedly onto *Short Serpent* and sliding off into the dark, rain-hissing river. In the storm's searing white light, her face was raised to mine, eyes bright, streaming with rain so that she looked as if she wept. I almost kissed her then, but the corner of my eye caught Finn's scowl in that eyeblink of light and I patted her like a wet dog instead.

In the dark, we had hauled a little way upriver, all that could be managed, before settling on the east bank to wait for daylight and the storm to growl out. By then the river was mud-coloured, frothing like a mad dog in the sullen light of morning and it stayed that way for the next few days, with no sign of stopping, so there was nothing to be done but pull.

'Bank is not made for towing,' Onund growled at me, coming up with an oar to fend off something that rolled and turned, shapeless in the water.

'Nor the current for rowing, nor the wind for sails,' I answered, more sharp than I had intended, for the truth of it nagged me like a broken tooth.

'Trees down to the water,' Onund added, which was true. Once they had been the edge of a considerable wood, set back from the river, but it had spilled over and swamped them; hip-deep in it, the men looped rope over one shoulder, padded a tunic, or a cloak or a spare serk under it and hauled, stumbling and sliding. To their left, Alyosha and a handful of men, weighed with shields, weapons and ring-coats, splashed to keep up, as a flank guard.

'The mast might go,' added Trollaskegg, watching the bowing curve of it.

'Or the line,' added Yan Alf, almost cheerfully.

I wondered if anyone had something good to say and asked it aloud. No-one answered – then Kuritsa appeared, sloshing calf-deep through the water and calling out, so that men stopped

pulling and braced instead, holding *Short Serpent* against the current.

He came up to where the water deepened to the river proper, stopping when it got to his waist. He had his unstrung bow in his hand and a young doe draped round his shoulders like a fur cloak, the hooves cinched on his chest; men yelled at him and grinned, for this meant good hot eating at the end of a wet misery of hauling.

It took some time, but we got *Short Serpent* closer to him, while he came out until the current threatened to sweep him off his feet. Crowbone threw him a line, he tied the deer to it and it was hauled aboard; another line drew him in like a fish, until he stood on the deck, streaming water and grinning. The rain had stopped.

'Good hunt,' I told him and he nodded, blowing snot from his nose. He pulled off his leather cap and checked that the bowstring was dry, then coiled it up again and stuck the hat back on.

'Up ahead is trouble,' he said. 'A barrier of drift.'

Trollaskegg grunted; that was a bad thing to have happen now, but you could have foreseen it without throwing rune-bones, on a river like this and weather like we had.

It was a fallen tree, undercut and ruined, a fine big oak – a keel tree, as Onund pointed out. If we had been wanting one that would be cause for grinning, as I told him; those nearest laughed, though it was a sound as grim as tumbling skulls.

Drift had piled against it, sodden birch and gnarled pine from far upriver, willow branches swollen with new buds, all forming a great dam the length of twenty men out from the east bank and solid enough that men could walk on it.

Around the end swept the water, rippling like muscle, then breaking into dirty-white foam and growling up spits of spray. The air stank with the cloy of death, for there were bloated bodies here, sheep and cattle that had drowned, bobbing and

sinking and rising again as they spun in a stately dance down to the sea.

Onund and Trollaskegg and others walked, cat-careful, out onto the barrier and peered and prodded here and there, while the men stood like patient oxen, hock-deep in the water and braced to stop *Short Serpent* spiralling backwards with the flowing current.

A tree came down, with an animal on it and men yelled and shouted cheerfully; it was a water-slicked wildcat, yowling and snarling, running this way and that as the tree caught the water's flow and half-turned beneath it.

'Shoot it,' Crowbone yelled to Kuritsa, who merely shook his head.

'Not me,' he declared. 'I almost died from shooting one once and I will not do it again.'

'How could you die from shooting a cat?' demanded Yan Alf, watching the tree in case it came too close. Kuritsa, his face serious, said it was the speed of the beast that had been his undoing and Crowbone made the mistake of asking how that was so.

'I came upon one while hunting deer,' Kuritsa said. 'Suddenly, without warning. I do not know who was the more surprised – but I had an arrow nocked and shot it, straight down the open mouth.'

He paused and shook his head.

'This was my undoing, for that cat, like all of its breed, was faster than Perun's thrown axe. It spun round to run away and my own arrow shot out of its arse. I felt the wind of it on my cheek; an eyelash closer and I would be dead.'

People laughed aloud and watched the tree and the yowling misery of its passenger spin away downriver.

Then Onund hauled himself aboard, dripping like a walrus, with Trollaskegg not far behind. Their faces were gloomier than Hel's bedspace.

'It will not be chopped up this side of summer,' Onund declared.

'Nor will it be hauled apart,' added Trollaskegg.

There was a pause and I waited, trying to be patient. Onund grunted and shrugged, the hump of his shoulder rising like a mountain.

'We will have to pull round it,' he said and all our hearts sank at that. It meant tethering *Short Serpent* and bringing everyone on board to take an oar – then loosing the lines and bending to rowing to the west bank. We would lose way, of course, probably back to where we had started pulling that day, before we could tether on the opposite bank. Then we would have to pull all the way back again, this time with the threat of Saxlander horsemen.

It would be a long, hard pull, too, for we would have to put some distance between us and the barrier; no-one wanted to spend a night on the west side of the river, so we would have to repeat the process to take the ship to the east bank again, on the far side of the barrier – with enough room to allow for losing way that would not carry us smack into that gods-cursed drift of trees and sodden corpses in the fading light.

The black, wet misery of it settled on us as we grunted and cursed and slithered the ship to where it could be tethered. The panting, exhausted crew slackened off, the linden-bast rope was hauled in and loosed from the masthead and folk spilled wetly over the side, sloshing towards rowing ports, sorting out their sea-chest seats.

I nodded to Finn and he went round with two green-glass flasks and men grinned wearily and brightened as the fiery green-wine spirit was passed down the line. Dark Eye and a couple of others offered soggy bread and hard cheese, pungent with its own sweat; men chewed and grunted and, slowly, began to chaffer and argue, so that I knew they were recovered.

Then Yan Alf called out that there was a boat snagged in the barrier.

This time, I went with Finn and Onund and others, stepping cautiously out onto the slick, wet tree, treacherous with stubs and broken ends, draped with crushed willow. The boat was half-swamped, cracked like an egg and ragged with splintered wood, but clearly a *strug*, the solid riverboats Slavs made. It would not have been important at all – there were lots of them and it was hardly a surprise to find one as part of the wreck of this swollen river – save for the crew it still held.

He was snagged by his own belt, hair drifting like weed, pale face fat with water and curdled as old cheese. For all that, it was a face I knew and I remembered him, stumbling back from where he had dug up my silver, showing handfuls of it to the rest of his oarmates, that bloated face bright with the wonder of it. Hallgeir, I remembered suddenly. His name was Hallgeir.

Finn nodded and growled when I told him this, peering up the river; he pinched one side of his nose and blew snot down into the wreck.

'So, Randr Sterki has met with some trouble,' he growled. 'Which can only be a good weaving for us, thank the Norns.'

I did not answer; I was too busy searching the water for signs of a small corpse, my belly sick with the thought of Koll, turning in a slow, stately dance like the sheep dead in the mucky water.

The oak finally behind us, days melted, one into the other and went unnoticed. No-one saw much else other than the red-brown water and the sucking mud as they stumbled, heads down and rope over one shoulder, through the shallowest parts they could find. The boat, that great shackle they were fastened to, fretted this way and that, the prow beast snarling and jerking.

The land changed, started to roll into short hills rising out of the flood, some of them flat-topped, others already undercut

by the merciless waters. Half-drowned trees shouted out all their green buds even as they died; others huddled like herded cattle on the hills above the water.

The rain sighed itself out and the sun broke through, so that the ground steamed up a crawling mist and the insects came, bloated and fat on carrion, yet still wanting more from the living.

Gudmund died, raving and bursting sweat off him, despite Bjaelfi's best prayer-runes binding the black-rotted holes where the hayfork had gone in, so we rolled him into the water and consigned him to Ran and Aegir, which was as much as we could do in that place.

Freed from that, Bjaelfi now went to treat the ones shivering and sweating and leaking their insides down their legs from some sickness or other – probably in the water, Bjaelfi thought, or perhaps poison from the insects.

'Not good, Orm,' he told me, as if I needed him to inform me of that. He slapped angrily and cursed the stinging insects.

'Perhaps it will rain again,' Crowbone offered cheerfully, 'and drive the insects away.'

'Not as if you suffer,' Yan Alf countered gloomily. 'I want that charm you have.'

Those on board – bailing, poling, or too weak and sick to pull – laughed, but uneasily, for the way the biting hordes avoided Crowbone was too close to magic for comfort and most remembered the reputation of the odd-eyed boy.

'They do not bite him,' Finn declared, bellowing from where he leaned on the sweep, fighting to keep the prow beast snarling into the current, 'because he has no man-juice in him.'

'They do not bite you, either,' observed Dark Eye suddenly, her clear voice made stranger by the silence that had gone before from her. Finn squinted calculatingly, then grinned.

'They do, but if you look closely, you will see them falling dead at my feet,' he growled, 'since there is too much man-juice in me for those little bodies to handle. One taste is all

it takes.' And he winked lewdly at her, so that I found myself bristling like an old hound and had to turn away with the shock of it, hoping no-one could see.

The next day, hungry and wet and tired as always, men looked sideways at Crowbone and at me, him for bringing the rain back, or so it seemed and me for . . . everything else. They were muttering more openly now, about forging on after this boy when there was little else in it for anyone. Yet they were fairly trapped, for they could not go downriver now, into the clutches of the waiting Kasperick. Ahead was not any more attractive.

Ahead, growling and spitting white lances and ferns, another storm fretted; the river, fresh fed, surged again the next day and the men started to stumble and fall and it was all I could do to keep them moving. We were close to the Vrankeforde now and I knew Randr Sterki would be there, what men he had as worn out as ourselves; if we were fast enough, he would not have time to find others, for when he thought he had enough, we would not have to chase him – he would come for us.

Then, so close I could almost taste the woodsmoke fires of Vrankeforde, there was a day that began under a vaulted sky of milk-silver, where the air clung to the skin and the men hauling and falling up the river, mouths open and panting, had almost lost the strength to put one soaked foot in front of another.

I saw Gunnliefr, best spearman we had, sink to his knees and weep, all his strength gone. I watched Osnikin, from Sodermannland, fall with a great splash and have to be hauled up by Murrough, or else he would have lain there and drowned.

'Orm,' Trollaskegg began and I did not need him to tell me what was best, so that my look was harsher than a slap and made him click his teeth on his next words.

'Pull, fuck your mothers,' roared Finn, seeing my face. 'Haul away, you dirty swords.'

She moved beside me and I felt a hand on my forearm, but when I turned, she was that little wooden carving, staring out over the river, saying nothing, looking at the distant rolling black of cloud, dragging all our eyes to it. As if, some said later, she had magicked it up.

The air tightened, twisting like the iron rods of a smith starting on a new sword. The wind rose, knotting with force, hissed stipples on the river and the dark swooped like a cloak of crows.

The storm broke on us, a great laughter of Thor howling out of the sudden new dark, his Hammer sparking blue-white with a banging that seemed to split the air and fist our ears. The men leaned and the linden bast threw up skeins of water and trembled, while the mast bowed and sang like a harp string.

'It will break,' shrieked Trollaskegg, but the wind grabbed his words and whirled them away down the river, which was a mercy for Yan Alf, since he was clinging to the top of that whipping pole, searching the river ahead while the rain drowned his eyes.

It was the end and it came swift as a secret knife. Through the sheeting veils of rain, I watched a tree blaze and heard the sky crack, looked up and half-expected to see the wheelrim of Redbeard's goat chariot breaking through the dome of the world.

Instead, there was Yan Alf, clinging to the *rakki* as the mast swung and sawed, his face a pale blob in the dark, shouting something the wind snatched away. He pointed out beyond the prow beast where, looming up like some snake-head goddess, the great tree crashed down on us, a huge ram with horns of clotted roots.

The prow beast rose up, dragging the men on the bank backwards, tearing the rope and the skin from their hands. I had time to turn, to think that all our struggle, all the days of effort to this place, hung on a thin, stretching line and the skidding crew who held it – when the linden bast spurted

water, snapped and whipped back. Ospak yelped with the lash of it, spun half-round and went over the side.

The *drakkar*, locked in what seemed a raging battle, spun round; timber shrieked, planks splintered and men were mouthing bellows no-one could hear. The ship seemed to rear up like a stallion in a horse fight, right up until the stern went under and it tilted. I saw oars and chests slide away – saw Dark Eye slide away and milled my arms to try and grab her.

Water slapped me, snagged me, dragged me down and round and round, so that the silver trail of bubbles from my mouth circled me like a flock of birds.

I saw them, like pearls, like the last thought trailing from my mind – Odin would have to fight Aegir for his sacrifice offering.

Then there was only darkness.

The moon was a bright eye and an owl shrieked, a thrown chip of a cry. From the rolling charcoal of hills came the scream of some animal, high and thin and trembling with loneliness and then there was Vuokko, sitting beside me on a flat, black rock, cradling his drum.

'I can only do this because it is Valpurgis,' he said, 'when the veil between the worlds is thinnest.'

May Eve, when the Wild Hunt staggered to a halt. Einmanuthur, the lonely month. I felt the crush of it, wanted to be home . . .

'There is a loss coming,' Vuokko said. 'Keener than winter. Odin will take his sacrifice soon.'

I wanted to be home more than ever, wanted to tell the Sea-Finn, who I knew was soaring in the Other watching me die, to take messages with him, of love and friendship and last words. But when I started to speak, he hit his drum and kept on hitting it, a thundering sound that jarred me, pounding on and on and on . . .

*　　*　　*

The blood thundered in my ears and my chest ached with each huge, retching breath; my throat burned and my nose throbbed. There was the iron taste of blood in the back of my throat. Ospak peered at me long enough to make sure I had come to my senses, then stopped pounding my chest and rose up, his knees cracking.

'It is a bad habit to get into,' he declared, 'this having to be hauled out of water just before you drown.'

Dark Eye, cat-wet and scowling, glared at him and then turned a soulful look on me.

'I shall try and break it,' I managed to hoarse back at him and he chuckled at that and the slap from Dark Eye as he reached out a grimy hand towards my nose.

'That neb of yours is cursed, I am thinking,' he said and then tilted his head slightly. 'It is only straight on your face if I stand like this. And it looks flatter than it did.'

If the pain was anything to go by, I did not doubt it, but I was more concerned with what had happened. I had thought him dead, for sure, a thought I shared with him while Dark Eye fussed.

'I thought the same when I went over,' he told me grimly and showed me the blue-black welt on his upper arm. 'That rope seemed set with a life of its own and it took me a while to get clear of it.'

'Double thanks, then,' I rasped, 'for hauling me out.'

He chuckled. 'Not me. The Mazur girl did that.'

I looked at her and she smiled.

'I was supposed to save you,' I said to her and she fixed me with her seal eyes; it came to me then that we were alone, the three of us, soaked to the skin on a patch of wet barely raised above a black swamp where the mud and water oozed and new, sodden reeds stood straight up like hairs on a boar snout.

'Where are the others?' I said, sick with the possibilities and scrambling to my feet. I was weary to my bones, my head

pounded, my chest burned and the whole front of my face felt seared, but I forced it off; I was ashore and the ground might squelch, but it was solid enough for me to feel safe after that muscling river. There was freshness in the air, too, as if the storm had finally gasped itself out, tangled and shredded in the branches and brush by the tiny sprigs of green. A bird sang somewhere unseen.

'Back upriver,' answered Ospak with a shrug, 'if they are still in the world at all. You and me and that girl were all tangled in the one rope, which is a strange thing. Perhaps the Norns wove it that way for a purpose.'

'Well,' I said, pushing the crushing weight of it grimly, like a bad plough, 'it seems we have a walk back to camp, then, if camp there is.'

I rose, weaving. Dark Eye straightened, wiped the palms of her hands down her sodden skirts and bent to pick up something beside me. My sword, still sheathed, the baldric loop missing a few silver ornaments.

'I hauled you ashore with it,' she said in her thin little voice. 'I had to take it off, for it was round your neck and strangling you.'

I felt the burning welt of that now, too, and fingered it, wondering at the strength in her to have managed that. I smiled and took the sword – Jarl Brand's sword. At least we still had that and I turned to Ospak and told him so, for the cheer in it.

'Aye, sure and that's a good thing, for I have an eating knife only,' he answered and then tilted his beard off to one side. 'And they were a worry.'

I followed his gaze and saw the six horsemen sitting at the limit of bow range, watching, resting easy on hipshot horses, bows out and arrows ready.

I looked back at Ospak and then at Dark Eye, whose face was a carving block.

'Magyar,' she said.

Which was hardly a comfort.

Two things happened then and it is sometimes strange how such weight as your life can hang on the thinnest thread – a voice understood and a scratch behind the ear.

Dark Eye moved two paces forward and hailed them, in her own Mazur tongue, which it was clear they understood. At the same time, a dog trotted out from the horsemen, a smooth, long-legged loper the colour of old bracken; it headed straight for me. Though smooth-coated, it reminded me of the big grey, wiry wolfhounds that had been with me not long before; we had eaten them out on the Great White and left nothing much more than the paws and I had been sorry for that later.

This one came close and sat while I moved to it, a few paces, no more. It let me scratch behind one ear.

The horsemen shifted then. The leader came forward, his hands out to either side and empty; when he got close, he halted and waited for me to walk to him. The dog followed me.

He was sallow, black moustached, with a clean chin and dark eyes over high cheeks. His hair hung under a fur-trimmed cone and was knotted in hundreds of small braids, like ropes and he wore an embroidered coat over loose breeks tucked into high boots which had what looked like silver coins down each side.

We fished for understanding for a while and found Greek. He grinned whitely at me and placed one hand on his chest.

'Bökény fia Jutos,' he declared, which I took to be a name. Later, I learned that he was Jutos, son of this Bökény.

'Orm,' I answered, slapping my own chest. 'Ruriksson.'

'You are *Ascomanni*, from Wolin,' he said and I put him right on that. He frowned.

'Sipos says you are to be trusted,' he answered and sounded as if that was strange to him. It took me a moment to realise he was speaking of the dog.

'Sipos,' said Dark Eye, coming up beside me; the dog licked

her hand and grinned, pink tongue lolling wetly. 'It means Piper. The Magyar call these dogs *viszla*, which means "deerhound" and they are much prized for hunting.'

'Mazur,' said Jutos, looking at her and it was a statement, not a question. Then he nodded and turned the horse.

'Come,' he said. Ospak looked at me and I shrugged. It was not as if we had much say in the matter, for the horsemen closed round us, like herders on cattle. We went a little east, away from the river which fretted me, for I thought it was further from the others and said so.

'If there are others,' Ospak answered moodily. 'That was a big tree.'

We left the floodplain for soft rolling hills and then, beside a rill that ran white between great smooth boulders until it made a large, dark pool, came up to their camp of wagons, some covered, some with two wheels and some with four. Horses snickered; smoke drifted, thick and pungent and a woman, squatting by the stream with her skirts spread for decency, took a piss and smiled at us.

The dog, wedge-head held low, snuffled and quested and answered a bark from the centre of the wagon circle with a hoarse one of its own, which seemed to be squeezed out of the red-gold body. It set ducks up off the water of the pool and Jutos laughed.

'Home,' he said and I could not disagree. We came up to a fire whose perfume was as heady as incense to me and the warmth made us all realise how chilled and cold we were.

People milled; we were given blankets to wrap ourselves and stripped of our clothes under the decency of them, made to sit down under a *wadmal* canopy and presented with bowls. A woman, grinning and nodding her head while she spoke a trill of softness I did not understand, cracked eggs in a cauldron of barley broth and meat, then filled our bowls. I ate, sopping fat chunks of bread with it, ravenous.

In the end, sated, we all sat back.

'By the gods,' sighed Ospak after a while, which said it all.

The camp moved with soft life while the sun of late afternoon slanted through the surrounding trees and Dark Eye curled up and slept with the dog, both cradled in the dry beech mast near the fire. The ducks came warily back to the pool, planing in to land with creamy wakes.

Folk passed and stared curiously, but left us alone. Ospak nodded, half-asleep; a woman came to where our clothes hung, studied them, poked a finger in a hole and tutted. Then she fetched needle and thread.

Jutos startled me from my half-sleep by looming up and squatting, face smiling.

'I have been told of others of your kind, not far. An hour's ride, perhaps more. They are by the river and their boat is badly damaged.'

That sounded like Finn and the others and I wanted to know if he knew how many. Jutos shrugged.

'Enough for my hunters not to go too near,' he answered, grinning. 'There are too many riders out on the land these days. Something has stirred them up.'

He said it in a way that let me know he thought part of that stirring was us, but he seemed friendly enough still and we talked until the shadows stretched and our clothes were dry enough to wear again.

These folk were, I found, Magyars, a trading party who travelled part of the old Amber Road, which once led to the north of Langabardaland and then down to Old Rome.

'Not now,' Jutos explained. 'Now we take it to our land and trade it on to the Bulgars and others, who take it down to the Great City, where the power and the gold now is.'

'I thought there was power and gold back in Old Rome,' I answered, to show I knew some matters of trade, 'now that Otto the Saxlander has declared himself Emperor, like his father of the same name before him.'

Jutos spat so that the embered fire sizzled.

'Best not to speak of the Ottos when my father comes,' he said grimly. 'Our *fejedelem* is Géza, who has eaten salt with the Saxlanders and Romans to gain peace. He has even taken a Christ worshipper to his household, a monk called Bruno – but friendship with the Saxlanders is not something that sits lightly with one of the Seven.'

I knew the word *fejedelem* meant something akin to 'ruling prince' and I had heard how this Géza had been forced to accept the Christ worshippers because the Great City and Otto had made an agreement. Of course, since Géza had little say in the matter, his Christ worship was not entirely full-hearted – but there it was again, that working of kings that always seemed to favour the White Christ. I said as much and Jutos grinned.

'Perhaps, after all, the Tortured God has more power,' he growled. 'It is certain our own gods did not help us when my father became one of the Seven.'

I did not recognise the reference to the Seven and wanted to know more, but Ospak bridled at this discussion, for he was an Irisher who had embraced Thor and loved him.

'This Christ has no power,' he argued. 'If you need proof of that, look at my god and him together. The Christ is nailed to a lump of wood; my god has a Hammer.'

He spat on one palm and slapped his hands together, as if he had made a good legal point at a Thing and even Jutos joined in my laughter.

Still, I did not have to wait long to find out about the Seven, for Jutos' father came to us soon after. At first he was just a tall, thin shadow against the red-dyed sky, moving slow and stooped, flanked by two other, stockier shadows who wore ring-coats and the high-crested helms favoured by Magyars and Khazars. Closer, the white blur of face resolved into features and what I had taken for a bald head was white hair, iron-streaked and dragged back.

Closer still and Ospak sucked in his breath, while Dark

Eye went still and quiet, as she always did when faced with horrors, sliding into the earth and stones, becoming invisible.

This Bökény had a face like a skull. There was no nose and he had no ears and age had shrunk the cheeks so that the skin on the knobs under his eyes looked to be splitting. Hard wrinkles marked him, deep-scored plough-lines across his forehead and great scars down the side of his mouth, deep enough to lose a finger up to the first joint. One eye was milk, the other black-bright as a crow and his hair was dragged back and tied at the nape of his neck, yet it spilled down almost to his belt.

I marked that. Finn had lost an ear long since and never tied his hair back. This man, this Magyar *horka*, did not care; more than that, he offered his face like a defiant, triumphant banner.

He squatted stiffly, and I saw his cloak, fastened at the shoulders by two discs, each marked with a bird holding a sword. That sight ran a shock through me, for the sword was a sabre and I had heard that these Magyars worshipped the sword of Attila, for they were Huns, when all was said and done. It also reminded me of something I had in my sea-chest – if I still had a sea-chest.

The old man gathered his cloak round him then spoke, while Jutos translated; it was the usual welcome and prettily enough done, so I gave him back the same.

He spoke again and Jutos answered him, then shrugged and turned to me.

'He wonders what you have to trade. You may count so far as hospitality, but if those are your men we found, they will perhaps need food and other things. Can you trade?'

Ospak grunted, for he did not like all this talk of trade, being – like the rest of the Oathsworn – a man who preferred to consider what he wanted down the length of a blade. Unless, as I told him sharply now in Norse, he was outnumbered and out-ranged, which he admitted with a scowl and another grunt.

I did not know what was left to trade and thought a salting of truth was best, so I said there had been riches enough aboard the ship before it was smashed and was sure all could not have been lost.

Jutos rattled this off to his father, who considered it for while, the blood-egg sun doing things to his face that would have sent bairns screaming into their ma's skirts. Then he spoke again and Jutos turned, almost resignedly.

'He wishes to know if you will trade the Mazur girl and what you will take,' he said. I looked at him steadily, so that he knew the answer without me having to speak. With a brief, almost relieved nod, he told his father, who grunted and muttered.

'He says,' Jutos told me, 'that you northers are hard to bargain with. He is fated to see unusual slaves he cannot get. He does not wish to meet any more of you on this trip.'

Ospak chuckled at that. 'Well, we are equal matched then,' he answered, grinning to take the sting from it, 'for this is one norther who does not wish to see a face like that again. How did he come by it?'

I closed my eyes and waited for the storm this would cause, but I had it wrong, for it was no insult to note this singular face.

'He is one of the horde of Bulcsú,' Jutos answered and the old man's head came up at the sound of that name. 'Last of the Seven.'

'Bulcsú,' the old man repeated and then began talking, in his own tongue, a great solemn, slow-rolling chant, thick as a saga tale and, though none of the three of us understood it, we were all struck by the telling of it.

He was as good as any skald versing on the giant Ymir whose skull forms the dome of the world, or of Muspell, at once burning and freezing, or of Odin and the gods of Asgard. But the old man's tale was no misted saga, but recent, from his own life and, as he poured it out, thick-voiced with remembering, Jutos translated the meat of it.

275

The old man told of Lechfeld some twenty summers before, when the Magyar, the fire of Attila still coursing in their veins, had come to take on the might of Otto the Great, the present Otto's father. The old man spoke lovingly of the clans all arrayed and the colours they wore and the myriad tiny, fluttering signal banners of the chieftains, Lél, Súr and Bulcsú.

He brayed and clashed his palms together to bring back the horns and the drums and the brass discs they struck, howled out the old warcries, showed how they were wild to fight. He stood up, no longer stiff but straddle-legged, riding an unseen horse, firing backwards as he feigned flight with all the others – twenty thousand and more – on that day.

I had heard of this battle. In the end, the bowmen on their light horses, fur hats scrugged down tight on their heads, had been mastered by the solid ranks of Saxlanders, had hurled themselves like heroes to be cut down, until only a handful were left, the chiefs among them.

Jutos, grim as a dark cliff and his eyes bright with water, watched the old man slump; someone brought him drink and it ran down the harsh grooves off his chin.

'The Saxlanders cut the ears and noses off the survivors and sent seven back to our ruling prince of that time, Taksony,' Jutos added blankly. 'They hung Lél and Bulcsú from a tower in Regensberg. Súr came back as one of the seven, and he was killed for causing such a tragedy, for he was not of the line of Arpad. The last warriors who survived that day were honoured for their courage, all the same, and my father is the only one left. The Magyar have stayed in their homeland since that day and have no love for the Saxlanders.'

'Heya,' said Ospak, his Irisher soul stirred by such a tale and the old man raised his head and nodded acknowledgement to that salute.

'Since then, we have travelled the Amber Road as traders,' Jutos went on. 'There are more of us now. All the men of this clan who rode with my father were killed in that battle,

276

but slowly we grow stronger. One day, we will be strong enough to pay the Saxlanders back.'

I looked at the old man, milk-white in the dusk, slumped and spent now, sitting in a ring of some forty wagons, with horses, men, women and bairns. I thought of Hestreng and how we were not so far from each other, Magyar and Northman.

Horses were brought, but I told Ospak to stay with the Mazur girl. Stone-faced Jutos sat on his horse and said nothing as I climbed onto mine, flanked by a half-dozen Magyars armed with lances and bows and wearing their pointed helmets with elaborate nasals. Bökény rose stiffly and nodded to his son, who returned it. Then he hirpled away to his tent, leaving me with the vague idea that some message had passed between them.

In silence, we rode out into the dying day and, for a while, nothing more was said. That let me work on how this horse moved, for it was a rangy, bow-nosed creature, not one of the short, stiff-maned, fast-gaited ponies I knew. After a while, I felt Jutos arrive at my knee, where he cleared his throat, like the dull rumble of distant thunder. Here it comes, I was thinking.

'There is a lot of happening up and down the Odra for the time of year,' he said in a low, even voice. 'Particularly when the rains have been so bad.'

I stayed silent, feeling my stomach turn slowly, like a dead sheep in the river; I gave great attention to the sitting of my horse.

'We came past an old settlement we had visited before,' he went on, 'and found it burned out and everything dead. Everything. Children, dogs. Everything.'

He shook his head with the memory of it and I swallowed the sick rise of shame in me.

'There are riders out everywhere,' he added, 'from the Pols. A force is out and not a small one – hundreds. I have not seen so many since the Pols marched this way two summers ago, heading for war in the north against the Pomorze.'

'I have heard the Pols are swallowing other tribes,' I said, in order to say something and give away nothing at all, even though the thought of hundreds of Pols searching along the Odra was a chill knife in my bowels. I had not thought they would be so stirred by the burning of a Sorb village. I had it right – they were not and the next thing Jutos said made that clear.

'They seek a Mazur girl and a band of northers,' he said flatly and that made me look at him. Here it was, then, out in the open. I waited to see what came next, strung tight as a drawn bowstring.

'You have eaten salt with us,' Jutos went on, slowly, carefully, like a man picking his way across a marsh. 'This means you will come to no harm from us, neither you nor your band by the river. My father, of course, is more honourable than I am, for he sought to buy the Mazur girl and so save your life; I argued that it was too much danger brought on us, but he insisted.'

I saw he was not lying and was both surprised and a little shamed at my thoughts, which had been along the path of how their elaborate hospitality was more to do with fearing to tangle with a band of armed growlers like the Oathsworn. Now I saw they pitied us and regarded us as already dead, which was not a comforting thing.

'Then we will trade for food and be gone,' I answered, 'before you are made sorry for your hospitality.'

Jutos crooked one leg casually over the saddle, an elegance I envied.

'Of course,' he added, white teeth gleaming in the dusk of his face, 'our obligation ends when trading ends. Usually, we allow a day between us before considering matters.'

I rode the gentle threat and stared him down.

'We are not so generous,' I gave him back, 'feeling half that is distance enough, should one side feel aggrieved.'

The dog, Sipos, ambled over to run alongside me and Jutos widened his grin.

'He likes you,' he said. 'Perhaps you have something to trade for him?'

I shook my head, feeling annoyed at the smile of this man, bland as oatmeal and curved sharp as a sabre blade.

'I like dogs,' I answered. 'All us northers do. With some winter roots, a peck of salt and the lees of old wine they make good eating.'

Scowling, he jerked the head of his horse savagely round and away and left me staring down into the mournful eyes of the dog until I blinked and looked away.

The rest of the ride was silence until, in the gathering dusk, Jutos hissed out a command and men galloped off and the rest of us reined in. A few minutes later, a rider returned and spoke briefly to Jutos, who turned to me.

'Your men have made camp, but lit no fires,' he declared, almost admiringly. 'None of my scouts have been able to approach closely without being seen. Perhaps you should ride out and hail them before there is unpleasantness.'

I was pleased as I edged the horse forward – and not a little anxious that Kuritsa would do something rash in the twilight, for I was sure he was watching. When I could no longer see the Magyars behind me, I decided enough was enough and bellowed out my name.

The voice, soft and almost in my ear, made me leap and teeter in the saddle with the shock of it.

'I see you, Orm Bear Slayer.'

Finn slithered out of the dark, with Kuritsa close behind, arrow nocked.

'Good to find you alive,' Finn growled with a grin. 'With a horse, too. And new friends.'

'Magyar traders,' I answered flatly, as if such a thing was no more than to be expected from the likes of me. 'Ospak and Dark Eye are safe in their camp. How are things with us?'

Kuritsa shook his head admiringly.

'I had heard that if Orm Trader fell in a barrel of shite he

279

would find the only bag of silver in it,' he laughed. 'Until now, I had not believed it.'

I acknowledged the praise with a nod and a grin, but kept looking at Finn for an answer to my question.

'Four dead,' he said flatly. 'Or so we believe. They were the weakest of the sick and have not, like you and Ospak, surfaced from the river.'

'The ship?'

He did not answer, but turned away, so I rode down to the river with him, past men iron-grey in the growing dark, shields up and helms on. One or two grinned and called greetings; just as many gave me blank looks, or even scowls.

Short Serpent was snagged tight to the heavy bole of a tree, which was furred green with moss. Slimy clumps of frog eggs drifted in tattered skeins along the riverbank, while the river itself growled and spat still, a mud-brown coil like a snake's back.

Men clustered round the *drakkar*, leaping on and off her, fetching and carrying; a smaller group stood by the prow – Onund, Crowbone, Trollaskegg and Abjorn – who turned as I came up.

'Odin's arse,' Onund said, his pleasure as clear as a dog's. 'Here is a good sight.'

'Doubled,' Finn said, 'for he has Ospak safe and found us food and shelter.'

'If my sea-chest survived,' I added and Trollaskegg said that it had and a lot of gear had been saved. Crowbone, eyes bright, nudged Abjorn.

'See? You owe me six ounces of silver – I said he was not dead.'

Abjorn looked at me and shrugged apologetically.

'It was a wild river,' he said by way of excuse, 'but I am glad it did not claim you, for we have been holding a Thing on it and could not agree on who would now lead.'

'Aye, well, include me out of that now,' shouted a cheerful

voice and Styrbjorn hurled something over the side of the ship, then followed it, both splashing wetly on the bank and spraying mud, to a chorus of curses. Undaunted, Styrbjorn hefted his prize and held it out to Onund; it was his carving of the elk head, antlers proud against the wood.

'Yours,' he said. 'All that is left of this ship.'

'The ship is exactly like my carving,' Onund agreed, mournful as a wet dog. 'Finished.'

I did not need him to tell me that, for the whole proud curve of the bow was staved in and the water frothed and gurgled in and down the length of it. The prow beast, white with gouges, still snarled even though the teeth in its mouth were broken and it hung by a splinter.

'We could cut new planks,' argued Trollaskegg and looked desperately at Crowbone for support, but even little Olaf knew, with all the wisdom of his twelve years, that we could not repair his wonderful ship.

'*Short Serpent* put up a good fight against that tree,' Crowbone said softly and Abjorn picked up the elk head.

'Lash that to a spear shaft,' I told him. 'We will have new fierceness yet. Light fires in hollows where they will not be seen – these Magyars are safe enough, but others are out hunting us – then give me half-a-dozen men with drag-poles to fetch back supplies. Finn – you command here. I will go back and stay with the Magyars, for the trading.'

Their faces asked all the questions, but their mouths stayed shut. Abjorn simply nodded and went off to see some of it done, handing his armful of prow beast to Onund, who gave a grunt and sloshed off to higher ground to see to the camp, rolling in his great, bear way. Crowbone and Trollaskegg stood, twin pillars of misery, looking at the ship.

'When it is empty of everything we can use,' I said, knowing I sounded crow-voiced and that they would not realise it was from the river and not from harshness, 'cut it free and let the

281

river take it. With luck, the Saxlanders will see it – or find it if it makes it to the opposite bank – and think us dead.'

I found my sea-chest, and Red Njal sitting on it, with Finnlaith and Murrough nearby. All the Irishers were happy to hear that Ospak had survived. Alyosha and Kaelbjorn Rog and others came up to see for themselves the marvellous event that was Orm, returned from the river with Ospak in tow. Not one of them, or anyone else, cared whether Dark Eye had lived or died, I noted.

I rummaged in the chest and found what I was looking for in the last of my treasures – a handful of hacksilver and three armrings, one of them already cut almost to nothing.

But there was a torc, too, and I took it out so that it gleamed pale in the last light of day. The Irishers were drawn to it like bright-eyed magpies and it has to be said it was a fine piece I had guarded carefully, an old necklet taken from Atil's hoard.

Not as fine as the one I wore round my neck, the torc of a jarl – even with its dragon-head ends battered and the twisted length of it nicked and cut – but a rich thing, of gold and amber-metal, which the Romans call *electrum,* with bird-head ends. It was those I had remembered, seeing the old man's cloak-pin.

Jutos' eyes widened when I presented it to him back at the camp as what I had to trade. He turned it over and over in his hands, the firelight sliding along it and folk coming up to look and admire. I saw them point to the bird-heads and heard the word *turul* repeated in awe and wonder. It turned out that I had been right – this bird, the *turul,* was worshipped by the Magyar.

Jutos wanted to know where it had come from and I gave him it straight, so he would know he dealt with more than just another trader from the north. The treasure hoard of Attila, I told him and watched his eyes grow round and black as old ice, for Attila was as good as a god to them.

Then he looked at Crowbone, who had come along because

he had never seen Magyars before, and you could see the thoughts flit across his face like hound and hare, for the distant, misted tales of the Oathsworn and the strange odd-eyed boy who was one of them had suddenly arrived at the fire where he was sitting.

So he went to the old man with the torc in his hand while we ate and drank in a dusk thick and soft as unseen smoke, with the quarrelling of women and the bark of dogs comforting as a cloak. Enough food for a night's decent meal was sent off back to the Oathsworn, so I was content enough with the start of this Thing.

Later, in the black of night, we went away from the others, to where the pool shimmered and there she moved to me. Others moved, too, so that the beech mast rustled; there was a laugh in the throat here, a groan from over there.

There was no love-talk – little talk at all between us, though she murmured soft, cooing sounds in her own tongue – nor even much kissing or hugging, but we moved as if we had known each other before and there was little need of any of the rest, for my heart was huge and urgent and in my throat and I knew it was the same for her.

She was white and thin, all planes and shadows, smelled of woodsmoke and warmth and crushed grass and there was not night long enough for us. As the dawn silvered up I lay back, with her breathing slow and even on my chest, snugged up under the same cloak.

'What will you do with me?' she asked.

'Give me a minute,' I answered. 'Perhaps two.'

She thumped me on the chest, no more than the flutter of a bird wing and I laughed.

'Will you take me back to my father?'

'Was that what this was about?' I asked, made moody by her now. She struck me again and this time it was a small, hard nut of knuckle that made me wince.

'You think that?' she demanded and her eyes were big and

283

round and bright in the dark. Just her eyes alone made me ashamed of it, so that I shook my head.

'If you are not taking me back,' she went on, slow and soft in the dark, 'then why am I here?'

I told her; because the Sea-Finn's drum had said to bring her. She was silent, thinking.

'Did it say to bring me to your home, after the ice-headed boy is found?'

That made me blink a bit, thinking of Thorgunna and what she would have to say about a second woman – wife, I realised with a shock, for I would have to marry Dark Eye. I was still thinking of an answer when she shivered.

'I will not marry you,' she said.

'Why not?' I wanted to know, chastened and wondering if she could read thoughts. She raised her head for a moment, then pointed out across the water of the tarn, where a mallard drake, all jewel-flashing in green and purple, swung down into the waters with a hissing splash.

'That is why not,' she said. The drake made for the nearest of the ducks and mounted her, vicious and uncaring, leaving her half-drowned and squawking.

'That is the lot of such as me,' she said, 'no matter whose I am at the time. A strange woman in a house of women. The men will all want to mount me, the women to peck my feathers off.'

Half-sick with the truth of it, I growled some bluster about what would happen to any who treated her in such a way, but she laid her head on my chest again and I could feel her soft smile.

'I do not know what path I am to take,' she answered. 'I am away from my people and cannot go back to them, since that would start a war. I am Mazur and if I am to marry I do not intend to do it in a land of ice.'

She stopped and looked into my face, her eyes looming like a doe's.

'But there will be a child,' she declared with certainty and I felt the skin-crawling whenever *seidr* presented itself to me. 'It will be a son and I can only offer it a safe place if I go with you.'

She stopped and shivered. 'Iceland,' she said. 'A country made from ice.'

I laughed, more from relief at being able to steer off the topic we had been on.

'It is not made of ice,' I told her. 'Anyway, I am not from Iceland. Onund is.'

'Somewhere as cold,' she muttered, snuggling tight to me. 'At the edge of the world.'

I liked the feeling and pulled her closer still.

'Iceland is not at the edge,' I answered, drifting lazily. 'Near the centre. North of Iceland is the *maelstrom*. You follow that star there.' I pointed to the bright North Star and she looked, squinting.

'What is the *maelstrom*?'

I told her; the place where the giant women, Fenja and Menja, turn the great millwheel Grotti, blindly churning out the last order they were given before the ship carrying them all sank – to make salt. Which is why the sea tastes the way it does. The *maelstrom* is a great whirlpool caused by them turning and turning the handle far beneath the waves.

Sleepily, she laughed. 'Good tale. The Christ worshippers, though, say the centre of the world is in Jorsalir, where their White Christ was nailed to his bits of wood.'

'What do you believe?' I asked, but there was no reply; she slept, breathing soft and slow and I began to wonder if it was not the will of the gods to bring her back to Hestreng. What other reason could the Sea-Finn's drum have had? It was never going to be possible to travel all the way across the land of the Pols to her own Mazur tribe, hunted every step of the way.

Of course, the gods laughed while we slept, were still laughing when the sun strengthened, rich and red-gold and

we dressed and moved back to the others, me prepared to endure the jibes from Ospak and Crowbone.

I started to hear the gods cackling when I saw Crowbone rise to his feet, slow and stiff, as if he had spotted a *draugr* coming across the space between the wagons. But he was not staring at us, but off to our right, where I saw the old man tottering forward with his two warrior pillars and his son.

Even then I thought Crowbone had spotted the old man's face and had been stunned by it, for it was a swung stick to the senses, that face, and I was chuckling when I came up.

'He is not half as fierce as he looks,' I said. 'I would not worry over much.'

Crowbone looked at me, then back to the old man, who came up closer to us.

'Nose,' Crowbone said, pointing and I turned.

The shock of it dropped my jaw; the gods' laughter grew harsh and loud as disturbed ravens.

The old man had come in his finery, from brocaded coat to red-leather riding boots and fine-hilted sabre. Round his neck he already wore the bird-ended torc, to show he had accepted the trade and we would now haggle only over the price.

But his last piece of jewellery was what staggered those who knew it by sight. Bound by a blue-silk ribbon, carefully tied to show his lack of ears, was the final statement on his flag of a face.

Sigurd's silver nose.

SEVENTEEN

We scarred the laden drag-poles over a sodden land steaming in the new sunshine, ripe with new life and old death, thick with the smells of dark earth and rotted carcass. We scattered birds from the raggled corpses of drowned cattle and, at the end of the first day, sent up a cloud of rooks like black smoke from dead sheep the retreating waters had left hanging in gnarled branches like strange fruit.

'Why are we pushing so hard?' panted Kaelbjorn Rog, who only voiced what others thought. 'We are leaving a trail a blind wean could follow, never mind some Magyar scouts.'

I said nothing, but grimmed them on through the fly-stinging, sweat-soaked day, the sick tottering along with the shite rolling down their legs rather than be bumped in drag-poles, for it was not the Magyars I feared, nor was I entirely running from enemies. Only Crowbone shared my thoughts on why we truly scowled our way so swiftly across the land and he was still mourning the distance between him and his uncle's silver nose.

Jutos had seen Crowbone's reaction and knew something was not quite right; slowly the tale of it was hoiked up and sense was made of things that had been said earlier, of northers encountered and hard bargains being struck.

The Oathsworn had not been the first band of Norse the Magyars had met; that honour had been given to Randr Sterki and some eighteen or so survivors of his own river-wyrd, stumbling out on the floodplain, starving and thirsting, for they dared not drink the foul water they sloshed through.

'My father wanted the boy they had,' Jutos told us, 'a rare child, white as bone. Their leader, a man with skin-marks on him, offered us a Greek Christ priest, but that was no trade for us. We said to take him to the Pols, who might give them a little food, for I thought the Pols might know better what to do with a priest from the Great City.'

'Where did they go?' I asked and Jutos shrugged, waving vaguely in the direction of the distant blue mountains.

'South, this side of the Odra,' he replied. 'After he had traded this marvellous nose for enough supplies.'

He paused and grinned widely. 'If you happen to have ears that match, we will make ourselves go hungry to acquire them.'

I told him the torc was rich enough and tried to get the nose back, for Crowbone's sake. In the end, though, we got supplies only – and the only bargain in it came as we were leaving, hauling the drag-poles away on a surprising gift of three horses.

Jutos came up and thrust out his hand, so I took it, wrist-to-wrist, in the Norse fashion and he nodded.

'We part as traders,' he said formally, then paused. 'I will give you a day, then send riders to find the Pols and tell them of you and the Mazur girl. That will stop them raiding us when they find out we helped you. The horses we have given you will let you travel faster away from them.'

It was as fair as you could expect from Magyars and, at the end of that first day, I told the rest of the Oathsworn what we could expect and that Randr Sterki and the boy we had come to rescue lay just ahead. There was silence, mainly,

and Finn had the right of it when, later, he demanded to know what else I had expected from the crew.

'The fact that we have enemies ahead as well as behind is not a joy of news,' he added, to which I could find no answer.

The next day we had grown used to the smell of rot, so used to it, in fact, that we stumbled into horror when we should have been warned long since.

When we came round the side of a hill and saw the *grod*, we slowed and came to halt; men unshipped weapons and shields and stood uncertainly, looking from one to another and then at me.

It was a good *grod*, a well-raised earthwork, wooden stockade surrounding a cluster of dwellings, with a big covered watchtower over the gate. It had been built on a hill above the floodplain and the rising waters had swept round it like a moat, save for a narrow walkway of raised earth and logs, which led to the gate. The watery moat had since sunk and seeped almost back to the river, leaving bog and marsh which steamed in the sun.

The gate in the stockade was wide open and there was not a wisp of smoke. No dog barked, no horses grazed. Then the wind shifted slightly.

'Odin's arse,' Finn grunted, his face squeezed up. He spat; the stink was like a slap in the face, a great hand that shoved the smell of rot down your throat.

'A fight, perhaps,' Styrbjorn said. 'Randr Sterki and his men, I am thinking. The villagers have all run off, save for those he has killed.'

Styrbjorn grunted out that this was good work from only eighteen men, but most ignored him, cheered by the idea of a whole village lying open and empty and ripe as a lolling whore – perhaps Randr and his men had left some loot, too.

Then I pointed out that Randr and his men might still be there, waiting to ambush us.

'Send Styrbjorn the Bold in,' Abjorn declared and men laughed, which made Styrbjorn scowl and go red.

I chose Finn, Abjorn, Kaelbjorn Rog and Uddolf to go with me, leaving Alyosha to organise the others into a cautious defence; when we moved to the gates, magpies and crows rose up, one by one, flapping off and scolding us.

The place was empty, just as we had hoped. Wooden walkways led to a central raised platform of wood, with a tall pole on it, carved with four faces – their meeting place, with their god presiding over it. No Christ worshippers these. At first there were no bodies either, yet the smell of death was thick as linen as we prowled, turning in half-circles, hackles up and wary as cats. A goat skipped out of an alley and almost died under Abjorn's frantic axe; a cow bawled plaintively from an unseen byre.

Uddolf poked a door open and then leapt back with a yelp; two dogs sidled out, whimpering, tails wagging furiously, tongues lolling from want of water – but they were full-bellied and the smell made my hair rise, made me breathe short and quick, not wanting to get the air anywhere deep in me.

I peered in, squinting through the gloom at the three bodies, black, bloated and chewed by the dogs. A man, his clothes tight against puffed flesh. A woman. A youngster, who could have been girl or boy.

After that we found others, one by one, two by two; a woman slumped against a wall, part-eaten, part-pecked. A boy whose face seemed to be peppered with scabs. A man with a bloated face that looked like oatmeal had been thrown at it and stuck. I grew afraid, then.

'Sickness,' Kaelbjorn Rog declared and he was right, I was sure, so I sent him back to fetch up Bjaelfi, who knew about such matters. We prowled on uneasily.

There were two handfuls of long timber houses, where kettles and cauldrons, horn spoons and looms sat, waiting for hands. There were storerooms and barns, hay in the barns

and barrels of salted meat in the storehouses, while the bawling cow had teats swollen and sore, being so overdue for milking. The strange stillness became even more hackle-raising.

'The livestock has been turned loose,' Finn said, nodding to a brace of chewing goats. 'So someone was alive to do that.'

Not now. We found them when we came up to a larger building, clearly a meeting hut. Here the truth unravelled itself from this sad Norn-weave.

'Look here,' Abjorn called and we went. A man and a woman lay at the door of the meeting hut, part-eaten but not as long-dead as the others. The woman had a wound in her chest, the man a knife in his throat and we circled, calling the tale of it as we read the signs.

'The last ones left alive. He stabbed the woman,' Finn declared.

'Thrust the knife in his own throat,' added Uddolf, pointing. 'Missed, but bled. Did it again by putting it against his throat and falling on it, so he could not fail.'

We wore that little tragedy like a cloak as we filtered through into the meeting hut, almost having to push again the smell. Here they were, on pallets or slumped against the walls, dead, swollen, scabbed, eaten by scavengers, brought here to be more easily cared for, though there was no care that kept them from dying.

Bjaelfi came up, the fear slathered on his face. He had seen the other corpses, but he took one look at the stabbed woman's body and turned it with his foot so that the flies rose up with the stink. One arm flopped and he pointed at the untouched, mottled flesh down her arm, where small red and white dots stared accusingly back.

'Red Plague,' he said and it hit us like a stone, so that we scrambled from the place. Fast as we were, the news of it was faster and, by the time we were hawking the bad air out of us, everyone knew.

Red Plague. We moved away as fast as we could, but I knew we would not outrun the red-spotted killer, that we probably carried it with us. I had expected to die for Odin, but the thought of thrashing out my life in a straw death, the sweat rolling off me in fat drops, my face pustuled and no-one wanting to be near me, was almost enough to buckle my knees.

We made camp at the top of a hill, in the shelter of some trees, where two fires were lit, smoking up from wet wood. Beyond a little way, bees muttered and bumbled, stupid with cold and spilled from their storm-cracked nest; men moved, laughing softly when one was stung, fishing out the combs of honey and pleased with this small gesture from Frey.

Warmth and sweetness went a long way to scattering the thought of Red Plague, as did Finn's cauldron of meat and broth, eaten with bread and fine, crumbling cheese. Their bellies no longer grumbled, but it would not be long, as I said to Finn when our heads were closer together, when their mouths did it instead.

That night one of the sick died, a man called Arnkel, who had bright eyes and a snub nose and told tales almost as good as the ones Crowbone had once given us. Bjaelfi inspected him for signs of plague, but it was only the squits he had died of and he had been struggling for some time.

'Ah, well, there's an end to truth entire, then,' Red Njal mourned when Bjaelfi brought the news of it to the fire in the dull damp of morning. 'No more tales from him.'

'Truth?' demanded Kaelbjorn Rog, his broad face twisted with puzzlement. 'In bairns' tales?'

'Aye,' Red Njal scowled. 'Told by those old enough to remember. Wisdom comes from withered lips, as my old granny told me.'

'Was this just before she told you one of her tales?' Kaelbjorn Rog persisted. 'Made up completely, for sure.'

'Only those written down,' persisted Red Njal and men

craned to listen, for this was almost as good entertainment as one of Arnkel's tales.

'You mean,' Abjorn offered, weighing the words slowly and chewing them first to make sure the flavour was right, 'that stories are only true if they are not written?'

Red Njal scowled. 'If you are laughing at me, Abjorn, I will not take it kindly. Let no man glory in the greatness of his mind, but, rather, keep a watch on his wits and tongue, as my granny said.'

Abjorn held up his palms and waggled his head in denial. Finn chuckled.

'Ask Crowbone. He is the boy for stories, after all.'

Crowbone, staring at the flames of the fire, stirred when he became aware of the eyes on him and raised his chin from where it was sunk in his white, fur-trimmed cloak.

'When you hear something told, you can see the teller of it and pass judgement. But if you read it, you cannot tell who wrote it, and so cannot say whether it is true or not.'

Red Njal agreed with a vehement growl and Finn chuckled again, shaking his head in mock sorrow.

'There you have it,' he declared, 'straight from an ill-matched brace of oxen, who cannot read anything written, not even runes – so how would they know?'

'You do not understand,' Red Njal huffed. 'There is magic in such tales and if you needed the measure of it, remember Crowbone when he told them.'

Which clamped Finn's lip shut, for he did remember, especially the one which had once snatched us from the wrath of armed men. He acknowledged it now with a bow to Crowbone and, seeing the boy only half notice it, added: 'Perhaps the prince of storytellers will grace us with the one he is dreaming of now?'

Crowbone blinked his odd eyes back from the fire and into the faces round it.

'It was not a tale. I was remembering the whale we found once.'

293

Short Serpent's old crew stirred a little, remembering with him and, bit by bit, it was laid out . . . on a desolate stretch of shingle beach, pulling in for the night, they had come upon a small whale, beached and only just alive. No matter that it was another man's land, they flensed it, cutting great cubes of fat, thick as peats, thick as turf sod. They ate like kings, bloody and greasy.

It was the dream of home, of north water and shingle and it fixed us all with its brightness. For a reason only Odin could unravel, I kept thinking of the patch of kail and cabbage at the back of Hestreng *hov*. Thorgunna had grown a lush crop there, using the stinking water from the boilings of bairns' under-cloths and it had survived everything, untrampled and unburned, when Hestreng was reduced to char and smoulder.

Uddolf crashed into the shining of this, asking for men to come and howe Arnkel up. His closest oarmates went and, in the end, we all stood by the mound; as *godi*, I placed one of my last three armrings in it, to honour him, which went some way against the grey grief of his loss.

It was a cloak that descended on us all. Onund wept and when he was asked why, said it was for the black sand and milk sea of his home. No-one mocked him, for we were all miserable with similar longings.

Through it all, two figures caught my sight. One was Dark Eye, still and slight and staring at the dark beyond the fire while men sighed and crooned their longings out; it came to me that this was how she must feel all the time, yet bore it without a whimper.

The other was the fire-soaked carving of the *Elk*, proud-antlered, lashed to its spear-haft. I was thinking that a prow beast was leading us still, further than ever from where we wanted to be.

In the morning, stiff and cold, men moved sullenly in our camp on the hill, hidden in trees where the mist shredded and

swirled. I was gathering my sea-chest together when Styrbjorn came up, with men behind him. Everything stopped.

'We have been talking among ourselves,' Styrbjorn said. Finn growled and men shifted uncomfortably. I said nothing, waiting and sick, for I had been expecting this.

'It seems to us,' he went on, 'that there is nothing to be gained by continuing in this way and a great deal to be lost.'

'There is a deal to be lost, for sure,' I answered, straightening and trying to be light and soft in my voice, for the anger trembled in me. 'For those who break their Oath and abandon their oarmates. Believe me, Styrbjorn, I have seen it.'

The men behind him shifted slightly, remembering that they had sworn the Oath, but Styrbjorn had not. One scowler called Eid cleared his throat, almost apologetically, and said that when they had held a Thing, as was right for *bondi* to do when they thought I was dead, it was generally understood that whoever was chosen would lead them home.

Men hoomed and nodded; I saw no more than a handful, all from Crowbone's old crew of *Short Serpent* and that, while Styrbjorn stood with his arms folded, pouting like a mating pigeon, it was to Alyosha that these men flicked their uneasy eyes.

'Now I am returned and there is no need for such decisions,' I said, though I knew it would not silence them.

'If I had been chosen,' Crowbone added defiantly, 'we would still be after the boy.'

Eid snorted. 'You? The only reason any of us are here at all is because Alyosha was sensibly tasked by Prince Vladimir to keep you out of trouble after he gave you the toy of a boat and men. If anyone leads here, it is Alyosha.'

Crowbone stiffened and flushed, but held himself in check, which was deep-thinking; if he started to get angry, his fragile voice would squeak like a boy. Styrbjorn, on the other hand, started turning red, though the lines round his mouth went white as he glared at Eid; he did not like this talk of Alyosha leading.

'Prince Vladimir gave *Short Serpent* to ME,' Crowbone answered his crew, sinking his chin into his chest to make his voice deeper. 'He gave YOU to me.'

'No-one gave me anywhere,' growled Eid, scowling. 'What am I – a horn spoon to be borrowed? A whetstone to be lent?'

'A toy, perhaps,' grunted Finn, grinning and Eid wanted to snarl at him, but was not brave enough, so he subsided like a pricked bladder, muttering.

Alyosha, markedly, stayed stone-grim and silent, with a face as blank as a fjord cliff, while Styrbjorn opened and closed his mouth, the words in him crowding like men scrambling off a burning boat, so that they blocked his throat.

'And there is the girl,' added a voice, just as I thought I had the grip of this thistle. Hjalti, who was named Svalr – Cold Wind – because of his miserable nature, had a bald pate with a fringe of hair which he never cut, but burned off and never got it even. He had an expression that looked as if he was always squinting into the sun and a tongue which could cut old leather.

'The girl is another matter,' I answered. Styrbjorn recovered himself enough to smile viciously.

'A sweetness we have all missed,' he replied, 'save you, it seems.'

I shot Ospak a hard look and he had the grace to shrug and look away, acknowledging his loose tongue and what he had seen and heard by the Magyar fires.

'Am I a chattel, then?' said a new voice and I did not have to turn to know it; Dark Eye stepped into the centre of the *maelstrom*, a hare surrounded by growlers. 'A thrall, to be passed around? A horn spoon or a whetstone, as Eid says?'

No-one spoke under the lash of those eyes and that voice. Dark Eye, wrapping her cloak around her, cocked a proud chin.

'I have a purpose here. The Sea-Finn's drum spoke it and

those who have heard it know its truth,' she spat, then stopped and shrugged.

'Of course,' she added slyly, 'if all it takes for such hard men to seek Jarl Orm's *fostri* is a sight of my arse-cheeks, I will lift my skirts and lead the way.'

There was a chuckle or two at that and Styrbjorn opened his mouth. Dark Eye whirled on him.

'You had all best move swiftly and catch me first,' she said loudly, 'for Styrbjorn is skilled at stabbing from behind.'

Now there was laughter and Styrbjorn turned this way and that, scowling, but it was too late – men remembered him for the sleekit nithing he was and that he had been the cause of all this in the first place. For all that, like a dog with a stripped bone, some still thought there was enough meat to gnaw.

'This chase is madness.'

His name was Thorbrand, I remembered, a man who knew all the games of dice and was skilled with a spear.

'Ach, no, it is not,' Red Njal offered cheerfully. 'Now, mark you, mad is where you chase a band of dead-eaters, who chase a thief, who is chasing a monk, and all in the Muspell-burning wastes of Serkland. That is mad, Thorbrand.'

'Aye, madness that is, for sure,' agreed Thorbrand. 'What fool did that?'

Finn grinned at him and slapped his chest. 'Me. And Orm and Red Njal and a few others besides.'

He broke off and winked.

'And we came away with armfuls of silver at the end of it. The best fruits hang highest, as Red Njal's granny would no doubt have told him.'

Styrbjorn snorted.

'That sounds like one of the tales Red Njal likes so much. Is it written down anywhere? I am sure it must be, since it smacks of a great lie.'

'As to that,' Finn said, moving slowly, 'I could not say, for reading other than runes is not one of my skills. But I can

hear, even with just the one ear and I am sure you just called me a great liar.'

The world went still; even the birdsong stopped. I stepped into the silence of it.

'There is only one safe way to stop heading the way I am steering you,' I rasped, feeling my bowels dissolve, 'and that is for one of you to become jarl. And there is only one way for that to happen – what say you, Styrbjorn? You will also have to take the Oath you have so far managed to avoid.'

There was a silence, a few heartbeats, no more, where Styrbjorn licked his drying lips and fought to rise to the challenge, even though his bowels were melting faster than mine. I relied on it; I knew how Styrbjorn liked to fight and it was not from the front.

It stretched, that silence, like the linden-bast rope that had held *Short Serpent* to the bank and the fear-heat spurted from it like water.

Just before it broke, Kuritsa loped up and parted it with a slicing sentence.

'Fight later – men are running for their lives and one of them is Randr Sterki.'

They were running like sheep, all in the same direction but only because they blindly followed a leader; the water sluiced from under their feet and their laden drag-poles were flung to one side.

'They will never get away,' Abjorn grunted, pointing. He had no need to; we could all see the horsemen, big as distant dogs now and closing.

'They are heading right towards us,' Red Njal said, his voice alarmed.

Of course they were – Randr Sterki was no fool and he saw high ground with trees on top, knew if he reached it the horsemen would be easier to fight if they decided to charge in

and, if they balked at that, the trees would provide cover from the arrows.

'Form up – loose and hidden,' I ordered, peering out, searching for what I had not yet been able to see.

'We are going to rescue Randr Sterki?' demanded Styrbjorn incredulously. 'After all he has put us through? Let him die out there.'

Finn spat, just missing Styrbjorn's scuffed, water-stained boots.

'*Fud* brain,' he growled. 'The boy is there.'

Styrbjorn, who had forgotten why we were here at all, scowled, while Alyosha and Abjorn slid away to give orders; men filtered forward into the trees, half-crouched, tightening helmet ties, settling shields.

'Randr Sterki will not thank us, all the same,' muttered Red Njal; I had been thinking the same myself and thought to leap that stream when we were near falling in it.

There – two figures, one half-falling, slower than the rest, stumbling. The taller one, black, stopped, hauled the little one up into his arms and half-staggered, half-ran to keep up; I could hear the rasp of his breathing from here, but I was puzzled as to why the monk should care so much to rescue Koll.

A man fell, got up and stumbled on, then fell again. Sick, I was thinking as the monk reeled past him, then let Koll slip to the ground, taking him by one hand. The pair of them ran on and the horsemen were closing fast, spraying water and clotted muck up.

'An ounce of burnt silver says that small one is first to die,' Eid muttered close to me, nudging his oarmate, one of Finnlaith's Dyfflin men.

'You never had an ounce of burnt silver,' this one replied and Thorbrand's curse was reeking.

'That small one is the boy we came all this way to get,' he spat at them.

Out on the sodden plain, the first of Randr's men had

299

reached the foot of the low hill and we could hear the desperate, ragged dog-panting of them. Randr himself stopped and half-turned, bellowing at those who lumbered past, almost on all fours, what he wanted them to do when they got the shelter of the trees. It was a good plan, but I was thinking to myself that none of his men were up for it.

The weak man fell yet again and the first long-shot arrows skittered and spat up water behind him, so that he scrambled up and weaved on, almost at a walk now. A dozen steps further on and he fell again and this time he lay there, so that the horsemen, almost casually, shot him full of arrows, whooping as they ran over him.

'The boy . . .' growled Eid and sprang to his feet. Thorbrand followed and, with a curse, so did the Dyfflin man. They roared out of the treeline, leaving me speechless and stunned with the speed of it all.

The horsemen, felt hats flapping, their bow-nosed ponies at full stretch, were heading for the bulk of the fleeing men; more arrows flew and two or three men went down. Randr himself stopped bellowing and started scrambling up the low hill towards us.

Two or three horsemen had turned off towards Koll and Leo the monk, but they had their sabres out, planning to run them down and slash them to ruin. The monk shoved Koll to the ground and then dived and rolled as the first horseman came on him, lashing out with his left hand as he did so; my heart thundered up into my throat, but the horseman missed and Leo's slap had no effect, or so it seemed, while the others over-ran the pair.

Then Eid and the other two came howling down the hill like mad wolves and the horsemen, bewildered, milled and circled. Two of them whipped out arrows; the third turned back to Koll and Leo. After that, I remember it in fragments, like a shattered mirror flying everywhere, all the pieces with a different reflection.

300

Two arrows felled Eid as he ran. Thorbrand and the Dyfflin man crashed down on the two horsemen, stabbing and hacking. The third man's horse staggered and fell as if Dane-axed, just as the rider urged it towards Koll and Leo; poison, I was thinking, even as I turned to fight. Enough in Leo's stab to fell a horse in a few heartbeats – so he did have a hidden dagger after all.

The rest of the horsemen came up the slope, slinging their horn and wood bows and hauling out that wicked curve of sabre, a long smile of steel for hacking down on the fleeing. They were Vislanians, I learned later, who wore skin breeks and felt coats and caps and could climb under their ugly dog-ponies and up the other side at full gallop.

Not in the trees, though. They reined in from a gallop; Randr Sterki's men were on their knees, frothing and gasping, with no fight in them and it looked to be easy enough for the riders – until they discovered the hornet byke they had stepped in.

Kuritsa began it by putting the last of his war arrows in the chest of one of the horses, so that it reared up and rolled its great eyes until the whites showed, pitching the rider off with a scream.

Then it was blood and shrieks and mayhem. Red Njal ran at them, hirpling on his lame leg, bellowing like a bull and his spear took one of the horsemen in the belly, so that his head snapped forward and he went over the plunging horse's arse. Red Njal let the spear go and whipped out his seax.

Axes scythed, spears stabbed, swords whirled. It was bloody and vicious and my part in it was brutal and short – I came up on the man doing the most shouting, sitting on his dancing, wild-eyed pony, waving a crescent-moon of steel and bellowing.

He saw me come at him and raised the sabre, his eyes wide and red, his black moustaches seeming to writhe as he yelled; then something seemed to catch his arm as he raised it and

I saw the shaft, through his forearm and into the shoulder, pinning his arm – a hunting arrow from Kuritsa.

The sabre fell from his fingers and he looked astonished, though he had only a few seconds to think at all, before I took Brand's sword in a whirling, two-handed backstroke at his waist. Finn and others called this 'opening the day-meal' and it was a death-blow even if the victim did not die at once, for his belly split and everything in it fell out, blue-white, red, pale yellow.

He fell like a gralloched stag – and the rest of them tried to flee.

Cut them down, I heard myself screaming, though it sounded far away. None must escape to tell of what had been found and where we were.

The Oathsworn wolfed them, snarling and clawing. The last man turned his pony and flogged it back downhill, men chasing him, screaming. Kaelbjorn Rog, panting and sprinting, fell over his feet, bounced up and hurled his axe at the fleeing back in a fury of impotent rage, but it fell well short.

The arrow hissed out, a blur of speed and the smack of it hitting the rider's back was almost drowned in the great roar of approval that went up as the fleeing man spilled from the saddle. The pony kept going and I knew, with a cold, heavy sink of feeling, that we had failed.

There was a heavy silence, reeking of blood and vomit and moans. Men moved, counting the cost, clapping each other on the shoulder in the sudden ecstasy that comes with surviving a battle, or else retching, hands on their knees and bent over.

Randr Sterki lay flat out, a great bruise on the side of his face and Onund looming over him like a scowling troll. He had made for Randr as soon as the fight started and slammed him in the face with the boss of his shield. Now Randr lay on his back, propped up on his elbows and spitting out teeth and blood.

'I owe you that and more,' Onund growled at him, touching

his chest where, under his stained tunic, the glassy scars of Randr's old burning still wept.

'The severed hand seldom steals again,' Red Njal pointed out, scowling. 'And a head in a tree plots only with the wind.'

'Your granny was never one for a boy to snuggle into,' Crowbone muttered, hunching himself against the black glare Red Njal gave him in passing.

The rest of Randr's men, cowed and gasping, sat sullenly, aware that they had leaped out of the skillet into the pitfire. As I came up, Onund handed me a sheathed sword, taken from Randr; it was mine, taken when he had me prisoner and the V-notch in it undammed a sudden, painful torrent of remembering – of my sword biting into the mast of the *Fjord Elk*, of being slammed into the water, of Nes Bjorn's charred remains, of the loss of Gizur and Hauk and all the rest.

Randr must have seen that gallop across my face like chasing horses, for he stayed silent.

There was a survivor from the horsemen, a sallow-faced scowler with blood on his teeth and still snarling, for all that he had the stump of a hunting arrow in his thigh and his left arm at the ugly angle only a twisted break would allow.

I wanted answers, but his black eyes were sodden with anger and pain and defiance. Then Dark Eye came up and spoke to him, a string of coughing sibilants. He replied, showing bloody teeth in a snarl. She answered. They shot sounds like arrows, then were silent.

'He is a Vislan,' she said. 'That tribe are all Christ worshippers.'

'All that for so little?' I answered and she sighed.

'He called me names. He calls you all flax-heads, which is what they call the Saxlanders. Barbarians.'

There was more, I knew, but caught the warning spark from her and let Finn erupt instead.

'Barbarian?' he bellowed. 'I am to be called this by a skin-wearing troll?'

'*Quisque est barbarum alio,*' said a weary voice and, turning, we saw Leo the monk, with Koll behind him and Thorbrand trailing after.

'Everyone,' Leo translated, with a wan smile at Finn, 'is a barbarian to someone.'

I gave him no more than a glance, my attention on Koll, who came up and stood in front of me.

'You have fared a fair way from home,' I said, awkward and cursing myself for not having more tongue-wit than that.

'I knew you would come,' he answered, staring up into my face with the sure, clear certainty of innocence. He was thin and his bone-white colour made it hard to see if he was ill or not, but he seemed hale enough. Yet the pale blue eyes had seen things and it showed in them.

'Well,' drawled Finn, circling the monk like a dunghill cock does hens. 'You have led us a long dance, monk.'

Leo acknowledged it with a wry smile. His hair was long and stuck out at odd angles and he had gathered the tattered ends of his black robe up under his belt, so that it looked like he wore baggy black breeks to the knee; beneath them, his legs were red and white, mud-splattered and bloody from old cuts and grazes. He reeked of grease and woodsmoke and did not look much, but I knew he had a needle of poisoned steel on him and said so.

He widened his eyes to look innocent and Finn growled at him.

'Find a rope,' Red Njal spat. 'Make him dance a new dance. The breathless tongue never conspires.'

'No.'

It came from two throats – Koll's and Finn's – and took everyone by surprise, even the pair who had hoiked it out.

'Kill him another way,' Finn growled, scrubbing his beard as he did when he was discomfited.

'Do not kill him at all,' Koll declared defiantly. 'He helped

me, saved me when the rest of these pigs wanted to sell me to the Magyars. Him and Randr Sterki stood against them.'

I knew why Randr would want to keep the boy, but not the monk and I said so to Leo, who shrugged.

'I took him as a counter in a game,' he said diffidently. 'He still had value.'

Koll blinked a bit at that, but I had expected not much more. I put my hand on the boy's shoulder, to show him he was safe once more – then Randr Sterki struggled weakly to his feet and growled to me across the trampled, bloody underbrush of the clearing.

'Well? Will you finish it, Bear Slayer? What you started on Svartey?'

I wondered how many of the Svartey crew were left and wondered it aloud; the answer was straight enough – only him alone. All the others had died and the men of his crew who sat, shivering and sullen, had no connection with that old *strandhogg*.

'Kill him and be done with it,' Styrbjorn said and Randr Sterki curled a lip at him.

'So much for fighting shoulder to shoulder,' he answered bitterly. 'Well done is ill paid, as the saying goes. Here is the dog who fought, the chief who led and the ring-giver who paid – only the fighting dog dies, it seems.'

I looked from Styrbjorn to Leo and back to Randr. He had the right of it, for sure – all of those who had helped the Norns weave the wyrd of what happened were here, including the Oathsworn, who had scoured Svartey in one bloody thread of it.

'Matters would have gone better for me,' Randr Sterki went on morosely, 'but for this bloody habit of slaughter you Oathsworn have. The death of that village you visited has called out an army of Pols, all bent on skewering Northmen – my bad war luck to run into them before you.'

'Truly,' agreed Onund coldly, 'when you annoy the gods, you are fucked.'

Finn added his own bloody growl to that by cutting the throat out of the Vislan and, while he choked and kicked, Abjorn and Alyosha counted the cost of the fight and the heads left.

There were fourteen of Randr's men left, including himself. We had two dead and four men wounded; the two dead were Eid and the Dyfflin man, whose name, I learned from Thorbrand, was Ranald. Finn could not understand what had made them charge out as they did and asking Thorbrand only brought a weary heave of his shoulders and the answer that he had followed the other two. I thought I knew, for I had felt it myself – little Koll, the prize for all that had been suffered, was in danger of being snapped up by someone else.

It had cost us, all the same and we would need Randr and his men, I was thinking and I said that to them and him. Red Njal cursed and one or two others made disapproving grunts, but I laid it out for them; we were alone and together made no more than sixty. Somewhere, hordes of Pols hunted us.

'Turn Randr Sterki and his men loose, then,' Kaelbjorn Rog offered truculently. 'Let the Pols hunt them down while we get away.'

'Tcha!' spat Red Njal. 'At least make it easy for the Pols – the foot removed cannot scurry far.'

'I am now sure I dislike this granny of yours,' Crowbone said, shaking his head, then stared his odd-eyes into the pig-squint glare Red Njal tried to burn him with.

'If the wind changes, your face will stay like that,' he added grimly. 'My ma told me that one and she was a princess.'

'It is too late for running,' I said, before matters boiled. 'The Pols will know where we all are in a few hours.'

'Why so?' demanded Crowbone, moody because he had been effectively kept out of the fight by his iron wet-nurse, Alyosha. 'We have killed all these dog-riders.'

'But not their horses,' Alyosha told him, seeing it now. 'They will track back and find us.'

It was then that folk realised some of the bow-nosed ponies had galloped off and those who knew their livestock knew what horses did when riderless. They went home. I knew it, as well as I knew we could not stay here to fight, nor run somewhere else out on the wet plain.

There was only one place we could go which would give us a chance of fighting at all and it was not one I wanted to visit. When I laid it out, the words fell into a silence as still as the inside of an old howe, which was answer enough.

Save for Leo, who always had something to say, even about stepping into a plague-ridden fortress.

'*A fronte praeciptium, a tergo lupi,*' he declared and turned to Finn, who stunned the monk even as he opened his mouth to translate it.

'A cliff in front, wolves behind,' Finn translated. 'I have heard that one before, priest. It is the place the Oathsworn fight best.'

EIGHTEEN

His breathing, as Bjaelfi took pains to tell us, was just a habit, for the fever had fired him so that his blood had boiled up into his thought-cage and destroyed his thinking entire. What was left sucked in air the way a deer kicks long after you have gralloched it.

It was a habit strong in him, for he took three days to be quit of it and, at the last, was open-mouthed and desperate as a fish. Ulf, his name was, called Amr by his oarmates, which meant Tub on account of his considerable belly. Well, it had been considerable, but in three days of vomit and leaching sweat he had melted like grease on a skillet, become a wraith, his face pocked red and white and pus yellow and his eyes gone white as boiled eggs.

Bjaelfi tied his mouth back up with a scrap of cloth and we sat back and stared; Ulf, the emptied Tub, first to die of the Red Plague and lying there with drooping hare-ears of cloth on top of his head, making him look as if he was being silly to amuse bairns.

'They are coming again,' roared a voice from outside the dim hut.

I heaved myself wearily up, took up the blood-gummed shaft of the bearded axe and looked at Bjaelfi.

'Burn him,' I said and he nodded. Then I lumbered out to war.

We first saw our enemy when they filtered out onto the soaked plain in front of the *grod* not long after we had panted our way into it and barred the gate; we made it easier for them to find us, for we burned the main hall, after tying bound cloths round our faces – for all the good it would do – and dragging all the scattered, half-chewed bodies there, where most of them already festered.

Their horsemen trotted up, spraying water up from the steaming ground, to be greeted by great black feathers of reeking smoke; close behind came foot soldiers in unbleached linen and only helmets and spears and round shields. Behind them came a knot of iron-clad horse soldiers, sporting lances with proud pennons and one huge banner with what appeared to be a wheel on it. Dark Eye said that was the mark of the Pol rulers, who had been wheelwrights until the favour of their god raised them up.

'They will think we slaughtered all the folk of this place and burned some of it,' Styrbjorn said bitterly. 'Someone should tell them there is pest here and that we are doomed. That will send them running as far from this place as they can get.'

'It would send you scampering,' Alyosha replied, watching the enemy closely as they assembled – counting heads, as I was. 'What they will do is keep a safe distance and shoot anyone who leaves with arrows. When we are all dead, they will burn it. The last thing these folk want is us running all over their land, spreading Red Plague.'

'Better they do not know we have disease here,' I said, loud enough for others to hear and spread the sense of it. 'It will mean the reddest of red war and no-one will be able to throw down their weapons and be spared.'

Finn and I exchanged looks; we knew no-one would be spared anyway, once the talking had stopped.

309

'I make it four hundreds, give or take a spear or two,' Alyosha said, coming quietly to me. I had much the same; the rest of the men, grim and silent on the ramparts, knew only that the plain in front of the *grod* was thick with men who wanted to kill us.

'Get them working,' I said to Alyosha, 'for busy hands mean less chance to think on matters. Send Abjorn to the river wall – there is a small gate in it, used by the fishermen, I am thinking. It may also be the only way to bring water in from the river unless you can find a well. We have small beer but not enough, so we will have to drink water in the end. Finn – since you can tally a little without having to take your boots off, find out what we have in stores. Slaughter the live-stock if we cannot feed them, but leave the cows until last, for they at least provide milk.'

There was more – making arrows from what we could find, ripping out heavy balks of timber and finding all the heavy stones we could to drop on heads.

Hot oil, Crowbone told us with all the wisdom of his few years. Or heated gravel where there was no oil, he added and Finn patted him, as if he was a small dog, then went off, shaking his head and chuckling. It was left to Alyosha to patiently explain that flaming oil and red-hot stones were not the cleverest things to be dropping all over the wooden gate and walls of our fortress.

Randr Sterki came up to me then, badger-beard working as his jaw muscles clenched and unclenched.

'Give us our weapons back and we will fight,' he growled.

I looked at him and the men clustered behind him. They wanted their hands on hilt and haft, were eager – even desperate – to defend themselves, if no-one else.

'We are in this leaking ship as one,' I pointed out, more for the men behind than him. 'Those dog-fuckers out there call us flax-heads, think we are all Saxlanders and will curl their lips at any man who crawls out to claim he can open

310

the gate if only he is spared. They will kill him once he has served the purpose.'

Feet shifted at that and I knew I had them; Randr Sterki half-turned to his men, then turned back to me.

'We will fight, until dead or victorious.'

It had been said in front of witnesses and was Oath enough, so I gave him my V-notched sword back, for I would not give him Jarl Brand's own. He grinned, then drew it and stood, naked blade in hand and within striking distance of me, who had nothing in his hand but old filth and callouses.

'If we survive, Bear Slayer,' he said flatly, 'there will be matters to discuss.'

I was sick of him and his matters, so I turned away, putting my back to him and the blade he held, though I felt the skin creep along my backbone as I did so.

'I would not count on living out the rest of this day,' I answered over my shoulder, going off to fetch Brand's sword, 'never mind having a cunning plan for tomorrow.'

When I was sliding the baldric over my head, Koll trotted up, followed by Yan Alf, whom I had set to guard him. The boy's white-lashed eyes stared up into mine, sullen as a slate-blue sea and he wanted to know why I had stopped him from going near the monk.

'He ran off with you,' I answered, annoyed at this. 'Is that not reason enough? Because of him we are here, a long way from home and . . .'

I stopped then, before the words 'dying for the matter' spat past my teeth; I did not want the boy – or anyone else – empty of hope.

'He saved me,' Koll persisted.

'He has done killing in the night,' I countered, 'with some strange magic.'

I broke off and looked at Yan Alf, who shrugged.

'Alyosha and Ospak stripped and searched him,' the little man said. 'The only way he could be more naked is if they

311

flayed him. They found no weapon. Ospak guards him now and he has asked to help Bjaelfi with the sick.'

Very noble and Christ-like – but Alyosha would have turned the monk inside out rather than leave him as a threat to his charge, little Crowbone, and, if he had found no weapons . . .

Yet I did not trust Leo and said so.

'Keep at arm's length from that monk,' I added and saw the hard set of Koll's lip and, worse, the dull sadness in those pale eyes. I had told him of his mother's death and he had taken it with no tears – and yet . . .

'Did your father tell how to behave as a *fostri*?' I persisted and he nodded reluctantly, then repeated the words all sons are told – obey and learn. I merely nodded at him, then had an idea and handed him Brand's sword.

'This belongs to your father and so to you. You are come early to it and it is likely too large and heavy for you to use, even if you knew how. One day Finn will show you the strokes of it – but for now you can guard it.'

The pale blue eyes widened and brightened like the sun had burst out on a summer sky. He took the sheathed weapon in both hands and turned, grinning to Yan Alf, before running off with it.

'Keep him away from the monk,' I said softly to Yan Alf as he passed me, chasing his charge. If he had an answer, I did not hear it and turned away to hunt out a seax or an axe for myself. The whole sick-slathered wyrd of it had come down to this tapestry woven by the Norns and the picture of it was clear enough – a cliff in front, wolves behind.

I would not survive it, whatever happened, for I was sure Odin had, finally, led me to the place where he would take the life I had offered him.

First, though, there were the dance-steps of the rite, beginning with horn blasts from them to attract our attention. I had seen this before, though from the other side, when we had arrived at the Khazar fortress of Sarkel with Sviatoslav, Prince

of Kiev. Ten summers ago, I suddenly realised, climbing the ramp to the tower over the gate, where Finn and others waited. I had Dark Eye with me, for she was the only one who could talk to these Pols in their own tongue.

A knot of riders came slowly, ambling their horses across the wet grass and scrub to where the raised walkway led to the gate. One of them, accompanied by a single rider bearing the huge red flag with a spoked wheel worked in gold threads on it, came forward a few steps more.

He was splendid in gilded ringmail and a red cloak, his elaborately crested helmet nestled in the crook of one arm, allowing his braided black hair, weighted with fat silver rings, to swing on his shoulders. His beard was black and glossed with oil and it was clear he was someone of note, which Dark Eye confirmed.

'Czcibor,' she said softly. 'Brother of King Dagomir, whom folk by-name Miezko as a joke, for it means "peace". He makes it by fighting all who resist him. This Czcibor is the one who beat the Saxlanders at Cidini and took the Pols to the mouth of the Odra.'

I had thought Miezko meant 'famous sword', but then his enemies would have a different take on it and there was no more bitter enemy of the Pols than Dark Eye. When this Czcibor spoke, I wondered if I could even trust what she said – then scattered the thought, half-ashamed at it.

Dark Eye listened and then spoke back to him and turned to me; heads craned expectantly.

'He says you should give in, for you cannot win. It is better if you submit. I would be careful of him, Jarl Orm, for he knows Norse well enough.'

She spoke in a guarded, level voice; I looked at Czcibor, who grinned.

'Is this true – you know the Norse?'

'Of course. My niece, Sigrith, is a queen in your lands.'

Styrbjorn suddenly thrust forward, eager as a bounding pup – if he had had a tail it would have shaken itself off.

'You are Czcibor,' he declared and the man, frowning at this breach of manners, nodded curtly.

'Ah, well,' Styrbjorn went on, 'then we are related, after a fashion, for my uncle is married to your niece. I am Styrbjorn . . .'

Czcibor held up a hand, which was as good as a slap in the face to Styrbjorn. When he spoke, it was a slow, languid, serpent-hiss of sound, made worse by the mush-mess he made of the Norse.

'Styrbjorn. Yes. I know of you. My niece sent word of it down the Odra.'

I saw Styrbjorn stiffen and pale at that, which he had not been expecting.

'I shall have a stake cut especially for you,' Czcibor went on. 'And for the little monk who killed the woman Jasna. Perhaps I will make it the same one for you both.'

My stomach roiled and my knees started to twitch against the rough wood of the rampart stakes, where I had braced them. For a man with a name like a fire in a rainstorm he could summon up a mighty vision.

'An interesting idea,' I managed eventually. 'I would enjoy watching it under other circumstances. But we are all comfortable here and our arses free from stakes and a lot more dry than yours will be, by and by.'

He cocked his head sideways a little, appraising me; I had made it clear that I knew his predicament – he could not surround the *grod* completely because of the swamps on three sides and the river the settlement was practically thrust into. His own camp was on a soaked flat offering little comfort and no chance to dig even the simplest of privy pits or earthwork defences that would not instantly fill with mud and water.

All he could do was attack and be done with the business as fast as possible, which was a hard option – but this was a man come fresh from victory and unmoved by such problems. He nodded politely, put on his splendid helm, dragged out a

314

spear and, with a swift throw and a gallop off, hurled it over the ramparts as the signal that the bloody matter had commenced. It skittered on the hard ground behind me and a few men scattered, cursing the surprise of it.

'That went well,' Finn declared, grinning, then scowled and thumped Styrbjorn's shoulder, making the youth stagger. 'You nithing arse.'

Styrbjorn had no answer to it and slunk away while others who heard about his fawning attempt to wriggle over to safety jeered him.

And Dark Eye came to me, snuggling under my arm – which gained us both a couple of scowls from those who saw a sweetness they were not allowed – so that she could whisper softly.

'He asked for me.'

I had guessed that and had made quiet warding signs to prevent him voicing it in Norse for all to hear; let the Oathsworn think they were sieged here for the settlement we slaughtered, for if they suspected Dark Eye was the cause, they would hurl her to them in an eyeblink.

Yet it nagged me, that thought, for there was a whiff of betrayal and oath-breaking in it. Worse, there was the thought that this was what the Sea-Finn's drum had spoken of, so that defying it was standing up and spitting in Odin's one eye. I thought I heard Einar's slow, knowing chuckle as I turned away, whirling with mad thoughts of how to get folk out of these closing wolf-jaws.

Them, of course. Not me. I was only offering prayers to Frey and Thor and any other god I could think of to help convince AllFather to spare me long enough to see the crew away.

All the rest of that day we worked to improve our lot, comforted by the distant sound of axe-work in hidden trees; the Pols were making scaling ladders and would not attack before that was done.

Just as the dusk smoked in and we lit fires and torches, Finn came back from where he had been checking the watchers on

315

the river wall; there were skin-boats on the river, crude and hastily made, carrying one man to row and one man to shoot.

'The ground between the river and the wall is sodden, knee-deep at least,' he added. 'It will take four, perhaps five days for the water to seep away back to the river and even then a man will be hard put to walk through it without sinking to the cods.'

We ate together, waving off clouds of insects under the awning of the sail, for no-one wanted to be inside one of the houses, as if the air was thicker with rot there than elsewhere. I made a Thing of it, once they were licking their horn spoons clean.

To get away we would have to cross the bog down to the river, go in quietly, so as not to annoy the watchers in boats, then drift downstream a way to safety. Those who could not swim should fill bladders with air to stay afloat – there were sheep and goats enough for it – and we could try this when the bog had dried out, in five days.

By then we would be ankle-deep in blood, which I did not mention, and there would have to be men on the ramparts to let the others escape, which I did.

'I will be one,' I said, hoping my voice would not crack like my courage at the thought. 'It would be helpful to have a few more, but I do not demand this.'

'I will stay,' said Crowbone at once and Koll piped up bravely on his heels. I saw Alyosha stiffen at that, so I shook my head.

'Not this time, little Olaf,' I said to Crowbone. 'I need you to make sure Koll Brandsson gets back to his father.'

'I will stay,' Koll shrilled.

'You will obey your foster-father,' growled Finn, 'whose duty it is to keep you safe.'

The white head drooped. Crowbone paused a moment, then nodded at me; from the corner of my eye, I caught Alyosha's relief.

'I will be at your shieldless side,' Finn declared and I acknowledged it; one by one, men stood up and were counted,

316

each louder than the last and each into cheers louder than the one before. At the edge of them, Randr Sterki glowered in silence, offering nothing.

In the end, I had to turn men down, keeping ten only – Abjorn, Ospak, Finnlaith, Murrough, Finn, Rovald, Rorik Stari, Kaelbjorn Rog, Myrkjartan and Uddolf. We broke out a barrel of the fiery spirit that passed for drink in this part of the world and men fell to flyting each other with boasts of what they would do in the morning.

Later, as the fire collapsed to showers of sparks and glowing embers, Finn and I walked the guardposts, pausing in the tower over the gate to stare out at the field of red, flickering blooms which marked the camp of our enemy.

Beyond it, the night was silver and grey, soaked with the scent of a rain-wind, fresh-cut wood and torn earth; the moon, blurred and pale, darted from cloud to cloud, as if trying to hide from the all-devouring wolf which chased her.

'Will you tell them about the girl?' Finn growled and I felt neither alarm nor surprise; Finn was no fool.

'They would hand her over,' I answered flatly and he nodded.

'Aye – was this not what the Sea-Finn's drum meant? Can you stand against it? Defy that wyrd?'

I must and hoped he would not ask me the why of it, for I had no answer. Every time I thought of it, all I saw were her great, seal eyes.

He nodded again when I howked all this out.

'Is she so worth it then, that everyone here has to die? Even if both you and she get away, I am thinking Thorgunna will not be happy to see a second wife come into her home. I am thinking also that the Mazur girl is not the sort to be settled with being a second wife. If anyone makes it out of here at all – you are under the eye of Odin, after all.'

I had churned this to rancid butter night after night, after every furtive, frantic coupling we had stolen and had no answer for him.

'Tell Red Njal to get her away to safety when the time comes,' was all I could manage. 'Tell him to take her back to Hestreng. I charge him with that and taking Koll home.'

Finn nodded, a twist of a smile on his face. 'Aye – I wondered why you did not include Njal in your hopeless *hird*,' he answered. 'So did he – this will go some way to calming him for it.'

There was a noise and a figure that turned us; she came up the ladder to the tower, wrapped in her too-large cloak and it was clear she had heard us talk. Her eyes had vanished in the dark so that her face, pale and seemingly pitted with two large holes, looked like a savage mask.

'You will not take me home, then, Jarl Orm?'

I shook my head. It was too far and I would not be there to do it myself, for my wyrd was on me. The best I could offer was safety at Hestreng.

'In time,' I added, limping the words out, 'it may be that you could be taken back to your people. Word can certainly be sent to your father that you are no longer held by his enemies.'

She nodded and paused, head raised as if sniffing the wind.

'My father is called, in our tongue, Hard-Mouth,' she said. 'He is well-named and has a hand to match. I have two brothers and he whipped them every day from when they were old enough to walk. Every morning, before they ate, so they would know what pain was before pleasure and that such was our lot in life as Mazurs.'

She paused; a dog fox screamed somewhere far away.

'But he called me his little white flower and it was the hardest thing he did, handing me over to the Pols. He had no choice and wept. I had never seen my father shed a tear.'

Again she paused and no-one offered words to fill the silence.

'When he finds I am no longer held by the enemy,' she went on, stirring suddenly, 'he will raise up his warriors and fall on the Pols. They will slaughter him, for they are much

318

stronger now. It will take them time, for my father is skilful and folk will follow him. They will run and fight and run again – but, in the end, they will submit, when all the young men are dead. Bairns and women and old heads will die, too. The Mazur will be rubbed out, vanished like ripples on water.'

It was as bleak as an ice-field, that vision and I felt Finn shiver next to me. Then she turned and smiled whitely in the dark of her face.

'I have prepared a hut for us,' she said brightly. 'It does not matter to me whether the red sickness crawled in it. Does it bother you?'

I could only shake my head and she wraithed down the ladder and was gone. Finn looked at me.

'Do not ask what that meant,' I told him, 'for up here I am as much in the dark as you.'

Later still, weary as I was, I went to find Koll and knew just where he would be. The door of the hut was open, spilling out yellow light and letting in cool air, for here Bjaelfi moved among the sick, murmuring softly.

The monk was there, wiping the neck and chest of a man, while Koll sat some way back from him, his father's sword across his knees. Yan Alf crouched like a patient hound nearby and gave me a despairing look and a shrug when I came in, as if to say 'what can I do?'

Koll leaped up when he saw me and Leo turned his head, a twist of a smile on his face.

'I obey,' Koll said and thrust out the sheathed sword as far as he could before the weight dragged it to the beaten-earth floor with a clunk. 'I am at arm's length.'

'So you are,' I said. 'I came to make sure you had a sensible place to sleep.'

'This is sensible,' he answered uncertainly and Leo chuckled as I jerked my head at Yan Alf, who rose and propelled the boy outside.

'Do you believe I mean him harm?' the monk asked. I did not know for sure, but I knew he meant him no good and that, if he was a counter in the game, then he was my counter. Leo shrugged when I told him this.

'It is, then, a matter of bargaining,' he said and smiled. 'You are, after all, a trader as well as a slayer of white bears and a finder of treasure.'

'You are short of items to trade,' I answered.

'I have the boy,' he replied and I cocked my head and told him it was the other way round.

'You seem to wish to die here,' he said, as lightly as if passing judgement on the cut of my cloak, or the state of my shoes. 'What will happen to your men? To the boy?'

I had not thought beyond them drifting to safety and saw the mistake. Leo wiped the man's fat neck with one hand, the other resting comfortably at his side. The sick man's belly trembled as he breathed, low and rasping.

'The quickest way to safety is through the Bulgar lands,' Leo said. 'I am more of the Emperor's envoy there. In the Great City, I can provide help and aid for those who survive.'

He turned his face, less moon and more gaunt these days; life had melted some of the sleek off him.

'I can ensure the boy is returned to his father from the Great City.'

'For a price,' I spat back bitterly. Leo waved his free hand, then settled it, like a small moth, lightly back on his leg.

'What do you care – you are dead?' he replied, crow-harsh in the dim; I heard Bjaelfi grunt at that.

'I will return the boy, unharmed to this father,' he went on. 'I will make sure Jarl Brand knows that this is because of what you have done, so that you fulfil whatever vow you made. I know how you people value such vows. If there are other agreements made – what of it? The boy is still safe and your fame is safer still.'

This last was sneered out, as if it held no value at all – which,

him being steeped in the Great City's way of doing things, was accurate enough. Yet there was merit in this and he saw me pause, knew he had gaffed me with it.

'What is the price?' I demanded and he waved his free hand again.

'Little enough – freedom of movement. When the time comes, let your men know you trust me to guide them, so they will take pains to help both me and the boy.'

I pondered it.

'Of course,' he went on smoothly, 'it also means you cannot carry out your plan to kill me when the enemy breaks down the gate.'

He turned his bland smile on me. 'That *was* your plan, was it not?'

It was not, exactly. I had planned to leave him tethered for the Pols to find and stake him for the red murder of Jasna and the threat to Queen Sigrith. I had the satisfaction of seeing him blink; I could feel his hole pucker from where I stood and laughed.

'How was that killing done?' I asked. He recovered and shifted wearily, then paused in his endless wiping of the man's head and neck.

'One day,' he replied slowly, 'you may profit from the knowing.'

Then he smiled his bland smile. 'Of course,' he went on smoothly, putting aside the cloth and lifting the man's limp, slicked arm up high, 'all this is moot. This one is called Tub, I believe. He is leaking a little and he is the first, I think. It may be that no-one goes home without God's mercy.'

I stared at the accusing Red Plague pus-spots crawling down the arms and up the neck of Tub and heard Bjaelfi curse as I left.

In the morning, all our enemies were at the gates.

There was no skilled planning; Czcibor used his foot soldiers

like a club and they came piling across the narrow causeway, fanning out under the looming cliff of earthwork and timber ramparts, throwing up makeshift ladders.

We had one good bow – Kuritsa's – and a few more hunting ones we had found, but the horsemen had been dismounted and launched great skeins of shafts to keep our heads down, so we could do little but lob heavy stones from cover.

When the Pol foot soldiers, in their stained oatmeal tunics, finally got to the lip of the timbers, their archers had to stop firing; then we rose up and the slaughter started.

That first morning, I plunged into the maw of it, sick and screaming with fear, sure that this was where Odin swept me up and trying to make it quick.

I kicked the head of the first man who appeared, open-mouthed and gasping, so that he shrieked and went backwards. I cut down at the ladder, hooked the splintering top rung with the beard of my axe and then ran, elbowing my own men out of the way and hauling the ladder sideways; men spilled off it, flailing as they fell.

Some others had made the top rampart anyway and I plunged towards them, took a slice on the shaft of the axe, where metal strips had been fitted to reinforce the wood. In the same move, I cut up and under, splintering his ribs, popping his lungs out so that he gasped and reeled away.

Another came at me, waving a spear two-handed, so I reversed the axe and batted him off with the shaft, my left hand close up under the head – then gripped the spear with my free hand, pushed it to one side and sliced the axe across his throat like a knife.

The blood sprang out, black and reeking of hot iron, and he fell, half-dragging me as he did so, so that I staggered. Something spanged off my helmet; a great white light burst in my head and I felt the rough wood of the walkway splinter into my knees.

Then there was cursing and grunts and a hand hauled me

away; when I could see, Red Njal was standing over me, his own axe up and dripping.

'You will get yourself killed with such tricks,' he chided, then hurled himself forward, now that I was climbing to my feet.

Between us we pitched the struggling men back over the ramparts; no sooner had the heels of the last one vanished than two arrows whunked into the wood and we dived behind the timbers, panting and sweating, to listen to the drumming of others, flocking in like crows on offal. Crazily, I was reminded of rain on the canvas awning on the deck of the *Fjord Elk*, though I could not remember which *Fjord Elk* that had been.

'Five days,' Red Njal said and spat, though there was little wet in his mouth, I saw. I was thinking the same thing – these would be five long days.

The rest of it is a dull, splintered memory, like a tapestry shredded by a madman. I am certain sure that it was on the day we tied up Tub's mouth that we suffered a moon-howling loss that drove us a little mad.

It was the same as any other attack, though the ramparts by now were scarred, the timber points black and soaked with old gore, the walkway both sticky and slick. They came piling up over their own dead, threw up the ladders and did what they had been doing for what seemed years.

And we stood, we three, last of the band of old brothers, struggling and slipping and sweating and cursing, while Uddolf and Kaelbjorn Rog and others fought their own battles a little way away, for we were veil-thin on the rampart now.

Red Njal set himself behind his shield, took a deep, weary breath and shook himself, like a dog coming out of water.

'Fear the reckoning of those you have wronged,' he muttered, moving forward. 'My granny said it, so it must . . .'

The spear came out of nowhere, a vicious stab from the

first man up a ladder we had not seen. It caught Red Njal under the arm, right in the armpit, so that he grunted with the shock of it and jerked back. It had hooked and stuck and, even as we watched, the man who owned it fell backwards, ladder and all, as Finn smashed The Godi into his chest. Fixed to the spear, like a fish on a gaff, Red Njal was hauled over the rampart, a silent slither of ragged mail and leather.

I was stunned; it was the roof collapsing, the earth vanishing beneath my feet. I could not move for the sick horror of it – but Finn screamed, skeins of mad drool spilling down his beard and launched himself at the pack on the walkway, hacking and slashing.

I roused myself, moving as if I was in the Other, walking in a mist and slowed. Twice, I know, I held his back, stopped the crash of a blade on him, but I only came into the Now of matters when he was pounding the head of the last man on the walkway, screaming at him.

'What is it called?' he shrieked. Slam. Slam. 'This place? What is it called?'

The man, leaking blood from his eyes and ears and nose and mouth, spattered out a word, so that Finn was satisfied enough to haul him up under the armpits and heave him over the rampart.

We huddled in the lee of the black-stained points, sitting in the viscous stink and staring at each other, while the arrows wheeked and whirred and shunked into the wood. Eventually, Finn wiped one bloody hand across his bloody beard.

'Needzee,' he said slowly and my blank eyes were question enough.

'Name of this place,' he explained. 'I was thinking we should know where we are dying.'

That night, he and Kaelbjorn Rog and Ospak flitted down the rampart on knotted ropes, but it was dark and they dared

not show any lights, so they could not find Red Njal in the heap, some still groaning, at the foot of our stockade.

His death was a rune-mark on matters coming to an end.

The end came two days later, when eighteen of us were rolling with sweat and babbling and twenty more had died, three from the plague. Almost everyone else was wounded in some way.

Worst of all, Koll was sick. The red and white spots started under his armpit and down his thighs in the morning and then erupted on the pale circles of his cheeks. By nightfall he looked as if someone had thrown a handful of yellow corn that had stuck to his face, each one a pustule that festered and stank.

The monk sat with him, in between tending the others, while Bjaelfi, half-staggering with weariness, moved back and forth, Dark Eye with him like a shadow, answering a whimper here, a cry there.

In the fetid, blood-stinking dark, we gathered round the fire, streaked and stained and long since too weary to wash. My braids were gummed with old blood and other, even worse, spills from the dead and my clothing stained and ripped; no-one was any better.

We carried Koll to the fire; no-one minded, for there was no escape from the pest and if the Norns wove that red thread into your life, that was it. Only Styrbjorn scowled, thinking that distance meant more safety.

Behind us, torches burned at the raised wooden platform that marked the centre of the village – Needzee, Finn had called it, but Dark Eye had put him right on that. The luckless man had gasped out 'nigdzie' as Finn pounded his head to ruin, screaming to know what the name of this place was that we were all dying for, the place where Red Njal had gone to meet his granny.

Nowhere, the man had said in his own tongue and Finn

had thrown back his head and bellowed with cracked laughter when Dark Eye told him that.

Now Dark Eye lit torches and knelt on the wooden platform, praying to her four-faced god, while the shadows flicked and men, too tired even to eat or talk, huddled in a sort of stupor, heads bowed, watching the smoke writhe. A pot steamed on an iron tripod and the men lay in a litter of helms and weapons, slumped with shields as backrests, crusted ringmail puddled like old snakeskins at their feet.

When Dark Eye wraithed herself back to the fire, a few heads lifted and dull eyes took her in. Styrbjorn, always ready with his mouth, curled his lip.

'Praying for rescue?' he asked.

'Only the fearful pray for rescue,' she replied, pooling herself into a comfortable squat. Styrbjorn stirred uncomfortably, for everyone could see that promised stake up the arse occupied most of his waking hours.

'The man who says he is not afraid in this matter is a liar,' he responded.

'Tell Finn that,' Uddolf chuckled harshly. 'He is well-known for having no fear.'

'Perhaps he can tell you the secret of it, Styrbjorn,' Onund added with his usual bear grunt. 'Then we will be quit of your whine.'

'As to that,' Finn said softly. 'Since we are all about to look our gods in the face, it may be that you want to know the secret of having no fear.'

Now men were stirring with interest, me among them.

'When I was young,' he began, 'I did matters which were not agreeable to certain men in Skane and, when they caught me, there was no Thing on it, no outlawing. Justice was rougher in those days and none rougher than Halfidi. He was as white-haired as any kindly uncle and as black-bowelled as a *draugr*. *Slátur*, men called him.'

There were chuckles at such a fine by-name – *Slátur* was

a dish made by stitching pungently strong black-blood sausage into a lamb's white stomach.

'They kicked and beat me,' Finn went on, 'and starved me for a week, which was to be expected. Each day Halfidi, or one of his sons, would dish out the meat of a whipping and take delight in telling me when I would hang. At the end of that week, they took me to the top of the cliff they used, where a rope was fastened to an iron ring. They put the other end round my neck and tied a cloth round my eyes. Then they spun me and pushed me to walking, so that I did not know where the cliff edge was.'

Men grunted with the cruel power that vision brought.

'Three days they did this,' Finn said, soft, lost in the dream of it. 'On the second day the shite was running down my leg and I was babbling promises not even a god could keep if they would let me go. On the third day I did the same, only for them to let me see.'

He stopped. Men waited; the fire flared a little in a wet night wind, throwing up a whirl of sparks.

'On the fourth day, they were careless with the bindings and I worked one hand free, so that when they came to prodding and pushing, I tore the cloth from my eyes. There were eight of them, who all saw I had one hand free and so they came at me with spears.'

He paused, a long time this time, until Styrbjorn – that child would never learn when to put his tongue between his teeth – demanded to know what happened next.

'I went over the edge,' said Finn. All breathing stopped at the dizzying vision of that, of what it had taken to do it.

'And died, of course,' sneered Styrbjorn. 'I heard this tale when I was toddling.'

'I did not die. I went over the edge and, when I hit the end of that bast rope it snapped clean through. I should have had my neck cracked, but had my free hand taking a deal of the strain, so I was spared that. I hit the sea and got through that, too.'

Men were silent, for such a matter was a clear intervention of the hand of some god. Frey, suggested one. Odin himself, another thought and those who favoured Slav gods offered their own thoughts on the matter.

'I have had no fear since,' Finn said. 'It was snapped from me by that bast rope. Nothing and no-one since has made me drip shite down my leg through terror.'

'That is why you did not want that Vislan hanged,' I said, suddenly seeing it and Finn admitted it.

'And why you follow the prow beast,' Kaelbjorn Rog added. 'Since you cannot return to Skane while Halfidi and his sons are waiting.'

Finn said nothing.

'They are not,' I said softly, staring at him, rich with sudden knowing. 'But you can still never go back, can you, Finn Horsehead?'

Finn stared back at me, black eyes dead as old coals. 'I went to their hall in the night. That same night. I barred all the doors and fired it. No-one got out.'

It might have been the wind, or the trailing finger of that horror, but men shivered. The burning of a hall full of his own kind was the worst act a Northman could do and he was never forgiven for it.

It was cold, that burning revenge, for there were women and weans in it. It came to me then that humping a dead woman on the body of a dying ox was neither here nor there for a man such as Finn. I had been wrong, telling Brother John bitterly that I was leading the charge into his Abyss, for no matter how hard I ran down that dark, steep way, Finn would always be ahead of me.

'Heya,' growled Rovald. 'That was a harsh tale – what did you do that so annoyed this Halfidi?'

We expected robbery, dire murder or killing his ma – or all of them, after what we had just learned. Finn stared at the fire, leaned forward and stirred the cauldron.

'I fished his river,' he answered. 'Fished it once by moon-light for the salmon in it. He was not even sure it was me that one of his men saw.'

No-one spoke for a long time after that – then Onund suddenly leaped sideways with a curse and lashed out. Folk sprang up, hands on weapons and Onund looked at them back and forth for a moment, then grunted sheepishly.

'Rat,' he said. 'Ran over my hand. I hate rats. They come out for the raven's leavings.'

Crowbone's new voice was still more of a clear bell than others and heads lifted when it spoke.

'Pity the rat,' he said. 'It was not always as you see it now.'

He shifted his face forwards, to have it dyed by embers. His odd eyes were glinting glass chips.

'In the beginning of the world,' he said. 'When Odin was young and still had both eyes and so was more foolish than now, he was more kind-hearted. So much so that he did not like to see folk die. So one day he sent for Hugin, Thought, who was his favourite messenger from Asgard to men. He told that raven to go out into the world and tell all people that, whenever anyone died, the body was to be placed on a bier, surrounded by all the things precious to it in life and then freshly-burned oak wood ashes were to be thrown over it. Left like that on the ground, in half a day, it would be brought back to life.'

'A useful thing to know,' Styrbjorn announced. 'Find some oak ash and we will have our own army round these parts by tomorrow's rising meal.'

'Not now,' Crowbone announced sorrowfully. 'When Hugin had flown for half a day he began to get tired and hungry, so when he spotted a dead sheep he was on it like a black arrow. He sucked out the eyes and shredded the tongue and made a meal of it. Then went to sleep, entirely forgetting the message which had been given him to deliver.

'After a time,' Crowbone went on, looking round the rapt,

329

droop-lipped faces, 'when the raven did not return, Odin called for the smallest of his creatures – the rat. It was not a skulker in sewage and darkness then, but a fine-furred beast, even if he had no discernible use other than sleeping. Odin, in his foolishness, sought to raise the rat in life and sent him out with the same message.'

'Odin sounds very much like every king I have ever heard of,' Onund Hnufa rumbled, 'while his rat reminds me of every royal messenger I have ever seen.'

The laughter was dutiful, but so weak it dribbled out like drool from a sleeping mouth and scarcely made Crowbone pause.

'The rat was, as you say, a poor messenger,' he went on. 'He fell asleep, went here, went there – and, though he eventually remembered the message, forgot what it was exactly; so as he went about among the people he told them that Odin had said that, whenever anyone died, they should be set on an oak bier, surrounded by all their prize possessions and burned to ash. In half-a-day, they would be brought back to life.'

Crowbone stopped and spread his hands wide.

'Well – by the time Hugin woke up and remembered he had a message, it was too late. He flew around furiously yelling at people to stop setting fire to their dead and telling them of the message Odin had given him – but folk said they already had a message and it was all too late.'

'And so,' Crowbone said, 'the Odin dead are always burned to this day; the god in a fury rescinded the secret of resurrection and went off to find the sort of wisdom that would stop him making any more mistakes like that.

'Now no-one trusts a raven when it speaks – and the rat is hated for the false message he brought.'

Folk shifted slightly as the tale came to an end; Rovald shook a mournful head.

'Think of that,' he said, nudging his neighbour, who happened to be Styrbjorn. 'If the raven had not stopped to eat – folk would all still be alive.'

'Blame the dead sheep for dying, then,' snarled Styrbjorn.

'Or having tasty eyes,' added Ospak moodily.

Koll stirred and moaned, came awake into his nightmare.

'Moonlight,' he said and a few folk looked up; like a pale silver coin, it seemed to drift across the sky between clouds.

'Rain on the wind,' muttered Thorbrand.

'This place is famous for it,' Ospak growled and that raised a weak chuckle or two.

'The same moon,' Koll whispered, 'shines on my home.'

It was a link, right enough and the tug of it brought every head up briefly. Styrbjorn wiped his mouth, gone dry with the thoughts that flitted nakedly over his face – home was there, under that silver coin in the sky and just as unreachable. He would die here. We would all die here.

'Tell me of your home,' the monk asked gently and Koll tried, in his shadow of a whisper, a thread of sound that stitched all our hearts. Of running barefoot on the strand's edge. Hunting gull eggs. Playing with his dog. Fishing. A bairn's things that, to these hard raiding men, were as far removed as that same moon – yet close enough to be remembered, to make them blink with the sudden rush of it. A man grunted almost in pain as Koll lisped about sliding on the frozen river on goat-bone skates. Then the boy's voice faded – mercifully – to sleep.

'What of your own home, monk?' I harshed out, eager to be rid of the pangs of Koll's memories, sure that tales of Miklagard would be more diverting, since most of the men here had never been to it more than once and that only briefly.

'The city walls rise like cliffs,' Leo said obligingly, 'and the towers and domes blaze with gold. In the morning, a mist hangs over the roofs, there is smoke and ships . . .'

He stopped and I was surprised to see his eyes bright. Murrough shifted his big frame and coughed, almost apologetically.

'I have heard they have women of great beauty there,' he

grunted, 'but veiled, like the Mussulmen women. I thought you were all Christ believers in Miklagard?'

'Veiled, unveiled, beauteous and plain as a cow's behind,' Leo answered with a small smile. 'All manner of women – but you are asking the wrong man, since they do not bother me. I am a priest of Christ, after all.'

'I had heard this,' Randr Sterki answered, frowning. 'It is a great wonder to me that a man can give up women for his god.'

'It is a great wonder to me that a god would ask it,' added Onund and men laughed now. I relaxed; this was better. Even Randr Sterki seemed to have covered the sharp edge of himself.

'Worse than that,' Finn growled, 'these Christ folk say you should not fight.'

'Yet they do it, all the same,' Myrkjartan pointed out. 'For these Pols we are killing are Christ men, or so I have been told – and there is no greater army than the one of the Great City itself, yet they are all Christ followers.'

Leo smiled indulgently.

'They are told not to kill,' Murrough corrected, 'according to all the canting Christ priests of my land. Perhaps it is different in the Great City. I have heard they follow the same Christ, but in a different way.'

'The rule,' Leo said slowly, picking his words like a hen does seed, 'is that you should not kill. A commandment, we call it.'

'There you are, then,' Finn muttered disgustedly. 'The Christ priests command the army not to kill and the chiefs command the opposite. It is a marvel that anything is done.'

Leo smiled his gentle smile. 'Actually, the original gospel commanded us not to murder, which is a little different and not too far from what you northers believe.'

There were nods and thinking-frowns over that one.

'This is what happens when such matters are written,' Ospak declared, shaking his head and everyone was silent, remembering Red Njal.

332

'Then confusion will be king,' Leo answered, 'for the Mussulmen have some similar rules written down in their holy works.'

'Are you Mussulman, then?' asked Crowbone, knitting his brows together. Leo shook his head and his smile never wavered; another priest of Christ would have been outraged.

'I wonder only,' Crowbone said, 'because I met a Mussulman once and he had sworn off women. He ate like you did, too, with one hand only.'

He looked at me when he said it, but just then Finn leaned forward, sniffed the pot, lifted the ladle and tasted it. Then he fished out his little bone container of emperor salt and poured generous whiteness into it.

'Salt,' he declared, sitting back. 'A man should eat as much salt as he can. It cleans the blood.'

There was silence, while the fire crackled and the cauldron bubbled and men sat slathered and crusted with other men's salt-cleaned blood and tried not think about it. Then Koll woke and managed to whisper out to Finn, asking him what he missed of his home.

Finn was silent and stared once out at the dark ramparts where our guards huddled and watched; I thought his head was back in Hestreng, was full of thoughts of Thordis and Hroald, his son.

I should have known. Thordis and he would never trade vows and Hroald was a boy ignored as much as acknowledged; Finn showed the truth of it all when he stretched out one long arm and pointed to where Onund's elk carving perched on the gate tower, slanted slightly, but still upright and proud, a symbol that the Oathsworn were here and not leaving in any hurry.

'I am home,' he growled.

NINETEEN

We had left it too late; Czcibor had more men and bigger boats on the river; it cost us three dead to find that out and Styrbjorn came staggering back from the little river gate, clutching his bloody arm and ranting with the fear howling in him, for we were trapped.

That was the day we started burning corpses in a mad, desperate fear-fever that sought to try and scour the Red Pest out before it killed us all.

That was the day they brought up the ram and smashed in the gate.

They had tried fire, but lacked oil for their arrows and we had water enough to soak the gates and timbers where they tried it. Then we saw men hauling back a good tree, sweated out of the river further down, where it had lodged. It was, as Finn pointed out, as good an oak for a ram as any he had seen.

We had to watch it being crafted, too, for there was no place to hide out on that plain and every hammer and axe-stroke that shaped it rattled us to the bone, for we had no way of stopping such a beast. Their archers would keep our heads down – it was almost impossible to put your head above the timber-teeth of the rampart now, unless there were enemy

climbing over it – and the ram would come up to the gate and splinter it to ruin.

'Barrier the inside of the gate,' I suggested and Alyosha nodded, then grinned.

'Battle luck for you, Orm Bear Slayer, that you have skilled men here. Better than a barrier is our wolf-teeth.'

Alyosha and the Rus were old hands, having fought in sieges on both sides of the ramparts and they knew what was needed.

They had a house demolished for the great timbers of the roof-tree and lashed them together like a cradle. Then they gathered up spears and split the heads from them, or cut the shafts short, so that they were fixed to the cradle, all odd lengths and all deadly.

After that, it was shifted to a point just beyond where the curved groove of dirt showed how far the gate opened inwards.

'Wolf-teeth,' Alyosha said, when his chosen men had sweated it into place; they beamed with satisfaction. Finn and others strolled round it, eyeing it with a professional air, for we were raiders, when all was said and done and avoided anything that looked like this bristling terror.

'A place to hang their cloaks and hats when they come,' Finn said eventually, which was admiration enough to make Alyosha beam.

'Growl not at guests, nor drive them from the gate,' Ospak added, 'as Red Njal's granny would say.'

'No more on that,' Finn growled. 'Without it coming from his mouth, I would sooner see Red Njal's granny laid to rest.'

Ospak merely nodded and smiled, twisting his dirt and blood-crusted face into a hard knot.

Not long after, hidden watchers peering through slits on the gate tower announced that the enemy were coming again.

I stood behind the barrier with Finn at one shoulder and Ospak at the other, fetid with fear and old blood, rot-red with rust. My bowels curled like waves on the shore and the

335

first great boom of the ram on the door almost loosened them entirely.

On the ramparts, Finnlaith and Alyosha and others hunkered down and heaved the last of our stones as well as spike-studded timbers down on the heads of the ram party; we heard them clatter and bounce off the roof of shields, though there was an occasional scream to let us know they were not having it all their own way.

We sweated and shivered behind the wolf fangs, while the gate rang like a bell and heaved in another little bit with each blow, the bar on it creaking and dancing in the locks. Great gouts of muddy slurry spurted up from the hinges.

Crowbone slid up to the tower steps with a party bringing up more timbers, manhandling them up the ladder, with the gate bulging in right at their ears. Alyosha, his helmet flaps up and laced across the top of his head so that his ears were free and he could hear better, saw it and bellowed out something, lost in the mad din. Crowbone merely waved at him and Alyosha, scowling, half-stood to make his way to the steps and tell Crowbone to go away.

The arrow took him in the neck, just under the ear; if he had had his helmet flaps down it might have saved him, but they were up like little birdwings and the arrow went in one side and out the other. He jerked and pawed at it, a puzzled look on his face, then reared up; blood came out of his mouth in a great, black gout and he fell sideways and clattered down the steps to Crowbone's feet.

The boy howled – but someone grabbed him just then, dragging him back and under the cradle of wolf fangs, just as the gate crashed open with a splintering rend of wood and hinge.

The first man through was a mad-mouthed frother, black hair flying, lunging in with a spear up and a leather helmet askew on his forehead; he had time to see what he was running at, time to skid to a halt – then the ones behind crashed on

336

him and he was shot forward, shrieking for his ma, to be impaled like a shrike's breakfast.

The first half-dozen ended up like that – there were longer blades with two and three bodies on them; some of the shafts snapped under the weight.

Those behind realised something was up when they were brought up short and found they could go neither ahead, nor to the side, while those in the gate tower above were hurling slabs of spiked wood down on them.

I hacked and stabbed and cut and slashed; the wooden cradle started to shift and slide back under the press, so men put their shoulders to it on our side and shoved, while others elbowed for room to fight. There was a fine haze of steam and stink and misted blood, a great bellowing shriek of fear and dying; the earth under the gate tower churned to a thick broth of muddy blood.

I saw Finn take a jaw off with a wild stroke. I saw one of Randr Sterki's men eat the point of a spear and go down, gargling. Arrows whirred and shunked and men from both sides screamed and died; the Pols were shooting through the open gateway, heedless of who they hit.

Yan Alf went crazed then and leaped up on top of the wolf-fang cradle and its smother of hanging bodies, then hurled himself, screaming, into the middle of the pack; I never saw him alive again. Finnlaith, screaming 'Ui Neill' and spittle, followed him, leaping off the top of the watchtower and I saw him once after that, rising through a frothing sea of enemy like a breaching whale; then he disappeared.

That broke them. One minute I was slashing and stabbing, my breathing high and shrill, my arm aching, seeing the blood curve off the end of the axe blade in fat, greasy spray – then I was slumped against the scarred, gouged cradle where bodies writhed and groaned. The Pols backed off through their own arrows and Finn yelled out a warning as the full weight of shafts fell on us.

Shields up, we stood there until men brought up some thick timber doors torn off the houses and used them as shelter. In the end, the arrows stopped and men went out to heave corpses aside and shut the gates again, though they were so badly splintered that they could not be barred.

I know I shouted instructions for some of this, for Finn told me. I know I helped carry Alyosha away and consoled a weeping Crowbone, while the crew of *Short Serpent* – what was left of them – stood, covered in gore and grim silence while Alyosha was shield-carried to a pyre. Ospak and Murrough, the last Irishers left, stood like dumb posts, unable to go out and find Finnlaith; in the end, Onund whacked their shoulders and gave them work to keep their minds off the loss.

I know all this, but was aware of none of it. I only came back to life later, when Bjaelfi was binding up my ankle – the old injury, which burned like fire. I had gone over on it, according to folk who saw, and limped about for a long time until Bjaelfi and others managed to pin me down and tend my wounds.

I had a scratch down one cheek, my ribs ached from a blow I did not even know I had come by and my nose thundered with pain and trickled new blood, so that Finn, unharmed and grinning through the stains on his face, shook his head.

'That neb of yours will not last much longer if you persist in getting it dunted,' he noted and Ospak, staggering past with an armful of timber to be spiked with spear and arrow points, stopped long enough to look and tilt his head almost onto his shoulder.

'Every time I look at it,' he said, 'I have to stand at more of a list to steerboard than before, just to keep it straight on your face.'

Then he laughed, a shrill, high sound. They all laughed, those that were left, hair stiff with clotted filth, armour red-rusted

and weapons stained with gore. They moved as though their legs were wood – yet they moved, getting ready for the next attack.

Finnlaith was dead, Yan Alf was dead. Thorbrand was dead. Hjalti Svalr had the Red Pest, had lost most of his right hand and was groaning and babbling of home. Others were stacked like winter wood, their weapons bound to cold hands. And those who were left mourned with laughter, like wolves.

I had no belly left for laughing. As the shadows lengthened and weary fires sprang up, Bjaelfi came to me, his face scored with misery, carrying a limp little bundle which he laid at my feet like an offering. It was so small, that bundle, yet it broke us all like a falling tree and men groaned and bowed their heads; some even wept, leaving wet white streaks through the filth of their cheeks.

Koll. He was wrapped warmly and his face was so swollen his father would not have known him but for the bone-white of his hair. One hand rested on his chest under the warm wrap, but one had flopped free and the blue veins on it stood proudly out, so proud it was hard to believe that blood did not pump through them. The rest of the hand was pale, the shrinking flesh spatterered with white pustules.

Bjaelfi looked at me, waiting to take the small body to the burning; men stopped and made Hammer signs for mourning and not just because Koll was dead. He was what we had struggled all this way to get, had fought for, had watched oarmates die for – and we had failed.

I tied his little hands round the hilt of his father's sword and gave him to the Odin-fire. It was like the death of hope itself, watching that small, wrapped body smoke up into the dark.

That night, Dark Eye came to me, silent as a summer breeze, yet when I reached for her she was limp and slick-sheened with sweat, hot as embers in my arms. To the question in my

339

eyes, she simply slithered from her shapeless tunic-dress and raised her arms; even in the dark, where her silver shape glowed, the red spots on her thighs and under her arms were clear, almost as big as the tender tips of her hard breasts.

She shivered and sweated.

'In the morning,' she said, 'I will go to them.'

I argued. I swore. I ranted. I babbled. In the end she pressed hot, cracked lips on mine to silence me.

'This is my wyrd,' she said, her breath fetid on my cheek. 'This is best. I am what they want – let them take me, for it will be their own doom. This is what the Sea-Finn's drum saw.'

I saw it, then, hot in her eyes, with a coldness deep in my bowels. It was her wyrd – at one stroke she saved us, saved her people and would spread the red, ruinous pest through Czcibor's army.

'It must be done in the morning,' she said, 'before I am too weak to pretend.'

I nodded then, still frantic with the loss of her, with the sight of those great, liquid seal eyes already filming blue-white with sickness. I held her most of that night, leaving her only long enough to take a stained, unbleached linen scrap and wrap it round a shield.

There was not enough dark in all the world that would keep back the creeping dawn.

When it spilled up, staining the rampart, making it like the jaw of some snarling prow beast, men stood, shaking and weary, beards and hair stiff with filth, eyes bright with the knowledge that today they would stand before their gods – and were amazed to see me walk Dark Eye to the gate.

I handed my axe to Finn and left Dark Eye with him while I shoved through the splintered ruin, stepping over the bodies and through the bloody crust of mud. I held the linen-wrapped shield high, hoping it was white enough to be noticed as a truce-sign. I paused only once to look Randr Sterki in his red-rimmed eyes. His grin was a curve of snarl.

Picking my way through the festering dead, I stumbled out to where Czcibor sat on his horse; he looked more gaunt now, I was thinking and I wondered if the Red Pest had already reached his army.

'Be quick,' he said harsh and haughty, so I was.

'Is she trade enough for our lives?' I asked and he looked over my shoulder to the small figure in the broken gateway, having to look across the heaped bundles of his own dead men, having to see the spears and blades still defending the rampart, the cradle of wolf-teeth gleaming just inside the gate.

When he looked back at me, his eyes were hard and cold and bleak, which did not bother me much – I knew he would agree, for he could not stay here longer. He ached to stake us out, but the cost was high and he was too much of a good commander to let his hate ruin his army and his ambition.

What stabbed me to the bone was the rest of his look, the bit just behind his eyes which curled a sneer at me for giving up this slip of a woman to save our lives.

Perhaps it choked him, perhaps he was too tired to do more – but he nodded, which was enough.

I walked back to the gate and took my axe back from Finn. Dark Eye, impassive as a carving, wrapped the tattered cloak round her and walked out, the way she had always walked, as if she had gold between her legs, into the maw of the Pols. She did not look back.

I came back into the faces of those who knew the business was finished and that they would not die today. Yet there remained, hovering like a waiting hawk, the knowledge that it had been the girl the Pols had wanted all along – but no-one who saw my face wanted to bare their teeth on that, all the same.

Save one, of course. There is always one.

'You fuck,' yelled Styrbjorn, trembling with the nearness of that fearful stake. 'It was the girl. All this time. We died so you could have a hump while the . . .'

I hit him with the haft of the axe, a wet smack in his face that sent him crashing to the ground, where he lay and snored out bubbling blood and teeth. Uddolf moved to him, turning him over so that he would not choke.

I was cold with it all, cold and sick. A little shape was burning on a pyre, another was staggering away to die among enemies and both had held skeins of my wyrd in their hands; with their loss, I could not see one more step in front of me. I was almost on my knees, begging Odin to take his sacrifice and I half-turned to where Randr Sterki stood, silent and watchful, almost willing him to make his move.

'Good blow,' said Bjaelfi after a swift look at Styrbjorn. 'Though I am thinking it would have been better to have used the edge. A head hacked off cannot conspire, as Red Njal's granny would say.'

Finn shifted slightly and cleared the rheum from his throat.

'Make that the last of Red Njal's granny,' he growled, so that everyone could hear, 'and be content that our Orm used the shaft and not the edge. He was always the one for leaving folk alive who should be dead, yet is known for a man who can fall in a bucket of shite and come up with a handful of silver. Perhaps there is worth in Styrbjorn yet.'

He frowned down at the groaning Styrbjorn, then hefted The Godi and clawed everyone with his gaze.

'This needs cleaning. Then we can quit this Nowhere place.'

There were twenty of us quitting, no more; the rest were dead, and those who were not, we killed for mercy's sake and then burned them, with all their gear and even their sea-chests, the black feathers trailing accusingly into a sullen sky behind us as we moved across fresh green and birdsong.

For most of that first day we moved grim and fearful, a scar on the land, always looking over one shoulder, for no-one trusted the Pols and we were on their side of the Odra now, heading for a tributary river called Notec, which we would

have to cross. After a while, when it seemed as if we had, truly, escaped, men began to look round at the green tips and buds, to turn to where a raven harshed, or a small bird peeped.

They took deeper breaths of spring air and started to grin at each other – except the sick, who staggered or were carried, babbling. The Red Pest stayed with us, tagging along like a dog that could not be sent home and still they grinned at each other, as if they had thrown particularly good dice.

I was the only one not exulting in survival, not cheered by avoiding the cliff and the wolves, moving like a man already dead and waiting, waiting, waiting, for Odin to strike. I was a scowl on the face of their cheerfulness and men avoided me, all save Finn and Crowbone – and the monk, strangely, who strode out alongside me now and then, the uneven dagged ends of his black wool robe flapping round his calves.

Eventually, because I knew he was waiting for me to do it and would never break the silence first, I asked him what he wanted.

'To knit you back, like the broken bone you are,' he said, easy enough with the words and looking ahead at the trail. Crowbone loped past us, an old bow in his hand and three arrows in the other.

'I am going hunting,' he declared and I knew it was to take his thoughts off the dead Alyosha, so I fought for words to rein him in and yet not make it seem so, for his nursemaid was gone.

Kuritsa appeared and slapped Crowbone manfully on the shoulder.

'Nothing with legs is edible when you kill it,' he declared. 'You gutshoot it and the meat is bitter when it runs. I will go with you and teach you how to hunt.'

He shot me a look over one shoulder, a reassuring grin with it, then the pair of them moved off ahead of the trail,

with men chaffering them, pleased that there might be more than old bread and oats that night.

'I do not need your Christ for my salvation,' I told the monk and he nodded.

'Then I do not offer him. But you need something.'

I was wondering why he cared and said so.

'I need you to get me back to the Great City,' he said, which was truthful enough, if not exactly the warm spirit of caring I had imagined. I laughed, the sound echoing as if my head was in a bucket and he smiled.

'See? Now matters are better.'

'What happens when we do get to the Great City, monk?' I demanded. 'It comes to me that taking such a dangerous man as yourself back to the place where he is powerful and we are not is foolish. Perhaps we should kill you here; it is no more than you deserve.'

Leo walked in frowning silence for a while, then smiled suddenly, bright and wide.

'You will just have to trust me,' he said. 'I will be more use alive in the Great City than dead in a heap out here.'

'So I will not have to offer some jewelled cross for our lives, then?' I offered wryly. 'Now that your bargaining counter is burned to smoke?'

'Jesus died on a wooden one,' he answered and I had no answer to that and felt suddenly washed with weariness, so that we walked in silence through the wood, which seemed never to end – so much so that I remember saying so and asking how far we had to walk into it.

'Only half-way,' Finn answered, peering at me, 'then we are walking out of it, as any sensible man will tell you. You look like eight ells of bad cloth, Trader. Perhaps you should rest.'

The day had slithered into grey twilight, where the *alfar* flickered and I was only vaguely aware of Finn calling a halt for it seemed that the grey light smoked round me, so that I saw and heard them as if in a mist.

There was a steading. Once, it had been a substantial *hov*, a shieling of some note, built low to the ground, but it had fallen to ruin, so that the moss had reclaimed it to a mound of green; grass hung, dried and withered off what was left of the roof, drooping like the bodies of the dead on the ramparts we had so recently left.

I woke to find myself under the shelter of the only roof-space left, sharing it with groaners with sweating, plaguey faces, or wounded from the fight, or moaning with belly-rot and boils. Fires were lit, the rest of the men huddled outside, under the stars and what cloaks they had, sharing them with those who had none.

Kuritsa and Crowbone had returned, the big archer with a buck over his shoulders and it was jumped on, gralloched, cut up and spit-roasted; the smell of meat sang round the house like a memory of better times.

They brought me slivers of succulent deer, bread softened and savouried in the blood-juices of it, but I had no hunger, which I found strange and even the bit I forced down tasted like ash. Bjaelfi came and peered at me and it was then I realised, with a shock, that I was sick.

For a time, I lay and listened to the men mutter softly and start in to weaving themselves together; straps were repaired, weapons cleaned, men tried to sponge the worst stains from clothing and cloaks.

They dragged out combs – all of them had them, good bone ones and, even if some of those implements grinned like gappy old men, they still dragged them through clotted, raggled hair. Bjaelfi produced shears and some of the worst matting was cut off; beards and hair were trimmed and Leo shook his head with wonder, for he had not realised that norther warriors are more vain than women.

In the end, I drifted off in my jarl-bed under the roof with the murmuring sick, listening to the gentle shift of Bjaelfi and the monk, moving like soft, clucking hens.

345

I moved into a dream of smoke and water, where familiar people and places shredded mistily away when I looked at them, living only at the edge of my dream-sight, like *alfar*. When I surfaced from this, it was like breaching from the ocean, whooping in air and shivering, blurred and blinking. Sweat rolled off me and I shook; I knew what ate me.

I got up and the place heaved gently as if I stood on a deck in a swell; my feet seemed too far below me and did not even seem to be mine as I moved, slowly, like an old, blind man, out past the soft glow of the fire, the snorers and farters, out to where a man stood on watch in ringmail and helm.

He looked at me and I stared blankly back at him; it took long seconds for me to recognise Ospak, by which time he had come close enough to give me his concern.

'You should go back to the fire, Jarl Orm,' he said flatly. I wanted to tell him to leave me alone, that I needed a shit – which was a lie, of course. What I needed was privacy to find out what I already knew in my heart.

All that I croaked out of me, all the same, was 'shit'. He nodded slowly, and turned back to his guard duty. I struggled on, to where the dark ate the fireglow and beyond, to where only the half-veiled moon gave light.

I dropped my breeks, bent my head to look. I saw the red spots crawling out of my groin and on to my thighs like embers from a forge-fire. I touched the burn of them, knew the truth and either it or the fever swam my head, so that I half stumbled and nearly fell.

'Steady, Bear Slayer,' said a voice, cold as quenched iron. 'I would not wish you hurt. That is my pleasure alone.'

Randr Sterki moved blackly out of the dark to stand in front of me, where I could see him if I could raise my head. I could do that only a little but the blade he held gleamed like an old fang in the moonglow. Naked from the waist, the white of his body seemed eaten by whorls of darkness, which I slowly realised were his Rus skin-markings.

346

The stupidity of him made me laugh and I saw myself as he saw me – swaying, head-bowed, breeks around my ankles. It only made matters funnier and the laughing choked me, so that I suddenly found myself with my arse on the wet grass.

'Get up,' he hissed angrily. 'Or die on your knees.'

On my arse, I wanted to correct. I am on my arse here and dying of the Red Pest and whether you slit me here or wait for me to die makes no difference and will not bring any of the ones you loved back again. Odin takes his sacrifice-life – in the cruelest way, of course, that being the mark of One-Eye.

But all that came out was 'arse'. Which, given the moment and the matter, was not gold-browed verse likely to sway him from his path.

He grunted, moved like a lowered brow, black and angry and the sword silvered through the shadows, seemed to leave a trail behind it as it moved, like the wake of a ship on a black sea. My sword, I noted dully; I could see the V-notch in it, as if the dark had taken a bite from the blade.

'Hold, Randr Sterki,' growled a voice and a figure scowled out of the shadows and grabbed Randr's arm. 'Do not kill him. We need him . . .'

Randr yelped with the shock of it and we both saw it was the monk, black-robed and tense as coiled wire, his hand gripping Randr's sword-arm. Randr, with a savage howl, flung Leo away from him and cursed in pain as he did so.

'Get away, you Christ-hagged little fuck,' he snarled, rubbing his forearm and scowling. 'Once I deal with this dog, you will be next.'

Leo rolled over and came up to his knees. Strangely, he was laughing through the blood on his mouth. Behind him, I saw Finn sprinting forward, The Godi in one fist, nail in the other.

'You *nithing fud*,' he shrieked, but it was desperation, for he knew he would never make it. I knew he would never

347

make it, watched the slow, silver arc of my own sword curl on me like a great wave. I smelled crushed grass and new earth, heard Odin laugh – though it may have been Leo. This way was better, I was thinking. Quicker than the Pest, praise be to AllFather after all.

The laugh sounded softly again as the wave of that silvering sword cracked and broke; Randr's hand faltered, seemed to lose the strength to grip and the blade fell from it, tumbling point over haft to land in the crushed grass. He stood, shook his head a little, looked like a bull which had just butted a rock.

'I . . .' he began and rubbed his forearm with his spare hand, the forearm where Leo had gripped him so tightly.

'Itches,' said Leo gently and spat a little blood from his mashed lip. 'Those scratches are deep.'

I almost felt Randr Sterki nod. He stood like a *blot* ox waiting for the knife, one which had been fed enough mash to still it, so that it barely managed to hold the great mass of its own head up.

Finn arrived in a rush and skidded to a halt, panting, uncertain, as Leo held up one hand to stop him striking Randr.

'Kill,' said Randr, blinking and dull-voiced. 'You. All.'

'I do not think so, Randr Sterki,' Leo said flatly.

Randr staggered two steps and then fell toward me, toppling like a great wind-blown oak; his head bounced at my feet.

There was silence for a moment – then shapes moved in the dark, sliding easily to the side of the stunned Finn, armed and ready and alerted by Ospak.

'It would be better, I am thinking,' said Crowbone, 'if someone were to help me with Jarl Orm. You, Styrbjorn, since you brought all this on us.'

Styrbjorn licked his lips, looked from one to the other and back again and could have been on the edge of pointing out how it had been Crowbone's bloody vengeance that had brought all this. He stayed silent and stared, finally, at the

toppled giant that had been Randr Sterki, the fear of *seidr* magic washing off him like heat from a sweating stallion.

There was no magic here, as Crowbone pointed out.

'Battle luck for you, Jarl Orm,' he said, stepping past where the monk still sat, working the jaw Randr had hit, his left hand sitting quiet as a white spider on one knee. Crowbone picked up my sword, handed it to a bemused Finn and looked at me with chiding sorrow.

'You should have paid more heed when I told you how the monk ate his food,' he added.

I blinked like a light-blind hare; then it came to me. Leo ate with his right hand – like a Mussulman, Crowbone had said. In fact, he did everything with his right hand. I had never seen Leo use his left hand at all, save to strike with. We had all wasted our time looking for a cunningly hidden needle.

The monk shrugged and held up the white spider, where long nails on thumb and forefinger, both splintered from use, gleamed balefully in the light.

'I have no idea how much is left,' he said, 'after so long without renewing.'

Enough to kill Randr Sterki dead as a flayed horse, I thought but could manage no more words. I watched Leo smile his bland smile, his face wavering as if he sat under water, while Bjaelfi and others pounded up, shouting.

'You are strong,' he said to me, though he seemed to be receding, growing pale as mist. 'With God's help and some simple skills, we will all get safe to Constantinople.'

'Aye,' said Finn, flexing his fingers on both sword hilts and glancing at the poison-dead Randr Sterki. 'You have saved our jarl for sure, monk – but forgive me if I do not grasp your wrist in thanks over it.'

HESTRENG, *high summer*

The rock was old and stained from use. Just a stone on a hill, flat here and hollowed there, small enough for a tiny body. It was here, then, that Odin had claimed the life I had offered him and there was nothing left to show for it after so long, for the birds and the foxes had picked it clean and scattered the remains.

A long, hard birth, Aoife told me, weeping with the memories of it. The bairn – a boy – had arrived with a head too big and a leg too short and the little chest heaving for breath, so that Aoife knew, as they all knew, that it was broken inside as well as out.

It was the last of Thorgunna's womb, too, and she must have known that wee crippled mite was all the bairn she would ever have, all the son she would ever give, for a man she did not even know would come safe home.

Yet it lived, so Thorgunna did what all good wives did when a bairn was born who would never be whole. She stumbled with it up to this place, offered *blot* to the gods to wrap it safe and warm in their hall and left it there, naked on the rock.

She had never been back to it, Thordis told me, even after she had been brought from the brink of death herself.

Not, she added with bitter accusation, in all the time I had been away.

Yet the bairn on the rock lived in front of Thorgunna's eyes every day, so that she could see nothing else and sat, staring. She left her own life on that rock, all that she was, all that she would ever be and Thordis took a long, hard time telling me how she had gone off with a Christ priest and others who followed him. West, Thordis said, to Jutland, perhaps even to Saxland or beyond, for the god of the White Christ, it seemed, did not condemn twisted bairns to the wind and rain and cold.

A hand on my shoulder; I knew it was Finn, his eyes doglike and round. The others were there, too, standing awkwardly as you do when you see someone you care for so stricken and not able to offer anything other than mumbles of sympathy.

I climbed to my knees from that stone and looked up at the sky, that great, cold, blue eye of Odin that watched all I did and regarded me now as I worked out the measure of what I had offered as sacrifice. It had been a puzzle, intricate as a secret box, when I recovered from the Red Pest with only a few pockmarks to show for it. Down on the strand, a *knarr* with our battered elk prow crudely tied to it rocked heavily, fat with flagons of olive oil and bales of silk; our rich prize from a grateful Leo. I had lived and prospered and did not understand why Odin had spared me and taken little Koll.

I heard Aoife calling on her son and turned, knowing what I would see.

The pale of him, the bone-white of little Cormac running in and out of the tide-shallow as men splashed back and forth. Laughing, with his hair like spume on a wave, he brought back the crushing sight of Brand when I had told him his son was dead.

He was already a wasted man, the muscle and bulk burned off him with wound-fever so that his knees and elbows were

351

big as galls on an oak, while one side of his face was a scarred horror. I told him his son, my *fostri,* was dead and sent to Odin with his sword. I told him his enemy, Styrbjorn, lived.

He said nothing, but when I left I knew there would be no more visits from him and that what friendship we had was ended. Soon, he would ask me for the boy Cormac and his mother, too, in a way that could not be refused, even if I had a mind to. Not long after that he would find a way to take Hestreng back.

One-Eye had been cold and cruel and wolf-circling as ever. He had taken the life I offered as surely as if he had struck me down with the spear Gungnir – Dark Eye, Thorgunna, my son, Hestreng, all made as dust, so that there was now nothing for me in the world save the Oathsworn of the *Fjord Elk.*

I looked at Finn and Ospak, Kuritsa and the others – Crowbone, his odd-eyed stare bland and cool and Onund Hnufa, his face strange, a cliff that set itself hard against the terror of old memories. I saw his unnatural, crooked shoulder and the way he stared at the flat, hollowed, stained stone and knew, with a shock of understanding, that this should have been his wyrd, yet somehow he had avoided it. I wanted to ask him how he had done it, but he caught my look, held it until it was me who looked away, sliding from gaze to gaze until I was back at the hollowed stone, feeling the eyes of the Oathsworn rest on me.

The Oathsworn, still bound one to another tighter than the ties of brothers – and now the only family I knew. In the bleak dark of me, a small ember glowed warmly.

'Heya, Jarl Orm,' Finn said softly and stared out to sea, his eyes narrowing against the glare. 'I am told that raiding has started again in the lands of the Englisc. Good pickings to be had, I hear.'

'Vladimir will want us in Novgorod, for sure,' Crowbone countered, with a glare at Finn. 'To fight for him against his brothers.'

'Anywhere but back to the Wendish lands,' added Ospak and looked meaningfully at me. 'I hear red sickness rages there.'

There was a long pause which the wind filled with a mournful, gentle sigh. I looked at them, one at a time, finally settling back on the grim-faced hunchback.

'We will need a new *Fjord Elk*,' I said to Onund Hnufa.

Down on the blue-grey water, the prow beast rocked, nodding as if satisfied.

HISTORICAL NOTE

The Odra – the Oder – in the tenth century was a boundary river and has stayed that way for a thousand years, marking the frontier between Germany and Poland – or, in A.D. 975, the Saxlanders of the Holy Roman Empire and the Slavs to the east, chief among them the Pols.

The Holy Roman Empire saw itself as a bastion of Christian civilisation against the heathens from the east and that view persists even to the twenty-first century, no matter what political correctness dictates – any manifesto of the right-wing parties of Europe is worthless unless it includes a diatribe against the economic migrants beyond the Oder.

Dealing with the tenth century along the Oder you can see the same strains, the same hatreds, the same divides, the same naked warfare not far from the surface of any meeting. Scores of small tribes clutched the last of their lands on both sides of the river, swearing allegiance to whichever of the major powers held most sway at the time. Like the river itself, politics were fluid in this region.

Yet this was a trade route of some note, part of the Amber Road, that lesser-known son of the Silk Road and the Silver Way, which led from the Baltic to the north of Italy when Rome was more of a power and that capital city the centre

of the world. In the tenth century, the Ottos of the Holy Roman Empire, father and son aspiring to be as great as the Emperor in Constantinople, had revived the fortunes of the city of Rome and trade was on the move again.

New breeds were straddling the tenth-century Amber Road, too, turning the Balkans into the forge-fire it has remained to this day – the Magyars, only recently brought to a stop in their westward expansion, were now settling in what would become Hungary and had been forced to become Christians though they, like everyone else, quickly saw the benefits of belonging to that club.

The Bulgars would bump against the Byzantine Empire with a friction so irritating that, in the end, one of the best of Byzantium's emperors would be known as Bulgar-Slayer.

The last thing such a delicate thread of a trade river needs is a boatload of pagan warriors snarling their way up it and scowling at everyone who gets in their way. The last thing a boatload of pagan warriors would want to do is go up it at all – so why would Orm and the Oathsworn?

Because of Koll, Jarl Brand's heir and, more importantly, Orm's foster-son. The importance of the *fostri* in Norse lands of the time is not so hard to work out – how many reading this would entrust their son with another family for the formative six or seven years of his life, trusting that he is brought up properly? If that son represented all the hopes and dreams for the future of a dynasty? Think of a public school – I mean a real one, not some limp-wristed Hogwarts – with one pupil and an ethos of edged weapon sport and you might get some idea.

The one so entrusted had a supreme responsibility from the moment the child was declared a *fostri* – not least for the safety of the boy – and this was doubled because accepting the task also acknowledged that the foster-father had bound himself to the real father, accepting a degree of fealty as well as admitting that his status was slightly better than your own.

To lose such a boy was the worst stain on your fame. Since 'fair fame' then was all that truly mattered, worth more than any amount of gold, retrieving such a reputation was worth any hardship, any risk.

As ever, I have tried to weave real people into a fictional tale. Queen Sigrith is real, as is King Eirik the Victorious and the babe that Orm fought so hard to defend went on to become King Olaf, called Skotkonung, the Lap King. Styrbjorn is also real, as is Pallig Tokeson – though his brother Ljot is fictional – and their subsequent fates are no part of this tale.

Leo is also real – Leo the Deacon is the prime historical record for this era in Byzantium, but I have almost certainly maligned the man by making him into a combination of Moriarty and George Smiley.

Real, too, of course, is Crowbone, Olaf Tryggvasson, and the relationship between him, Queen Sigrith and King Svein Forkbeard might have been different if Sigrith had been nicer to a teenage boy. In later years, the widowed Sigrith tried to interest Olaf in marrying her and he took advantage of it, enjoyed the fruits and then, at the last, cast her aside in revenge for the slights she gave in his youth.

Enraged, Sigrith then had more luck with Svein Forkbeard and worked at turning that king against his former ally and friend. In the end, Olaf went under the swords of all his enemies, brought together by Svein as much for Sigrith's revenge as any gain in lands.

Crowbone's stories of Dyl U'la-Spegill are my take on the origins of the later tales of the trickster Till Eulenspiegel, or Dyl Ulenspegl – the name translates, roughly, as 'mysterious owl-mirror' – although the original Low German is believed to be *ul'n Spegel*, which means 'wipe the arse' and altogether is a more satisfying soubriquet for a character who so viciously ripped the pith out of the venal and pompous in society.

Till Eulenspiegel's social satire tales are almost certainly older than the tradition that has him born in 1300. Since the

same tradition has him dying in the sixteenth century, I have no trouble assigning him to an altogether darker time, before his tales were sanitised for children and turned into a tone poem by Richard Strauss in the nineteenth century, thus bringing him to the attention of an English-speaking culture.

As ever, this tale is best told round a fire against the closing dark. Any mistakes or omissions are my own and should not spoil the tale.

ACKNOWLEDGEMENTS

As ever, the list of people who made this book possible is enough to crew a longship – but, at the head of it stand the real Oathsworn, the members of Glasgow Vikings (www.glasgow vikings.co.uk) and the rest of the Vikings, national and international (www.vikingsonline.org.uk) who provide entertainment and education in several countries as well as striking fear into publicans everywhere.

Treading on their heels is Clare Hey, my editor at HarperCollins, a delicate fragrance of a woman whose skill in spotting how a story should be is matched only by her bloodthirsty love of the Oathsworn.

As ever, all the Oathsworn raise their swords to my agent, James Gill of United Agents for without his vision they would not be being enjoyed at all.

My wife, Kate, deserves all the silver of the world for putting up with muddy Vike boots, a litter of swords and my endless absence at a computer with indulgent patience.

Finally and most importantly of all – the dedicated band of Oathsworn fans who actually buy the end result. More power to you for your praise, criticism, comments and unfailing humour. I hope this one pleases you as much as the others seem to have done.

ROBERT LOW

The Prow Beast

HARPER

I raise my hand. 'Mr Henderson, could I borrow some goggles?'

'No, Joe. If you had been listening you would know that this is survival swimming and thus has to be done unadorned with either goggles or flippers. The government in all its wisdom has decided that too many children are drowning and they want to make sure that you have the skills to survive any accidental falls off boats or into rivers. It's a new scheme and, as a Sports Academy, we've been asked to pilot it. So it has to be done properly.'

'I can't do it without. I'm sorry.'

Some of the boys laugh, not too nicely. Carl says, 'Got a problem getting your hair wet. have you? Think it'll spoil your looks? Think your mascara will smudge? Well we'll help you out.' Two of his gorilla gang grab my arms and Carl pushes my head under the water.

I'm fighting and struggling and kicking, and breathing in water through my nose and my mouth . . . and bubbles of air are escaping in great gulps, and my lungs are bursting . . . and I can only see sparkles and dots and . . . I'm dying. . . Then they let go their grip on my arms and I leap up to breathe again.

I'm coughing and gasping and I hear Mr Henderson yelling his head off: 'What the hell do you think—'

but I don't stop to listen. I launch myself at Carl, my arm goes back and – whack! – my fist crashes into his piggy face. He screams, hand flying to nose, and falls backwards, spraying a fountain of blood which stains my hand and clouds the water.

'Grab him, lift him out of the water,' shouts Mr Henderson, and Brian and Jamie fish Carl out. They haul him up to the edge where he quivers, snivelling, with blood streaming down his face, and then he spews up his breakfast all over the side of the pool.

'For God's sake,' says Mr Henderson. 'Go get a towel,' he barks to Brian. Brian goes running and comes back with Carl's towel, and is told to get changed as quickly as possible and go for the school nurse. 'And tell her she's probably going to have to call an ambulance. And then get Terry the caretaker to come and clean this up.'

I can't stop staring at the blood on my hand and the blood in the water. I'm starting to shake, like I did that time in the gym. The blood is dripping into the water and it's on me, and I'm going to drown in blood. It's only Mr Henderson's icy voice that pulls me into the present.

'All of you, get out of the water and go and get changed. You can then go to lunch. Joe, as quickly as you can to my office once you are changed.'

As soon as we're in the changing room Jamie and Max pat me on the back. 'You were totally within your rights,' says Max. 'He was trying to drown you.'

'Where did you learn to punch like that?' asks Jamie. 'Can you teach me?' Carl's lot, I notice, keep as far away from me as possible.

I shower – making sure that my hands are clean, that no blood remains – and dress as slowly as I dare, trying to put off the interview with Mr Henderson. Brian comes back into the changing room to get his stuff and finds me there alone apart from Jamie and Max who are asking if they should come with me. 'Because it's not fair,' says Max. 'You were only defending yourself, but he's let Jordan and Louis get away with it.'

Brian's flushed with excitement. 'Carl's gone off to hospital in an ambulance, still in his trunks, wrapped in a blanket, and the school nurse thinks his nose is definitely broken and they're worried he might have inhaled some blood and vomit into his lungs because he can't stop wheezing,' He too slaps me on the back. 'Great stuff, mate. Haven't had such an entertaining lesson for months. Not since Ashley slapped Kelvin's face in Geography for daring to ask her out.'

'I'd better go,' I say. 'He's going to be even more angry if I'm late.'

Brian offers to come as well but I think Mr Henderson might not appreciate a support party. 'OK,' says Max, 'but if he's really not fair and chucks you out, we're ready to go and protest for you. We'll make a petition or something.'

'Thanks,' I say, and I really mean it. I'm feeling very alone at the moment, and it's good to find people who are prepared to stick their necks out.

Mr Henderson is on the phone when I sidle into his office. He points at the armchair and I sit, head down, while he talks: 'Yes, yes indeed. Yes, yes, to casualty. No. No, nothing like this. Yes, indeed.' It's one of those conversations that sounds like it could go on forever and I'm almost surprised when eventually he puts the phone down.

'That was the headmaster,' he said, 'and you won't be surprised to hear that he wants to see you, with your parents, in his office on Friday morning. 10 am You will be suspended from school until then.'

My throat is very dry and it's hard even to speak. 'My mum's away and I don't know if she'll be back on Friday and she's all the parents I've got.'

'She's away and you're by yourself?'

'No, there's someone staying with me.'

'Then if she's not back, that person is in *loco parentis* and will have to come with you.'

I'm trying to imagine Makeover Maureen, who I have met all of twice, by my side as I am excluded from school, and the total global explosion that will take place when my mum finds out.

'Am I going to be excluded?'

'I have no idea, Joe. I would say you've made a pretty good attempt at it. What on earth did you think you were doing? You could have killed him.'

'Could I?'

'Knocking someone out in a swimming pool? What if he'd hit his head against the side? What if no one had brought him out of the water in time? He's probably suffering from concussion and a broken nose. Where on earth did you learn to punch like that?'

'Oh, I used to go to boxing club.' I'm actually amazed that I can punch so hard. I was the most useless boy in the club. All the training must have massively enhanced my strength.

'Boxing club. Lord deliver us.'

'What about him and his mates? They were drowning me.'

'There's no excuse for what they did, but you were actually under the water for less than a minute and they let you go as soon as I told them to. And there was absolutely no need for you to retaliate in the way that you did, whatever the provocation.'

I shrug. And again I feel that sharp pain in my side. I must have winced because Mr Henderson asks, 'What's the matter?'

'My side hurts. I got kicked this morning.'

'When you were messing around on the floor?'

'I wasn't messing around. I fell over someone's kit bag.'

'You fell over someone's kit bag and then someone kicked you?'

'Carl.'

'I see.'

'He didn't like me getting the access card. And he doesn't like me anyway.' There's no real need to mention mildly winding him up at the shopping centre.

Mr Henderson is looking puzzled. 'Joe – you look different. Is there something wrong with your eyes?'

He's spotted that the contact lenses have gone but he doesn't know what's different. He's never really clocked what colour my eyes are. What can I say?

'I have contact lenses and they shouldn't go in the water. Now they've gone. Maybe it makes me look a bit different.'

'So that's why you were making a fuss about swimming underwater! You should have brought a note from your mother. Joe, the fact remains that you punched and injured another student in the swimming pool.

I'm going to have to rescind your access card and I'm not sure that I can let you go on having special training with Ellie.'

Now I'm angry. This is really not fair. 'But it was him . . . he attacked me first. . . I had to defend myself. . . If you don't defend yourself you can end up dead.'

I'm so nearly crying that I have to shut up right away. Right away, before I start howling like a five year old. . . Oh no . . . I can't hold back the tears at all and I have to bite the back of my hand to stop sobbing out loud.

Mr Henderson shoves a box of tissues towards me. He sounds less angry and more disappointed. 'Joe, you know we think you're very promising and we've been very happy with your progress. I'll certainly be reporting good things about you to the head as well as this unfortunate incident.'

Now I've started crying, I really can't stop. The pain in my side is burning into me and I keep on imagining Gran's face, all swollen and cut, bleeding and mashed to a pulp. The thought of having no training, no Ellie as well, is too much.

Mr Henderson says, 'Joe, maybe I should call the person who's standing in for your mum and get them to come and pick you up? Who is it, a grandparent?'

'No . . . my gran's in hospital.' My voice is all over

the place. 'That's where my mum is. But they won't let me see her.'

The bell rings for the end of lunch. Mr Henderson sighs and says, 'I'm going to have to go and take 7P for rounders. Stay here and calm down a bit, and hopefully things will look a bit better on Friday. I'll try and make sure you're not disturbed. And when you're ready, then you can just go home.' He reaches into his pocket and pulls out a toffee. 'Try this. It might make you feel a bit better.'

He leaves me alone in the office and I force myself to take deep breaths and stop the crying. Chewing the toffee does help a bit. Eventually I'm able to dry the tears and the snot, and by then there are no tissues left in the box.

I've got to get out of here before the end of school when there will be hundreds of kids milling around. I've got to get out before anyone sees me and spots that my eyes are green and my nose is red and I've turned from cool hard Joe into jelly-baby Ty.

CHAPTER 14
Skeleton Soul

No one spots me sprinting across the playing fields and escaping through the side gate. I carry on running down the hill and into the High Street. The sensible thing is to go home right away, find my spare set of lenses and tell Maureen what's happened. I don't do the sensible thing. I cross the road and head for Ellie's house.

I have to explain. Maybe she can persuade them that I can go on with the training. I don't want her to think that I didn't value her training. I'm worried that she's going to despise my lack of focus, my lack of control, my basic weakness.

I ring the doorbell and Ellie's mum comes to the door. She looks surprised. 'Hello, Joe,' she says. 'Not in school today?'

I shake my head. 'Is Ellie here?'

'No, sorry, love. She's gone to a training camp for

Paralympic potentials. Her Dad's driven her and Magda, the new helper we're trying out. She won't be back until Sunday. I thought you knew she was away.'

She's right, I did know. I just didn't remember. I'm numb with disappointment. 'Sorry to bother you,' I say.

'It's no bother. I tell you what, why don't you come and have a cup of tea? You look like you could do with one.'

That's just what my gran would say. As I follow her into the kitchen, I realise that my eyes are filling up again. What the hell's happening to me? I bite my lip hard, but I can't speak at all as I slide into a seat at the big table.

Luckily, Ellie's mum doesn't seem to expect a lot of chat. She puts a mug of tea in front of me, and makes me a chicken sandwich. I can't remember the last time I ate anything and it doesn't last long. She follows it up with a slice of fruit cake.

Then she sits down next to me. 'That's better. It's good to see someone who likes his food.' She pats my hand: 'Joe, don't mind me asking but is everything OK? You seem a bit upset.'

I shake my head. Everything is not OK. Nothing is OK. Where to start?

'My gran is in the hospital. She's been hurt.

She's in intensive care. But I can't go and see her and I don't know what's happening.'

'But surely you can go with your mum, Joe? Maybe next week when you've got half term.'

'I don't think they'll let me.' I say hopelessly.

'They?'

'Er . . . the people in the hospital. I don't know.'

'Well, I'm sure they know what they're doing. They don't tend to like a lot of visitors in the ICU. Maybe things will look a lot brighter by next week.'

'Maybe. And I don't think school is going to let me go on working with Ellie.'

She laughs and says, 'I'd like to see them try and stop Ellie working with you,' which makes me feel a bit better. Then she asks, 'But why would they want to stop you? I thought everyone was very happy with the results?'

'I punched someone in the swimming pool. Mr Henderson said I could have killed him. I think perhaps they are going to exclude me permanently.'

'Why did you punch him?' She sounds pretty calm.

'He and his friends were trying to drown me . . . I thought . . . and he'd kicked me this morning.'

'Kicked you?'

'In the ribs.'

'Can I have a look? I'm a nurse, you know. I work three nights a week up at the General.'

Carefully I lift up my shirt and show her the two big bruises. She puts her hand on one and I jump away. 'Ow!' It's hurting like crazy now. Much to my shame I feel more tears running down my face. She tactfully hands me a tissue.

'Joe, you have to go to hospital and get that looked at. I think you might have broken a rib there.'

'But there's nothing they can do about that, is there?' It sounds like a big waste of time when I could easily take a few aspirin.

'Let me ring Michelle. You've not got a car, have you? I could run you two up there.'

'She's not here. She's gone to London to be with my gran.'

'So who is staying with you?'

I shrug and she gives me another tissue.

'Joe, she's not left you all by yourself, has she?'

'No, there's someone staying with me. Called Maureen.'

'Well, then. Get Maureen to take you to casualty for an X-ray. Joe, it's very important. A broken rib could puncture your lung, and that could kill you. Or at least bring your sporting career to an end.'

'Oh.'

'And if you have broken a rib, well, it's good for the head teacher to know that, isn't it? Fair's fair.

No good punishing you for violence if the other boy gets away with it. Look, I have to go and get the boys from school. Stay here, have some more tea, help yourself to cake and when I get back I'll take you home and talk to this Maureen.'

I'm not sure this is a good idea and it must show on my face. 'Really, Joe, you can't be too careful about things like this. You don't want permanent lung damage.'

Left alone in the kitchen, I go over and look at the many photos of Ellie on display alongside a shelf of her trophies. She looks so happy and determined. I wonder if there's another side to Ellie, full of rage at what life's done to her. I'm very tempted to sneak a look at her room but that would seem like I'm some sort of mad stalker, which wouldn't be a great idea.

I'm just cutting myself another piece of cake – OK, it's my third – when I hear a gasp, and a small voice says, 'Wh— what are you doing here?'

It's Claire, home from school. I turn around and suddenly I'm really fed up with her constant scared rabbit expression.

'I'm eating cake. What about you?' I say rudely, cramming it into my mouth.

'No, I mean why you are in my house? And why . . . how . . . have your eyes gone green?'

She noticed. Damn. Bugger. I'd totally forgotten

about the stupid lenses.

I stand there for a minute and then I put down the knife and walk towards her. My side is hurting so much that I feel dizzy but I put out my hands and grip her wrists. She looks absolutely terrified. Good.

I lean towards her and shift into gangsta. Menacing. Angry. Scary. 'You keep yer mouth shu' abou' my eyes. Forget you ever saw they was green.'

She's almost crying. I tighten my grip. She whispers, 'No, no . . . I won't say anything.'

'Not to Ashley or Lauren or Emily – none of dem, none of your mates.'

A blotchy red blush spreads over her face. 'They're not my friends. I'd have thought you'd know your girlfriend has no time for me. Hasn't she told you what a stupid freak I am?'

I let go and turn away. 'Who says she's my girlfriend?'

'She's told everyone you belong to her.'

'She doesn't own me. We're just messing around.'

'Whatever.'

'Whatever,' I echo. 'Anyway, keep it quiet.'

She's rubbing her wrists. I must have really hurt her. What am I turning into?

'Did you really punch Carl?' she asks in a whisper.

'Yup.'

'They say he's got to have plastic surgery.'

'Do they?' This strikes me as quite funny. Maybe Carl's porky features will be transformed by my efforts. Maybe he'll end up looking like a chimp. I can't help smiling.

Claire is looking at me like I'm a psychopathic maniac. Her voice is shaky. 'Joe, if I don't tell anyone about your eyes – and I won't, I really, really promise you – you won't tell Ashley that we talked, will you?'

Not this again. 'What is your problem with talking to me? Most people seem to like me.'

'Ashley doesn't like other girls talking to her boyfriend.'

I think back to Ashley telling me, 'If I want a guy I make sure no one else goes near him.' I think back to Claire's crumpled note. And I know, deep down, that Ashley, who I want like a kid wants candyfloss, is not a nice person at all.

But I still want her.

'Don't worry,' I say to Claire. 'I don't tell tales if you don't. But please don't treat me like I smell or something.' It feels crazy to say this when I've just been terrorising her, but I add, 'Right at the moment I could do with some friends.'

She gives me a little uncertain smile. 'I think a lot of people will be your friend now that you've smashed

Carl's nose. He used to pick on the year seven boys – they were chanting your name in the playground. And Max is organising a petition to go to the head to ask that you shouldn't be punished.'

Brilliant. I am the figurehead of a popular revolution. By Friday there will probably be riots in the dining hall and book burning in the library. I can't see this working in my favour with the head teacher. And what about when he tells keep-your-head-down Doug?

There's the sound of a key in the door and Sam and Alex erupt into the room, shouting and whooping when they see me. 'Boys, you stay here with Claire and I'll run Joe home,' says Janet. 'Claire, is that OK?'

'Yup.' I can sense her relief. What if she tells Ellie and her kind mum how I scared her? What have I done?

When we get to our house Maureen instantly spots my not-brown eyes and her own widen in alarm. I go upstairs to find the spare set of lenses while Janet suggests a trip to casualty. Maureen agrees right away: 'She's absolutely right, Joe – we've got to get this checked out, especially with your mum away.'

I don't protest. The pain is getting worse and my breathing is feeling a bit difficult. But I don't say so because that would be making a fuss.

By the time we've waited for a few hours at the hospital, Maureen knows the whole story. Well, everything except what I did to Claire. She's actually a nice lady – best police officer yet – and easy to talk to. She seems to think that I'll get away with punching Carl, although she doesn't really approve.

'In my opinion, schools should be a lot tougher about these incidents and then we wouldn't have the problems we do out on the streets,' she says. 'In the good old days it was zero tolerance. You and Carl, you'd have been out of that school. Nowadays it'll be a slapped wrist.'

They take the X-ray. I lie all alone on a table while a white machine clicks and whirrs above me. I wonder what it would be like if these machines could look inside your mind as well as your body and see the tangle of stories and lies and thoughts and problems inside; if they could make an image that captured the inner truth, the real person, the skeleton soul. Who would they see if they could look inside me?

We wait a bit longer and then a doctor comes and tells me that I've cracked two ribs and should take it easy for a bit. She prescribes painkillers and says, 'No rough sport because there is a danger of puncturing a lung if you have another impact. And no alcohol while you're taking these.'

'He's thirteen, for heaven's sake,' says Maureen, and the doctor asks, 'Have you been here on a Saturday night?'

'What about running?' I ask. 'That should be fine,' she replies, 'but if you have any trouble with your breathing, then stop right away and seek medical advice.'

We're about to leave when Carl and his mum emerge from another cubicle ahead of us. Carl's face is hideously swollen and he's holding an ice pack to his nose. His mum must have brought in some clothes because he's wearing a tracksuit. They've been here for hours.

I pull on Maureen's arm. 'It's him. Can we wait? I don't want him to see me.'

Carl doesn't look tough and strong any more, but like a little boy who's clinging to his mum for comfort. When I see how his mum has her arm around him, I long for my gran. She's the one I need right now.

'Come on, they're gone,' says Maureen and we walk to her car. Every step is painful and I'm sure I've screwed up my training schedule for the next few days, whether I can use the school gym or not.

Back at home, she makes me baked beans on toast. I switch on my mobile. I have eighteen texts and ten messages. Almost all the texts are from people at school sending their congratulations and pledging their support, like I'm the leader of a resistance movement under some oppressive regime. They must have got my number from

Ashley. She's sent me a text: *u r my hero. Cant w8 2 c u. park 2moro 4pm? Xxxxxx.*

And then I listen to the messages and there's a voicemail from Mum.

Maureen is buttering the toast. I go into the living room and listen to the message. Mum sounds breathy and anxious: 'Hello, Ty. I can't really talk but Gran is stable and we're all here with her. I'm sending her lots of love from you. Hope you're OK. Can't talk more. Take care, sweetheart.'

I may be wrong. Maybe Doug told her she could ring. But it doesn't seem right to me. Surely she's potentially giving away where we are? Doug said no phone calls. What if someone's monitoring calls or something? I dither for about two seconds, then, as Maureen calls, 'Food's ready,' I make a decision.

I sit down at the table and hold out my phone. 'Maureen. My mum left me a message. I thought maybe it wasn't such a clever thing to do.'

She takes the phone from me and listens. She shakes her head. 'I'm not going to lie to you, Ty – I think she's done this without telling Doug. It's understandable – poor girl, she's under a lot of strain, but she shouldn't have. I'm going to have to tell him.'

I nod, although I feel I've betrayed my mum. 'Eat up,' says Maureen. 'None of this is easy, I know.'

173

'Nope. . . Maureen, do you know a lot of families in witness protection?'

'Quite a few,' she says. 'I tend to get involved, as I did with you, in changing the way people look. You're unusual, though, because most of the people we deal with are criminals themselves. They're looking to escape prison by informing on their former colleagues. Complete low lives, to be honest. It's hard to be helping people you feel so little respect for. You two are different. I'm sorry it's been so hard for you.'

'It's not all hard. Some of it's been good.'

'I hope it stays that way,' she says, but she's being kind, I can see.

We sit and watch some stupid reality programme where two women change families and have to live in each other's houses. After about two minutes they are going crazy, shouting and sulking and threatening to leave. As I watch, I'm feeling older and older, like an ancient old man who's done it all and seen it all and all the adults are like children to me. I bet really old people feel incredibly lonely when everyone their age is dead.

I take a painkiller and go to bed. My ribs are still agony, though, and my head's full of violence – the real kind between me and Carl, and the infinitely worse sort that I'm imagining happening to Gran. But what I can't bear to think about is the way I tightened my grip on

Claire's wrists when I knew I didn't need to, and the terrified look on her face.

There's only one way to block it out. I grab my mobile and send a text: *OK 4 pm* And I shift on to my less painful side, close my eyes and start imagining – in fantastic exotic detail – what Ashley and I are going to get up to tomorrow.

But even that's not enough to bring sleep. I'm relaxed all right, but I can't get rid of the fear. I'm scared of the faceless people out there who want to hurt me like they hurt Gran. I'm terrified that Mum's phone call is going to lead them to me.

But the biggest fear is what I'm becoming inside.

CHAPTER 15
Old Habit

Ashley's annoyed with me. I can tell the minute I spot her coming along the path, by the way she's frowning and flouncing and pouting.

It's a shame because she looks *fantastic*. She's in summer uniform, which means a really short skirt and a tight white polo shirt through which a purple bra kind of shines. I'm dimly aware that my aunties wouldn't have been so impressed – they'd use mean words like chav and tart – but I don't care what they'd think because to me she's really sexy, incredibly attractive.

'Hey Ash,' I say, as she sits down next to me. 'What's up?' I'm hoping that we can keep any talking to a minimum so I can explore this new look as thoroughly as possible. And I'm also worried that if I allow myself to dislike Ashley any more than I do now, I'll have to chuck her, which I'd rather not do quite yet.

We're just finely balanced right now.

'I thought you'd call or text or something yesterday or today and tell me exactly what happened – the whole story,' says Ashley in a huff. 'Everyone was asking me about you and I felt a right lemon not being able to tell anyone anything. You could have waited for me after school. And then you just texted '4 pm OK', no kisses nor nothing.'

Blah, blah, blah, blah. Loud and annoying, just as I thought. Me, me, me, me. And I suspect she's a bully. Why am I even here? 'I can give you kisses like this,' I say and lean in to do just that.

She's not having it though. 'But why didn't you call me yesterday? My mum knew more about what was going on than I did.'

'I was in the hospital for hours, Ash. Look.' I lift up my T-shirt to show her my bruises, which are nearly the same colour as her underwear. 'Two broken ribs from that thug Carl.'

Her hand goes to her mouth. 'Oh my God. You must be in agony.'

'Only you can make it feel better,' I lie, because today the painkillers are doing an excellent job and I was able to go out for a two-hour run this morning, no problem at all.

'Oh, I suppose I forgive you,' she says, and moves

in close for the kind of mouth-to-mouth resuscitation that Carl very nearly needed yesterday at the pool.

We're there for an hour, during which I discover that Ashley will let me go quite a bit further than Arron ever got with Shannon Travis, although – somewhat to my relief – there do seem to be limits. But one minute she's pushing my hand away and the next she's placing it right back where it was, which is kind of confusing.

And then we hear something. A rustling noise. . . We freeze. Nothing. 'It's OK,' I murmur and my hand creeps on to her thigh. And then muffled laughter, a bright light and – bugger– he's taken our photo on his mobile phone.

'Slag!' he yells at Ashley. 'Slapper. . . Wait till all the boys see these. . .'

It's Jordan. Carl's sidekick. And Louis is by his side. Ashley's never moved so fast in her life. She launches herself at them: 'Bastards! Delete them!'

They're laughing at her and at me, and they're taking the opportunity to feel her up a bit. Inside me there's cold fury. This is threatening. This is unacceptable. This is an emergency. And I reach into my back pocket and I pull out the knife that I took from the kitchen before I came out to meet her.

'Gimme da phone,' I say in my hardest gangsta

voice, slowly unwrapping the handkerchief I'd wound around it.

Now it's their turn to freeze. They look uncertainly at each other. 'Gimme da phone,' I repeat, except this time I throw in a bit more cussing. 'Den no one's gonna be hurt.'

'Oh my God, Joe,' says Ashley.

'You knows I can fight. And you knows I can run. And you see dis blade.' I wave the knife at them. 'So give. Me. Da. Fu'in'. Phone.'

Jordan throws it on the ground. I look at Louis. 'And you.'

'But I never took any.'

'Gimme da phone coz you is disrespectin' me and dis gel, and you is gonna pay for dat, muvverfu'er.'

He throws his phone down too and I say, 'Ash, get 'em.' She picks them up and I can see she's crying.

'Delete all their data and then give them back.'

She does it and I say, 'OK, now you're gonna apologise to the lady.'

They shuffle their feet. 'Sorry, Ashley. Sorry.'

'Get outta here.'

They stumble along the path, looking behind them every two seconds. Ashley and I follow – I don't want to let them out of my sight so they can ambush us halfway down. At the park gate I put the knife back in my pocket and make sure they've got on to a bus. Then I turn to Ashley, who has stopped crying but looks pretty upset. There's this little tiny bit of me that thinks it's not such a terrible thing for her to find out how she makes people like Claire feel.

'Are you OK?' I ask.

'Yes,' she whispers. Then, 'Joe, why did you have a knife?'

Because there are people out there who beat and tortured my gran to discover where to find me, and my mum may have stupidly given them my address. I shrug. 'Old habit.'

I wonder whether Jordan and Louis are going to go home and start looking in their kitchens to be ready for the next time they meet me. But most of all, I wonder what I'd have done if they hadn't thrown down their phones.

'How come you talked like that?'

It's just another language, I want to say, like Urdu or Turkish or Portuguese. We played around with the way we spoke all the time at primary school. And then at eleven some of us went to a school where you could go on doing that (St Jude's) and some of us went to a school where you spoke in gangsta and you wrote in text (Tollington) and two of us went miles across town to St Saviour's where it was, 'yes sir, no sir,' and the other boys laughed at you for coming from East London.

'Dat's da lingo in da hood, innit,' I tell her.

'You sound like another person altogether,' she says. I kiss her goodbye as her bus draws up, but her heart doesn't seem to be in it.

I lie low for the next few days. I don't answer anyone's texts – even Ashley's – and I don't go near the school. The only message I'd like to get would be one from Ellie but I don't hear anything from her. Maybe she's too disappointed with me to bother. Maybe Claire told how I hurt and scared her.

Maureen keeps me up to date with news from the hospital. Gran is still in a coma and although they say she's stable, they have no idea when she might wake up. Mum and my aunties are staying at the hospital. 'Are you guarding them properly?' I ask, and Maureen assures me that yes, there's a police guard there all the time. 'Have you found the people who did this?' I ask, but she shakes her head.

I watch a lot of daytime telly and I keep the curtains closed. It seems that one way or another I'm going to get permanently excluded from school. Jordan and Louis will report me for threatening them with a knife. Claire will tell someone that I bullied her. Carl will have suffered irreversible brain damage.

And then what? I won't be Joe any more and I'll

have to start all over again. I can't decide if that's a good thing or not. It seems that once Mum left, once no one knew me as Ty, then Joe turned into a monster. It's safest to stay at home and watch *Cash in the Attic*.

Friday morning, I come downstairs dressed in jeans and a T-shirt and Maureen sends me straight back again to change into uniform. She even cuts my hair a bit to make it tidier and combs it for me like I'm six. She drives us to school: 'Just remember, tell him you're sorry and promise it won't happen again. And look like you are sorry. No back chat, no arguing.'

Luckily everyone's in lessons and no one I know sees us as we walk through the corridors to the head's office. There's an outer office and Maureen knocks on the door and tells the woman, who answers, 'Joe Andrews and Maureen O'Reilly to see the head teacher.'

I get a horrible shock when I see this woman. It's like Ashley's aged thirty years overnight. Same dark hair, same spidery eyelashes, same pouty mouth, even the same strain on the buttons around the chest area. She makes me feel a bit sick. She looks at me like I'm a dung beetle – interesting but revolting. I remember how unprofessional she is and glare right back. I wonder if she knows about Ashley and me.

We wait for ten minutes, and then the door of the head teacher's office opens and Carl and his parents come out. Carl's nose is still swollen and there's a huge bruise that covers both eyes. I can't imagine that, having seen that, the head teacher is going to want me to stay in the school. To my surprise they come over to us, but only to sit down – it seems that they're not finished with the head. We all ignore each other, which is a lot of ignoring. I stare at the ceiling and in my head I rerun my 1500-metre triumph.

'Mr Naylor will see you now,' says Ashley's mum, and we walk into his office. I'm actually relieved that Mum isn't here. Maureen is a lot calmer than she would have been.

Mr Naylor is sitting at his desk and we sit down in front of him. He's quite old; grey hair, beard and specs, and I know from assemblies that he's nuts on order and discipline.

'Mrs Andrews,' he starts, and Maureen interrupts. 'Excuse me, but I'm not the boy's mother, Mr Naylor. She's away at the moment and I'm *in loco parentis*. The family is in severe crisis: Joe's grandmother has been the victim of an extremely violent crime,' – my stomach lurches – 'and is still unconscious. Although it in no way excuses Joe's behaviour, I think it may go some way towards explaining it.'

Mr Naylor and I are both a bit dazed by this opening speech. 'Ah,' he says. 'Well. I'm sorry to hear that,

Mrs . . . er. . .'

'Maureen O'Reilly,' says Maureen, offering him her hand to shake. 'Friend of the family.'

'Ah. Oh. Right.' Mr Naylor is trying not to look too nosy. 'Well, I was hoping we could hear from Joe his explanation of the event in the swimming pool.'

Event? That's a good one. Perhaps they'll add drowning and fighting to the next swimming gala. I give him a brief outline.

Mr Naylor reaches for a piece of paper on his desk. 'And Carl suffered a broken nose, concussion and severe bruising.'

Maureen says, 'Yes, but what Joe hasn't told you is that Carl broke two of his ribs earlier in the day. Show him, Joe.'

I unravel my uniform to display the bruises. It's kind of embarrassing stripping off in front of the head, but I suppose it's worth it.

'How did this happen?' asks Mr Naylor, peering over his specs at my torso.

'I fell over a kit bag in the changing room and Carl kicked me. I didn't realise anything was broken though.'

'I would suggest that any punishment you give Joe should apply equally to Carl,' says Maureen.

'Carl's parents are talking about taking the whole

matter to the police,' says Mr Naylor.

'That would be very foolish of them, unless they would like Joe's mother to press charges against their son as well,' counters Maureen with quick-fire speed.

'Joe, what are the roots of this argument between you and Carl? You've hardly been in the school any time at all, and I'm very disappointed to find you mixed up in what seems to be an escalating feud.'

'I . . . er . . . Mr Henderson gave me an access card to use the fitness suite and stuff out of hours and Carl was really angry, said the football team should have them too. That's the main reason, I think.'

'And there's nothing you've done to exacerbate matters?'

'No, I don't care if they have cards as well.'

'And over the last few days you've done nothing to stir up popular feeling in the school? This petition, for example,' – he points to a wodge of paper – 'and the protests that have been taking place?'

'I didn't know anything about that,' I say, and Maureen kicks into action again.

'Mr Naylor, over the last few days I've seen the very sad sight of a bright, athletic, sociable boy turn into a virtual recluse who sits and watches television all day and won't even open the curtains. He's had dozens of messages from supportive friends and he hasn't replied to one. Joe and his mother are new to this town and they came here not knowing a soul. He's had to find friends and get used to a very different atmosphere, and I think the school's let him down by failing to protect him from this sort of bullying behaviour.'

She pauses, but only to draw breath. 'At the hospital they told me that his breathing may have been affected all day, and that the supply of oxygen to his brain was obviously further restricted by being held under water. This could well have affected his judgement. Joe's come from a tough area and his mother sent him to boxing club to learn to protect himself. I'd ask you to consider that he was acting on instinct and in pure self defence.'

She ought to be a lawyer. That was brilliant! Mr Naylor opens his mouth to reply, but Maureen has more to say.

'He's been at home all week. Surely he's had his punishment.'

Mr Naylor clears his throat. 'I've certainly heard some good things about Joe and I have a letter here from Ellie Langley, the student responsible for his training. She makes a strong case for allowing him to keep on with the athletics programme. I'd like to hear Joe say he's sorry for his behaviour and make a commitment to behaving better in future.'

'He's certainly happy to do that,' says Maureen,

giving me a quick glance, 'but I'd also like to know what your strategy is for avoiding this kind of bullying in the future. I don't need to tell you what the consequences could have been if one of the broken ribs had punctured a lung.'

'Well,' says Mr Naylor, 'we're trialling a form of restorative justice at the school, which involves the two parties coming together to discuss the effect such an incident has had and jointly find a way forward. In this case, I was keen for Joe's mother to talk to Mr and Mrs Royston, as well as to try and avoid police involvement. So why don't I ask them to come in and we can see if Carl and Joe can, as it were, make peace?'

He gets up to go to the door, and Maureen rolls her eyes at me and mimes slapping her wrist. I'm so impressed at how she managed to turn me from villain to victim. But I wonder if a real court is also so open to twisting and turning the facts. Maybe there's no such thing as real truth, just lots and lots of different ways of explaining the same thing.

Carl and his family file in. We're all squashed into the space in front of Mr Naylor's desk and there aren't enough chairs, so Carl and I have to stand up.

His mum and dad make a lot of noise about how disgusting I am and how Carl's sporting career may be affected by the re-routing of his nasal passages.

Maureen counters with her poor-little-bullied-new-boy story, adding in some scare stuff about punctured lungs and a bright future in athletics that could have been blighted.

Everyone threatens to report both of us to the police. Everyone agrees that it's not necessary to involve outside bodies and criminalise two previously blameless teenagers.

Mr Naylor says, 'I'd like Carl and Joe to speak about how this incident has affected them and make a commitment to having a better relationship in the future. Carl, you go first, please.'

'You've smashed my entire face and I might not be able to play football for weeks,' says Carl. 'I might even have to have an operation on my nose. I only like playing football, so you've taken away the only thing I like.'

'Now, Joe,' says Mr Naylor.

'You set up that kit bag so I'd fall over and you could kick me, but I'd never done anything to you. I thought you and your mates were going to drown me in that pool. It wasn't my idea to give me an access card and not you, so none of this is my fault. And now it's been taken away from me.'

'Now, how sad it is to hear two of the school's most promising young sportsmen battling each other like this,' says Mr Naylor, sounding like we're all in church.

'Can we make a commitment to working together for the good of the school from now on? Perhaps there's a way that you two can find a joint project to work on?'

'I don't mind,' I say warily. I do feel a tiny bit sorry for Carl, if it's really true that he's got to have an operation.

'OK,' grunts Carl.

'So perhaps you two could apologise to each other, and then I'll ask Mr Henderson to work with you on finding a joint project to bring you together.'

'Sorry, Carl,' I mutter.

'Sorry, Joe,' he growls.

'Good,' says Mr Naylor. 'I shall expect to see a much more positive relationship in the future. You boys have great potential to bring glory to the school.'

We're dismissed. I'm not excluded. I'm no longer suspended. I suppose I might even get the access card back.

I ought to be happy, but I'm not. Joe's been given a second chance. I'm just not certain that he deserved one.

CHAPTER 16
Private

Half term is when they said I might be able to see my gran. But nothing seems to be happening. I keep on asking Maureen and she keeps on saying be patient, and I never hear anything from Mum. I'm beginning to feel she's forgotten me, even though I know she's not allowed to phone.

Ellie never contacts me either. I've been going for a run every day and do as much of the other training as I can with the few machines that they have at the local swimming pool – they have concessionary rates for under-sixteens, it turns out – but it hurts that she's not in touch. Maybe she feels that I've let her down and she can't be bothered any more.

Ashley's gone off to Spain for the week with her family. I texted her on the Friday night: *ddn't gt xcldd, hv a gd time, c u Jx*. I didn't hear anything back.

I'm almost sure that means she's chucked me.

Half way through the week Ellie's mum rings Maureen to find out how things are going and invites me over for lunch again. I think Maureen's relieved to get a few hours off – it can't be great fun being a permanent babysitter to a moping teenager. She drops me off at noon on the dot, although Janet had told her any time between twelve and one.

I'm really nervous. I'm worried about seeing Ellie again. Is she even going to talk to me? Have I mucked everything up? And I'm even more anxious about Claire. Ever since Mr Naylor made me apologise to Carl I've known I must say sorry to Claire for hurting her and scaring her. Only then will I be able to forgive Joe.

Alex lets me in. 'Come and play football in the garden!' he yells, and I follow him out to where Ellie's dad Gareth is setting up the barbeque. 'Hello, lad. How's it going?' he says, handing me a can of Coke. Ellie and her mum are out but will be back soon, he explains. The boys shout for me to play with them, but I ask, 'Where's Claire?'

'Upstairs, I suppose. Why don't you see if you can persuade her to come and get some sunshine for once?'

I creep upstairs as quietly as possible. Claire's room is up a second flight of stairs – it's a converted attic. There's a sign saying 'Private – Keep Out', but I don't even knock. I push the door open and for a moment I'm completely confused. The curtains are closed and it's totally dark in there.

I stay still and quiet while my eyes adjust. I don't think Claire's even in there; there's no sign of life. Then I see a slight movement and realise that she's sitting on the floor, half hidden behind the bed. She's got headphones on and her eyes are closed and she's got a strange look on her face, a look that reminds me of something, but I can't quite think what.

This is incredibly awkward. The only way I can attract her attention is to touch her arm, and I don't really want to scare her.

I'm frozen with indecision and about to give up and go downstairs again when I see it. A knife. In her hand.

It's a small, sharp knife, the type you use in art classes sometimes. What's she holding it for? As she holds out her arm and kind of strokes it with the knife I know what she reminds me of. Her face and her pose and the way her body relaxes as the blood oozes out are just like the junkies I've seen sometimes, shooting up in the park.

I feel as sick as I've ever felt, and I have to bite my tongue to make no noise. At the same time there's a tiny undercurrent of . . . I don't even want to say it . . . but there's something almost exciting about being there to see her gaze at the blood running down her arm. I feel like I'm watching something very private and very real.

She dabs at it with a tissue and pulls out a plaster and carefully sticks it over the cut. It's all planned I realise. She's got everything there ready. And then she unrolls her long sleeves and lies back against the bed.

I pull the door silently to try and escape. But she must have seen something out of the corner of her eye. She starts up and tugs the headphones from her ears. And shouts at me.

'What the hell are you doing in my room?'

I'm so amazed to hear her make a noise – quiet, mousey Claire – that I can't speak for a minute. I step forward and then sit down on her bed.

'I'm . . . uh . . . sorry. I mean I came to say I was sorry for the way I behaved the other day. I was out of order.'

'How long had you been standing there? No one is allowed in my room!'

It's very tempting to lie. It's very tempting to say, 'Only a minute,' and escape downstairs. What do I care anyway what she's up to? If she wants to hurt herself it's her business. But I say, 'Long enough to see what you did,' and after a moment's silence she whacks me in the mouth.

She's got the strength of a rag doll. 'Ouch,' I say unconvincingly, and I collapse backwards, lying on her bed. 'I'm sorry Claire. I could have said I didn't see anything. But I did and, to be honest, I don't think it's a great thing to be doing.'

'I s— suppose you and your g— girlfriend are going to tell the whole school about this are you? How dare you sneak up here and spy on me? I kept your stupid secret. You can just leave me alone!'

'I don't think Ashley wants to know me any more,' I say. 'I don't give her enough attention.'

'She's a cow. I hate her.'

'I thought you used to be friends?'

'Yeah, until the first day at Parkview when she and Emily and Lauren pretended they didn't know me, and they wouldn't talk to me and they didn't let me sit with them in class or at lunch and they told everyone that I was a dork.'

'I kind of know a bit how that feels,' I say, remembering the look on Arron's face when he realised that the rest of our gang would be going to St Jude's and he and I would spend two hours a day together just travelling to and from school.

'Oh, do you?' she asks, obviously not believing me.

'Yes. Look, Claire, I really won't tell anyone. After all, you never told anyone about my eyes and

I really appreciate that.'

'How did they change colour anyway?' she asked. 'Are they brown again now?'

I go and open her curtains. She blinks as the sunshine streams in. 'Look,' I say and I stare into her eyes. 'Now they're brown.' I flip one of the lenses out. 'And now one's green. I really trust you, and you can really trust me.' And I put the lens back.

'What the hell was that?' she says, but she's not so angry any more. She's still staring intently at my eyes. 'Is that your party trick?'

'No, no, really, Claire, no one must know. No one. Only you.'

'Not even Ashley?'

'Especially not Ashley. To be totally honest, I only went out with her because I was a little bit scared of her. And because she's quite . . . you know. . .'

'A slapper?'

'A twenty-first-century post-feminist,' I reply, a bit shocked, to be honest, by her unsisterly sexism. I was brought up by my aunties on a diet of *Cosmo* magazine and I know that you're not meant to disrespect women who want a full and active sex life. Especially if they want to have one with me.

She starts giggling and says, 'That's one way of putting it,' and I'm laughing too, and I know it's OK and we can trust each other. But there's a slight niggling doubt in my mind about keeping her secret. Maybe I should tell Ellie or her mum that she's hurting herself?

Ellie. What's going on there? 'Claire, is Ellie angry with me?'

'Oh I don't think so,' she says. 'She's just totally wound up about her preparations for this race at the weekend. When she's really focused, then she doesn't think about anything else. I think that's why mum arranged this barbeque, to take her mind off it. And also she's getting used to Magda, her new helper, and she hates that.'

'Hates what?'

'Ellie doesn't really like to admit she needs a helper, but mum and dad feel they can't always be there for her, so she has to have Magda, but she resents it. It's hard . . . for everyone. Ellie can get really cross sometimes.'

'Oh. Look, I really am very sorry about the other day. I was completely wrong to hurt you, I don't know why I did it.' I think about what Maureen said about my judgement being affected by lack of oxygen, but I don't think even that's really an excuse for hurting someone as delicate as Claire.

'I knew all the time you were scared,' she says. 'I just didn't know why you were scared of me. Why do you make your eyes brown when they're really green?'

For one crazy second I think I might tell her everything, this girl with a deep, scary secret of her own. This girl who understands that I'm scared. 'It's a long story,' I say, and I'm thinking how much I'd love it if someone my own age knew what's been going on. 'It's hard to know where to start.'

Bam! Alex and Sam crash through the door shouting their heads off. 'What are you doing? You're missing all the food! Mum says you've got to come downstairs right now.'

'Get out of my room, monsters,' yells Claire, and we chase them down the stairs. But as they disappear outside I ask, 'Can we talk more later?'

And she says, 'I'd like that.'

The garden is full of people. There's Janet and Ellie and Magda, who's blonde and Polish and seems sweet and shy. I say hello to her in Polish and you can see she's amazed that anyone's bothered to learn her language. Pity Doug cut off my lessons in the hotel. Maybe I can ask Magda to teach me more.

There's Alistair, who's Ellie's trainer and has one of those ludicrous, super-gelled, boy-band hairstyles; and there's Kieron who's another wheelchair racer with incredible pumped-up arms; and Tim and Sue who turn out to be the next-door neighbours. I can hardly get near Ellie. There're four small boys – two belong to Tim and

Sue – and they're nagging me to play football with them so, after I've swallowed a burger, that's what I do.

We play for about an hour and then we're all burning hot and sweaty and lying on the grass. 'We won! We won!' shrieks Alex, dancing around, and Janet comes out of the house with a bowl of cut-up watermelon. I look around and catch Ellie's eye. She doesn't look too unfriendly.

'Joe, come and tell me what's happening with your training,' she shouts.

'Yes, and Joe, you can tell us what Ellie's like as a trainer,' says Kieron. 'Is she as impossible to work with as she is with her teammates?'

'No, she's fantastic,' I say, and they all laugh. I don't know why.

Ellie says, 'Stop messing around. I really need to hear how Joe's getting on. And why on earth have you lost your access card? Did you know I had to write a letter to the head teacher to stop him kicking you out of school?'

'I'm sure that was never going to happen, Ellie,' says Janet.

'Oh it was,' says Ellie. 'Mr Henderson said you smashed another boy's face in and he nearly drowned.'

'That's not true at all,' says Claire angrily. 'Joe was nearly drowned by him.'

Everyone looks amazed to hear her speak. She's blushing again and looks like she wishes she hadn't bothered. I feel like everyone is looking at me, and I don't like it. 'I'm going to go,' I say. 'Thanks for lunch. Ellie, can you let me know when you want to do more training? Good luck for the weekend.'

'Oh, don't go, Joe,' says Ellie. 'Come and tell us all about it.' But I shake my head and make for the back door. I'm sure that as I go I hear one of her friends say something like, 'So that's your toy boy, Ellie.'

Claire follows me and we walk through the house together. 'Ellie gets a bit over-excited sometimes,' she says.

'Yeah, I'm just bored with talking about it now. And there's other stuff going on that's more important.'

'Oh. Look, Joe, don't go. Why don't we go upstairs again? Then we could talk.'

I'm not sure. I'm kind of disappointed with Ellie and I want to get away from all those laughing strangers. I want her to stay the perfect, golden girl that I can rely on, not someone who uses me to entertain her friends. I only really like it when Ellie's attention is focused on me.

But I follow Claire up the stairs because I've found someone that I can be as near to honest with as possible.

I'm really curious to know why she wants

to cut herself. And in my most secret, secret heart –
and I'm wondering how sick and twisted I really am –
I'd be quite interested in watching her do it again.

CHAPTER 17
Invisible

The first thing she does is draw the curtains so it's dark again. The next thing is to wedge a chair against the door so no one can come in. Then she sits down on the floor, as she did before. I can see she's got some cushions down there – it's her little nest.

I sit next to her. 'Why do you do it?' I ask.

'I try not to,' she says. 'I know it's a crazy thing to do. I'm really trying to stop.'

'When I saw you, I thought you looked like a junkie, you know, an addict, shooting up.'

'It feels like how I think an addiction must feel like,' she says. 'It builds up, and all I can think about is cutting myself, and then I do it and I'm OK again for a while.'

'How come no one's noticed?'

She shrugs: 'I'm not the sort of person that anyone notices much.'

I'm not having that. 'What about when you're in a T-shirt? What about swimming or PE?'

'I always wear long sleeves, for PE as well. I don't know what to do about swimming. We were going to have it for the first time last week and I was so worried. I'd made up a letter from my mum, but then you punched Carl and the pool was closed for cleaning.' She chuckles. 'I was very grateful to you.'

'Oh. Well, glad I could help you out.'

'That's OK.'

'But what builds up? Why do you do it? When did it even start?'

She considers, staring into space. It's like she's never asked herself these questions before. 'I started out just scratching myself. Then one day it wasn't enough, so I used my comb. I liked the feeling and I liked seeing the marks on my skin. But it was never quite enough. And then I cut myself by accident in art when we were lino printing and I knew that's what I'd been looking for.'

'But what is the feeling that builds up?'

She shrugs again. 'Could be anything. I might be feeling scared, or worried or upset. Sometimes I feel like I'm invisible, like I'm not as . . . as real as other people. But when I cut myself and see the blood and feel the pain I know I'm real. I can see . . . feel . . . myself better.

Does that make any sense? Probably not.'

It sort of does, in a funny way. I'm almost tempted to try it myself.

'But you're not invisible, you just hide yourself. I mean you're really quiet all the time, and you wear those long baggy clothes, and you've always got your hair all over your face. Even your school uniform is too big.' I have an idea. 'Why don't you stop hiding? Stop covering up who you are and what you're doing to yourself. Show me your arms.'

She blushes again, that red blotchy heat rushes into her face, and I realise what I'm suggesting. 'I don't mean . . . I mean, umm, put a T-shirt on or something. I won't look.'

But she's unbuttoning the top buttons of her shirt which is black and about five sizes too big for her. 'No, it's OK. . .' And she takes it off over her head.

She's sitting there in her jeans and little white bra, and all I can look at are her arms. Her poor arms. They're scratched and patched and scarred, and the new piece of plaster is already stained with blood. In between the wounds, old and new, I can see goosebumps standing up on her skin. The cuts are in a neat little line, like train tracks, with the oldest scars faded to white and the newer ones pink and shiny. It's the neatness that's the saddest thing, the way she's tried to be good and tidy while cutting herself till the blood pours out.

She reminds me of the assembly hall at St Saviour's, the crucifix with Our Lord hanging from it, bloodied and suffering. It's not that I'm at all religious, of course, but Gran used to take me to church with her sometimes and Mum and I had to go for a full year to get me into St Saviour's. I've always gone to Catholic schools and it's given me the idea at the back of my mind that pain is somehow more than just pain, that it's got supernatural power and meaning. What the meaning is though, I'm not too sure.

How could I ever have found the idea of her hurting herself exciting? I'm disgusted with myself.

She must have seen something of that in my face and she thinks it's directed at her. She's crying silently and trying to cover up her arms. As gently as possible I take her hand. 'No, it's OK. Look at them. Look at what you've done to yourself. Look at all that pain. You don't need to hide it from me.'

We sit there for a while, hand in hand in the near darkness. Far away I can hear the sound of people laughing and talking in the garden. Then she says, 'You won't tell anyone, will you?'

'I won't because I promised, but I think you should. I'm sure you can get help with this. Claire, there're enough bad people out there in the world who can hurt you without you hurting yourself.'

'Maybe,' she says.

'Yes,' I say.

She leans her head against my shoulder and I stroke her long hair away from her face. 'You can't hide away all the time, if this is what hiding does to you,' I say, and then wonder if I'm talking to her or me.

'Tell me your story now,' she says. 'Tell me why your eyes change colour.'

'Claire. . .' I hesitate. I know I can trust her. But what if someone threatens her?

'Yes?'

'What I'm going to tell you isn't just a bit secret. It's really secret. You can't tell anyone in your family or anyone at school. But if anyone really scary tries to make you tell them. . .'

'Yes?'

'Then tell. Don't protect me and don't put yourself in danger.'

'Danger?'

'Yes. Look, I'm not really called Joe. We didn't move here because my mum broke up with her boyfriend. We're here because I . . . I. . .'

'Because what? What is your name? Who are you?'

I've never seen Claire look like this. I mean apart

from the fact that she's hardly wearing anything. She's come alive, eyes shining bright blue, pink cheeks. Now I can see her face properly, she's so much prettier – but can I really tell her my story?

'I'm called Tyler. Most people call me Ty, but it's short for Tyler. Tyler Michael Lewis.'

It feels so strange to say my full name out loud, but what a fantastic relief. 'Tyler's after my dad and Michael's for my grandad.'

'Tyler,' she says. 'It's a nice name.'

'I saw something. I saw someone get killed. And when I told the police they said it wasn't safe to stay at home. We went home anyway but there was an attack . . . a petrol bomb. . . The shop underneath our flat got bombed, it all burned up. They had to give us new identities and send us away from London and they sent us here and that's how I became Joe and my mum became Michelle. Her name's Nicki really. They changed my eye colour with contact lenses and they dyed my hair – it's light brown, a bit like yours – and they put me down a year at school. I'm fourteen, not thirteen, and I should be finishing year nine.'

'Who did you see get killed?'

'A . . . a boy. They tried to mug him for his iPod and he had a knife too. It was a mess. Three against one.'

'Oh God, how terrible.'

I'm remembering the red, red blood on Arron's white shirt. 'And I ran to get help, and I managed to stop a bus and shout to the driver to call an ambulance, but it was too late by the time they got there. Much too late.'

I should have stayed. I should have been there when the ambulance got there. But instead . . . instead . . . there are some things I'm not ready to tell. Even Claire. Even now.

'Why wasn't it safe to stay at home?' she asks.

'Because someone wants to . . . to shut me up so I can't give evidence at the trial. And that person, those people, are really ruthless and they might even kill me I suppose.'

'Oh my God, Joe – oh, should I call you Tyler?'

I shake my head. 'Too confusing. And you might forget and get it wrong at school or something.'

She laughs. 'Oh, I'd never dare speak to you at school.'

'Bollocks to that, Claire, you're going to stop being invisible.' I laugh too. 'I'm meant to be being invisible and I'm doing really badly at it. But you don't have to be invisible at all.'

'I can't believe you ever could be invisible,' she says softly and I think – aha! – you *do* have a crush on me. Obviously someone like Joe would take advantage of the opportunity presenting itself. But I'm Ty right now. 'You're so wrong. I was completely invisible in London. My best friend thought I was babyish and no one at my school wanted to know me because I wasn't rich and I wasn't very . . . anything really. And I was short, and a bit podgy.'

'No!'

'It's true.'

She's laughing at me and I'm feeling incredibly happy to have found someone that I can tell all this stuff to. It occurs to me that no one knows all this – not Mum, not Gran – only Mr Patel in the shop downstairs had any idea of how difficult I was finding St Saviour's.

'When do you have to give evidence?' she asks.

'They said in the autumn, probably. I don't know for sure. The police come and ask questions sometimes but they don't tell me anything. And now my gran . . . she was beaten up because they wanted her to tell them where I was. Even though she didn't know. And she's in intensive care, and my mum's there with her and I don't know if I'm ever going to see her again.'

'That's terrible,' she says again. 'I don't know what to say. I feel such a wimp, making a fuss when you have real problems.'

'No, don't be daft, you have real problems too.'

I touch her arm, careful to avoid a scar. 'What will you do about this?'

'What can I do?'

'Here's my mobile number.' – I'm writing it down on a scrap of paper – 'You can call me if you feel it building up, if you feel like you're going to need to cut again.'

'But what if . . . if it's the middle of the night or something?'

'No problem. It's fine.'

'Have you got an email address?'

'I used to. . .' And I wonder if anyone's been emailing me any more on that address. How can I find out? Would it be safe to use the computers at school? But maybe it's better not to look.

'You need a new one. Shall I make one for you?'

'Yes, please.' I could do it myself easily but it's nice to think of Claire doing something to help me.

'Thanks, Joe. Thanks for trusting me.'

'Thanks for trusting me too.'

We're so close and so intent on each other, it's like the whole world's stopped. It's really easy to talk now. She tells me about the books and music she likes and I tell her about learning lots of different languages and being a football interpreter one day. She says, 'The first time I heard you speak French I thought you were French,' which is pretty nice to hear. There's no more noise coming from the garden and it's like we're in our own little dark cave. I lean towards her. . . Our lips brush together . . . and . . . crash! Someone's trying to open the door.

'What's going on?' calls her mum. 'Why have you blocked the door, Claire?'

Bugger. I was meant to have gone home hours ago and now she's going to find me barricaded into her half-naked daughter's bedroom. Maybe I can hide under the bed? Claire has the same idea and points to the floor while she whips her shirt back on.

'It's OK, Mum – just wanted some peace and quiet. The boys came in here earlier. You know they're not meant to.' Claire moves the chair out of the way and her mum opens the door.

'I don't know what's the matter with you, Claire. Why do you have to spend a nice sunny afternoon up here in the dark when we have guests and everything. I get no help from you at all.' Janet sounds completely fed up. 'You could at least let some light in.' She marches across to pull the curtains and almost falls over me. I scramble up quickly. 'Oh, sorry . . . I was just, er, having a rest on the floor.'

Janet is stunned, you can tell, and not sure whether to be angry or not. I can see her adding it all up – little Claire plus dark room plus chair against door, multiplied by violent boy (whose mother was obviously a teenage slag) – and failing to work out a satisfactory answer.

She obviously has the same opinion of Claire's pulling power as my mum had of mine. I'm sure that any minute she's going to notice that Claire's shirt is not done up to her chin as usual.

'Oh. You're still here, Joe? Maureen rang and asked where you were and I told her you'd gone home hours ago.'

'We were talking,' I say uncomfortably, and Claire says, 'Joe was just leaving, weren't you?'

Janet is still looking a bit suspicious. 'Thank you very much for lunch,' I say, and she says, 'You can stay for supper if you like. It's nearly six.'

'No, thanks, but I'd better get back if Maureen was looking for me.'

I sprint down the stairs and say goodbye as quickly as possible. Claire is looking pink and embarrassed, and I can hear her mum hissing at her, 'Claire, what was wrong with coming downstairs if you and Joe wanted to talk?' As I leave, I turn around and mouth, 'Call me.' And Claire nods and smiles.

Maureen's looking a bit annoyed when I get home. 'Where have you been? Janet said you left there at about three.'

'What's the big problem?' I don't really think it's any of Maureen's business where I've been. She's not my mother, after all.

'No problem, but I'd suggest you have a rest now. Doug's going to be here at midnight and we're taking you to see your gran.'

CHAPTER 18
Hail Mary

Maureen does a kind of reverse disguise on me before we go to the hospital. I have to take the contact lenses out and put on a black woolly hat, pulled down to cover up all of my hair – which looks pretty stupid and feels way too hot.

She wants me to wear shades too, but I tell her she has to choose between them and the hat because otherwise I will look like a total freak. Who wears shades at night? She pulls out some fake tan but I protest so strongly – after all, I'm due back at school on Monday – that she backs down. 'The main thing is not to draw any attention to yourself,' she says, which is pretty rich considering she was trying to turn me into a cut price Craig David.

And then Doug arrives and we drive and drive on nearly empty roads, and almost immediately we get in the car I fall asleep and I don't wake up for ages. And when I do, I lie quietly on the back seat and listen to their conversation without letting on that I'm awake.

'DI Morris seems to be happy to go with his evidence,' says Doug. 'He'll be interested in your input now you've spent a bit of time with the lad.'

'Oh, he's not talked to me about the evidence at all, sorry to say. He's very bound up in the here and now. Very upset he was when he thought he was going to be kicked out of school. It's good that the school scared him like that. He's learned a lesson. He's a good kid really, nothing like as hard as you made out.'

'Well that's your feminine intuition speaking, Mo, but I'm not so sure. Very manipulative, and the mum's no match for him. You know one of the defence teams is going to go on the line that he was involved? Went along with the whole thing, initiated it even, then ran off to get the ambulance. Pretty cool-headed if that's the case.'

'Don't believe it myself. That'd be a hell of a lot of lying for a young kid to sustain. And I thought there was no blood on him? That's what the bus witnesses say.'

'Took his time coming forward though, didn't he?'

'Hmm,' says Maureen, 'I can't see it. Why make up such a twisted story and come forward as a witness if it's going to make you a target for one of the biggest criminal families in London? These people have the money and the contacts to eliminate him like they're swatting a fly. He's pointing the finger at their son and they want him to disappear. Poor kid, I think he had no idea what he was getting into.'

'True enough,' says Doug.

They're quiet for a while – and I try not to let them hear that my breathing's gone a bit fast and shallow – but then I hear her say, 'So the sister's kicking off? Can't say I blame her.'

'She'll see sense,' says Doug, 'but it hasn't been plain sailing, believe me. Lots of aggro. Hard for our girl. Not in a great state.'

'Dear, oh dear. They'll go, though?'

'Have to. First Julie's got to be well enough to travel, and that's not so certain.'

Julie's my gran. Where are they sending her?

'Sooner the better, even if she's not well enough to go with them,' says Maureen. 'I wouldn't be happy having them hanging around that hospital. Not exactly secure, is it? How about our two? I think young Ty wants to stay where he is. I suspect there's a girlfriend in the picture somewhere.'

'Not decided what to do with them. That little stunt at school, bloody kid, made me think we'd better send them too. Crack down on him a bit, keep him out of trouble. But it's all expensive, you know. They'll be querying the costs on this one. If we can leave them be, all the better.'

They talk a bit softer and I'm desperate to hear what they are saying and make sense of it.

'No more news on . . . *mumble, mumble*?' asks Maureen.

'Not that I know of. Cliff's on surveillance. They're bloody clever, though. Know how to cover their tracks. We've not been able to prove any link.'

'Always the way. We switching cars on the way back?'

'Yes, it's all organised.'

'I wish we weren't doing it though,' she says. 'It's too bloody risky for the boy.'

'They think it'll help his granny,' says Doug. 'We don't want it turning into another murder investigation.'

'Exactly,' says Maureen. Then she looks around and says, 'Time to start waking up Ty. We're nearly there.'

I make a good act of stretching and yawning and Doug brings the car round to a side entrance of the hospital. I look at my watch. It's 3 am. Not exactly normal visiting hours.

He pulls out a police radio and talks into it for a while, and then a burly man approaches the car. Doug gets out and talks to him for a minute and then reappears.

'OK, Ty, you go with Dave here, and we'll see you later.'

'Aren't you coming with me?'

'No, we'll pick you up later. Don't worry. Dave will sort you out.'

What if Dave's some sort of a double agent? What if, when they're gone, he shoots me or something? I take a deep breath and get out of the car.

'Come with me,' says Dave, and we walk into the hospital. We walk up some stairs and along a corridor. He never speaks to me the whole time. Then through some double doors and up in a lift and we walk for a bit until we're in a corridor where there's a policeman in a uniform carrying a huge gun. Like a machine-gun sort of thing. Dave and he nod at each other.

'OK, this way,' says Dave and we walk into a ward. I wonder what the other families that come here make of the police guard. I wouldn't like it much if I had to worry about some sort of potential shoot-out at my relative's bedside. I feel incredibly guilty to have caused so much hassle to so many random people.

Dave opens a door to a side room, and says, 'Thirty minutes.' I don't really believe him. We've driven for three hours to stay for thirty minutes?

He stays outside. I walk through the door, nervous and jumpy. What am I going to see? Who's going to be there?

There's a bed and lots of bleeping machines and my gran in the middle. Just her and me. I thought Mum and my aunties would be here too. Where are they? Didn't they want to see me? It's so creepy being here by myself.

Gran's almost unrecognisable – she looks really old and her face is a kind of greeny-white colour, except for the bits which are purple and swollen. Her eyes have big blue-black bags underneath. She doesn't even smell nice, and her head is all bound up in bandages.

I'm only certain it's her because, in between the tubes coming out of her arm, I can see the little tattoo on her arm – the heart with Mick, my grandad's name, written inside. Gran had that tattoo done when they went on honeymoon. 'All the girls were getting them in those days,' she would tell me when I was little and wanted to know what it was.

It's only her heavy, rattling breaths that let me know she's even alive. She'd hate me to see her like this. I hate seeing her too. I take her hand. 'Gran, it's me, it's Ty,' I say. 'I'm really, really sorry, Gran. It's all my fault.'

She moans and her eyes flutter. My heart is beating really fast and my hands are sweating. I don't know what to say next. Then I remember Doug and Maureen's conversation in the car and I begin to wonder. Maybe this is some kind of trap? Maybe they've put me in here by myself because they think I'll tell Gran something that I've never told anyone else. Could they be secretly filming or recording me?

'Gran, I'm trying to do the right thing, like you said,' I say. 'I never hurt anyone. I just tried to keep Arron out of trouble. I didn't know what to do for the best.'

I tried and failed. I failed so badly. . .

The door opens and I spring round. Oh my God. It's my auntie Lou, but looking so pale and gaunt, and her roots are so dark that it's like the ends of her hair have been dipped in yellow paint. We hug, and it's amazing to be able to feel her and know that she's really here with me in this stuffy room.

'Ty, my love, what do you look like?' she says. 'You must be boiling in that ridiculous hat.'

'I am, but they said don't take it off,' I say nervously. Sweat prickles on my forehead and the hat feels really itchy.

'Idiot police,' she says, reaching over to hold Gran's hand. 'We think she's regaining consciousness, that's why we asked them to bring you here. She's opened her eyes a few times and even said a word or two, but she goes back again. We thought it might just nudge her in the right direction if she heard your voice. She adores you so much. We never thought they'd leave you in here on your own. You must have been terrified.'

'I'm OK.'

'Look at you, how you've grown,' she says. 'You're becoming a man.'

'Yeah, well. . . Where's Mum?'

Lou gives me a strange look. I suppose she's never heard me call Nicki 'Mum' before. 'Nic's in the waiting room with Emma. You'll see them later. They only want two or three of us in with your gran at any one time and they said that you and me and him' – she nods towards Dave, stationed outside the door – 'were more than enough. Talk a bit to her. She'd be so happy to see you again.'

I lean over the bed again. 'Gran, please will you wake up for me? I'm only here for a little while – they won't let me stay.' Again her eyes seem to flicker a little.

Lou coughs. 'Ty, you know what she's like. We've had the chaplain here every day. We thought if you said a prayer for her, it might just. . .'

'Oh bloody hell, Lou.' I'm not at all sure that I'm up for that.

'Just try it, Ty. It wouldn't work if any of us did it. She'd know we didn't mean it.'

And I would? 'Do I have to?' But I know I do. 'Where's her rosary?'

'It's still in her flat. The police won't let us go back in there and I asked them to bring it but they haven't yet, but the chaplain gave us this one.'

It's very simple – ivory plastic beads, nothing like Gran's beautiful olive-wood rosary which Grandad bought her when they went to Rome and is her most special possession. But I suppose it'll do.

I put the rosary in one of her hands and take hold of the other. I stick my head as near to Gran's as possible and reach across to hold the rosary too. I like the way the beads feel smooth and slippery, and they remind me of being a little boy when we still lived with Gran.

'Hail Mary, full of grace,' I say really slowly. I'm kind of hoping that my thirty minutes will be up before I have to get to the end. 'The Lord is with thee. Blessed art thou amongst women. . .'

Gran makes a kind of coughing noise and her eyes move again. Louise pinches my arm: 'It's working, keep going. . . I knew this would work.'

'. . . and blessed is the fruit of thy womb, Jesus.'

She opens her eyes. She opens her eyes! It's a flaming miracle.

'Holy Mary, mother of God . . .'

Gran's hand is clutching mine. Her eyes are open. She's mouthing the words with me. I'll have to finish.

'. . . pray for us sinners now and at the hour of our . . . our . . .'

'Death,' says Louise. Her eyes are full of tears and

she kisses me on the stupid woolly hat. 'Amen.'

'Amen,' echoes Gran in a really frail and wobbly voice. And then she says, 'Louise, is that you? Can you help me?'

After that, everything seems to move really quickly. Dave wants me to go after thirty minutes but I say no, it's too soon. The nurses and doctors need to see to Gran and Dave says I shouldn't be in there with them, so he takes me to the waiting room to see Mum and Emma. 'We'll give you fifteen minutes together and then fifteen minutes back with the old lady and then that's that.'

'She's not an old lady, she's only fifty-eight,' I say. Gran looked about a hundred and eight in that bed.

'Fair enough, son. Well done for bringing her round.'

The waiting room is just as hot as Gran's room. My mum's asleep on a sofa. She looks totally different – a bit like her old self again, because her hair is long and blonde. How did they manage that? Oh. It must be a wig. Emma's sitting in the dark, reading *Grazia* magazine with a little torch. She jumps up when she sees me. 'Ty! I can't believe it!'

It's so good to see her again. Emma's the easiest-going person in our family and she's the nearest thing

I've got to a big sister. 'Emma, Gran woke up!'

'I knew she'd wake up for you,' she said. 'They didn't want to bring you, you know, but it seemed like the only thing we could try to get to her. Ty, did you know they're going to send us abroad for a while? Me and Louise, and Mum, as soon as she's ready to leave hospital.'

'What about us?'

'Not you. I think, they think it's safer to keep us apart.'

'Yeah, well, they're experts at keeping people safe, aren't they?' She misses my sarcasm and answers, 'I certainly hope so.'

I think about Emma and her job in fashion and her boyfriend Paul. I think about Louise and her university degree and her flat in Hoxton and her job as head of English at a girls' school in Westminster. I have totally messed up their lives.

'I'm really sorry, Emma. It's all my fault.'

'No it's not, Ty, don't ever think that. You're just a witness. It's those boys on trial, they're the ones to blame. And whatever bastard threw that bomb into the shop.'

'Did you see it? Did you see Mr Patel?'

'I saw the shop,' she says, and she's looking the most serious I've ever seen Emma look. 'He was OK. Trying to sort out his insurance claim.'

'What . . . what does Lou think about going away?'

'Well, she's not very happy. She's giving up a lot. But no one is blaming you, darling, never think that.'

'Where will they send you?'

'I don't know, they won't tell us. It'll be a magical mystery tour until we get to the airport. I'm keen on Spain. Get a bit of sunshine.'

She gently shakes my mum's shoulder. 'Nicki, look who's here.'

She takes time to wake up and I'm shocked to see she's lost weight. Even the new red top, the one that looked so pretty before, is hanging loose on her. My mum is disappearing like a snowman when the sun comes out. She's blinking at me and says, 'Ty? Are you OK? What's been happening?' Her voice sounds like a little girl.

'I'm fine. Everything's fine. Gran woke up.'

'She did? Louise said she'd wake up for you.' She's not as happy as I'd have expected. In fact, she sounds a little bit pissed off.

'We can go back and see her in a minute. Nicki, when will you come home?'

She shrugs: 'When they say . . . I don't know. Maybe they think I should come now with you.'

She's lost it again, I can tell. She's back to how she was a few weeks ago, unable to make decisions, all her independence and fight and spirit drained away.

'What do you want to do?' Emma asks gently. 'Maybe it's time to be with Ty again? I'm sure Mum will understand.'

Nicki looks a bit confused. 'It's not really up to me. . .' she says.

'I'll talk to the police,' I say to Emma over her head. 'I'll work something out.'

She looks even more worried than before. 'Nicki, why don't you ask them to take you into Mum's room now? Then Ty and I will come along in a minute.'

My mum wanders out of the room and I hear her talking to Dave in the corridor. Emma puts her arm around me. 'Ty, sweetheart, I'm a bit worried about Nicki. She seems spacey, out of it, not really herself.'

'I know. . . She was getting a bit better but now she seems worse. Is she eating anything?'

'Not much, and she and Louise haven't been getting on very well. Nicki feels very sensitive and like she's being blamed, which isn't what Lou means at all. It's been difficult.'

'Why would she be blamed? It's down to me.'

'Well, she feels like Lou is saying she isn't a very good mother, which obviously doesn't go down very well.'

Well, obviously. So Louise does think it's all my fault.

Dave knocks at the door: 'I can give you another fifteen minutes with your gran, Ty, and then you really must go. They don't want to move you when it's light.'

I'm like an owl or a bat. A creature of the night. Or maybe a werewolf.

Gran is looking much more awake when they take us to see her again. She's not really up to talking though, and doesn't seem to know what's going on. 'Ty?' she says faintly and reaches out to touch me. 'What's that thing?' She's puzzled by the hat.

'Take it off,' hisses Mum, and I don't know what to do. So I whip it off really quickly, and Louise and Emma both gasp when they see my jet-black hair and Lou says, 'God, he looks exactly like his dad.'

Poor Gran is confused: 'Are you Ty?' I pull the hat back on and tuck my hair underneath. 'You've been ill for a while, Gran. My look's kind of changed.'

'Oh, that's it,' she says, and she seems happy again.

'Time's up,' says Dave, and I quickly hug them all. I lean over and kiss Gran. 'Gran, take care. Get yourself well again.'

'I'll see you soon, darling boy,' she says, and I wish it could be true.

'I'll be back with you soon,' says Mum, but she doesn't sound very sure.

Louise kisses me. 'It's so good to see you. Take care.'

'Take care,' echoes Emma, and Dave says, 'That's it, I'm afraid.'

He leads me away, through corridors, down in the lift and through an empty hallway. Out of a door into the cold. It's not so dark now and the birds have started singing. 'That all took far too long,' he says, and he lifts up his radio.

And then a car comes screeching around the corner and there's a loud cracking noise – bang! – and Dave shoves me back through the door before he stumbles and falls, blood seeping bright though his shirt.

CHAPTER 19

Under the Blanket

'Run!' he shouts at me. 'Run!' The blood is spreading out over his side.

'But . . . you. . .'

He points back along the corridor. 'Run, go . . . they might come after you. . .'

I'm backing off. I don't want to abandon him, but . . . he said. . . I run. I run away from the blood.

I run and run along the corridor and crash through two sets of double doors. The hospital is starting to wake up now and I nearly barge into some cleaners. 'There's a man back there,' I gasp, 'been shot. . .' And I run on past their gaping faces.

Hospitals are strange places. This one seems to be lots of buildings jumbled together. The floors have lots of different lines on them, blue, red, yellow, A, B, C. Very helpful if you know where you're going, but I don't. I'm just running, along echoing corridors, through tunnels, up stairs and past wards full of people who can't help me.

I'm trying to run as I would for Ellie, but I can't. I can't get my breathing under control. It's coming in short, sharp bursts, a jittering, terrified breath, a breath that slows me down and gives me a shooting pain in my side. What's the point of being a good runner if you can't run when you need to?

I need to pee. There's a loo and no one around and it seems like a good place to hide. Luckily there's no one in there. I find a cubicle, lock myself in, do the business, and climb up on to the toilet seat. I curl myself into a ball and try to think clearly. If I were watching this in a film it'd be really exciting, an action adventure. But when it's me on my own and I don't know what to do or where to go, it's not as exciting as you'd expect.

What if the gunman goes to the intensive care unit? What if he knows where to find my family? I'm going to have to get there first.

I hear a creak as the door opens. Someone's come in. I hold my breath, try not to make a sound, waiting to hear them use the loo, wash their hands, leave. Nothing. There's someone right outside the cubicle door just standing there. Oh Christ. . . Can bullets go through doors? I bet they can.

I'll have to do something. I stand up on the loo seat and kick the door open as fast and strong as I can. And kick again as I jump down. I can feel my foot crunch into some guy's groin – and he goes flying backwards into the urinals. I don't even look at him or wait to see if he's got a gun or not. I clatter through the door and leg it along the corridor.

Intensive Care. I need to go and warn them that he could be coming there. There's a signpost up ahead and I stop for a moment to search for the name. There it is . . . follow the red line . . . here and here and stairs or lift? I opt for the stairs and dash up three flights. At the top I'm gasping for breath but feeling triumphant. I'll get there, I'll save them. . .

The lift door opens and a large man steps out. 'Stop!' he yells at me and launches himself in a rugby tackle which I meet with another kick. Crash! My foot smashes against his teeth. I'm just about to follow through with a punch when I look at him properly for the first time.

Shit.

It's Doug.

'Sorry, sorry, really sorry, Doug. I didn't know it was you.'

He recovers slowly, blood dripping from his lips.

'What the hell did you think you were doing? First you kick me in the balls, then in the teeth.'

I'd have thought that was obvious. 'I didn't realise it was you. I was trying to escape. I thought you were the guy who shot Dave. . . Did you know? He needs help. . .'

'Don't worry about him. He's OK. We need to concentrate on you.'

'How did you find me?'

'We put a trace on you before you went in, just in case anything happened. To be honest, I was worried you might do a runner. You're an unpredictable little bugger.'

'What do you mean, a trace?'

'Electronic tagging device. Useful when someone goes AWOL.'

'Dave said to run. . . I didn't want to leave him. . .'

He pulls out his mobile. 'Got him. Main entrance in ten.'

'Main entrance? Isn't that a bit dangerous?' I'm like a suicide bomber. Anywhere I go, I could bring death and destruction to innocent people.

'It's the only place they won't be expecting us. Walk slowly, try and look normal.'

We walk back down the corridor. My breathing is still coming in painful bursts and I'm constantly looking behind and around me. 'What about Mum and

Gran. . .?' I ask, and Doug says, 'Lots of people to look after them.'

We're nearly there. 'Stay calm,' mutters Doug. 'Once we're with other people, don't do anything to bring attention to yourself.'

I can hear police sirens and hope that means that someone's got to Dave in time. What about the guy that shot him? Is he going to be lying in wait for us?

We're at the main entrance. There are people here. They look normal – some old men, a woman with a baby, but what do I know? They might have guns, they might be about to shoot us. Suddenly I don't feel so brave any more. I can't do this. 'It's OK,' says Doug, but what does he know?

And we're walking through the door and out into bright sunlight and there's a big black car, and Doug opens the door and pushes me in, a bit more roughly than necessary, in my opinion. Maureen's sitting there and gestures for me to crouch down on the floor, and I scrunch myself down as low as possible. Doug gets in the front, next to the driver, and Maureen covers me with a blanket. 'It's just for a little while, just to get out of here.'

It's stiflingly hot under the thick scratchy blanket, and I'm getting cramp and I'm desperately hungry and thirsty. The motion of the car is making me feel sick too, and I retch a bit, but there's nothing there to be sick with, just a foul taste in my mouth.

But worst of all is sitting in the dark feeling more and more panicky about what nearly happened to me, and what could be happening right now. I'm seeing the gunman standing in that little room and blasting them all away. My family turned into little scraps of blood and bone and hair and flesh.

I'm wedged against Maureen's legs, and after we've been driving for a bit, she leans down and rests her hand on my shoulder and whispers, 'Don't worry. Try not to worry.'

Eventually, after what feels like hours, they stop and Maureen pulls off the blanket and says, 'Oh dear,' when she sees me. I am so hot that I can feel my whole body burning up and my hair and shirt are completely wet with sweat, and I suppose I might look a little bit like perhaps I've been crying.

'OK, quickly now, out of the car and over to that one.' I kind of groan because I was really hoping that we were going to stop driving for a bit and my legs are so cramped that I can hardly walk, but I half hop, half stumble to the other car. Doug's already transferred to the driver's seat, and he's not looking too sympathetic.

'Just lie down on the back seat,' says Maureen. 'Try and relax.' Doug reverses and then speeds along the little country lane we're parked in. 'Here, have some water,' says Maureen, and I prop myself up on my elbow and gulp it down gratefully. She says, 'You're looking a bit green. Take one of these,' and passes over a little white pill which I assume must be for travel sickness.

I must have gone to sleep then, a blissful sleep with no dreams, because it's nearly night when I wake up again. We're pulling in at a service station and Maureen shakes my shoulder and says, 'You could do with some food, I should think.'

'Wh— what time is it?'

'It's nine at night. You've slept almost all day,' says Doug.

'I gave you a sedative. Thought you could do with it,' says Maureen.

'Why are we still driving?' I have a sudden horrible thought. 'You're not taking me to a new place to live, are you?'

They both laugh. 'No, even we can't work that quickly,' says Maureen. 'Let's just say we thought it was best to bring you back by the scenic route and get back after dark. We can have some food here, then we'll go to the house around midnight. Doug'll have to stay over.'

'I'm really sorry, Doug, about what happened.'

'Attacked me not once but twice, you little bastard,' says Doug, but he sounds OK about it. 'Given that

234

you thought I was a vicious gunman, I'd say you were pretty brave. Of course, if you didn't think that, I'd have to take it personally. And now I'm going to have to stay over. Don't think the missus'll be too happy with me but needs must.'

It's never occurred to me before that Doug and Maureen both have lives of their own which they've put on hold to look after me.

'I didn't know you had a missus.'

They laugh again. 'Oh yes, he most certainly does,' says Maureen. 'Keeps you on a very short leash, doesn't she, Doug.'

'A fine woman,' says Doug, and Maureen winks at me.

We go into the service station. I'm still a bit nervy, but the sedative seems to have slowed me down. My body feels heavy and my eyes keep trying to close. I'm so stiff and cramped that Maureen has to help me walk from the car to the cafe. I'm hobbling like an old man and I don't feel like someone who fought off a police officer twice. Even if it was only Doug.

They both want sausage and chips, and Maureen realises that I can't make a decision and chooses fish and chips and a cup of tea for me. We sit down and I start mushing up the fish with my fork. 'Have you got a husband, Maureen?' I ask.

'No chance. Married to my work I am. Luckily for you, eh?'

I nod, and she says, 'Try and stop messing with the food and eat some of it. It's no good to you if all you're going to do is play with it.'

Maureen really reminds me of my gran. She's about the same age and she's got the same sort of friendly face. 'Maureen, did you know my gran woke up? She did it when I was there.'

'I do know, and I'm really pleased for you. Why don't you tell me about it?'

So I tell her what happened, and she ruffles my hair like I'm a baby and says, 'I think you did a fine job there.' Then she pauses and says, 'I didn't realise you were a church-going family. Should I find you one for Sunday?'

'Not me and Mum, just Gran.' I wish I did have the comfort that Gran gets from prayers and church and stuff. But it's never seemed to connect with me, and Mum would have kicked up big time if I'd gone holy on her.

'Oh, shame,' says Maureen, which I think is a bit odd. 'The jury would like to hear about you going to church,' she adds, which is even weirder.

'How did you think your mum was looking?' asks Doug.

'Crap.'

'Yes, we're a bit concerned about her. We can't contact

the hospital right now. We want to get back first with no risk of anyone making any connection between us and them. But I'm pretty sure that they'll move everyone right away. Your mum will be back with you very soon.'

'So . . . will you go away then, Maureen?'

She hesitates, and I'm desperate for her to say no, she's going to stay and look after both of us. She can see it in my face, I think, because she says briskly, 'Let's cross that bridge when we come to it.' And then, 'Right, you're going to eat something if I have to pick up that fork and feed you,' which makes me try a chip and find it surprisingly tasty.

I'm asleep again as soon as we get back into the car and I don't wake up until we're back at the house. Joe's house. For the first time it feels like home. My anonymous beige room is so peaceful. A safe place, our safe house. I need to believe it, so I do. I collapse on to the bed and it's incredibly comfortable.

Downstairs I can hear the television. Doug's switched on Sky News. I hear snatches of headlines drifting up the stairs . . . 'shooting . . . hospital. . .'

Shooting? Hospital? I pull myself up and stumble down the stairs. There's an aerial shot of the hospital, and then the reporter standing by the main entrance. 'The policeman who was shot was an armed officer protecting a woman who had been injured in a violent assault. Questions are being asked about security in the hospital, with families of patients complaining that their loved ones were put at risk.'

'The woman at the centre of this incident has now been moved to an undisclosed location. The injured policeman is recovering and his condition is said to be stable.'

'They've moved Gran?'

'Sounds like it.'

'It's a good thing,' says Maureen. 'Now you won't have to worry about her.' She gets up. 'I'm going to run you a bath, and then see if you can sleep some more.'

I do sleep, but it's not the easy, empty sleep I slept in the car. I'm back in the hospital running along the maze of corridors, but this time I go through some double doors and I'm in my gran's room, with all the bleeping machines and the smell and the bandages . . . and in the bed it's not Gran, but Claire, and it's not her arms that have been cut, but her throat, and there's blood everywhere, on the walls and the bed and dripping on to the floor, and there's a screaming noise – and it's coming from me. . .

And Maureen's sitting on my bed in her dressing gown and handing me another little white pill. 'Better take another one,' she says. 'No good sleeping if it just gives you nightmares.'

I take it and as I swallow, I wonder whether my life – awake or asleep – will ever just be normal again.

CHAPTER 20
Sharon and the Pope

In the morning I try to go running. I put on my kit. I lace up my shoes. I open the door and I think about how I'm going to warm up, then stretch, then run for at least an hour.

And then a car comes along the road and I shut the door again.

Three times I open the door and three times I close it again. In the end I sit down on the step and just watch the road for a bit, hoping that if I see what a boring, quiet street it is, then I'll be able to jog down it.

What I see is Ashley Jenkins walking up the hill towards me.

She's tanned and wearing skimpy shorts and a crop top, and I'm surprised that I don't feel more than a flicker of interest. Maybe Maureen's sedatives have shut me down, switched me off. I bloody well hope it's not forever. I'd have to sue the police, which would be totally embarrassing.

It can't be coincidence that Ashley's walking along my street. But how could she know where I live? Of course, I'm so stupid. Her motor-mouth mother must have fished my address out of the school records.

'Hello, Joe,' she says. 'Are you going to invite me in?'

'OK,' I say, not quite sure what's going on. Am I meant to take her up to my bedroom, where I haven't even picked up my sweat-stained clothes from yesterday? Is Ashley about to take things to a new, fantastic but terrifying level? Am I capable right now? Are we even together any more? 'Do you want a coffee?'

We go into the kitchen where Maureen and Doug are sitting at the table and looking very interested in my visitor. I try and ignore them while I fill the kettle, which just makes me look really stupid because Maureen immediately says, 'Hello, my name's Maureen and this is Doug,' and Ashley says, 'Hi, I'm Ashley,' and then everyone looks at me and I don't say anything.

I make coffee and say, 'We're going upstairs,' to see if they object, but she spoils it by saying, 'Actually, Joe, maybe we'd better stay in the lounge if no one's in there.' I can see Doug and Maureen exchanging knowing glances and I feel like a complete prat.

It's clear to everyone that I am about to go through the ritual of being officially chucked. Doug and Maureen will probably listen at the door and then have a good laugh about it.

We go into the lounge and I shut the door behind us. 'Where's your mum?' asks Ashley. 'Or are they your real parents and you were just pretending that your big sister was your mum?'

'No, she's away right now and they're staying here with me. They're just friends.'

'Oh.'

'How was your holiday?'

'It was good.'

I'm not going to ask her why she's here if she's not going to say. We can go on having this sort of conversation for hours if she wants.

'Nice weather?'

'Yes, very sunny.'

'Nice hotel?'

'Yes, lovely.' She sighs. 'Look, Joe, I didn't want to go upstairs because I thought we needed to talk.'

'Oh, yeah?'

'It's just. . . Look, I think maybe we should stop seeing each other.'

There are two things I can say. I can say, 'Yes, fine, OK, it was good for the two weeks that it lasted, especially when you were in Spain,' and show her out. Or I can ask why. Stupidly I go for option two.

She looks uncomfortable. 'It's just. . . Thing is, Joe, I don't know if you know but I didn't grow up round here. My family came here when I was nine from Catford – you know where that is?'

Of course I do. She's a South Londoner. If you're from north of the river like me, then South London is somewhere you know about but have never been to. Most of the things you've heard aren't good.

'And the reason we left was to get my brother away from that area. My brother Callum, he's six years older than me, and he was getting involved in gangs and carrying a knife and one day he got stabbed.'

'Was he . . . was he killed?'

'No, of course not. I said we moved here to get him away from London, duh. Anyway when I saw you with that knife the other day, I knew . . . I knew I couldn't be with you.' Her lip trembles and I think she's about to cry. 'I saw a different side of you.'

This is totally unfair: 'But I only did it for you. They were touching you, and they had those pictures. . .'

'I know, and they're sick bastards, but you know what, Joe, we might have been embarrassed by those pictures, and it wouldn't have been nice, but it wouldn't have been the absolute end of the world. But say you'd stabbed one of those boys. . .' Her voice trails off.

She's not altogether wrong and I know it. 'I'm sorry, Ash. I never meant to scare you.'

She's crying now, and the sedatives seem to be wearing off because I really would like to try and cheer her up a bit. I go and sit on the sofa next to her and tentatively snake my arm around her almost-bare shoulders. She doesn't object, and my other arm manages to rest itself against the bit of her back between the shorts and crop top. And then I'm kissing her tears away and we're lying down on the sofa, and I'm hoping very much that Doug and Maureen will have the sense to leave us alone while I find out whether she was doing any topless sunbathing in Spain.

She pulls away. Eventually. Half-heartedly. 'And that's the other thing,' she says.

'What?' I'm still stroking her bare stomach and the other hand is doing some really successful exploration.

'You and me. It's too much, too soon.'

'Mmm . . . I don't see you complaining. . .' I'm nibbling her neck and she smells all coconutty.

'That's the problem.'

'What do you mean?'

'I know everyone thinks I'm a slag who'll do anything, but I'm really not, Joe.'

That's just not fair. 'I never thought anything like

that. I think you're amazing and sexy and . . .' I kiss her glossy lips, '. . . very sophisticated.'

'Yes but the thing is that I don't seem to be able to say no to you, Joe, like I can to other boys. The boys I've been out with before, they knew that they couldn't . . . you know . . . go too far. I made sure they knew. But I keep on forgetting to tell you to stop, and I'm getting a bit scared. I mean if we'd gone up to your bedroom, I can imagine, you know, one thing leading to another. And I don't want to end up like. . .' She hesitates, but I can see this one coming a mile off.

'Like my mum.'

I very deliberately remove my hands, wipe them on my jeans as if I'm cleaning off something dirty and move away like she's giving off a bad smell.

'I don't mean— '

'I know what you mean. I know *exactly* what you mean. But you know what? My mum was happy to have me. She wanted to have me. And we've never scrounged off the state. She's got qualifications, and she's worked and worked to look after me.'

I'm so furious I can hardly speak. It's incredible how much shit you take in life just because your mother happens to be a teenager when you're born, and your dad can't be arsed to know you.

Ashley says, 'Joe, don't take this the wrong way.

I don't mean anything against your mum. I think she's really cool, but she must have been ever so young when she had you. Not much older than us. And I just wouldn't want to have to make those choices.'

I can't stand looking at her. 'Oh yeah, Ashley, I bet you say this to all the boys.'

'No really, Joe, it's really true.'

'I bet you found yourself some waiter in Spain and you've been at it with him all week.'

'No . . . no. . . I've really thought about this a lot.'

'Why come here dressed like a tart, then?'

Her face falls. My aunties would kill me if they heard me speak to a girl like that. But I don't care. I only want to hurt her like she's hurting me.

'I'm not. . .'

'Yeah, yeah. . . Well, you've done what you came for, Ashley. What are you going to tell everyone? "He was so hot I couldn't trust myself with his body, so I chucked him"? Or "I thought he was a psycho with a knife"?'

'I don't know,'

'Maybe I'll tell everyone I chucked you because you're just a slag.'

She stands up and I can see I've made her angry. Good. 'Go on then,' she says. 'See if I care. It's what they all think anyway.'

'No, I won't do that.' Her unexpected dignity has shamed me. 'I'm sorry, Ashley. I thought you were disrespecting my mum and I've had enough of that for a lifetime.'

'I'll tell people we broke up because my parents told me I had to chuck you after you punched Carl. That's true, by the way. And all the girls'll be after you whatever I say.'

'Yeah, but they're too scared of you to speak to me.'

She shrugs: 'It's OK. I'll tell them they can talk to you.'

'All of them?'

She looks suspicious. 'Why . . . who were you thinking of?'

'Oh, no one. . .'

'Hmmm.' She's not quite sure what to think, but I hope I've made things safe to talk to Claire at school.

She leaves then, and I lie down on the sofa and I feel quite upset, although it's not being chucked by Ashley that's bothering me, but the memories she's stirred, the days and days and years and years of being told that there's something wrong with you because your mum is young and poor and had a baby when she wasn't much more than a child herself.

It's not just stuff like Father's Day when you've got no one to make a card for, and politicians on the telly saying that single mothers cause lots of problems in society. It's not just Vicky Pollard on *Little Britain* and the word pramface and the word bastard as well.

It was the way everyone looked that first parents' evening at St Saviour's, when I realised with a horrible grinding feeling in my stomach that all the other parents came in pairs – even Arron's, although his dad wasn't the one he used to have – and Mum was at least ten years younger than anyone else's, and she didn't dress the same way as the other mums who were either suits or frumps.

And in the playground, the voices, the voices that I pretended not to hear. Your mum's a slut. Your mum's a whore. Will your mum do it with me?

No one I tried to talk to really understood. Auntie Emma said I was making a big fuss about nothing and she was sure that loads of kids at school had single mothers, and when I explained that most of them had dads as well, she said, 'From what I hear, you're better off without yours.' Mr Patel said every woman needed a good man and perhaps I should come with him to the mosque some time, learn a more traditional way of life.

Arron said, 'The problem, mate, is that she's too fit. She's nothing like a normal mother. She looks like she had you when she was eight.'

And then he said, 'You just have to pick one of them to fight and they won't do it any more. Come on, bro, remember the stuff we learned at boxing club.'

And I shook my head because there were so many of them and they were all bigger than me, and I thought if I fight one I'll have to fight them all. And I could see he despised me. And later he started with the 'pretty boy'. And the 'girl'. And the 'gay'. And I had to take it because he was my only friend. But I worried that if I took it, it made it true.

And none of this would have mattered so much if I hadn't worked out a conversation that had bothered me for years; since I was about eight or nine and Nicki and I were watching *East Enders*, and Sharon was weeping and wailing about a baby she'd been pregnant with and hadn't had. Had somehow decided not to have.

And I turned to Nicki and said, 'I didn't know you could quit a baby.'

And she said, 'Well, sometimes you can.'

And I said, 'Could you have?'

And she laughed and said, 'What a question! Not with your gran and the Pope on my case!' And when I looked puzzled she kissed me and said, 'I wouldn't ever want to be without my lovely boy.'

But it nagged away at me for ages, as things do that you don't really understand but you think might be important, and I stored it away until the day before I was due to start at St Saviour's. I was trying on my new blazer and Nicki said, 'You know Ty, at this new school they're going to be much heavier with the God stuff. It's all very well, and I'm so proud you're going there, but remember you've got a mind of your own. Don't let them fill you up with Jesus and Mary and the Pope until you can't make your own decisions.'

And I saw sadness in her eyes and I pulled that old conversation out of my memory and I kind of realised that if it hadn't been for Gran and the Pope then Nicki would have decided to be like Sharon on *East Enders*. And just then I still didn't really understand how or why but a bit of my inner certainty, my basic happiness, died that day. Which wasn't a great way to start a new school.

I'm still lying on the sofa, feeling a bit sorry for myself, going over it all again and again when there's a knock at the door and Maureen comes in. 'Doug's gone,' she says. 'He's going to find out what's happening, and maybe he'll be collecting your mum.'

She's trying not to look too nosy. 'Your friend gone too?' she asks, although quite where she thinks Ashley is hiding I'm not sure.

'Yup.'

'All well?'

'She chucked me, if that's what you want to know.'

'Sorry to hear that. Long relationship?'

250

'Two weeks, but we had some amazing moments,' I say gloomily, and then I realise how stupid that sounds and I start to laugh because actually I'm kind of bubbling with happiness inside to be able to be Claire's friend. I'm thinking I can go shopping with her and help her chose nicer clothes, and take her long rippling hair and tie it back with a silky ribbon, and have someone to talk to that I can trust and feel close to. A real friend.

Maureen laughs too and says, 'You must be absolutely devastated. Why don't I make you a cup of tea?'

'Yes, OK. Thanks.'

We sit at the kitchen table and I tell her about not being able to go running. She says, 'Look, Ty, that was a very frightening experience yesterday. Don't kid yourself. Some evil bastard tried to kill you and that's a big thing to cope with.'

'Yeah,' I say and she says, 'You know, Ty, what doesn't kill you makes you stronger,' which is pretty amazing because I would have thought that Maureen'd be way too old to have even heard of Kanye West.

'Anyway,' she goes on, 'We're happy that your identity as Joe is very secure, and no one can connect you here with Ty. It's possible we might be able to arrange some counselling for you in the future, but right now you're going to have to take a bit of advice from me.'

'What's that?'

'Keep calm and carry on. It was a poster during the Second World War – no, I'm not that old, cheeky bugger – and I've always thought it was a good motto.'

It's a good one for a runner, I think, and I wonder about giving it another try. Maureen seems to read my mind. 'Go on,' she says. 'Maybe you can do it this time.'

I hesitate a bit on the step, then I fiddle with my iPod until I find the Kanye West song she was talking about, and I walk down the garden path. I almost turn around and come back when I get to the garden gate. But with Maureen watching me and Kanye in my head telling me to be strong, I manage to jog down the street and around the corner and I'm running again. And maybe, just maybe, I can take her advice.

CHAPTER 21
Lost Property

My mum arrives back at about 9 pm on Sunday, just as I'm ironing a shirt for school the next day. She's pale and dazed, blinking like she's just woken up. I put the iron down and come and hug her. 'Hi, Nic. How was Gran?'

'I don't know,' she says in a faraway little voice. 'They took her away from us. And then they put us in some hotel place. . . And then we were there, and now we're here, except Emma and Lou are somewhere else. I don't know where.'

I wonder if it was a hotel at all. She's acting like she's been in a loony bin. 'It was because of the shooting,' I say impatiently. 'They had to move you in a hurry.'

'Oh God, yes, the shooting,' says Nicki, like she's a TV and someone's turned her on. 'You could have been killed. Are you all right? Oh, God, Ty.'

'Yes, yes, would I be doing the ironing if I'd been shot?'

The screen goes blank. 'Oh. I don't know. They didn't tell me anything.'

'They must have told you that I was OK.'

'I suppose so.' She's doubtful. 'They talk to Louise mostly and she doesn't tell me anything.'

Maureen has been listening to this, standing tactfully by the door and she comes over and puts her arm around my mum. 'Nicki, love, you have a good sleep now and you'll feel more like yourself in the morning. I was wondering, would you like me to see if I can stay on a few days? Just to help you get back on your feet again, and tell you how Ty's been doing while you've been away.'

Nicki looks like there's no one there at all. 'Yes, whatever you want,' she says. 'Whatever. . .' and her voice trails off and she wanders out of the room.

'Blimey,' says Maureen, 'what is she on? I'd better go and help her get ready for bed. She's so away with the fairies that I don't think she can even do that. Don't you worry, Ty, whatever my boss says, I'm not going anywhere in a hurry.'

I just bend my head over the ironing and concentrate very, very hard on getting all the creases out. I iron six shirts, five handkerchiefs, ten T-shirts and two pairs of trousers. I move on to tea towels, underpants and even socks. When there's nothing left in the house that I could possibly iron, I gather together all the books I'm going to need for the morning. And then I find an episode of *The Simpsons* on telly and I watch it without laughing once.

Doug and Maureen come and sit either side of me. 'OK, Ty, I am definitely going to stay,' says Maureen. 'Doug thinks your mum may just be a bit out of it because she had a sleeping pill in the car, so you should see a great change in her in the next few days.'

'She was a bit like this in the hospital,' I say doubtfully.

'She's been under a lot of stress,' says Doug. 'She just needs some recovery time.'

Why can't she just keep calm and carry on like me? It's not as though she was the one who was shot at, or the one who's going to have to get up in court and tell her story, or even the main person involved here anyway. Stress . . . it's just an excuse really. An excuse for being useless.

I get up and collect my pile of ironing to take upstairs.

'I'm going to bed.'

Maureen follows me up the stairs. 'I'm going to

put half a sleeping pill and a glass of water by the bed, just in case you have nightmares again.'

'Thanks, Maureen. Thanks for staying.'

She looks at me and says, 'It'll get better, Ty. This'll pass, you know.'

She's great, Maureen, but she's also police. And the police told me that Gran would be safe in her flat, and that I should go into the hospital with Dave. So I don't altogether believe what she has to say.

Mum's still asleep when I get up in the morning. Maureen makes me some toast and wishes me luck, and I trudge off down the hill. It occurs to me that last time I was properly at school – apart from my date with the head teacher, of course – I was in floods of girly tears, sobbing my heart out in Mr Henderson's smelly office. What if somehow everyone knows about that? What if there's some secret CCTV footage that has been sent to everyone's mobiles? I very nearly turn back a few times before I reach the school gate.

Brian, Jamie and Max pounce on me the minute I walk through the gates. 'Hey, Joe, good to see you back, mate.' We do a bit of high-fiving, and Brian asks, 'So, what's the story? Did they throw the book at you?'

'Nah. Carl and I have to work on a joint project together.'

Everyone has different ideas. Jamie thinks we'll be

running cricket club for year seven. Brian reckons we might be sent to some sort of boot camp for delinquent youth.

'Or maybe you'll have to scrub out the swimming pool,' suggests Max.

'With our toothbrushes?' I suggest.

The boys go silent, nudge each other and look at me. Ashley's directly ahead of us in the playground, at the centre of her group. They're all looking over at us and several have supportive arms round Ashley who is wiping away a tear.

'We heard the news, mate,' says Brian. 'What a bummer. But her parents are very strict, I hear.'

'It's always the ones with the strictest parents who are the real goers,' says Max.

'Maybe she'll be up for a secret affair?' asks Jamie. I shake my head: 'Nah, time to move on. There'll be plenty of other opportunities in this school.'

Brian sighs: 'For you, maybe, but it's a desert for some of us.'

As the bell goes for registration, I'm vaguely aware that I'm attracting quite a bit of attention. People are looking my way, pointing me out, and there's a general murmur that seems to be directed towards me. Girls are smiling, some year seven boys start clapping and cheering before being shushed by the playground supervisor.

I'm trying to ignore all the attention and just look out for Claire.

She's quite easy to spot because there're only about three girls still wearing winter uniform. Her hair is still all over her face. She looks as scared and lonely as ever, like I used to feel at St Saviour's, although I hope I wasn't such an obvious loser.

I can't imagine how I'm ever going to get people to accept that Joe could be friendly with this girl – especially when really fit girls like Lauren and Emily and Zoe from 8P are giving me a lot of glances and winks and secret smiles whenever Ashley's back is turned. I'm pathetically concerned that Joe's image shouldn't be tainted. But is Joe cool enough to give Claire a boost?

I try and catch her eye but she completely blanks me. Maybe she's not aware of my official status as Ashley's ex. When we sit down in assembly we're so close that I could almost reach out and touch her hand. I'm inching towards her, little by little, trying to make a tiny bit of skin to skin contact which no one else need see – but she moves her hand away and puts it in her pocket.

I'm almost snubbed, but, OK, it's best to be cautious. And then I remember. Ellie's race, Ellie's big, important, qualifying race was yesterday. And I didn't wish her luck and I didn't ask how it went. I've blown it.

I've totally blown it. This nice supportive family who've only been good to me must think I'm a selfish scumbag. Claire is obviously furious on her sister's behalf. And Ellie will never want to train with me again.

Assembly passes in a blur as I try and think of plausible excuses. As we leave, Claire casually takes her handkerchief out of her pocket and as she does a scrumpled piece of paper falls out. She glances at me, and I reach down and pick it up. I shove it in my pocket but I know what it's going to say. It's going to tell me that she wants nothing to do with me, and nor does Ellie.

Geography and Science pass me by. I know it all anyway. I'm trying to think what I can do, how I can make some sort of excuse. I can't think of anything.

As the bell goes for break I jump up to try and find a quiet place to face the worst and read Claire's angry words. But the science teacher says, 'Joe, you're to go straight to Mr Henderson's office.' Carl is already there, looking a lot less mutilated than he did last time I saw him. Mr Henderson keeps us waiting outside for an awkward five minutes, then calls us in. He doesn't suggest that we sit down, so we don't.

'Well,' he says. 'I appear to have been left picking up the pieces.'

I study my shoes. Carl gazes at the ceiling.

'The head teacher has some idea about you two

learning to work together. Some sort of joint project. Something that will help the school and also use your undoubted talents. He was thinking of . . . he suggested . . . something like helping with the annual five-a-side tournament that we run for local primary schools.'

That could be a laugh. Carl looks enthusiastic too.

'But that's not the sort of thing I have in mind at all,' says Mr Henderson. He opens the door to the corridor and points out a large cupboard. 'See this? Every piece of lost property we've acquired over the last three years is in here.' He opens the door to show us mounds of mouldering clothing. The stench is overwhelming. 'Your job is to sort all this out, return every bit of labelled clothing to its owner, then wash the rest so that it can be used by those disorganised creatures who forget their kit.'

Oh, for God's sake. I can see that Carl's equally unimpressed. 'You can do this while the rest of your class are having swimming lessons because I am not having either of you use the pool for the rest of the term. And when it's finished, you can tidy the equipment cupboard for me.'

That's it. I wonder if it's worth mentioning the access card, given that Ellie's never going to speak to me again.

'Um, Mr Henderson?'

'Joe?'

'I was wondering,' – I glance nervously at Carl – 'about my access card.'

'Ah yes, the famous access card. The start of all this trouble.'

He goes to his desk drawer. 'Joe, you are having your access card back, but you are specifically barred from the pool. Ellie has said that she will not continue working with you. . .'

Oh no.

'. . .unless you have the card back. She wants you to enter for some more competitions during the summer – I think she's going to talk to you about it, and now that she's all but qualified for the Paralympics next year she needs you to be able to work intensively on your own. I hardly need tell you that if there is any breach of any school rule – and that includes the most minor uniform regulations – then you will have the card taken away.'

'What about me?' asks Carl.

'What about you?'

'Can't I have one too?'

'We've been through this, Carl. If I give one to the football team, then there are so many others that I will have to give them to that the whole system will become unworkable.'

'Yes, but you don't have to give one to the rest

261

of the team. Just to me. And then Joe and I could train together.'

I'm quite impressed by Carl's cheek in making a case for himself.

'So the two of you get rewarded for your appalling behaviour, is that it?'

'No, we get to improve our sports performance. Joe, wouldn't you like to be on the football team?'

I nod. Actually I'd love to be on the football team. I've always wanted to be good at football. It was a real disappointment to me to find when I went to primary school that I was so crap compared to the boys who had dads and brothers to play with, and even though I nagged Nicki to let me join a football club it never really happened. I'm good at the stuff you can practise by yourself – keepie uppies, that sort of thing – and obviously I'm fast, but I go to pieces a bit when I play in a team.

'Well, we can work together, get you skilled up, on the team.'

Mr Henderson looks extremely unconvinced but says, 'We'll try it for a fortnight. If you two genuinely work together then we'll make it permanent – and we'll send you out to make peace in the Middle East.' Carl gawps. 'It's a joke, boy. Joe, I'm going to give you a key to the lost property cupboard – guard it with your life.'

We're just leaving the PE block and I'm wondering whether I can ask Carl if his offer was genuine, when I hear someone calling me. 'Joe! Come over here a minute!'

It's Ellie. She's heading for the running track, clipboard in hand, and Magda, her Polish helper, is standing by her side looking a bit gloomy. Ellie hands the clipboard to Magda and says, 'Can you just go and tell them that I'll be five minutes?'

Magda looks blank. 'I . . . tell?'

Ellie rolls her eyes. 'The girls' group – over there. I'll . . . be . . . five . . . minutes.'

I can just about do this in Polish. 'Girls must wait a little,' I say, and Magda flashes me a grateful smile. She walks off in the direction of a clutch of girls who must be the young sportswomen that Ellie mentors. Zoe from 8P is among them and she gives me a wave. She won the girls year eight race at the inter-schools competition, and she actually looks great in shorts. But I've got other things on my mind.

'God, that girl is annoying,' says Ellie, eyes still on Magda.

'Ellie, I'm really sorry,'

'Sorry? It's not your fault that yet again I have a useless helper. In fact, it's really helpful that you can speak her language.'

'I never wished you luck . . . or asked how you did. . .'

She grins: 'Too busy with your love life, eh? I hope it was because you were too busy training.'

I wonder what she'd say if she knew the truth. 'I have done my best with the training.'

'Anyway, I won, which is great, so I forgive you,' she says airily. 'Start training again with me tomorrow? We're celebrating at home tonight. You can come if you want.'

'Oh, great, thanks, I'd like that.' Then I remember. 'But I might not be able to. My mum's a bit . . . not very well. . .'

'Oh well, if she's feeling better then bring her along. Anyone can come. Just a little party to celebrate.'

'Thanks, Ellie.' Her shining happiness is the sort that swallows up all your worries and concerns. She's like a kind of superperson, a celebrity. Everything about her is *more*, somehow, than ordinary people. It's strange that Claire isn't like that – in fact, Claire is the opposite, somehow smaller, quieter and less of a person than everyone else.

'Oh, but one thing, Joe,' says Ellie. 'I'm going to ask you because no one else will. What on earth were you doing locked in my little sister's room for three hours?'

'I . . . er. . .'

'Claire won't tell us, and my mum is completely confused about what you might have been up to, and she's all worried that you've got bad intentions. I said I thought you had plenty of girls to choose from so it'd be pretty unlikely you'd be after Claire like that, but Mum seems to think different. Says you were in the dark.'

'We were just talking and then I was feeling a bit tired so I had a lie down on the floor. . .'

Ellie looks pretty unconvinced. 'I can't think what you were talking about. She never speaks. Or are you saying she bored you to sleep?'

'No, we were talking about school and that. She's OK to talk to. Maybe you should try talking to her a bit more often.'

I'm feeling a bit annoyed on Claire's behalf. After all, Claire seems to care so much about Ellie's feelings that she won't even speak to me, even though Ellie doesn't seem bothered at all that I forgot her race.

Ellie shrugs. 'Whatever. See you later. . .' And I have to run all the way to Maths while she goes off to the running track.

It's only as I walk home that I'm able to pull out Claire's note. There's an email address and a password, and that's it. She's kept her promise and made me an account. We can communicate wherever I am, whatever happens, whatever my name is. With Mum crumbling and Gran ill and my aunties disappeared abroad – where in the world are they? – it's a promise of continuity, of support, of friendship. I decide I am definitely going to Ellie's party tonight.

CHAPTER 22
Claire

Nicki's in the kitchen when I get home. Maureen doesn't seem to be there and I wonder nervously if she's left already. But Nic certainly seems a lot better. I can even cope with calling her Mum again. She's put on some make-up, and the radio's on for the first time since we moved into this house.

'Come and have a cup of tea,' she calls. I sit down at the kitchen table: 'Are you feeling OK?' I ask.

'Ty, darling, I'm so sorry. Did I scare you?'

I have a whole new concept of being scared. Things like horror films and getting told off at school, things that used to scare me a bit, wouldn't even register now. I'd hardly describe last night with Mum as scary compared to, say, being shot at. But the idea that I was going to be left alone with a zombie – that was pretty worrying.

'No, but you were really out of it.'

'They gave me a tablet and I hadn't eaten all day, and hospitals do my head in at the best of times. Ty, Maureen told me about what's been happening at school.'

'It's all OK now. You don't have to worry about it.'

'But I do worry about you, I do. . . I'm so sorry I've not been here for you.'

'You had to be with Gran.'

'That's not what I mean, and you know it. I've been useless since we left London.'

I'm not going to disagree. 'So you're not angry about the swimming pool thing?' She shakes her head: 'Don't make a habit of it. But Maureen explained it all to me and it does sound like these boys were being very nasty to you. Are they still? Are you being bullied?'

It's so ironic that she never asked me this when I was at St Saviour's, when I was bloody miserable every single day and she was so busy with work and everything and so happy that I was at a good school that we never talked properly at all unless it was about homework.

'No, it's fine. Everyone likes me except these few boys and it's because they're jealous.'

'And Maureen said you've been seeing a girl? But you split up?'

'Ashley. The one you liked at Top Shop. We went out a few times, but her parents said she had to chuck me because I punched Carl.'

'Are you upset?'

'No, she wasn't really my type.'

Mum looks like she's trying not to laugh. She pats my hand. 'You don't want to get too serious, anyway.'

'Not with her, anyway.'

'Not with anyone – you're only fourteen, for heaven's sake. You're still my baby.'

Huh. Outrageous. I could point out what she and my dad were doing when they were fifteen. But I won't.

'Mum, there's a party at Ellie's tonight, to celebrate because she won her big race. I'm going to go . . . you can come too if you want, and Maureen, I suppose.'

'Maureen's gone to see her boss and talk about how we're coping,' says Mum, frowning. 'I get the impression that she's worried about us.'

'Maureen's really nice – she'd only be helpful.' Christ. Am I about to be taken into care? Would Maureen do that to us?

'Sat me down and said I had to be more supportive of you, look after you better. Louise was saying the same thing, that you wouldn't have been running around the park getting involved in fights if I'd been more on the case, talked to you more, not left you so much to Gran.'

'Oh well, Lou's always like that,' I say soothingly.

In our family no one ever holds back when it comes to telling people how they could be doing things better.

Her eyes fill with tears: 'I just can't believe that there are people out there who want to kill you, Ty. You're a kid, not a gangster. What would I do without you? I love you so much.'

'I'm not going anywhere,' I say uncomfortably. She's been really together so far but she's probably not up to talking about the shooting business. Also, I suspect she might not think it was so clever to kick someone who could have had a gun twice.

'What about the party, then? Do you want to come with me?'

'It's a school night. I don't know if you should be going,' she says, which is such an Auntie Lou thing to say that I don't take it seriously.

'It won't be late. It's just a few friends round.'

'Oh, well. OK. They are a lovely family. She's fantastic, isn't she, Ellie, really inspiring.'

'She thinks you ought to get running again. Join a club or something,' I say.

'Oh. Well. I do think about it sometimes.'

I get up. 'I'm going to get changed.' And she decides she will come, and at 7.30 we're knocking on Ellie and Claire's door again.

Ellie's mum looks happy to see my mum and gives

her a hug and asks about Gran. She's obviously not so sure about me, although she asks about my ribs. I can't wait to see Claire in her dark little den again. But we're going to have to be clever about it.

When I get out into the garden I think it'll be possible to disappear in this crowd. There are tons of people here, and kids running around all over the place. People are drinking beer, the barbeque is sizzling and someone's set up a karaoke machine in the kitchen. It's a proper party. Mum looks a bit nervous, but Janet introduces her to some of Ellie's mates from the gym and I can see the old Nicki, the flirty, funny, have-a-laugh girl coming out again. Give her an hour and a few drinks and she'll be belting out 'Dancing Queen'.

It's hard to spot Claire. She seems to fade into the background so easily, like a lizard or a moth. It takes a good ten minutes to find her, sitting in the garden being talked at by an old lady. I wait patiently until the old lady trots off and then Claire looks over and smiles and says, 'Hi, you.'

'Can we go and talk?' I ask. She shakes her head: 'My mum said I should stay down here.'

'Oh. It's too noisy. Where can we go?'

She thinks, then says, 'There's always Ellie's room. That's not upstairs. She only said not upstairs.'

It's funny. With Ashley, I knew where I was. I didn't

like her, but I did fancy her. The evidence was completely unarguable.

But with Claire, I don't know. I care about her. I think about her . . . but not in, you know, the sort of way I'd think about Ashley in bed at night. I daydream about looking after Claire, and her looking after me, about being close and talking and sharing and soppy stuff like that.

If I see her at school, I don't fancy her at all – she's too much of a freak – and I try not to remember that time she was cutting herself because being turned on by that is just wrong. I know it's wrong. I'm not some sort of perv. I just thought for a misguided second that it was kind of interesting.

But sometimes, when I remember that day she took off her shirt, I feel a bit stirred up, and right now, looking at her big blue eyes, the prospect of being alone with her is very attractive indeed. I wish I could just be consistent.

'We'll have to be really quiet,' she says.

We wander out to the hallway and miraculously there's no one there. Claire pushes the door to Ellie's room and we slip inside. But it's hopeless. It's noisy, boiling hot, even when I peel off my hoodie; there's the constant sound of people passing through the front door and, worst of all, anyone in the front garden can see us through the window. I'm beginning to feel breathless. 'We can't talk here,' I say, 'it's no good.'

So we scuttle up the stairs, hoping that no one notices. Once in her room Claire wedges the chair against the door again. I pull the curtains. And we sit in the dark on her cushions and I put my arm around her and I feel about as happy as I've ever felt.

'So, thank you for making the email address,' I say.

'It's nothing. You could have done it for yourself.'

'I thought you were upset with me because I forgot Ellie's race.'

She snorts: 'I wish I could have forgotten about it. We've had nothing but race, race, race for weeks. And now she's won and now Magda's quit, we'll hear nothing but Paralympic training for the next year, and Mum and Dad will always be going away, and everyone will be running around Ellie as usual.'

'Magda's quit?'

She chuckles: 'They always do. Couldn't take being bossed around.'

I like being bossed around by Ellie, but I can see that it might not be great if you aren't being trained by her.

'Aren't you pleased she won?'

'Pleased for her, but not for me.'

I touch her arm as softly as possible. 'Are you OK? No more . . . you know. . .'

'No . . . but it's not always easy. I did try and ring you the other day but there was no answer.'

She's wearing a kind of floaty tunic thing and leggings – it's nicer than her usual over-sized shirts but it still swamps her. I push her sleeves up and look at her arms. At least there are no new plasters, although the latest cut, the one I saw her do, looks pink and sore. I stroke her arm with my finger. 'I'm sorry. I was away.'

And I tell her about Gran and the hospital and Gran waking up and coming out of the door with Dave. And the blood, and the corridors, and kicking Doug twice. And how the worst bit was afterwards, alone under the blanket.

And she listens, and she takes my hand and she asks, 'Who are they, these people who want to kill you?'

I've been thinking a lot about that myself in the last few days. 'It's the family of one of the guys that was in the park that day. I think they are professional criminals, you know, real gangsters. I don't know who they are.'

'And they want to kill you because you saw their son do the killing?'

'I suppose. . .' I think about what I actually did see. 'I think he must have been the leader, the one who started it all. I mean, I don't actually know which one it was that's threatening me. Unless. . .'

'Unless what?'

'Well, Nathan. He's the brother of my friend Arron. It was Arron that I followed to the park. And Nathan told me to keep quiet or else. But I don't think Nathan's part of a family of criminals. I mean, I know the family, I'd know if they were criminals, wouldn't I?'

And if they were, they'd be living in a big house somewhere, not in a flat on an estate in Hackney. And you'd have thought Nathan would want me to be a witness because I'm doing it for Arron. I mean, I'm doing it for Gran and I'm doing it for me and I'm doing it for other people too, but if it wasn't for Arron I wouldn't be doing it at all.

But I remember the smell of Nathan, the sour-sweet smell of sweat and fear as he pushed his face into mine, and I'm not sure. Maybe Nathan would know a hitman. He certainly knew where my gran lived.

Claire says, 'Can't the police tell you more? Now that this has happened? It doesn't seem fair that they know more than you.'

'None of it is fair. . .'

I'm not all that sure I want to know any more. 'Let's talk about something else, Claire.'

Claire leans against me: 'Is it true you've finished with Ashley?'

'She finished with me.'

'Is it true her parents told her to chuck you?'

I'm torn. I don't want to tell Claire about the knife. I don't want to tell her about what Ashley said. It's really embarrassing, and it might put her off me if she knows what I've nearly been up to with her enemy. She's probably going to think I'm some sort of opportunistic sex maniac, which wouldn't be totally inaccurate. And it is true about the parents. It just isn't the whole truth. But I need to practise this whole truth thing, and Claire's my best listener. So I tell her everything.

She's shocked, eyes wide, but laughing as well: 'I can't believe she said that to you. Do you think she says that every time to every boy she goes out with?'

'No. . .' Of course not. 'Well, maybe.'

'Pathetic. She's pathetic. What a fake. Although she's not wrong about the knife.'

'No, I was stupid and wrong to carry one again. But I did feel less scared.'

'Again?' she asks.

'I used to carry one in London. Lots of people do there.'

'Yeah, and lots of people get stabbed. Do you watch the news?' she says. Then she says, 'It's a deal: I don't cut myself, you don't carry a knife.'

'No knives for anyone,' I say, and wonder if I can keep this deal.

'The thing is, you can fight to defend yourself,

and you can run away. You didn't need a knife in that hospital, did you?'

'If I'd had one I might have killed the wrong guy.'

'There you go.'

I'm feeling so much better and so fond of her that, as I stroke her hair away from her forehead, I want to kiss her, but I don't think I should. It's so unclear what sort of a friendship we have, and I'm worried that she's only about twelve. But she leans over to me and says soft and shy, 'Let's seal it with a kiss,' and the next thing I know we're in the tightest hug possible, and my heart's done a massive flip.

'I think you're incredibly nice,' I say, and realise immediately that I've picked the wrong word.

'Nice?' she says. I don't think she's very impressed. I'm flustered and all confused because I've never felt like this before – so close, so equal, so caring and cared about. Tenderness kind of sums it up, but I feel shy just thinking about it. Arron never gave me instructions for this.

'I think you're great,' I say. And then, because it's bothering me, 'How old are you, anyway?'

'I'll be fourteen on November fifth.' She's exactly a year younger than me. That's fine.

'That's amazing . . . it's my birthday too, except I'll be fifteen. But the police have changed it to the fifth of September.'

'It must be horrible to have even your birthday changed.'

Mum always used to take me to see the fireworks for my birthday. Gran would never come because she thought Guy Fawkes night was an anti-Catholic celebration, but Mum said it was all about anti-terrorism and just a bit of fun anyway. I suppose we can go to the fireworks this year, but it won't be the same.

I clutch at her hand. 'Will you talk to me at school now it's OK with Ashley?'

'I suppose so, but people will think it's very strange. No one's friends with me, and everyone wants to be your friend. And Ashley's such a bitch . . . you have no idea, Joe, she's so horrible. She likes to control all the girls. She told them that I was a freak and they all started to be mean to me.'

I don't like to tell Claire that the way she looked and acted might have contributed a little to her freak status. I believe her when she says that Ashley bullies her.

'I don't care what anyone says,' I say, and I hope I'm telling the truth. I kiss her again, really slowly, just to make sure. She smells of soap and she tastes sweet and minty. She's lovely. 'You're very special,' I say, but I say it in Portuguese, so she just laughs at me.

And then – damn and blast – there's a pounding on

her door. Her mother's come to check up on her and she's found just what she'd forbidden. Claire's blushing and panicky as she dislodges the chair from the door, and I'm totally embarrassed.

'Claire!' says Janet. She's not happy. Her lips are pursed together. 'What's going on?'

'Nothing,' I say, jumping away from Claire, who goes pink and says, 'We just wanted to talk.' She's so unconvincing that even I don't believe her.

'You could have talked downstairs. . . I don't think it's very suitable to be sitting here in the dark,' Janet says.

I get up. 'It was just very noisy, Mrs Langley. We didn't mean to cause any problems. . . I'm going to go. Ummm . . . thank you for inviting me.' And I take to the stairs without looking back.

I head for the garden. I need to find Mum and get home before it gets too late – I'm still nervy about walking around when it's dark. It's chilly when I get out there and I remember my hoodie, still in Ellie's room. I'd better get it.

But when I open the door to her room, there's someone in there. Two people, sitting on Ellie's bed. One's a bloke . . . I think it's Alistair, Ellie's trainer, the one who looks like he should be in Boyzone. And he's kissing my mum.

CHAPTER 23
It'll Do For Now

Of course this isn't the first time. I've met an unexpected visitor at the breakfast table once or twice, and when she's seeing someone I spend even more time than usual staying with Gran or downstairs with Mr Patel or in my room. It's not like I've never seen her kiss anyone, obviously.

But she's never got off with anyone at a party that I've been at before, probably because the only kind of parties we've been to together were things like Great-Aunt Edith's funeral, or trampolining at the leisure centre for someone's seventh birthday.

'Don't mind me,' I say, reaching for my hoodie while they jump apart. Alistair obviously thinks I'm a complete clod and says, 'Look, mate, could you just give us a minute?' And Mum pretends we're all at some polite tea party and says, 'Oh, Alistair, I don't know if you've met my son T— Joe.'

'Son? Cho?' says Alistair.

'No, Joe,' she says.

I can see him looking from her to me and back again and trying to do some quick maths in his head so I say, 'It's OK, she is about the age that she looks,' adding meanly, 'which still makes her about five years older than you.'

'Joe!' says Mum. I can see she's wishing we still had our cosy Nicki 'n' Ty relationship when she'd quite often pass me off as her little brother.

'I'm going,' I say. 'Will I see you later? Or not?'

'Can I give you a lift?' asks Alistair. I can see my mum doesn't know what to do, but she doesn't want to send me home alone on a bus while she's swanning around on the back of Alistair's flash motorbike or whatever, and she says, 'That's so kind of you, Alistair – we'd both like a lift, wouldn't we, Joe?'

So I scrunch up in the back of Alistair's motor, which turns out to be a grotty Ford Fiesta, and they sit in the front talking about Ellie's training and Ellie's gym and how Michelle used to love running until she unfortunately got pregnant and blah, blah, blah, blah, blah, blah. Both of them pretend I'm not there and so do I.

By the time we get home I'm in the foulest of foul moods, and I stomp into the house and slam the door while Mum takes her time saying goodbye to Alistair at the front gate.

Maureen's back and she looks a bit startled when she sees the expression on my face.

'Are you OK?' she asks. 'Where have you been?'

'None of your business,' I say rudely and crash on up to my bedroom. I'm expecting Mum to follow me right away so I can tell her what I think of her, but she stays downstairs for about an hour and I can hear her and Maureen chatting and laughing together, probably about me.

I get ready for bed, do my Maths homework with the book propped up on my knees, then lie in the dark and remember how it felt to hold Claire in my arms. She doesn't seem too young and small any more. She's not a freak at all. She's pretty and delicate and her lips felt so soft and her skin was warm and smooth. I'm just moving on to imagine what might happen next time . . . and then my mum barges into my room and switches the light on.

'Oi! Go away! This room is private!' I protest.

'You've got no secrets from me,' she says. Huh. That's what she thinks. I don't bother to reply.

'Are you OK, darling? I'm sorry about what

happened.'

She doesn't sound sorry at all.

'You should be ashamed of yourself,' I say.

'Well, I was a bit embarrassed. But he's a really nice guy, and guess what, Ty? I think I've got a job!'

'What job?' I ask suspiciously.

'Well, Ellie asked if I'd think about being her helper because she's fed up with the sort of girls she gets usually and she'd like someone a bit more on her wavelength. And Alistair thought it was a good idea too.'

'And that was him giving you your final interview, I suppose?'

'Oh come on, Ty, it was a party and we were just getting to know each other. We were having a chat and then he gave me a quick kiss. It was just unfortunate that you walked in just then. He's asked me out for a drink tomorrow night. Where were you anyway? I couldn't see you anywhere.'

Huh. That is classified information. I'm thinking about this idea of her helping Ellie. Mum'd be hanging around my school all the time. She'd get to know Mr Henderson. She'd be there when I was doing my training. It's a terrible idea.

Also it's totally wrong for my Mum. A helper has to look after the other person, doesn't she – help with things like showers and getting changed and so on? I would say

I'm uniquely placed to judge that she'll be unsuited to that kind of role.

'What do you mean, you could be Ellie's helper? That's not what you do. You're a qualified legal secretary and you want to be a solicitor.'

'Yes, but it'll do for now, won't it? And it could be interesting, and I like Ellie a lot.'

There's something incredibly sad about my ambitious, hard-working, clever mother saying, 'It'll do for now.'

'She'll boss you around all the time.'

'No, she won't.'

'And you'll have to go away with her when she has training camps and competitions and then I'll be left here on my own.'

'Janet said you could stay with them. She really loved the idea, thought it would take a big strain off their family.'

I think she means Janet loved the idea of Ellie having Mum as a helper. I can't see her being thrilled about me as a house guest. Presumably this invitation was issued before she discovered me in Claire's room. But if she would have me to stay, it'd be fantastic to spend more time with Claire, not to mention the excellent food in that house . . . and the Wii. . .

'Do what you want. But you're not coming to my

training sessions.' And I cover my head with the duvet to indicate that I've had enough of her today.

'It's not all about you, you know,' she says as she switches off the light and shuts the door.

In the morning, Carl's there when I get to the fitness suite. "Hello, mate," he says, sounding a bit nervous. Neither of us is quite sure how to play this, but both of us want to hang on to the access cards. So we work out a programme for him based on the one Ellie did for me. As we're getting changed afterwards, he suggests that I play football with his mates at lunchtime so he can give me some tips. I'm not sure though, because I'm wary of Jordan and Louis, and because my ribs may not be ready for football yet.

'Don't worry about Jordan and Louis, they'll behave themselves,' he says. And then he adds, 'And they'll keep their distance from you anyway because of you-know-what.'

'What?' I ask.

'What?' he echoes.

'What's you-know-what?' I ask.

'Your . . . you know . . . knife.'

'What knife?'

'They said you threatened them with a knife at the park one day.'

My heart is racing but my face is calm.

'You what? Christ, dem boys have been watching too much telly,' I say. My voice seems to be sliding back to East London.

'They said it.'

'Nah . . . I didn't need no knife to scare them off. You know, Carl, they act all brave but they ain't got no bottle.' *Bo'ul*, I pronounce it, and it gives me a flash of Arron's face as I say it, Arron saying, 'He ain't got no bo'ul,' and meaning me – 'They made it up to make themselves sound like big men but, you know, I just had to show them this . . .' I turn my hand into a fist, 'and they ran off, peein' their pants.'

He laughs a bit nervously and I think I've got away with it.

'Don't worry about it,' he says. 'See you at lunchtime.'

But I do worry about it. If this story gets to the head teacher then Joe Andrews will be excluded from school and exterminated by Doug. Then Tyler Lewis will probably be charged with murder. Because if they think I'm regularly waving a knife around, then they'll believe the people who say I was involved that day in another park far, far away. I think and think about what I can do to stop anyone talking, but I can't come up with an answer short of mass murder and obviously that's not the way to go.

Claire and I manage to pair up in Science and I forget all my worries. She's very serious about the work, and it's sweet the way she scrunches her face up when she looks at the test tube to read measurements out for me to write down. She's clipped her hair back from her face and she's wearing summer uniform, her arms covered with a cardigan. She's beginning to look normal. I scribble a note in faint pencil on my table of measurements: *I like your hair like that*, and she blushes and spends ages rubbing it out.

I whisper to her, 'Was your mum very cross?' and she nods and then writes another pencil note which says, *It's OK, I think.*

When we've finished and are clearing up, I tell her about Mum's plan to be Ellie's helper. She says, 'I know, they were talking about it last night. Ellie's really pleased. She thinks your mum will be great.'

'I don't know . . . it's not really her sort of thing.'

She looks at the test tube she's drying and says, 'Mum said you'll come and stay sometimes.' And when she looks up, we've both got silly grins on our faces.

'No talking,' shouts the teacher, and we get ready for Maths. It's the first time I've ever been sad to finish a Science lesson.

Playing football with Carl's lot goes well at

lunchtime. I take Brian and his mates along with me and they join in too. Carl mixes up the teams so we're not obliterated. He offers some good tips – 'You're faster than anyone on the pitch but you need to think about passing the ball. Your problem, mate, is that you forget you've got anyone else on your team.' – and I even score a goal, so I'm feeling pretty pleased with myself when we hear the bell go for the end of lunch.

But Ashley is waiting for me as I come off the football pitch. 'Walk with me?' she says, and I know it's an order.

'OK.' I can see people all around us noticing that we're together and nudging each other.

'How are you?' she asks.

'I'm fine.'

'Not missing me then?'

'I didn't say that.'

She's got her full warpaint on today and I don't fancy her at all, thank goodness.

'So . . . are you seeing anyone else then?'

'Give me a chance, Ash, we've not been split up for five minutes.' And anyway, what business is it of yours?

'Because I saw you with that retard Claire in Science.'

What? I can't believe it. 'I . . . you . . . what?'

'I saw you. Smiling at her . . . touching her hand. . .'

Bloody hell. 'And so? Your point is?' I say, cold and distant.

'Well, it doesn't look good for me, does it, if you split up with me and immediately start going out with the dorkiest girl in the year. I want you to keep away from that minger.'

I stop still and say, 'You can't talk about her like that. You shouldn't talk about anyone like that.' People are jostling all around us and I'm sure some of them are listening.

'Oooh,' she says, 'so you do like her? I didn't really believe it.'

'She's my friend. And you don't have any right to tell me who to be friends with.'

'I can tell you that she's a weirdo. And I can tell you that if she ever took her cardigan off, you wouldn't like what you'd see underneath.' And she laughs, a really nasty, sneery laugh.

'You bitch!' I say. I want to hit her. My hand flies up and I'm ready to lash out.

Then Brian bashes into me and says, 'Steady, mate.' And I come to my senses and lower my hand.

And there's a crowd of people all around and Ashley's laughing and saying, 'If you want to know any more about your little friend, just come and ask me, any time.' And I hear a squeaking sob and Claire's running away, pushing through the crowd to escape into the playground.

CHAPTER 24
Finding Claire

Should I run after her? I'm tempted to go off to my next lesson, let her recover on her own and not give the gossips anything more to chew on. But when do I ever do the right thing? Instead, I push my way through the crowds streaming into their classrooms then sprint after her and, being pretty fast, I catch up with her in the middle of the playground.

That's the middle of the deserted playground, overlooked by about fifty classrooms all packed with people.

'Come on, we can still get to PE,' I shout.

I thought she'd be crying but she isn't. She's white-faced and her fists are pressing to her mouth. She's looking from side to side, like a mouse cornered by a cat, desperate to escape. She gasps, 'Go away,' in what would be a fierce whisper if it hadn't had a hiccup in the middle that sounded like another sob.

'I'm not going away. Tell you what, I'll take you to the nurse. But we need to go inside right now.' And I jerk my head towards the watching windows, grab her elbow and pull her towards the door.

She gives a little yelp. And then she follows me inside and I can see the tears coming so I search my pockets for a handkerchief, but of course I haven't got one. I nobly offer my tie instead. She shakes her head and pulls a tissue out of her cardigan pocket.

A teacher comes out into the corridor and asks us what we think we're doing. 'Claire isn't feeling very well so I'm taking her to the nurse,' I say.

'Do you even know where the nurse's office is? Because it's not along here,' she says, looking curiously at Claire.

'Yes, we're just going.' And we walk along the corridor to the flight of stairs that leads to the sick room.

'Look, it's OK, it's OK,' I say as we get there. 'Ashley's only shown herself up as a complete bitch. No one knows anything about you. You have nothing to worry about.'

'I. . .' but she can't say anything.

I knock on the door and tell the nurse that Claire

has a migraine. She takes one look and puts her arm around Claire. 'I'll come and see you later,' I say. 'I hope you're feeling better soon.'

I sprint to the PE department. I should be swimming but I'm actually going to be sorting vile-smelling lost property. Carl's already knee-deep in ancient knickers and crusty shorts.

'Blimey,' he says, 'what was all that about in the playground? You looked like you were fighting her.'

"What? You couldn't see us from here."

"Mate, the whole school was watching," he says. "We were all late for PE. What's the story?"

'Women,' I say. 'You know what they're like.'

'Too right,' says Carl, and we sort the smelly piles into labelled and non-labelled while discussing Man Utd's prospects for the next season which, frankly, is exactly the kind of conversation I need right now, and by the end of the period I feel like Carl's my main man.

I want to make a swift exit, but they're all waiting for me. Lauren, Emily, Dani and Becca. Only Ashley's nowhere to be seen.

'What happened?' asked Becca. 'What happened to Claire? What were you doing in the playground? Had she had . . . you know . . . some kind of mental breakdown?'

I shrug. 'She wasn't feeling well. Had to go to the nurse. Migraine.'

'Yes, but what was it all about?' says Becca. 'Why were you shouting at her?'

'You're not seeing her, are you?' asks Lauren in a way that suggests that only someone very strange would have anything to do with Claire.

'Maybe she's got some sort of weird crush on you?' suggests Dani.

'What was Ashley going on about?' says Emily.

'Look, it's not for me to say what's going on in Ashley's mind. First she chucks me, and then she bitches about Claire because we happen to be friends.'

'Friends?' says Emily, like she can't believe her ears.

'Yup. Friends. I do athletics training with her sister, right. I know the whole family.'

'Yes, but *Claire*. . .'

I'm worried that I'm going to start blushing. 'There's nothing wrong with Claire. She's just a bit shy.'

As soon as I can shake them off I go back to the nurse's room. But Claire's not there. 'She left about five minutes ago,' says the nurse. 'What a shame, she could have done with someone to see her home. She was in a bit of a state.'

'You didn't ring her mum?'

'At work. Claire said she was OK to walk home.'

I don't think this is a good idea. What if Ashley's lying in wait for her? I'd follow her right away but I have to meet Ellie at the running track. As I walk there my mind's on Claire. She'll go home, no one will be there and . . . oh, my God.

I sprint up to Ellie, yelling, 'Keys, Ellie, keys. I need your house keys.'

'What on earth. . .?' says Ellie, but she fishes her keys out of her bag and gives them to me.

'I'm going to run to your house. Can you get there really quickly too? It's Claire . . . she's in danger. . . '

'You what?' says Ellie, but I'm running. I'm running down the High Street and around the corner. I'm bashing into people and swearing, and running across roads without looking properly so cars screech to a stop and swerve to avoid me.

And I'm at the top of their road and I'm running down and I'm praying – to Jesus, to Mary, whoever – that I'm going to get there in time.

And I run up Ellie's wheelchair ramp and I fumble with her set of keys and then I leave the door open so she can get in.

And I run up the stairs, two at a time and I get to Claire's door. Of course she's blocked it with a chair, so I kick and push and shout, 'Claire! It's me! Let me in!'

But she's done it really well and it takes an

almighty kick to finally topple the chair away.

I slam into the room and fall over the chair – damn – it's so bloody dark in here. But I know where to find Claire. I drag myself up and feel my way round her bed, while my eyes adjust to the darkness.

'Claire? Are you here? Are you OK?' Far, far away I hear Ellie calling me. 'Joe? What's going on?'

But I've found what I'm looking for. Claire is sitting propped up against the bed but she's fallen forward so her nose is touching her knees. She's not speaking – is she even conscious? – and when I touch her arm my hand feels wet and sticky.

I leap for the curtains and tug them apart so fiercely that the whole lot clatters to the ground. And I can see then that I feared right – she's cut herself, but it's not a neat, tidy little cut like usual, it's a big angry slash which is pumping blood over her skin and shirt.

'Ellie! Call an ambulance!' I yell.

Christ almighty. I need to do something fast. I take the knife from the floor and grab the sheet from her bed. I cut a strip of fabric from the sheet and loop it around her arm, just under and then over the wound, lifting her arm up as high as I can. I need a stick – the only thing I can find is a pencil which isn't really long enough, but I wind the sheet around it and then turn it around and around so the sheet tightens on her arm. I'm so scared that she's going to die. I'm screaming, 'Claire, wake up, Claire, wake up,' and her eyes flicker open and she stares at me as if I'm a stranger. And we sit there like that, waiting for help, with me concentrating all my effort on winding the sheet as tight as possible.

Ambulances come quicker here than they do in London. The door crashes open again and there're two paramedics, a man and a woman, who run over to Claire and push me out of the way. One takes the pencil from my hand. And I can't bear to look any more and I stumble down the stairs to Ellie, who gasps when she sees that my shirt's soaked in blood.

'Oh my God, what's happened? Did someone attack her? How did you know?'

I shake my head. 'No one attacked her. She did it herself. She cuts herself when she's upset, and she was very upset.'

'She does what? Oh, my God. Is she all right?'

'I don't know. She opened her eyes.'

One of the paramedics comes downstairs and says, 'Who put on the tourniquet? Was it you?'

'Yes.'

'Good job. When did you do it?'

'About ten minutes before you arrived.'

'Well done. We'll bring her downstairs now and we'll take her to hospital. Can one of you come with us?'

It should be Ellie really, but I'm not sure how it'll work with the wheelchair. She says, 'You go Joe, and I'll ring my dad and see what's happening about the boys. Mum's at the hospital already – that's where she works – general surgical.'

They bring Claire down the stairs on a stretcher and we get into the ambulance. Ellie shoves a jacket of her dad's into my hands and I put it on – it's a huge, smelly fleece thing but it covers the blood and it warms me up because although it's a hot summer's day I'm feeling cold and shivery.

We speed through the streets with the siren blaring and I'm remembering the ambulance I called to the park that day. The ambulance I never saw. The ambulance I didn't wait for. And I'm holding Claire's hand and I'm saying the Hail Mary in my head, because if it worked a miracle for Gran it might work one for Claire as well.

And we're in casualty, and Ellie must have got hold of her mum already because she's waiting there for us in her nurse's uniform, which reminds me a bit of Arron's mum, and she doesn't even speak to me, but she grabs Claire's hand and says, 'It's all right, darling, it's all right. Mum's here now, it's all right.'

They disappear down the corridor and I don't really know what to do, so I just sit down in a corner and wait.

And I see Ellie and her dad arrive, but they go straight past without seeing me and get taken off somewhere.

I suppose I should just go home but I don't seem to be able to move. I wish I could call up my gran to come and look after me. After a bit I think about Mum saying, 'It'll do for now,' and I think, well, sometimes you have to compromise. And I send her a text: *pls Nic cm n gt me, at hsptl, a&e Ty*.

Her first text says, *wtf*? And then she sends another, *omg r u OK*? And then she sends another, *on way*. She and Alistair arrive about twenty minutes later – I must have interrupted their big date. She spots me right away.

'Are you OK? What happened? Did someone attack you?'

Alistair looks a bit bemused, given that I am pretty obviously unharmed.

I shake my head. 'No, I'm fine. It's Claire, you know. Ellie's sister.'

'What happened to her?'

But I can't say. And Mum sees it and she gives me a hug, and we just sit there for a bit with her arms around me until Alistair says, 'There's Ellie. Hey, Ellie, over here.'

Ellie comes over and she's obviously a bit surprised to see Alistair, and she's looking from Mum to him and back again and working out what he's doing there. I don't think she's all that delighted.

She leans forward: 'Joe, Claire's all right. They stopped the bleeding. They're stitching it up. She's got to stay overnight, but she'll recover. They say you might have saved her life with that tourniquet.'

'Oh,' I say. 'Good. Is she awake? Will you say hi from me?'

But Ellie shakes her head and says, 'She's asleep and they'll keep her asleep for some time. You might be able to come and see her tomorrow.'

So Alistair takes us home in his Ford Fiesta, and when we're in the car, Mum asks me, 'However did you know how to make a tourniquet? You've never even done a first aid course.'

I answer, 'I watched Arron's mum do it once.'

She's satisfied with that because Arron's mum is a nurse and I did spend a lot of time at their house. And it was true what I said.

But if I'd been telling the whole truth I would have said a bit more. And this is what I would have said: 'I watched Arron's mum do it once. I watched her that day after we ran out of the park. I watched her that day I stabbed Arron.'

CHAPTER 25
Ashley's Story

Alistair isn't the complete waste of space he looks. At home, he makes me a cup of horribly sweet tea and says I have to drink it for shock. Then he looks in our fridge, which is empty as usual, and drives to Tesco to stock up. When he comes back, he cooks stir-fry chicken and noodles and opens a bottle of wine for him and Mum. I'm feeling a lot more friendly towards him as I eat, although he should realise that the way to my Mum's heart isn't through feeding her.

She's already run me a bath and I'm having supper in my pyjamas. Maureen's not here – there's a note which says, 'Had to go, called out on urgent job elsewhere. Your gran is doing well. See you soon.' I'm kind of grateful she didn't see me covered in blood.

Mum pushes the noodles around on her plate and then goes and looks at my school uniform. She's got a look on her face like she's going to throw up.

'God, what on earth happened? There's so much blood here – what the hell did she look like?' I don't want to think about that, and I think she realises because she doesn't ask me any more.

'Ellie never talks about her sister,' says Alistair. 'She comes along to training sometimes. Just sits there in the corner reading, never gets involved. Poor kid, she must have been in a terrible state.'

Mum's still looking at the clothes. 'The shirt doesn't matter, you've got plenty, and I think the stains will come out of the blazer if we put it in to wash now – good thing it's black – but the tie is ruined.' She holds it up – the grey and blue stripes are splattered with dark brown. 'We'll get a new one tomorrow. You may as well take the day off school, get over the shock and tell me what happened properly.' And I nod and say, 'Yeah,' and duck when she tries to give me a kiss. Luckily there's still a sleeping pill by my bed, so I know I can avoid bad dreams.

But I'm up early as usual and get ready for my gym session. I'm not giving anyone a chance to take my access card away; I'd rather not wait and see if Alistair is still here to cook us breakfast, and I'm not up for a heart-to-heart with Mum about Claire. I'll go to school, I reckon, and then I'll swing by the hospital and hopefully Mum will be out with Alistair again tonight. And maybe she'll overlook that I skipped the debrief.

The blazer looks fine, I have a clean shirt, but the tie is no good. I finger the key to the lost property cupboard – there are plenty of old, unlabelled ties there. I sneak one out on the way to the changing room. Now no one will know a thing about what happened yesterday.

Carl and I have a good training session. We're competitive and we set targets which push us both further. It's working well, I think, this restorative justice scheme. I'm really feeling OK, considering what happened yesterday. In fact, when I think about Ellie telling me that I might have saved Claire's life I feel really chuffed with myself. Surely, saving someone's life is such a great thing to have done that it counts against other bad stuff? I can't be such a bad person after all; sometimes I get it just right.

This good feeling lasts all the way to registration. I'm there on time, properly dressed, ready for the day ahead. I'm talking to Brian about our football match, getting my books together for French. Ashley ignores me and no one else asks about Claire. They don't know. Maybe no one will ever find out. I hope not – Claire would find it so humiliating to be gossiped about. For a moment I feel sick when I think about what it would be like if all the bitchy girls knew that she was cutting herself.

Then Mr Hunt comes into the classroom, looks around the room and says, 'Joe Andrews, Ashley Jenkins, straight to the head teacher.'

We walk there together in silence. She's looking nervous, thoughtful. I don't feel I have anything to worry about. I'm the hero of this particular episode and she's the villain. I saved Claire's life. I did something good. We reach the door of her mother's office.

And then she turns to me and says, 'You better back up everything I say.'

'What?'

'Don't contradict me. Don't tell Mr Naylor what I said about Claire. Or I'll have Jordan and Louis down here quicker than you can say . . .' she gives me a flickering smile, 'knife.'

Oh, my God. Oh, Jesus. And we go into the office and she says, 'Hi Mum, we're here to see the head teacher.'

Mr Naylor is seated at his desk and gestures for us to sit down opposite him. I'm keeping a wary eye on Ashley. 'Good morning, Mr Naylor,' she says, all demure. I mumble something.

'I'm sure you both know why you're here,' says Mr Naylor. 'The very shocking news about Claire Langley in your class.'

'I don't know, I'm sorry, Mr Naylor,' says Ashley. She lies like an expert. I close my eyes and pray that he will be discreet. But no.

'Claire slashed her wrist yesterday afternoon. She lost a lot of blood and had to be rushed to hospital. Thankfully she is now making a good recovery.'

He makes it sound like she was trying to kill herself. I have to say something.

'She didn't slash her wrist . . . she just cut herself.'

Mr Naylor and Ashley both look at me like I'm mad. I shut up.

'Claire's parents spoke to me this morning and I want to find out exactly what was happening in the lunch break and afterwards yesterday – the period, Joe, when you were seen acting aggressively towards Ashley here, and then straight afterwards were witnessed by half the school shouting at Claire and manhandling her in the playground.'

Eh? 'No . . . it wasn't like that,' I say, but I don't sound very convincing, even to myself.

Ashley says, 'Mr Naylor, I've known Claire for years. She's a really sweet girl, not very confident . . . you know . . . she's quite young. I noticed Joe had his eye on her and I thought that was totally wrong. I know him and what he's like. I wanted to protect Claire from him . . . from what he gets up to. So I told him to stay away from her . . . from my friend. And he didn't like it and he called me a bitch and I thought he was going to hit me.'

'I . . . I . . . never hit you. . .'

'Only because Brian told you not to. Anyway, I think Claire overheard and got a bit upset. She's never had a boy interested in her before. I think she was really easy prey for Joe. Joe was angry with me and I was scared. And she ran away and he chased her. I don't know what happened after that. I felt a bit upset and I went to the girls' loo to . . . to recover. . .'

She should get an Oscar. Even I am beginning to be taken in by her. I don't know what to do. . . She's twisting everything, she's lying, but I can't risk Jordan and Louis telling about the knife.

Mr Naylor says, 'What do you mean, Ashley, what Joe gets up to? I know it's embarrassing, but it's important to get these things out in the open.'

Old perv. I know what he's hoping for, and Ashley gives it all she's got.

'We went out for a bit and at first I thought he was great but. . .' she wipes away a tear, 'he wanted too much. Too much, too soon. And he's very forceful – pushy – in getting his own way. I had to finish with him. I was a bit scared.'

Oh my God. What is she accusing me of? Forceful? Pushy?

'Is this true, Joe?'

Is what true? 'I . . . I . . . I didn't think I was doing

anything wrong. Ashley . . . she said her parents made her chuck me because of what happened in the swimming pool. . .'

Now why did I have to remind him of that?

'Ah, yes. You haven't had a very happy start at Parkview, have you? It's probably very different from what you're used to,' says Mr Naylor, like I'm a Neanderthal caveman or something. 'Now, Claire's mother backs up what Ashley's been saying here. She tells me she's been very worried because you've spent hours on end locked in Claire's bedroom in the dark with her, and she's also worried that you might have been trying to pressurise her into something she wasn't ready for.'

Ashley's glaring at me.

'Claire's my friend,' I say. 'A really good friend. My best friend. I wasn't pressurising her . . . I saved her life yesterday. Didn't her mum mention that?'

'She was very perturbed that you seemed to know that Claire had been regularly cutting herself yet had not sought help for her. She even suggested that you might have been involved somehow with this . . . this mutilation.'

'I saved her life. . . I would never do anything bad to her.'

'Joe, half the school saw you shouting at her and

pushing her around in the playground. I have a report here from the deputy head. She says Claire seemed terrified of you.'

'No . . . really . . . I was just trying to help her. . . I took her to the nurse. Ask her . . . she'll say I was being nice. . .'

Mr Naylor turns to Ashley. 'Ashley, thank you very much for coming here today. I am sorry if this has been difficult for you and I can assure you that we will do everything possible to protect you from aggressive behaviour in the future.'

This doesn't sound good. I try again.

'Why don't you talk to Claire?' I plead. 'She'll tell you I wasn't doing anything bad to her.'

'In due course I will, I am sure. Now Ashley, if you go back to class I will talk to Joe alone.'

As Ashley leaves she shoots me a glance that makes it very obvious that the news that I've been spending time with Claire while officially still with her did not go unnoticed.

'Joe,' says Mr Naylor, 'bullying girls, bullying girls for sex, that is really the lowest of the low. Boys who don't understand that no means no are a danger to society.'

'But I didn't. . .'

'I am going to have to think very hard about how to deal with this. I shall need to speak to Ashley's parents and also Claire's. I am going to suspend you for the rest of the day and . . . is your mother now returned?'

'Yes.'

'I would like to see both of you tomorrow morning, eleven o'clock. Now leave. And try not to get into any trouble between now and tomorrow. Do you think you can manage that?'

I nod – yes, you sarcastic old tosser – but I'm beginning to wonder. Maybe I'm destined to get into trouble again and again and again, and it's going to get worse and worse until fate or God or whatever has severely punished me for everything I'm getting away with.

CHAPTER 26
The Wolf

Joe Andrews can't survive this. This is beyond bad. Sexual harassment? Or was Ashley suggesting something even worse? But what the hell can I do?

Claire's mum and dad. I need to talk to them, explain, make them understand. Maybe they can explain to Mr Naylor that I'm actually a hero. I need to go to the hospital and find them. I need to go now. But I really don't feel up to telling Mum I've been suspended again.

I go to the nurse's office. 'Hello again,' she says. I tell her that I think I'm about to vomit. It's not altogether untrue. 'You are looking pale,' she says. She calls home and I can hear Mum's voice at the end of the line saying, 'I don't even know why he went in today. I told him last night he wouldn't be up to it.'

Twenty minutes later Mum and I are walking out

of the school gates. Alistair's Ford Fiesta is parked outside – so he *did* stay the night. I decide I don't care. I have enough to worry about. 'Can you take me to the hospital?' I ask.

'I didn't know you were feeling that ill, darling,' says Mum, all concerned, and I say, 'No, I'm not, but I want to see Claire. I need to see her now.'

So they drive me to the hospital and insist on coming in with me, which I'm not happy about, but then we find out that Claire's just been discharged and so it's good, really, that they are there to drive me to her house.

'Look, I'll leave you here,' says Alistair. 'I think it'd be a bit much for everyone if I come too.'

'Mum, you go with him,' I say, but she replies, 'D'you know what, I'm a bit fed up with taking orders from you. I think I should know what's been going on.' As I walk slowly to Claire's front door she gives Alistair a kiss, a long lingering kiss – this is so *not* the moment – and he says, 'I'll call you later.'

She catches me up and rings the doorbell. Claire's dad comes to the door. He looks tired and annoyed. 'We've only just got back from the hospital,' he says. 'It'd be better if you could come back later.'

'Please,' I say, 'I really need to talk to you, to you and Janet. I don't have to bother Claire if you don't want me to.'

'If you'd be kind enough to give him some time,' says Mum. 'He's very upset over what happened.'

He scratches his head and says, 'Look, son, we owe you because she could have been dead if you hadn't helped her out when you did. Come in and we'll have a chat.'

He takes us through to the kitchen and we sit down at the big table. Then he disappears upstairs for a long time. As we wait I look around. There are so many pictures of Ellie, so much stuff that belongs to the boys, but you'd never know Claire lived in this house. But what made her so invisible – was it her, or did the rest of her family just not leave her enough space? What would Claire be like if she was an only child like me?

Eventually they come and sit at the table with us. Janet and Gareth. Two nice people who look about ten years older than they did last time I saw them. Janet has little red puffy eyes and the tip of her nose is scarlet. Gareth's face is white under his freckles. And now they are here, I don't know what to say. Lucky that my Mum tagged along.

'Janet, Gareth, we're just so sorry about Claire,' she says. 'I'm sorry to intrude, but Joe was anxious to find out how she was. He had quite a shock.'

'Did he now?' says Janet in a cold voice that you wouldn't think could come from such a kind person.

'Well, we'd like to talk to him, find out what's really been going on.'

They all look at me. I don't know where to begin. It's hard when you suspect people are thinking bad things about you but they haven't said them yet.

'I knew she was cutting herself, but she said she would stop,' I say. 'I was trying to help her . . . she's my friend. . .' I fade to silence. I can feel massive hostility radiating from the other side of the table.

'How did you know this about Claire?' says Janet. 'What have you been doing to her, locked in her room? We trusted you, Joe, invited you into our home . . . made you feel welcome. . .'

'I didn't do anything to Claire. Really nothing. We were only talking.' I'm getting a little bit louder. It's not nice to be accused of things you haven't done.

'Talking about what?'

'Just things. I like talking to Claire and I think she likes talking to me.'

'Oh yes, she certainly likes you all right,' says Janet, and she sounds like she's only just holding herself back from screaming at me. 'Crazy about you. I just wonder what else was going on apart from talking.' I bet she did notice about the shirt buttons that time.

'He's said they were just talking,' says Mum.

'Are you accusing him of lying?'

'Well . . . you must admit it's a bit suspicious. I mean, no offence, but they are very different. Claire's so young for her age, very shy, very quiet. She's still a child. Joe's so streetwise, and he seems much older. What would they have in common?'

Streetwise is just one harmless word, but she rolls a lot more into it: dirty, violent, chav, liar, molester and ASBO, with just a touch of pram-face as well. I tense, waiting for my mum to explode.

'Maybe they were both a bit lonely and looking for a friend,' she says, and I could hug her.

'I didn't do anything bad to Claire,' I say. 'It's true. . . I totally respect her and I care about her and I think she's the nicest person I've ever met. To be honest, we did kiss twice, but nothing bad, really nothing . . . please ask her. Ask her if I did anything bad to her.' I'm almost crying by the time I get to the end of this speech, mainly from complete and utter embarrassment.

They're all looking a bit more sympathetic. This might be all right. But then I remember. I did do something bad to Claire. I did bully her. Here in this kitchen. Janet's watching me intently and she says, 'What's going on, Joe? Why do you suddenly look like that? Why are you chewing your lip?'

'I . . . just remembered something.'

They're all waiting. My mouth is completely dry.

'I . . . I was mean to Claire. Once. Here. But not in the way that Mr Naylor means.'

This means nothing to them as – thank God – they weren't there to hear what Mr Naylor had to say. But I've said enough anyway.

'What the hell did you do to our daughter?' shouts Gareth, and I think for a minute that he's going to punch me.

'I . . . I . . . she found out a secret and I just sort of scared her, sort of hurt her, just a little bit so she wouldn't tell. But I did apologise, I really did, and I think she understood.'

I catch a quick glimpse of Mum's face and have to look away. She's looking disgusted, frightened and sad all at once. Janet gets up. 'I think we've heard enough. I think you'd better leave now, Joe, and don't bother Claire again. And I'm going to tell Ellie to stop training with you as well.'

'But can't I just see Claire?' I ask hopelessly. 'Just to explain . . . to say goodbye?'

'I don't think that's a good idea, is it?' says Janet, and Mum says, 'Come on now, you've said enough.'

She gets up and turns to Claire's parents: 'I had no idea . . . no idea about any of this. He's never acted remotely like this in his life before. I can't apologise enough.'

We're walking towards the front door and I'm walking out of Claire's life forever and I don't know how I'm going to do it. And then I hear her voice.

'What's going on?'

I turn around. She's standing at the top of the stairs, wrapped up in a dressing gown, hood pulled up over her head. She looks pale and small and her hair is all over her face again. She could be about ten years old. I can't bear not to say goodbye. And I run up the stairs and pull her into my arms.

'You get down here at once,' yells Claire's dad, but I can't because Claire is clinging on to me. We must look like Little Red Riding Hood and the big bad wolf. I'm the wolf, obviously.

'Claire, I'm sorry, I told them about that time in the kitchen . . . and they're all furious with me, and they don't want us to see each other again . . . I'm sorry, it was my fault. . .'

Her face is buried in my shirt and all I can feel are her arms around me. Just for a moment I feel safe and loved. And then she takes my hand and sits down on the top stair, pulling me down next to her. She pushes her hair away from her face. 'We're going to talk about this,' she says. 'Joe's not going anywhere.'

It's quite funny really. They're all looking up at us cuddled together and no one's saying anything. Then her mum says, 'For heaven's sake, Claire, you ought to be in bed,' and Claire says, 'I'm not going back to bed unless Joe comes with me,' and she blushes bright red and I think I do too, because that wasn't the most helpful thing to say just now.

Mum says, 'Why don't we all go upstairs, then Claire can lie down and we can all talk a bit more?'

And everyone seems to agree that's a good idea, so we go into Janet and Gareth's bedroom and Claire gets into the big double bed and I sit down nervously by her side and the three parents stand over us.

Janet says, 'Claire, Joe's just admitted hurting you. We can't allow you to go on seeing him, love. You don't want friends like that.'

Claire looks tiny and pale and weak, but she's really determined.

'Mum, in case you hadn't noticed, I haven't got any other friends. Joe only hurt me for about twenty seconds, then he immediately started begging me to be his friend. He thought he was being all scary but I could tell he was just putting it on. He was scared, I could see. He apologised, and he explained and I understood why he did it. He would never do it again.'

I'm really hopeful after she says this, but then my

mum opens her big mouth.

'Claire,' she says, and she's not looking at me. 'Claire, it's never acceptable for a boy to hurt a girl. Never. Not even for twenty seconds.'

I can't believe she's doing this to me. I'm her son. Doesn't she care about me? How can she? Why?

And then she says, 'Believe me, I know what I'm talking about,' and I know. It's like I never knew and I always knew. I know why my dad disappeared out of our lives all those years ago. And I know what we're both scared of in me.

CHAPTER 27
When I Was Joe

Claire opens her mouth to argue, but Mum says, 'I'm going to take Joe home now, and we're going to have a talk, and I think you need to talk to your parents too. I'm sorry, but I think you'd better say goodbye for now.' She looks at Janet and Gareth. 'Maybe we could give them a few minutes?'

They go out on to the landing and we're left together. I put my head down on the pillow next to her. 'I'm so sorry,' I say, 'I've screwed everything up.'

And she says, 'You talk to her and explain and I'll talk to them. Don't give up. You're so important to me.'

'I don't know what's going to happen now. There's a load of stuff going on at school. Ashley. . .' But I can't even finish the sentence.

'It'll be all right,' she says. 'Don't give up.'

And we kiss, and it's the best feeling in the world to taste her sweet lips, and to stroke her soft hair.

But I have almost given up, and I think she realises.

Mum and I walk to the bus stop in silence, and we sit on the bus and get all the way home without saying a word. And all the time I'm getting more and more angry with her for interfering. And for all the things she hasn't told me. And for letting this happen. All of this. It's her fault. I think the anger is going to choke me.

I'm not talking to her about anything. I'm not talking to her ever again. I'm going to ask the police to provide a different appropriate adult. I throw myself down on the sofa and switch on the television. There's a new episode of *The Simpsons* and it's really funny. I concentrate hard on zoning everything else out of my head, and it works. I can do this. It's all about focus.

She gives me five minutes and then she marches in and switches it off. 'Hey! I was watching that.'

'For Christ's sake, Ty, don't you think it's more important to talk about what just happened?'

'No,' I say, and I switch it back on again.

'Ty, I want to know what's been going on. What did you do to Claire? Why?'

'Why didn't you find that out before you told her she shouldn't see me again? I'm not telling you anything.

I'm not even talking to you.'

I turn up the volume. She stands in front of the screen and puts her hand out for the remote.

'Give it to me.'

'No.'

'Give it to me.'

'Make me.'

She can't make me. I'm bigger and stronger than her. This thought freaks me out so much that after a minute's furious silence, I fling it on the floor by her feet.

'Leave me alone, you interfering bitch,' I say, but I mutter it in Turkish, so she ignores me.

'Right. Now. Tell me,' she orders.

'You know it. You know . . . I already told.'

'No, you didn't. You didn't tell us any details.'

'It was the day of the swimming pool thing. You were in the hospital with Gran. My contact lenses came out underwater and Claire saw that my eyes were green. So she asked and I had to . . . I tried to scare her . . . not to tell anyone.'

'What the hell did you do? Did you . . . you didn't hit her, did you?'

'No!'

'Thank Christ for that. So what did you do?'

'I took hold of her wrists . . . and kind of squeezed.'

'Oh. That wasn't a nice thing to do, Ty. A sweet little

girl like that. How could you?' She sits down in the armchair, which is better than having her stand over me. Her face looks all twisted and ill.

'I said I was sorry. And I explained . . . I explained why. . .'

I stop. Her eyes are wide and her mouth's dropped open.

'What do you mean, you explained?' she says slowly.

Oh, God.

'I just sort of explained . . . that it had to be secret. . .'

'What exactly did you just sort of explain?'

I'm not telling. I'm actually scared of her.

'Just that it had to be secret. . .'

'I don't believe you. Why did she say she understood?'

'She's very understanding.'

'Tell me exactly what you said. Or I will go back to their house and ask her, and I will embarrass you so much that when I've finished she will never want to speak to you again.'

I can't believe that my own mother is doing this. Gran would never ever treat me like this.

'I told her. I told her about witness protection and being Ty and Joe and everything. But she'll keep it secret. It's OK.'

'Ty! What were you thinking? You've put her in danger.'

'No . . . she won't ever tell anyone. Claire's sound, you can trust her. '

'You're not meant to tell anyone anything. How could you? She's in danger and you're in even more danger. What if she tells someone? What if someone gets their hands on her and does what they did to your gran? I'm going to have to ring Doug.'

'Please Nicki, please, *please*. . . I'm begging you, Nic, please don't tell Doug.'

'Jesus, Ty, what's happened to you? You used to be such a sensible boy, so gentle . . . so nice. . .'

'Shut up! I hate you!' My volume control has gone and this comes out as a shout.

'Don't talk to me like that,' she snarls. 'It's completely unacceptable for you to tell the truth to every girl you fancy. You were nearly shot, for God's sake. Think about Mr Patel's shop. Want that to happen to Claire? To Ellie? We can't mess around here.'

I go back to begging. 'Please, Nic, *please*. . .'

'Look, it's not so good for me either, right? I've just met a really nice bloke and it's all been screwed up. Story of my bloody life.'

She goes into the kitchen to phone Doug and I stamp upstairs and lie on my bed. I think about all the things I'm looking forward to as Joe. Running proper races over the summer. Joining the athletics squad. Maybe being in the football team one day. The end of term party – I'd been planning to give Claire a makeover and take her to the party and everyone would realise she was actually completely beautiful, and I'd be the one who had transformed her.

And talking to Claire, and going places with Claire, and kissing her again, and spending time generally with Claire.

None of these things are going to happen. I'm even feeling miserable about not being able to finish the lost property cupboard with Carl.

Mum comes upstairs and sits down on the bed next to me. 'What did he say?' I ask, and my voice comes out all shaky.

'He'll come as soon as possible with Maureen. They're going to talk about it with you and make a decision.' She puts her hand on my shoulder and I angrily shrug it off. 'But it doesn't sound good, I'm sorry.'

Doug and Maureen arrive about nine o'clock, just as I've decided they've had an accident on the motorway and we're never going to see them again. Mum talks to them first and then calls me to come down. I don't want to look them in the eye. It's Maureen who says, quite nicely, 'It's all gone a bit wrong, hasn't it, Ty? Doug had a call from your head teacher to say you were suspended again.'

They must have told Mum about it because she's looking even more devastated than before, and she stubs out her cigarette like she's trying to grind the entire ashtray into dust. 'How come you never told me?' she says. 'Bullying another girl? Suspended for the second time?'

'I never – she's just a liar. . .'

And then I remember Maureen and Doug heard me trying to get Ashley to come up to my bedroom and I shut up again. They won't believe me.

'It's no good, mate,' says Doug. 'It's a shame, but I think you're going to have to be moved on. Too much trouble here. You've become too visible. And we can't have you putting another family at risk.'

I don't say much. They're all sitting there looking at me and I know that somehow I've screwed everything up again. It seems such a big punishment for the one time I did something good. But maybe life works a bit like Tesco Clubcard points in reverse – you do your normal stuff and it all adds up without you thinking about it, and then suddenly you get a load of vouchers in the post. Or, in my case, you make lots of crap decisions and they all add up to your life falling apart altogether.

I pack my iPod, I pack my Man Utd scarf from Dad. I pack my photos and two lots of school books. I pack all Joe's cool new clothes, his running shoes, his contact lenses and his hair dye. I pack Claire's two scrumpled notes. I try very hard not to feel anything at all. And I lie down on my bed and remember the time when I was Joe.

When Mum's ready, they load the bags into the car. But I don't get up. I'm thinking crazy thoughts about running away. Going to live secretly in Claire's bedroom or her garden shed or something. Maureen comes and sits on the bed next to me. 'Time to go,' she says.

'I'm not going,' I say. 'It's not fair. I like it here. I need to be here.'

'You'll do all right somewhere else,' says Maureen. 'You can't hang on here and put yourself and other people in danger.'

'I don't care.'

'Think how your gran would feel if anything happened to you. She doesn't deserve to lose you. She's doing so well too, off to join your aunties any day. Think about how this Claire would feel if you were hurt because of her. Is she a bit special?'

And I can only nod and gulp, and Maureen gives me a hug and says, 'It'll work out.'

'Am I a bad person, Maureen?' I ask. It feels like

I've never known for sure.

She says, 'Seems to me you've always been a very good boy, very hard working, never in trouble. But a lot of difficult things have happened to you in the last few weeks and, just occasionally, you've not shown good judgement. Happens to everyone. Doesn't make you a bad person. I don't think you're a bully.'

It's reassuring, but she doesn't know the whole truth. And she's police, so I can't tell her.

CHAPTER 28
Mel and Jake

So now I have to get into the car and watch the street lights of this not-so-boring little town disappear into dark country roads. And then a motorway, lit up orange and eerie. And then we're checking into another hotel, another little room, where there's no room to unpack and nothing to do but watch a big screen TV.

It's different staying here though. The hotel is pretty similar, but we've changed. I go for a run every day, and there's a leisure centre where I swim and use the gym. Mum comes with me sometimes. And we talk a bit too, and I tell her a little about how awful St Saviour's was and how Arron and I weren't really friends any more. I don't tell her what the boys used to say about her. She doesn't need that. We avoid talking about

Claire, but I explain a bit about Ashley and she seems to understand.

One day I'm feeling brave and I say, 'What did you mean that day – you know – when you told Claire you knew what you were talking about?' And she replies, 'Oh, I heard so many terrible things working for a solicitor. I know how important it is for girls to realise that they mustn't take any kind of abuse.' I say, 'But it wasn't abuse,' and she shakes her head at me. And I know she's not telling the whole truth, and I think she knows that I know.

Maureen chops my hair a bit and dyes it a different colour, a kind of dark reddish brown, which doesn't look right to me. The eyebrows are still in place and she says I can go back to having green eyes, which I'm pleased about, but she wants me to wear glasses, which I'm not. I suspect she's designed my new look to make me as unattractive to girls as possible. She didn't try and change anything about my clothes though, so I still feel there's a basic Joe-ness about me. Joe with geeky specs and a bad haircut.

I try and find a computer to use, but there's no internet cafe and the only library I can find won't let you have a ticket unless you have a permanent address. So I can't even email Claire. And I don't know if I should anyway. I feel some scary emotion which is beyond sad whenever I think about her – you could call it despair, I suppose – so I'm working on blanking her out. It's like she's left an aching emptiness inside me.

Maureen comes to see us to talk about where we're going next. This time, she says, we can choose our own names. It's surprisingly difficult. I want a cool name, something like Spike. Mum is reading *Heat* magazine and suggesting stupid celebrity mother/son combos like Jordan and Junior, Gwen and Zuma, Angelina and Knox or Maddox or Pax. Pax isn't too bad, I suppose, but I think she's joking anyway. I counter with Marge and Bart but she's not having it.

Maureen says we're both daft and we have to be sensible. So we agree on Melanie and Jake. Mel and Jake Ferguson. I suggested the surname after Sir Alex. He's the manager of Man Utd and it'd be fantastic to be part of his family, except I think he'd shout at me a lot because that's what he's like.

And on a burning hot summer's day we leave the hotel and Doug takes us to another small town, a seaside town, with noisy seagulls circling overhead and a crumbling pier and a long grey beach.

This time we're in a flat and it's small, but it's bright and white and it smells of fresh paint and there's a stepladder which leads out on to a flat roof with a view of the sea. It's not bad. It feels a bit like being on holiday.

'Is this really a good idea?' says Mum. 'Don't these seaside places get a lot of visitors?'

'You're a long way from London,' says Doug. 'We think it'll be fine. This isn't a big place for day trippers. There's not much going on here.' Doug really knows how to sell a place.

We go and buy school uniform three days before the start of term. As I look at myself in the changing room mirror – dark green blazer, black trousers, grey jumper, white shirt, green tie, stupid red hair (I really don't like the hair) and steel-rimmed glasses – I'm trying to get an idea of what sort of a person Jake is going to be. He doesn't look as cool as Joe, that's for sure, but he's tougher than Ty ever was. He looks a bit miserable, to be honest, hiding behind his specs.

We get back to the flat and we're unpacking all the stuff, and Mum is talking about getting Maureen to call the Open University and see if her credits can be transferred to her new name so she can pick up her studies again. 'Only two more courses and I've got a law degree,' she says. And then we hear a knock at the door.

'Who on earth is that?' says Mum. 'Doug said he wouldn't be back until Tuesday to hear how your first day went.'

We both freeze, looking at each other nervously.

She says, 'You go out on to the roof and I'll see who it is.'

So I'm lying on the roof, watching the seagulls circling overhead and pretending they are vultures about to pick out my eyes, when DI Morris and DC Bettany step out to join me. 'Don't get up,' says DI Morris, and he sits down next to me. DC Bettany gets out his notebook. I'm beginning to hate that notebook.

So there's nowhere to run when DI Morris says, 'I've been talking to a friend of yours and I'd like to ask you some more questions.'

'Oh, yeah?' I say cautiously, watching three gulls fight viciously over a piece of fish. I'm wondering if he's been to see Claire, and hoping he doesn't mean Ashley.

'I want to ask a bit more about what happened before you got to the park,' he says.

And I know who he means. He doesn't mean Ashley. He doesn't mean Claire.

He's been talking to my friend Arron Mackenzie.

CHAPTER 29
Rio

Arron promised. He promised me. 'I'll never tell it was you,' he said. But of course six months in a youth offenders' institution can change anyone. I wouldn't blame him if he's told them what I did. But that doesn't mean I'm giving anything away right now.

I sit up. 'I thought you weren't meant to be talking to me without a lawyer here. Or my mum, anyway.'

DI Morris says, 'Here she comes.' And Mum's climbing out on to the roof as well. She sits down and says, 'Are you sure you don't want to come back downstairs? It's a bit more comfortable.'

'We shouldn't be too long,' says DI Morris.

Oh. That doesn't sound like. . . I'll just wait and see what he asks. No point rushing into anything.

He's asking about the paper round. About whether I ever saw anyone using the bags to transport anything other than newspapers and magazines. Whether any little packages were involved. And I say no, I was always the first one to get my bag and I had the longest round and they were all finished before me. It's true. I don't know if anything else I tell him will be.

Then he says, 'I want to ask you about a meeting that you and Arron had with the youths that you identified as being with Arron in the park. Julian White – known as Jukes – and Mikey Miller. Is that correct?'

'It wasn't a meeting like that. They were just there when we got off the tube on the way home from school. . . I thought maybe they'd been bowling. The bowling alley's just there by the tube station, you know. . .' Of course I realise now that Arron must have arranged it.

'I just knew them from boxing. Friends of Nathan, at least, I think so. . . '

They were scary, these guys. We met them by the bowling alley on the way home from school and walked with them down to the bus stop. We stopped outside one of those shops that sell knocked-off mobiles. 'What you want from us, boys?' asked one, and Arron said we needed protection. He'd been mugged the week before, threatened with a blade and robbed of his watch, and he was jumpy. That's when we both started carrying knives.

'You gotta earn dat protecshun,' said Mikey. He's one of those white guys who talk all the time in gangsta, have massive tattoos and go heavy on the bling. He had huge diamond studs in his ears and a gold tooth, and the sort of gold chains that you only wear in our area if you're tough enough to defend them. 'You gotta do some li'l jobs for us.'

I was too scared even to speak but Arron said, 'OK, man, no problem.' And they all laughed together.

'Wha' abou' 'im?' said Jukes, jerking his thumb at me. Jukes isn't one for the bling, and if you saw him in the street, the only thing that might make you look twice is the eagle tattooed on his arm. It's only because I've seen him fight at boxing club that I know how much power is packed into his stocky body. I shook my head and stared at the gum-splattered pavement, and the two of them laughed. And Arron joined in after a few minutes and said, 'He ain't got no bo'ul.'

'So you thought Arron was looking for protection from Jukes's gang,' says DC Bettany.

'No . . . yes . . . sort of. I didn't think they were a gang.'

'And you knew he was going to the park to do a job for them?'

'Umm . . . I didn't know exactly. He asked me to come along, and then he started talking about protection again, said I'd be a target for everyone unless I had it. But I said I wouldn't come. I didn't know what to do. I didn't want to get into trouble.'

I don't tell him that Arron wanted me to do the job for Jukes and Mikey. That he said, 'Prove yourself a man.' When I said no, he spat on the ground and said, 'You're letting me down, Ty. You're just a big girl.'

'You didn't want to get into trouble,' said DI Morris, and then, 'Well, you seem to have changed your tune recently. Suspended twice from school in as many weeks.'

'Sorry. It was an accident. I don't really know how it happened.'

'Don't let it happen again.'

'No,' I say, and think about what a completely boring person Jake Ferguson's going to have to be. He's going to have to make much better choices than Joe or Ty. I don't know if I'm up to it.

'So then you followed Arron?'

I've told them about this again and again. I'd followed him all the way to the lower entrance. It's only a small park. It stretches between two streets, up a hill, with a pond at the bottom and a children's playground at the top. Arron and I used to play a lot in that playground when we were younger. There's a wooden castle with walkways and a slide, and the usual swings and stuff.

We loved it there.

He'd gone in towards the pond and I ran around the perimeter fence, up the hill on the other side, and climbed over the fence at the top. No one was playing in the playground because it was getting dark and it was drizzling. I climbed into the castle, because from there you can see the whole path and everyone coming up the hill, but no one can see you.

'I followed him. Just in case he got hurt or anything. I didn't know what was going to happen. '

'Right. And when did Jukes and Mikey turn up?'

'They were walking up with Arron. They must have met him down by the pond. And then they all hid themselves and waited for someone to come along. But I've told you all this before. '

I'm thinking about that boy walking up the path towards them. I think about him a lot. He was singing along to his iPod. He was only the same age as me. He wore a hoodie and baggy trousers and he was eating chips and he looked just like all of us, except he was black and we were white. And I wanted to shout and warn him, but he wouldn't have heard because he was plugged into his music.

Arron leapt out at him. He had his knife out and he hit the boy's chips out of his hand. 'What've you got for me?' he said. You'd have thought the boy would have just given up right away, handed over the iPod and run away. That's what I would have done. But he didn't. He had his own knife. And he started waving it back at Arron.

If I'd done what Arron wanted and been the one mugging the boy, then I'd have dropped my knife and run away. And I can run so fast that there wouldn't have been a fight. But Arron didn't run. He was backing off, looking around, unsure what was going to happen next.

Jukes and Mikey jumped out and pushed him forward. 'Go on, man, don't let him disrespect you,' said Mikey. The knives waved in the air. I stayed frozen in the castle. What if I'd tried to help . . . shouted out . . . had some credit on my phone?

Then Jukes grabbed the boy's arm and twisted it. The knife in the boy's hand grazed Arron's ear, sending blood gushing over his shirt. And Jukes pushed the boy away, and he fell against Arron. And Arron's knife. And they splashed into the mud together and they were fighting, and all I could see was a tangle of bodies. And blood. And mud. And Jukes and Mikey running away.

And there's no point going through this with DI Morris because this was all in my original statement. They know this bit, every last detail.

'And how close did you get, before you called the ambulance?' asked DI Morris.

'Not close at all,' I said. I'd jumped down from the castle and run away. I could have just run and run and never come back, but I didn't. All the time in my head there were the two thoughts – first ambulance, then Arron. How to get an ambulance. How to help Arron. How to make certain he didn't take all the blame.

I got out on to the road and I saw the bus coming up the hill towards me. And I stuck my hand out to stop it. When the door opened I shouted, ' Ambulance . . . call an ambulance. In the park, by the playground . . . someone's really hurt.' And then I ran back.

'And then you helped Arron run away,' says DI Morris. 'Yes,' I say, and I wait. But he doesn't know. He doesn't know. Arron didn't tell him what really happened then.

'When did you realise he'd also been hurt?'

'When we were running. It all happened really quickly.'

'His idea to run, or yours?' he asks.

'Both,' I say firmly.

He's looking curiously at me, like he knows there's something wrong with my story. But he doesn't ask. He doesn't ask. So I don't have to lie.

He asks a few more questions, but nothing I can't

handle. And then he says, 'We're nearly there with the case that we're building but there may yet be some delays before it goes to court.'

'Oh, yeah?'

'Be patient. Keep your head down. We'll have a new statement which covers this meeting outside the bowling alley for you to sign in a week or so.'

'What about Arron? What's going to happen to him?'

He shakes his head. 'I can't tell you that,' he says.

I don't know a lot about courts and law but I'm hoping that, by telling DI Morris that Arron wasn't meaning to stab anyone, I can help him. Arron was injured as well. I'm sure he'll be able to argue self-defence. He's a lot younger than Jukes and Mikey. As long as the court believes me about what they did. I wonder what Arron's statement says.

'How come you never thought I was involved?' I ask. I want to make absolutely sure that I'm in the clear.

'Luckily for you, we found traces of your DNA on the castle, which backs your story, and the timing of you appearing on the bus route also seems to rule out much involvement. Anyone who'd been in that fight would be covered in blood and mud, and every passenger on that bus says you were spotless. It'd be hard to prove joint enterprise – that you were working with the others. Of course, you could have been acting as their look out, but we're not pursuing that line. We checked your computer as well and there's absolutely nothing on the hard drive to link you with any gang activity.'

I think about them checking my laptop, reading every message I've ever written, every word of the diary I kept for a bit – which was mostly about Maria at the tattoo parlour – and I feel a bit like someone's just gone through my underwear drawer or filmed me in bed at night. It's not good to be spied on. It makes you feel automatically ashamed.

'Can I talk to him, to Arron?'

'No, Ty, because you're a witness in the case against him.'

All these months I've been worrying that Arron and his family hate me for going to the police. All these months I've been confused about who's after me. But when I think clearly, I know who I have to worry about. I'm pointing the finger at the one who pushed the boy on to Arron's knife.

'OK,' I say, 'why can't you arrest Jukes's family? Because you know they were the ones that threw that bomb and beat up my gran, don't you? Why can't you lock them up?'

He sighs. 'It's a fair question,' he says. 'The problem

is proof. These are organised criminals. They're probably responsible for half of the drugs on the streets of North London. They control a large number of people and they have vast resources. Nothing that's happened to you will have been done directly by them. Getting people to testify against them is a problem, and getting hard proof that they are ultimately responsible for any one crime is extremely difficult.'

Fair enough, I suppose. It makes me feel a bit stupid, though, that I didn't realise what a risk I was taking when we went to the police in the first place. I wonder how they're keeping Arron safe in prison. Or did Arron even name Jukes and Mikey in his statement?

And then DI Morris says to me, 'OK son, behave yourself from now on,' and they leave me alone on the roof.

I lie on my back again and look up at the seagulls. And I'm back in far, faraway London, running back to Arron in the park.

I can see that the boy is dead. He couldn't look more dead. There is blood everywhere. But Arron is desperately shaking him and shouting at him, 'Wake up, man, help is coming, it's gonna be OK.'

'Come on Arron, leave him. You can't help him now.'

'Shut up, man,'

'Come on Arron, you can still escape.'

'Shut the fuck up.'

So I get out my knife. And I wave it in his face. And I say, 'You do as I tell you.'

'Make me, gay boy.'

I slash the knife at his arm. Harder than I meant to. And he's bleeding and gasping and looking at me like he never knew me.

The strange thing is that sometimes, when I remember it, my knife slices hard into his arm and blood spurts out in a fountain. And sometimes my knife just scratches his arm, leaving a straight red line which oozes little drops of blood. I have no idea which memory is right. I've been over it again and again in my head.

We run down the path, with the sound of sirens getting louder and louder. And we run through the trees and bushes to the bit of fence that backs straight on to his estate. Amazingly, no one sees us as we crash through the double doors leading to his block, and we call the lift.

Incredibly the lift arrives – it's usually broken – and we're all alone in the piss-stinking space. And it's there that Arron looks at me and says, 'I never thought you'd do that. Don't worry, I'll never tell.'

There's respect in his eyes for the first time for years – at last he sees I'm as good as him. He doesn't despise me any more. But then I wonder what sort of respect I've earned, and, ever since, that confusion has tangled my brain. Because I needed that respect, I was desperate for it.

Sometimes I dream of that moment and I'm high with relief – I'm not a pretty boy, I'm a real man – and then the joy drains away when I remember why he's looking like that, and I'm just a shapeless blob of nothing again. It's the worst dream because sometimes humiliation is worse than fear. And then I wake up and despise my selfishness because nothing that's happened to me means anything compared to what happened to the boy with the iPod.

By the time the lift stops, Arron's breathing is more of a gasp, and he's collapsing into my arms and we stagger along the last bit of walkway and fall against his front door. His mum hears the thud and comes to the door. And as we fall into the flat she sees the blood pouring down. And she's screaming and falling to her knees. 'He got stabbed,' I pant. 'You gotta do something.'

And luckily her nursing instinct takes over, and she makes a tourniquet and calls an ambulance.

After they've gone, I change into some of Arron's clothes. I put my bloody clothes into a Tesco bag and

I wipe the knife clean on them.

I go home and I boil up the kettle and pour steaming water over the knife, and then I put it back in the cutlery drawer. The Tesco bag goes under my bed and then I have a shower. I don't need to tell Nicki anything because she's down at the Duke of York for karaoke night.

I curl up on the sofa and all I can think about is blood and death and Arron and the boy. The way he was singing. The dead stare on his face. I'm shaking and crying a bit. But then I hear a knock at the door and I creep along and open it, and Nathan bursts into the room. He's sweating and shaking too, and he says, 'They've arrested him. The fu'in' hospital called de police to him. He's under arrest.'

And then he pushes his face next to mine and tells me to keep quiet. And I say, 'Yeah, yeah, I'm not saying anything.' All these months I thought he was threatening me. But now I wonder if he was trying to protect me, to keep me out of it. Nathan's scary, but he did always seem to like me. And maybe he knew what Jukes's family were capable of.

The next day I say I'm ill and I can't go to school, and Nicki calls Gran and asks her to come and be with me. And Gran makes me toast and tea and puts her hand on my forehead and says, 'Maybe you're running a temperature, my darling. Go back to sleep.'

But then she reads the paper and listens to the radio. She calls my mum and asks her to come home from the office. When she does, Gran sits both of us down in front of the lunchtime news and we watch a press conference. It's about a murder which may have racist motives. A press conference given by Mr and Mrs Williams, the grieving parents of Rio Williams, aged fourteen.

They're appealing for help, for anyone who was in the park that day to come forward. In particular for the boy who stopped the bus. There's a pretty clear description of me – green eyes, brown hair, grey hoodie – and Gran just looks at me. Then she says her bit about the precious child. This poor family's precious child. And then we go to the police.

The police take my statement, which names Jukes and Mikey and Arron, and then they take us to the canteen where I eat crisps and custard creams. Then they take us home and, well, you know what happens next.

CHAPTER 30
Fish and Chips

Another first day at another school. This time the school is stricter, more old-fashioned, more like St Saviour's in fact, minus religion but with the yes sir, no sir and the tons of homework. Mum will be over the moon.

It's only for boys. Doug and Maureen obviously decided that I need to be kept away from girls. I don't like it, it doesn't feel natural to me. You can't grow up among women and then easily flip over to everyone being male. Or I can't, anyway. I feel flat and gloomy. I'm worried it's going to be St Saviour's all over again.

They put a boy called Nigel in charge of showing me around and making sure I get to the right classroom at the right time, and he does it, but he's not really interested. At break he talks to his friends and I stand around until he's ready to take me to our History lesson. By lunchtime I'm so fed up that I tell him I'm OK by myself and just wander around a bit. I'm not hungry, just waiting for the day to end. And then I see the sign saying Library.

I push the door cautiously and see a room with hundreds of books. It's twice the size of the library at St Saviour's and I don't think there was one at Parkview – they had a learning resource centre instead. What's most interesting here are the computers.

'Hello,' says a woman who's got the most amazing ginger curls. 'We don't usually see many people in here on the first day of term.'

'Can I use the computers, please?' I ask. 'Is there internet?'

And she says yes, and I sit down and I log on to the email address that Claire set up for me.

There are twenty messages. Twenty. All from Claire. She's been writing and writing for weeks, even though I haven't replied. I can't believe it. I'm happy and sad and excited and terrified all at the same time.

The first messages are just short: *Call me, write to me, where are you? We need to talk, what's happened? Are you OK? I'm worried about you.* That kind of thing.

She wrote:

I found out what Ashley said about you and I told the head teacher that she'd been bullying me, and that you were only good and supportive to me. I know it's too late for you, but she's on full report now. I'm not going back until next term, and I think they'll move me to another class. I wish you were still here.

Then she wrote about a month ago:

At last I know what's happened to you. A nice lady called Maureen came to see me. Mum thought she was just a friend of your family, but she told me who she really was and how she knew you. She told me why you'd had to be moved away and that you were all right. I was getting really scared for you.

I'm going to keep writing and maybe one day you will reply. Surprise me! You know I'm not angry with you. I wish other people hadn't interfered with us. I know they were just trying to be protective but I wish they'd have left us alone. I love you. Claire.

And then she writes message after message about her life, about how things have changed and how her mum's asking her all the time how she feels and is taking her shopping and stuff.

One message makes me stop and think for a bit.

I thought about what your Mum said about you hurting me and I want you to know that I didn't even mind at the time.

All the time I was thinking that you were actually touching me, someone like you had noticed me. Any pain came second to that. It's OK, you mustn't feel bad about it.

When I read this I *do* feel really bad, because I realise that Claire's quite screwed up about all sorts of things, and I see more what my mum was going on about. I wish Claire and I could have worked it out together though. She needs so much love and friendship and I have it here for her.

The last message was written yesterday when she went back to Parkview.

The first day is over and it wasn't as bad as I'd thought. Did you ever meet the school counsellor? They rushed me off to see her as soon as registration was over. She's a bit annoying to talk to – really nosy, assumed all sorts of things about you and me – but she had a good idea. She suggested that I pick about four girls in my new class, and then she got them to come to her room so I could talk to them about what had happened and they could sort of protect me in the classroom, tell other people to leave me alone, that kind of thing. I asked for Evie, Anna, Zoe and Jasmine from my PE group – did you ever meet them? They're OK, I think. They never teased me, just ignored me.

They were quite shy when they came in, and Miss Wilson

explained what she wanted them to do and I thought, this'll never work. But then she left us alone and I talked to them a bit about why I used to cut myself and how it felt and why it all went wrong and how I'm feeling now. I felt really sick and ashamed when I was talking, but they were all kind and nice and they said they were sorry they'd never talked to me and known what was going on. Zoe is a specially nice person and she asked me to go shopping with her at the weekend.

They all wanted to know about you. They wanted to know if you were cutting yourself too, and I said no, absolutely not, he was the one who saved my life and made me stop. And I have stopped, I really have. They wanted to know why you suddenly disappeared and I told them that your mum wanted to go back to London.

After that we went back into class, and at break and lunch I went round with them, and no one else has bothered me. Carl and Brian both asked about you and I told them I thought you were OK, and I told them the London story as well. Carl said in that case he forgave you for leaving him the rest of the lost property to sort out, which was nice of him.

Are you starting a new school too? Could you write and tell me about it? Are you OK? I love you so much, Claire x

I finish reading this and I hit reply and then I stare at the screen a bit and try and think about what to say. And I don't realise it but my eyes are a bit watery and the screen is blurry when I try and type. I've taken my stupid glasses off. They give me a headache.

'Are you OK?' asks the nice librarian lady. 'Because the bell for the end of lunch went ten minutes ago.'

I rub my eyes. 'Oh . . . I'm in trouble on my first day.'

'Never mind, they'll understand,' she says. 'Tell them you got lost. Where do you have to be?'

I pull out my new timetable. 'Maths. A7.'

'Shall I show you where that is?'

'Yes, please, but I really have to write something first.'

I think any other teacher would have told me off and pointed to the timetable, but she waits patiently while I write: *I finally found a computer I can use. I'll write properly soon. Missing you, love you too, Jx.*

'I'm done,' I say and get up to go and she says, 'Don't you need to put your glasses back on?' and looks at me as though she thinks I'm a bit strange.

She takes me along a corridor and points the way upstairs.

'Through the double doors, turn left, second door on your right,' she says. Then she adds, 'Welcome to Trenton Boys. I'm Miss Knight and you can always find me in the library.'

'I'm Jo— Jake,' I say, and she says, 'If you need any

help just come and ask.'

When I get home Doug's sitting at the table in our tiny living room and I don't mind him so much now, so I tell him and Mum all about how hard I'm going to have to work, and how I'll be doing Spanish which is obviously essential for a Premiership interpreter, and that someone mentioned that they might set up a Mandarin class after school. And I think there's an athletics club. So I can keep going with the running too.

Mum looks really pleased and says, 'I'll get you into university yet,' and Doug says, 'We looked for a school which would keep you busy. Your Mum thought this one would be good because they specialise in languages.' He looks really smug, but that's just the way his face works. I grin at Mum because I recognise this as a peace offering.

And then Doug says, 'I've got some news for you, young Ty,' and Mum looks a bit strange. Happy but also kind of stressed.

'What news?' I ask and Doug says, 'Your gran is coming back to England and so are your aunts. Your aunts are going to live in Manchester – we're getting them a flat there and you'll be able to visit because it's not so far away.'

'What about Gran?'

'Aha! She's going to come and live with you here.'

'Yay!' I'm so happy I whoop out loud and I see Mum wipe away a tear.

'But how can she live here? It's really small.'

'There's a studio flat downstairs which is empty. We thought she could have that. It's not what she's used to but she'll be very happy to be with you both.'

'You especially,' says Mum, and she goes off to make me a cup of tea.

Later, when Doug's gone and I've changed into jeans and a T-shirt, we decide to go and get fish and chips and eat them on the beach. It's a sunny evening and it's kind of relaxing to watch the waves crashing in. I've been wondering about trying surfing – I can see it's a big thing here and Mum says she thinks it's a great idea.

'Are you OK?' I ask her. 'Aren't you happy about Gran coming to live with us?'

'Oh. Well. Of course I am.'

'No you're not. Don't pretend with me.'

She sighs. 'It's just that she's never really approved of me, you know, Ty. I was never the good Catholic daughter she wanted.'

'Neither are the others,' I point out, but she says, 'Pregnant at 15? Beat that.'

She goes on, 'She adores you so much, and of course we lived with her on and off until you were five, and, even when we had our own place, you spent so much time there. After school every day, in the holidays; I sometimes used to feel I didn't get a look in with either of you. Like my mother had stolen my son and my son had stolen my mother.'

'Oh. I'm sorry. I never knew.' I feel guilty but cross as well, because I never asked her to hand me over to Gran. Stolen is a bit of a strong word. And then I ask, 'Why did we live with her on and off? I thought we just lived with her.'

'It's a long story,' she says. 'We had a go at living with your dad, just the three of us. It didn't really work. I'll tell you properly one day. Look, it wasn't your fault. I let her do all the mothering. Thought she was better at it than me, and I was probably right, eh?'

'You don't do so bad,' I say, reaching over and nicking a big handful of her chips.

'You liar!' she laughs, and a seagull nips in and pinches the end of her fish.

'I miss our flat in London,' I say. 'I really liked living there.' And she takes that as a compliment and says thanks.

'But it's OK here, isn't it?' she asks, and I don't know what to say because some things are good, like fish and chips on the beach, and doing Spanish is massive, but some things are rubbish, like not having any friends and missing Claire so much that it hurts and not doing training with Ellie any more.

And there's the constant nagging worry about our safety, and the exhausting job of remembering to lie all day every day about the most basic things. But I suppose that's going to be the case for a long time wherever we are.

'I suppose so,' I reply, and she says, 'Missing Claire?' and I nod, and she says, 'Well, it's much better not to get too serious at your age. At least you can concentrate on your homework,' which is just typical.

'You can't help what you feel,' I point out, and she says, 'I'm hardly one to preach, am I?' Then she sighs and says, 'I'm sorry everything's so difficult for you. What a useless parent I am.'

'You're about a million times better than my dad,' I say, and she says, 'You're underestimating,' and then we walk along the sea front and back to our new home.

CHAPTER 31
Confession

Jake's social life is crap. Watching *EastEnders* with Gran, that's about as good as it gets. He's a sad git, Jake. Good thing he's not really me. Funnily enough, when I was Ty, I was quite happy to spend an evening in front of the telly. But now I've been Joe, I expect more.

We're halfway through *EastEnders* when some guy starts beating up Ian, slapping him across the face and holding him by the throat. Nothing terrible. Normal stuff in Albert Square.

And then I look at my gran, and her eyes are full of tears and she's trembling and looking away from the television, so I quickly change channels. Gran will never talk about what happened to her and she gets upset if we ask, but she doesn't like loud noises, and she'll only open the door if I knock three times, and she asked Doug the other day if there was any chance we could move to a bigger flat which would have room for all of us because she's nervous on her own. Which isn't like my gran.

Anyway. On Channel 4 there's a programme about knife crime. About all the killings and stabbings. About the crisis among Britain's youth. About what the government plans to do about it.

I grab the remote to zap on to something like sport or *The Simpsons*, but Gran shakes her head and says, 'No, Ty darling, you need to watch this.'

So she goes to make tea and I watch. London, they say is the worst place for knives. In other British cities, things are more organised. Gangs have guns. In London, it's a free-for-all. We all have knives, gangs or no gangs.

The Mayor of London – the weirdo blond guy off the telly – goes on about kids not having enough to do . . . needing more facilities. Youth clubs. Boxing. Latin. *Latin?*

Some woman says that kids should be taken into hospitals to see stabbing injuries being treated. That's totally random – I mean, you'd have to wait around for ages before someone with the right sort of injuries came in. And you'd get in the way of the doctors and nurses. She's obviously not thought it through. Which is a bit worrying because apparently she's the Home Secretary.

A police guy says it'll take a generation to change

things, that they can solve murders really easily, but it's another story trying to prevent them.

And then they show a slide show of the victims, the teenagers stabbed to death in London this year so far. It's only September but the pictures seem to go on forever. Face after face of boys – almost all boys – black and white, big and small. One guy has a silly moustache and I cringe for him – imagine having your life end when you've just started experimenting with facial hair and you look like a complete dickhead. One boy looks a bit like Arron. Another looks more like me.

And then there's Rio, filling up the screen, Rio with his big brown eyes and his black hoodie and a smile that I never saw. I'm curled up on the sofa now, rocking slowly back and forward, a fist against my mouth.

Gran sits next to me and says softly, 'I know it's terrible, darling, but it's important to watch. This is why we're here. This is what we're fighting against.'

They're interviewing someone in a young offender institution now. A young guy, tall and dark, skin the colour of a frappuccino when you've stirred in the cream. For a moment I think it's Arron, but it can't be. He's not been to court yet. No one's found him guilty.

This guy is guilty. 'I carried a knife because my brother gave it me,' he says. 'He told me I needed protection.' I sneak a little look at my gran. She's shaking her head.

'The boy you stabbed – was he threatening you with a knife?' asks the interviewer. Slowly the prisoner shakes his head. 'I was drunk, innit?' he says. 'He disrespected me. I just shanked him.' He looks at his hand like he can't believe what it did.

He's serving four years for GBH. That could be me. That ought to be me. That might be me if the police ever find out the truth.

Here's another politician. A posh one. The one my mum likes – he talks a lot of sense, she says. You can tell from his smooth, certain face that he's had a pretty easy life. I bet he never worried about being attacked on his way home from school. He doesn't live in a world of fear.

He says that everyone who carries a knife should be locked up. I try to imagine how many prisons they'd need – hundreds and hundreds – and I laugh out loud. My gran gives me a look and I shut up.

The programme ends and she switches off the television. I hide my face in my cup of tea and she says, 'They should bring back National Service.'

'Why? Then you're just teaching people to fight.'

'Give these kids a bit of discipline,' she says. 'Give them a trade. Teach them some responsibility.'

She pats me on the shoulder. 'I'm so glad you're not like them, Ty darling.' I disappear into my mug again.

'Do you like it here, Gran?' I ask after a bit. I have to change the subject.

She shakes her head. 'I'm a Londoner, darling, I'll never adapt to living somewhere this quiet. Please God they'll find a way that we can go back home one day. This is fine for a holiday, but it's not real life.'

Then she smiles and says, 'But I popped into the church around the corner and introduced myself to the priest – very nice man, comes from Walthamstow, looks a bit like what's-his-name . . . George Clooney . . . and he says they've got a nice congregation on a Sunday. I don't suppose you'll come with me, will you? I do think it'd be good for you.'

'Umm . . . probably not. I've got a lot of homework,' I say. 'Actually, I'd better go and do some now.'

I go back upstairs to our empty flat – Mum's got a part-time job three evenings a week behind the bar at the local pub – and then I realise I actually have got quite a lot of homework, and some of it needs research, so I decide to go to the internet cafe. By thinking very hard about Jake's geography project I manage to shut out the thoughts of knives and prison and Rio and all those other faces – at least I shut them out of the front of my mind, but I know they're hiding in the back.

On the way I pass Gran's church and I wonder why you'd become a priest if you look like George Clooney. For one crazy minute I think about going inside and sitting in the confession box and telling the whole story to a dark iron grid. And finding out what Father Clooney would suggest for penance and contrition, and whether it's really true that priests keep the darkest of secrets.

But I'd be there for hours because it's so long since I last confessed. And I'd have to tell him all about Ashley and that. I think not. Just the idea makes me shiver and hurry on past the boxy grey building. Confession isn't meant for me. It's for people like my gran who only do good things.

But a memory is nagging me: assembly at St Saviour's and Father Murray telling us that confession was about the future as much as the past. 'It's Jesus's way of giving your soul an insurance policy,' he said, and everyone laughed because we imagined Jesus popping up on telly selling us a no-claims bonus.

Anyway, no one'd give my soul insurance now because I'm like a driver who's had too many accidents and I never really knew how to drive in the first place.

I go on into the cafe and get myself a Coke and log on. I spend fifteen minutes researching the Zuiderzee dam and printing out pages. And then I switch over to hotmail to see if Claire's sent me any messages. She has. Just a short one. Enough to take me through another few days.

Is it fair to lean on Claire when she doesn't know my whole story? Is it right? I'm already wondering if the Claire I'm relying on is real or a kind of made-up Claire that I've magicked up in my head. She's my best friend and I love her, but really I hardly know her. And she certainly doesn't know me.

And I know it's not fair to dump it all on Claire, but I have to tell someone and she's better than George Clooney hiding in a box or Jesus with his fully comp cover. She won't mess around with prayers. She'll either go to the police or she'll trust me. My fate is in her hands. It's a better place than anywhere else I can think of.

Hey Claire, my Claire.

I've been thinking a lot about why we got so close so quickly, and it's still a mystery. One minute I was being mean to you – and I am so sorry, you know, don't you – and we were fighting, and the next I just felt this incredible closeness and trust. I always will, even if you never want to speak to me again when I've told you this. I have to be honest with you. It's what we're about.

I'm a liar, Claire. I'm lying to the police and if I get into court as a witness I'm going to lie there too. I'm not just a liar, I'm someone who did something terrible. I hurt someone. I've never admitted it to anyone before.

It's up to you what you want to do. You could ask me lots of questions, and I will answer them all. I'll tell you anything. Maybe you will understand why I did it and forgive me.

You could never contact me again and I will understand. Or you could pretend you never got this email. It's your choice. Whatever you do, take care of yourself. I'm trusting in your strength. I love you. I always will. You are my best friend.

I know you think of me as Joe, but it was Tyler who did this and that's who I want you to love or hate or forget.

Ty x

The End

Read on for an exclusive preview of the
first chapter of the continuation of Ty's story in

almost true

CHAPTER 1
The end of Fake Jake

They come to kill me early in the morning. At 6 am when the sky is pink and misty grey, the seagulls are crying overhead and the beach is empty.

I'm not at home when they arrive. I'm the only person on the beach, loving my early morning run – the sound of the waves and the smell of seaweed. It all reminds me that my new name is Jake and Jake lives by the seaside.

Jake's normally a bit of a sad person – no friends, poor sod – but here right now, working on my speed and strength, I'm happy that wherever we are and whatever my name is, I can always run, my body is my own.

For a bit I even forget that I'm supposed to be Jake and I run myself back into my last identity, which was Joe, cool popular Joe. I miss Joe. It's good that I can be him when I run. I never want to be Ty again, my real name, the basic me, but I still dream of being Joe.

Joe never feels lonely, running on his own. It's Jake who's miserable at school, where no one talks to him.

Jake never thinks about Claire – *my* Claire, my lovely Claire – because just her name throws him into a dark pit of despair, but when I'm Joe I pretend I'm running to see her and I let myself feel just a little bit of joy . . . excitement . . . hope.

So it's a good morning, and even when I get near home and have to readjust to being Jake again, there's still a kind of afterglow that clings to me. A Joe glow for Jake the fake. I'm hot and sweaty and that's as good as Jake's life ever gets, but then, when I turn our corner, there are police cars everywhere and ambulances and a small crowd of staring people, and they're putting up tape to stop anyone getting through.

'Get back, get back,' a policeman is shouting, but I push on forward through the crowd to the edge of the tape.

And then I see it. A dark pool of blood at our front door. For a moment the world stops, and my heart isn't even beating. I'm swaying, and everything is going whiter and smaller and I'm like one of the seagulls flying overhead, looking down on the crowd and screaming to the sky.

I don't know what to do. I think about just running away, so I never need find out what happened. Then arms hug me tight and it's Gran, oh God, it's Gran, and she's pulling me over to a police car. My mum's hunched up in the back. She's making a weird noise – a kind of gasping, howling, hooting noise. It reminds me of when Jamie Robins had an asthma attack in year three – it was scary then and it's hideous now.

All her face is white, even her lips, and she's staring right through me – and then Gran slaps her face hard and Mum stops the terrible noise and falls into her arms. They're both still in their dressing gowns. There's blood on Gran's fluffy pink slippers.

Gran sits with her arms around my mum rocking her back and forth and saying, 'You'll be OK my darling, stay strong Nicki, you'll be OK.'

'What . . . who?' I ask, but I know. I'm already beginning to piece together what must have happened.

They must have rung our doorbell. Most days it would have been my mum stumbling down the stairs to the front door. If she had, then I think they would have grabbed her, dragged her upstairs and searched the place for me. When they found no one, what then? Kept her gagged and silent until I came back, then shot us both, I should think.

But Mum didn't open the door. She's sitting here in the car, retching and sobbing, doubled over like she's in pain. It must have been Alistair who went downstairs. Alistair, the guy she had just started seeing before we had to move here.

Alistair, who spent the night in her bed.

Alistair, who turned up last night, out of the blue.

No one bothered to tell me why or how.

Alistair, with his gelled hair and muscled arms. He looked like a prat from a boy band, but he was OK really. He was a good cook. My mum liked him a lot.

Alistair who worked in a gym and trained Ellie so well that she's going to the Paralympics next year. She was the first person to realise that I've got potential as a runner. Ellie's sister is Claire, my Claire. I'm probably never going to see either of them again.

Anyway. Alistair opens the door. He knew I was going out running and he probably thought I'd forgotten my key.

He's half asleep, hair all over the place. And they shout at him, 'Ty? Ty Lewis?' He stares, yawning and bewildered – he doesn't even know I have a real name, let alone what it is – and they must take that as a yes because then they shoot him. His hands are trying to keep his brains from spilling out. Then he drops to his knees on the doorstep and blood leaks from his broken body and he dies right there on the path. And they don't hang around because they think they've done their job. They've killed me.

This isn't the first time that someone's tried to silence me forever. It's just the first time that someone else has died instead.

My mum's woken up by the noise of the shots. She's standing at the top of the stairs, screaming and screaming, and then my gran, who's lived downstairs for the last few weeks, wakes up too. Gran spots Alistair's body – the blood. She screams and rushes to hug my mum. And then she calls the police.

Then the cars arrive, sirens shouting and the tape goes up and I get home from my run.

At the police station, they put us into a room on our own and say they'll send someone to take our statements. Gran pulls her mobile out of her pocket and starts ringing: first my aunties, then Doug, the policeman who's meant to be keeping us safe. Our witness protection officer. The man who's meant to keep us safe from the people who want to stop me testifying in court.

It seems like hours, but then they all start to arrive. Gran's trying to explain about witness protection to the local cops, and my Auntie Louise just says, 'Take us to whoever's in charge.'

Then Gran and Louise disappear into a room with the police guys and when Doug arrives he goes in there too. Doug looks incredibly rough. He doesn't even say hello to us. Mum and my Auntie Emma and I sit side by side in the corridor outside and I'm straining to hear what's going on. All I can hear is Lou's raised voice. She's good at shouting – she has to be, she's a teacher.

Mum is still shaking and crying and no one is doing anything to help her except Emma who's hugging her and saying, 'It'll be OK, it'll be OK,' in a really unconvinced voice. Deep, deep inside me there's a tiny muffled scream

– he's dead . . . he was shot . . . that should have been me – but shock has sucked all the feeling out of me and I'm getting that distant feeling again. It's like I've been laminated.

'I'm fed up with this,' I say. 'I'm going in there.'

Emma says, 'Ty, you can't just interrupt,' but I say, 'Watch me,' and I push the door open. They all go quiet as I barge into the room. It's almost funny to see Gran sitting there in her pink dressing gown in a room full of coppers.

'Look,' I say, 'we've been sitting here for hours. My mum's just seen her boyfriend shot. We all know they wanted to shoot me. What's going on?' I top it up with a lot of words that I don't usually say in front of my Gran.

Louise shakes her head and says, 'Just because there's been a murder is no reason for you to be foul-mouthed.'

'Oh for Christ's sake, Lou, you're not in the classroom now,' I say and I can see the police officers smiling. I sit down at the table with them. She frowns at me, but I'm going nowhere.

'Right,' she says, 'I think we've finished here anyway. Ty, you're coming with me. We've lost confidence in witness protection for you. We'll coordinate with the police when it's time for you to give evidence. But only if we're satisfied with their security arrangements.

'Your Gran's going to stay here with Nicki so they

can make their statements, and maybe someone'll be thoughtful enough to get them some clothes and then they'll have a discussion with Doug about where to go next.'

What does she mean? How is she going to look after me? What's going to happen to my mum? And Gran? Will the police even let me go?

Doug says, 'We'll give Ty 24-hour protection now this has happened. I don't think you should be too hasty.'

Louise is very near completely losing her temper. I can tell by the way the end of her nose has gone pink.

'As far as I can see, Ty is pretty safe right now. The bastards who are out to get him think they've succeeded. Until you release the victim's name that'll be the case. I'm assuming you won't do that right away. So I've got time to get Ty somewhere where no one will know where he is. And that includes the Metropolitan Police, and every other bloody police force in the country.'

'Are you suggesting *we* had something to do with this?' says Doug, who sounds pretty upset himself.

'I'm suggesting you launch an inquiry right away to find out how they got Nicki and Ty's address. I'll bet you'll find there was a leak somewhere close to home. And just in case you don't do that, I'm going to get on the phone to the Police Complaints Commission just as soon as I've sorted my nephew out.'

She's not finished with Doug. 'I want you to go to the flat and pack all of Ty's things, so I can leave here with him in half an hour. And then you can concentrate on making sure that Nicki and my mum and Emma – oh and me as well – have somewhere reasonably safe to go. You can keep your 24-hour protection for us.'

She leads Gran and me out of the room. Doug follows, and when he sees my mum he says, 'Nicki, I don't know what to say,'

Louise snaps, 'An apology would be nice, but that's not allowed, is it Doug? That would be admitting liability.'

Then she asks for some privacy to make phone calls and a policeman takes her away down the corridor.

Emma's rocking Mum back and forth, and Gran holds me tight.

'Ty, my love,' she says, 'this isn't going to be easy, but Louise knows what's she's about. She's rock solid that girl, always made the right choices, she'll know what's best for you.'

'I want to stay with you,' I say. 'I only just got you back.'

Gran's always been more like a mother to me than my own mum. I nearly fell apart without her these last few months. I can't believe I'm going to be taken away from her again. I cling on to her like I'm a baby monkey, not someone who's going to be fifteen in just over a month.

She kisses my forehead and says, 'I'm always with you darling, I always love you. But Nicki needs me more than you do right now.'

And that's it. Doug comes back with my bag, and puts it into Lou's car. I have a final hug with Gran and Emma. My mum is throwing up in the Ladies, so we wait for her, and I give her a hug too, even though she smells of vomit. She can't stop crying and I'm not even very sure that she understands that I might not see her for . . . for weeks? For months? Ever?

'Take care,' she says. 'Take care. Lou, take care of him.'

Louise says, 'Don't worry Nicki, I'll do what's best.'

My mum stops crying, mid-sob. She does an enormous sniff, which doesn't even begin to retrieve the snot on her face, looks Louise straight in the eye and says, 'He's *my* son, Louise, don't you forget that.'

And my auntie says, 'No one's ever in danger of forgetting that, Nicki. I'll be seeing you soon. Take care of yourselves.'

Then she puts her arm on my back and leads me away, underground where her car is waiting.